Campbell Biology

Tulane University

Simon/Dickey

| PEARSON COLLECTIONS |

PEARSON

Attention bookstores: For permission to return any unsold stock, contact us at pe-uscustomreturns@pearson.com

Pearson Learning Solutions, 501 Boylston Street, Suite 900, Boston, MA 02116

A Pearson Education Company
www.pearsoned.com

ISBN 10: 1323663320

ISBN 13: 9781323663325

Printed in the USA

Table of Contents

Introduction: Biology Today

From Chapter 1 of *Campbell Essential Biology with Physiology*, Fifth Edition. Eric J. Simon, Jean L. Dickey, Kelly A. Hogan, Jane B. Reece. Copyright © 2016 by Pearson Education, Inc. All rights reserved.

Introduction: Biology Today

Why Biology Matters

If you've ever wondered what an unusual or especially beautiful animal is called, you're curious about taxonomy.

Although you may not realize it, you use the scientific method every day.

One of the primary missions of the Mars rover is to search for signs of life.

Biology All Around Us   BIOLOGY AND SOCIETY

An Innate Passion for Life

Do you like biology? Wait, let's put this question another way: Do you have a pet? Are you concerned with fitness or healthy eating? Have you ever visited a zoo or an aquarium for fun, taken a nature hike, or gathered shells on the beach? Do you like watching TV shows about sharks or dinosaurs? If you answered yes to any of these questions—well, then, it turns out that you do like biology!

Most of us have an inherent interest in life, an inborn curiosity about the natural world that leads us to study animals and plants and their habitats. We wrote this text to help you—a student with little or no college-level science experience—harness your innate enthusiasm for life. We'll use this passion to help you develop an understanding of the discipline of biology, one that you can apply to your own life and to the society in which you live. We believe that such a biological perspective is essential for any educated person. So, whatever your reasons for taking this course—even if only to fulfill your school's science requirement—you'll soon discover that exploring life is relevant and important to you, no matter your background or goals.

An inborn curiosity about nature. This student is interacting with a woolly monkey (*Lagothrix lagotricha*) during a school trip to the Amazon River in Peru.

Topics as varied as medical uses of radiation, the importance of a flu shot, and the community of microscopic organisms that live in and on your body help to illustrate biology's scope and show how the subject of biology is woven into the fabric of society. Throughout this text, we'll continuously emphasize these connections, pointing out many examples of how each topic can be applied to your life and the lives of those you care about.

The Scientific Study of Life

Now that we've established our goal—to examine how biology affects your life—a good place to start is with a basic definition: **Biology** is the scientific study of life. But have you ever looked up a word in the dictionary only to find that you need to look up some of the words within that definition to make sense of the original word? The definition of biology, although seemingly simple, raises more questions: What is a scientific study? And what does it mean to be alive? To help you get started with your investigation of biology, this chapter expands on important concepts within the definition of biology. First, we'll place the study of life in the broader context of science. Next, we'll investigate the nature of life by surveying the properties and scope of life. Finally, we'll introduce a series of broad themes you will encounter throughout your investigation of life, themes that serve as organizing principles for the information you will learn. Most important, throughout this chapter, we'll continue to provide examples of how biology affects *your* life, highlighting the relevance of this subject to society and everyone in it. ☑

The Process of Science

Recall the definition at the heart of this chapter: Biology is the scientific study of life. This leads to an obvious first question: What is a scientific study? Notice that biology is not defined as the "study of life" because there are many nonscientific ways that life can be studied. For example, extended meditation is a valid way of studying the nature of life—this approach might be well suited to a philosophy class, for example—but it does not qualify as biology because it is not a *scientific* means of studying life. How, then, do we tell the difference between science and other ways of trying to make sense of nature?

Science is an approach to understanding the natural world that is based on inquiry—a search for information, explanations, and answers to specific questions. This basic human drive to understand our natural world is manifest in two main scientific approaches: discovery science, which is mostly about *describing* nature, and hypothesis-driven science, which is mostly about *explaining* nature. Most scientists practice a combination of these two forms of inquiry.

Discovery Science

Scientists seek natural causes for natural phenomena. This limits the scope of science to the study of structures and processes that we can verifiably observe and measure, either directly or indirectly with the help of tools and technology, such as microscopes (**Figure 1**). Recorded observations are called **data**, and data are the items of information on which scientific inquiry is based. This dependence on verifiable data demystifies nature and distinguishes science from supernatural beliefs. Science can neither prove nor disprove that ghosts, deities, or spirits cause storms, eclipses, or illnesses,

▼ Figure 1 **The protist *Paramecium* viewed with three different types of microscopes.** Photographs taken with microscopes are called micrographs. Throughout this text, micrographs will have size notations along the side. For example, "LM 300×" indicates that the micrograph was taken with a light microscope and the objects are magnified to 300 times their original size.

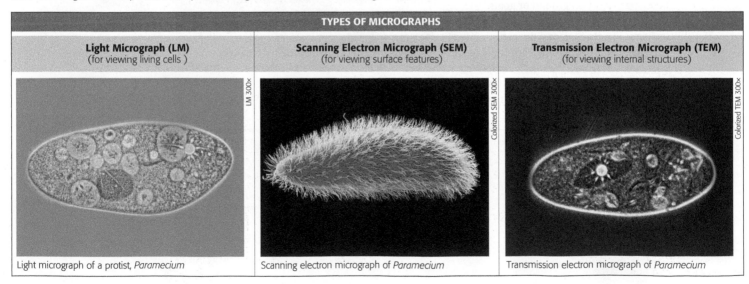

TYPES OF MICROGRAPHS		
Light Micrograph (LM) (for viewing living cells)	**Scanning Electron Micrograph (SEM)** (for viewing surface features)	**Transmission Electron Micrograph (TEM)** (for viewing internal structures)
LM 300×	Colorized SEM 300×	Colorized TEM 300×
Light micrograph of a protist, *Paramecium*	Scanning electron micrograph of *Paramecium*	Transmission electron micrograph of *Paramecium*

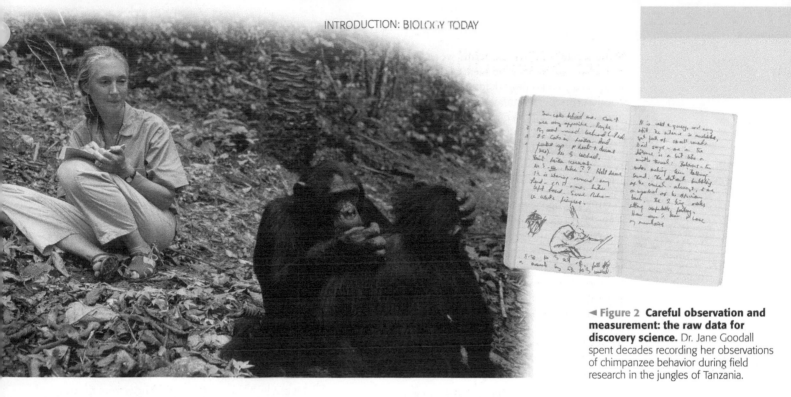

◀ Figure 2 **Careful observation and measurement: the raw data for discovery science.** Dr. Jane Goodall spent decades recording her observations of chimpanzee behavior during field research in the jungles of Tanzania.

because such explanations are not measurable and are therefore outside the bounds of science.

Verifiable observations and measurements are the data of **discovery science**. In our quest to describe nature accurately, we discover its structure. Charles Darwin's careful description of the diverse plants and animals he observed in South America is an example of discovery science. More recently, Jane Goodall spent decades observing and recording the behavior of chimpanzees living in the jungles of Tanzania (**Figure 2**). And even more recently, molecular biologists have sequenced and analyzed huge amounts of DNA, gathering data that shed light on the genetic basis of life.

Hypothesis-Driven Science

The observations of discovery science motivate us to ask questions and seek explanations. Ideally, such investigations make use of the scientific method. As a formal process of inquiry, the **scientific method** consists of a series of steps (**Figure 3**).

These steps provide a loose guideline for scientific investigations. There is no single formula for successfully discovering something new; instead, the scientific method suggests a broad outline for how discovery might proceed. The scientific method is a bit like an incomplete recipe: A basic outline of steps to be followed is presented, but the details of the dish are left to the cook. Similarly, working scientists do not typically follow the steps of the scientific method rigidly; different scientists proceed through the scientific method in different ways.

Most modern scientific investigations can be described as hypothesis-driven science. **A hypothesis** is a tentative answer to a question—a proposed explanation for a set of observations. A good hypothesis immediately leads to predictions that can be tested by experiments. Although

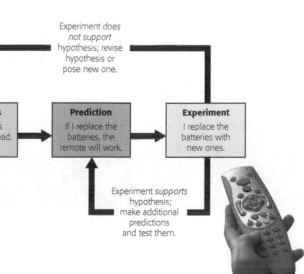

Experiment *does not support* hypothesis; revise hypothesis or pose new one.

Revise

Observation	Question	Hypothesis	Prediction	Experiment
The TV remote doesn't work.	What's wrong with the remote?	The remote's batteries are dead.	If I replace the batteries, the remote will work.	I replace the batteries with new ones.

Experiment *supports* hypothesis; make additional predictions and test them.

▶ Figure 3 **Applying the scientific method to a common problem.**

we don't think of it in those terms, we all use hypotheses in solving everyday problems. Imagine that you've completed your homework for the day and are going to reward yourself with some time in front of the TV. You press the power button on your TV remote, but the TV fails to turn on. That the TV does not turn on is an observation. The question that arises is obvious: Why didn't the remote turn on the TV? You could imagine a dozen possible explanations, but you can't possibly investigate them all simultaneously. Instead, you would focus on just one explanation (perhaps the most likely one based on past experience) and test it. That initial explanation is your hypothesis. For example, in this case, a reasonable hypothesis is that the batteries in the remote are dead.

Although you may not realize it, you use the scientific method every day.

Once a hypothesis is formed, an investigator can make predictions about what results are expected if that hypothesis is correct. We then test the hypothesis by performing an experiment to see whether or not the results are as predicted. This logical testing takes the form of "If . . . then" logic:

Observation: The TV remote doesn't work.

Question: What's wrong with the remote?

Hypothesis: The TV remote doesn't work because its batteries are dead.

Prediction: If I replace the batteries, then the remote will work.

Experiment: I replace the batteries with new ones.

Let's say that after you replace the batteries the remote still doesn't work. You would then formulate a second hypothesis and test it. Perhaps, for example, the TV is unplugged. Or you put in the new batteries incorrectly. You could continue to conduct additional experiments and formulate additional hypotheses until you reach a satisfactory conclusion to your initial question. As you do this, you are following the scientific method, and you are acting as a scientist.

Let's back up and examine what you would probably *not* do in this scenario: You most likely would not blame the malfunctioning remote on supernatural spirits, nor are you likely to meditate on the cause of the observed phenomenon. Your natural instinct is to formulate a hypothesis and then test it; the scientific method is probably your "go-to" method for solving problems. In fact, the scientific method is so deeply embedded in our society and in the way we think that most of us use it automatically (although we don't use the terminology presented here). The scientific method is therefore just a formalization of how you already think and act.

In each of these sections (titled The Process of Science), we will, as a reminder, highlight the steps in the scientific method. The questions we will address include: Does lactose intolerance have a genetic basis? Why do dog coats come in so many varieties? Do the organisms living in your intestine affect your weight? As you become increasingly scientifically literate, you will arm yourself with the tools you need to evaluate claims that you hear. We are all bombarded by information every day—via commercials, websites, magazine articles, and so on—and it can be hard to filter out the bogus from the truly worthwhile. Having a firm grasp of science as a process of inquiry can therefore help you in many ways outside the classroom.

It is important to note that scientific investigations are not the only way of knowing nature. A comparative religion course would be a good way to learn about the diverse stories that focus on a supernatural creation of Earth and its life. Science and religion are two very different ways of trying to make sense of nature. Art is yet another way to make sense of the world around us. A broad education should include exposure to all these different ways of viewing the world. Each of us synthesizes our worldview by integrating our life experiences and multidisciplinary education. ☑

☑ CHECKPOINT

1. If you observe the squirrels on your campus and collect data on their dietary habits, what kind of science are you performing? If you come up with a tentative explanation for their dietary behavior and then test your idea, what kind of science are you performing?

2. Place these steps of the scientific method in their proper order: experiment, hypothesis, observation, prediction, results, question, revise/repeat.

Answers: 1. discovery science; hypothesis-driven science 2. observation, question, hypothesis, prediction, experiment, results, revise/repeat

---

▼ Figure 4 **Some properties of life.** An object is considered alive if and only if it displays all of these properties simultaneously.

(a) **Order**   (b) **Regulation**   (c) **Growth and development**   (d) **Energy processing**

Theories in Science

Many people associate facts with science, but accumulating facts is not the primary goal of science. A telephone book is an impressive catalog of factual information, but it has little to do with science. It is true that facts, in the form of verifiable observations and repeatable experimental results, are the prerequisites of science. What really advances science, however, are new theories that tie together a number of observations that previously seemed unrelated. The cornerstones of science are the explanations that apply to the greatest variety of phenomena. People like Isaac Newton, Charles Darwin, and Albert Einstein stand out in the history of science not because they discovered a great many facts but because their theories had such broad explanatory power.

What is a scientific theory, and how is it different from a hypothesis? A scientific **theory** is much broader in scope than a hypothesis. A theory is a comprehensive explanation supported by abundant evidence, and it is general enough to spin off many new testable hypotheses. This is a hypothesis: "White fur is an adaptation that helps polar bears survive in an Arctic habitat." And this is another, seemingly unrelated hypothesis: "The unusual bone structure in a hummingbird's wings is an evolutionary adaptation that provides an advantage in gathering nectar from flowers." In contrast, the following theory ties together those seemingly unrelated hypotheses: "Adaptations to the local environment evolve by natural selection." This particular theory is one that we will describe later in this chapter.

Theories only become widely accepted by scientists if they are supported by an accumulation of extensive and varied evidence and if they have not been contradicted by any scientific data. The use of the term *theory* by scientists contrasts with our everyday usage, which implies untested speculation ("It's just a theory!"). In fact, we use the word "theory" in our everyday speech the way that a scientist uses the word "hypothesis." As you will soon learn, natural selection qualifies as a scientific theory because of its broad application and because it has been validated by a large number of observations and experiments. It is therefore not proper to say that natural selection is "just" a theory to imply that it is untested or lacking in evidence. In fact, any scientific theory is backed up by a wealth of supporting evidence, or else it wouldn't be referred to as a theory. ☑

The Nature of Life

Recall once again our basic definition: Biology is the scientific study of life. Now that we have an understanding of what constitutes a scientific study, we can turn to the next question raised by this definition: What is life? Or, to put it another way, what distinguishes living things from nonliving things? The phenomenon of **life** seems to defy a simple, one-sentence definition. Yet even a small child instinctively knows that a dog or a bug or a plant is alive but a rock is not.

If I placed an object in front of you and asked you whether it was alive, what would you do? Would you poke it to see if it reacts? Would you watch it closely to see if it moves or breathes? Would you dissect it to look at its parts? Each of these ideas is closely related to how biologists actually define life: We recognize life mainly by what living things do. To start our investigation of biology, let's look at some properties that are shared by all living things.

The Properties of Life

Figure 4 highlights seven of the properties and processes associated with life. An object is generally considered to be alive if it displays all of these properties simultaneously. (a) *Order.* All living things exhibit

(e) Response to the environment

(f) Reproduction

(g) Evolution

complex but ordered organization, as seen in the structure of a pinecone. (b) *Regulation*. The environment outside an organism may change drastically, but the organism can adjust its internal environment, keeping it within appropriate limits. When it senses its body temperature dropping, a lizard can bask on a rock to absorb heat. (c) *Growth and development*. Information carried by DNA controls the pattern of growth and development in all organisms, including the crocodile. (d) *Energy processing*. Organisms take in energy and use it to perform all of life's activities; they emit energy as heat. A cheetah obtains energy by eating its kill, uses this energy to power running and other work, and continuously emits body heat into the environment. (e) *Response to the environment*. All organisms respond to environmental stimuli. A carnivorous Venus flytrap closes its leaves rapidly in response to the environmental stimulus of an insect touching the plant's sensory hairs. (f) *Reproduction*. Organisms reproduce their own kind. Thus, monkeys reproduce only monkeys—never lizards or cheetahs. (g) *Evolution*. Reproduction underlies the capacity of populations to change (evolve) over time. For example, the giant leaf insect (*Phyllium giganteum*) has evolved in a way that provides camouflage in its environment. Evolutionary change is a central, unifying phenomenon of all life.

Although we have no proof that life has ever existed anywhere other than Earth, biologists speculate that extraterrestrial life, if it exists, could be recognized by the same properties listed in Figure 4. The Mars rover *Curiosity* (**Figure 5**), which has

▲ Figure 5 **A view from the Mars rover *Curiosity* searching for signs of life.**

been exploring the surface of the red planet since 2012, contains several instruments designed to identify biosignatures, substances that provide evidence of past or present life. For example, *Curiosity* is using a suite of onboard instruments to detect chemicals that could provide evidence of energy processing by microscopic organisms. As of yet, no definitive signs of the properties of life have been detected, and the search continues. ☑

One of the primary missions of the Mars rover is to search for signs of life.

☑ **CHECKPOINT**
Which properties of life apply to a car? Which do not?

Answer: A car demonstrates order, regulation, energy utilization, and response to the environment. But a car does not grow, reproduce, or evolve.

Life in Its Diverse Forms

The tarsier shown in **Figure 6** is just one of about 1.8 million identified species on Earth that displays all of the properties outlined in Figure 4. The diversity of known life—all the species that have been identified and named—includes at least 290,000 plants, 52,000 vertebrates (animals with backbones), and 1 million insects (more than half of all known forms of life). Biologists add thousands of newly identified species to the list each year. Estimates of the total number of species range from 10 million to more than 100 million. Whatever the actual number turns out to

◄ Figure 6 **A small sample of biological diversity.** A primate called a tarsier sits in a tree in a rainforest within the Philippines. The scientific name for this species is *Tarsius syrichta*.

DOMAIN BACTERIA

Colorized TEM 10,000X

DOMAIN ARCHAEA

TEM 18,500X

Kingdom Plantae

Kingdom Fungi

Kingdom Animalia

Protists (multiple kingdoms)

LM 150X

DOMAIN EUKARYA

▲ **Figure 7 The three domains of life.**

be, the enormous diversity of life presents organizational challenges to biologists who study it.

Grouping Species: The Basic Concept

To make sense of nature, people tend to group diverse items according to similarities. We may speak of "squirrels" and "butterflies," even though we recognize that each group actually includes many different species. A **species** is generally defined as a group of organisms that live in the same place and time and have the potential to interbreed with one another in nature to produce healthy offspring. We may even sort groups into broader categories, such as rodents (which include squirrels) and insects (which include butterflies). **Taxonomy**, the branch of biology that names and classifies species, is the arrangement of species into a hierarchy of broader and broader groups. Have you ever seen a fish, or found a mushroom, or watched a bird and wondered what kind it was? If so, you were asking a question of taxonomy. First, let's summarize the broadest units of classification of life.

The Three Domains of Life

On the broadest level, biologists divide the diversity of life into three domains: Bacteria, Archaea, and Eukarya **(Figure 7)**. Every organism on Earth belongs to one of these three domains. The first two domains, Bacteria and Archaea, identify two very different groups of organisms that have prokaryotic cells—that is, relatively small and simple cells that lack a nucleus or other compartments bounded by internal membranes. All the eukaryotes (organisms with eukaryotic cells—that is, relatively large and complex cells that contain a nucleus and other membrane-enclosed compartments) are grouped into the domain Eukarya.

The domain Eukarya in turn includes three smaller divisions called kingdoms—Plantae, Fungi, and Animalia. Most members of the three kingdoms are multicellular. The kingdoms are distinguished partly by how the organisms obtain food. Plants produce their own sugars and other foods by photosynthesis. Fungi are mostly decomposers, obtaining food by digesting dead organisms and organic wastes. Animals—the kingdom to which we belong—obtain food by ingesting (eating) and digesting other organisms. Those eukaryotes that do not fit into any of the three kingdoms fall into a catch-all group called the protists. Most protists are single-celled; they include microscopic organisms such as amoebas. But protists also include certain multicellular forms, such as seaweeds. Scientists are in the process of organizing protists into multiple kingdoms, although they do not yet agree on exactly how to do this. ☑

If you've ever wondered what an unusual or especially beautiful animal is called, you're curious about taxonomy.

☑ **CHECKPOINT**

1. Name the three domains of life. To which do you belong?
2. Name three kingdoms found within the domain Eukarya. Name a fourth group within this domain.

Answers: 1. Bacteria, Archaea, Eukarya; Eukarya 2. Plantae, Fungi, Animalia; the protists

Major Themes in Biology

Biology is a big subject that, as new discoveries unfold every day, grows continuously in breadth and depth. Although we often focus on the details, it is important to recognize that there are broad themes running throughout the subject. These overarching principles unify all aspects of biology, from the microscopic world of cells to the global environment. Focusing on a few big picture ideas that cut across many topics within biology can help organize and make sense of all the information you will learn.

In this section, we'll describe five unifying themes that recur throughout our investigation of biology **(Figure 8)**. We'll highlight each theme as it appears by using the icons from Figure 8 and repeating the section headings used below.

 ## Evolution

Just as you have a family history, each species on Earth today represents one twig on a branching tree of life that extends back in time through ancestral species more and more remote. Species that are very similar, such as the brown bear and the polar bear, share a common ancestor at a relatively recent branch point on the tree of life **(Figure 9)**. In addition, all bears can be traced back much farther in time to an ancestor common also to squirrels, humans, and all other mammals. All mammals have hair and milk-producing mammary glands, and such similarities are what we would expect if all mammals descended from a common ancestor, a first mammal. And mammals,

reptiles, and all other vertebrates share a common ancestor even more ancient than the common ancestor to mammals. Going farther back still, at the cellular level, all life displays striking similarities. For example, all living cells are surrounded by an outer plasma membrane of similar makeup and use structures called ribosomes to produce proteins.

The scientific explanation for the common characteristics found throughout such diverse species is evolution, the process that has transformed life on Earth from its earliest beginnings to the extensive variety we see today. Evolution is the fundamental principle of life and the core theme that unifies all of biology. The theory of evolution by natural selection, first described by Charles Darwin more than 150 years ago, is the one principle that makes sense of everything we know about living organisms. Any student of biology should begin by first understanding evolution. Evolution can help us investigate and understand every aspect of life, from the tiny organisms that occupy the most remote habitats, to the diversity of species in our local environment, to the stability of the global environment. In this section, we will present a basic introduction to this important topic. You will learn, for example, how evolution can shed light on such topics as our quest to develop better biofuels, how cancer cells grow and spread through the body, and the development of antibiotic-resistant bacteria.

The Darwinian View of Life

The evolutionary view of life came into focus in 1859 when English naturalist Charles Darwin published one

---

▼ Figure 8 **Five unifying themes that run throughout the discipline of biology.**

MAJOR THEMES IN BIOLOGY				
Evolution	**Structure/Function**	**Information Flow**	**Energy Transformations**	**Interconnections within Systems**
Evolution by natural selection is biology's core unifying theme and can be seen at every level in the hierarchy of life.	The structure of an object, such as a molecule or a body part, provides insight into its function, and vice versa.	Within biological systems, information stored in DNA is transmitted and expressed.	All biological systems depend on obtaining, converting, and releasing energy and matter.	All biological systems, from molecules to ecosystems, depend on interactions between components.

Giant panda bear

Spectacled bear

Sloth bear

Sun bear

American black bear

Asiatic black bear

Polar bear

Brown bear

▲ **Figure 9 An evolutionary tree of bears.** This tree represents a hypothesis (a tentative model) based on both the fossil record and a comparison of DNA sequences among modern bears. As new evidence about the evolutionary history of bears emerges, this tree will inevitably change.

reproductive success that Darwin called **natural selection** because the environment "selects" only certain heritable traits from those already existing. Natural selection does not promote or somehow encourage changes, but rather it serves to "edit" those changes that have already occurred. And the product of natural selection is adaptation, the accumulation of variations in a population over time. Returning to the example of bear evolution in Figure 9, one familiar adaptation in bears is fur color. Polar bears and brown (grizzly) bears each

▼ **Figure 10 Charles Darwin (1809–1882),** *The Origin of Species,* **and blue-footed boobies he observed on the Galápagos Islands.**

of the most important and influential books ever written: *On the Origin of Species by Means of Natural Selection* **(Figure 10).** First, Darwin presented a large amount of evidence in support of the evolutionary view that species living today descended from a succession of ancestral species. Darwin called this process "descent with modification." Darwin's phrase was an insightful one, because it captures the duality of life's unity (which is possible because of a shared descent) and diversity (which is possible because of gradual modification). In the Darwinian view, for example, the diversity of bears is based on different modifications of a common ancestor from which all bears descended.

Second, Darwin proposed a mechanism for descent with modification: the process of natural selection. In the struggle for existence, those individuals with heritable traits best suited to the local environment are more likely to survive and leave the greatest number of healthy offspring. Therefore, the traits that enhance survival and reproductive success will be represented in greater numbers in the next generation. It is this unequal display an evolutionary adaptation (white and brown fur, respectively) that resulted from natural selection operating in their respective environments. Presumably, natural selection tended to favor the fur color that provided each bear lineage with an appearance that provided an advantage in its home territory.

We now recognize many examples of natural selection in action. A classic example involves the finches (a kind of bird) of the Galápagos Islands **(Figure 11)**. Over a span of two decades, researchers working on these isolated islands measured changes in beak size in a population of ground finch that

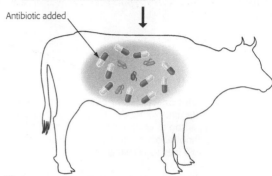

▲ **Figure 11 Finches of the Galápagos Islands.** Charles Darwin personally collected these finches during his time in the Galapagos.

prefers to eat small seeds. In dry years, when the preferred small seeds are in short supply, the birds instead have mostly large seeds to eat. Birds with larger, stronger beaks have a feeding advantage in such an environment, and greater reproductive success, and thus the average beak depth for the population increases during dry years. During wet years, small seeds become more abundant. Because smaller beaks are more efficient for eating the plentiful small seeds, the average beak depth decreases over generations. Such changes in structure are measurable evidence of natural selection in action.

The world is rich with examples of natural selection. Consider the development of antibiotic-resistant bacteria **(Figure 12)**. Dairy and cattle farmers often add antibiotics to feed because doing so results in larger, more profitable animals. **1** The members of the bacteria population will, through random chance, vary in their susceptibility to the antibiotic. **2** Once the environment has been changed with the addition of antibiotics, some bacteria will succumb quickly and die, whereas others will survive. **3** Those that do survive will have the potential to multiply, producing offspring that will likely inherit the traits that enhance survival. **4** Over many generations, bacteria that are resistant to antibiotics will thrive in greater and greater numbers. Thus, feeding antibiotics to cows may promote the evolution of antibiotic-resistant bacterial populations that are not susceptible to standard drug treatments.

Observing Artificial Selection

Darwin found convincing evidence of the power of natural selection in examples of *artificial* selection, the purposeful breeding of domesticated plants and animals by humans. People have been modifying other species

1 **Population with varied inherited traits.** Initially, the population of bacteria varies in its ability to resist the antibiotic. By random chance, a few bacteria are somewhat resistant.

2 **Elimination of individuals with certain traits.** The majority of bacteria are susceptible to the effects of the antibiotic and so will die off. The few resistant bacteria will tend to survive.

3 **Reproduction of survivors.** The selective pressure of the antibiotic favors survival and reproductive success of the few resistant bacteria. Thus, genes for anitbiotic resistance are passed along to the next generation in greater frequency.

Many generations

4 **Increasing frequency of traits that enhance survival and reproductive success.** Generation after generation, the bacteria population adapts to its environment through natural selection.

▲ **Figure 12 Natural selection in action.**

for millennia by selecting breeding stock with certain traits. For example, the plants we grow for food today bear little resemblance to their wild ancestors. Have you ever had wild blueberries or wild strawberries? They are much different (and, in many ways, much less desirable) than their modern kin. This is because we have customized crop plants through many generations of artificial selection by selecting different parts of the plant to accentuate. All the vegetables shown in **Figure 13** (and more) have a common ancestor in one species of wild mustard (shown in the center of the figure). The power of selective breeding is also apparent in our pets, which have been bred for looks and for useful characteristics. For example, all domesticated dogs are descended from wolves, but people in different cultures have customized hundreds of dog breeds as different as basset hounds and Saint Bernards **(Figure 14)**. The tremendous variety of modern dogs reflects thousands of years of artificial selection. You may not realize it, but you are exposed to the products of artificial selection every day!

Darwin's publication of *On the Origin of Species* fueled an explosion in biological research that continues today. Over the past century and a half, a tremendous amount of evidence has accumulated in support of Darwin's theory

► Figure 13 **The artificial selection of food crops.**

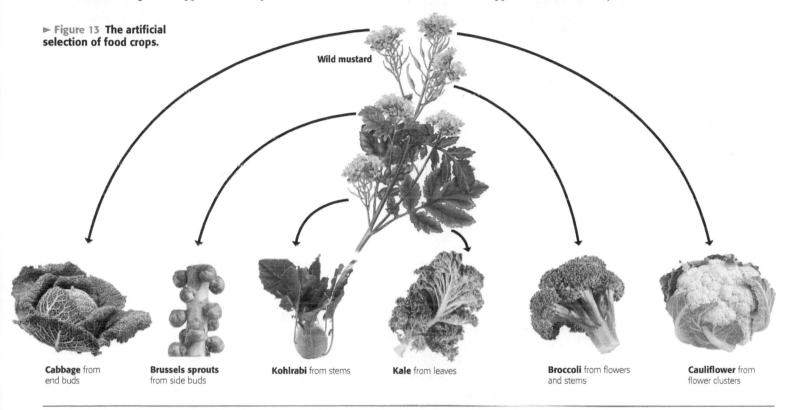

Wild mustard

Cabbage from end buds

Brussels sprouts from side buds

Kohlrabi from stems

Kale from leaves

Broccoli from flowers and stems

Cauliflower from flower clusters

▼ Figure 14 **The artificial selection of pets.**

Gray wolves

Artificial selection

Domesticated dogs

13

of evolution by natural selection, making it one of biology's best-demonstrated, most comprehensive, and longest-held theories. Throughout this text, you will learn more about how natural selection works and see other examples of how natural selection affects your life. ☑

Structure/Function The Relationship of Structure to Function

When considering useful objects in your home, you may realize that form and function are related. A chair, for example, cannot have just any shape; it must have a stable base to stand on and a flat area for holding your weight. The function of the chair constrains the possible shapes it may have. Similarly, within biological systems, structure (the shape of something) and function (what it does) are often related, with each providing insight into the other.

The correlation of structure and function can be seen at every level of biological organization. Consider your lungs, which function to exchange gases with the environment: Your lungs bring in oxygen (O_2) and take out carbon dioxide (CO_2). The structure of your lungs correlates with this function (Figure 15). Increasingly smaller branches of your lungs end in millions of tiny sacs in which the gases cross from the air to your blood, and vice versa. This branched structure (the form of the lungs) provides a tremendous surface area over which a very high volume of air may pass (the function of the lungs). Cells, too, display a correlation of structure and function. As oxygen enters the blood in the lungs, for example,

▲ **Figure 15 Structure/function: human lungs.** The structure of your lungs correlates with their function.

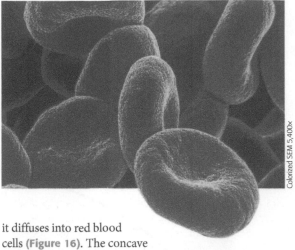

▼ **Figure 16 Structure/function: red blood cells.** As oxygen enters the blood in the lungs, it diffuses into red blood cells.

Colorized SEM 5,400x

it diffuses into red blood cells (Figure 16). The concave indentations of red blood cells provide a large surface area through which oxygen can diffuse.

Throughout the text, we will see the structure/function principle apply to all levels of biological organization, from the structure of cells and their components, to DNA replication, to the internal organization of plants and animals. Some specific examples of the correlation of structure and function that you will encounter include explaining why ice floats, the importance of a protein's shape, and structural adaptations within the bodies of plants. ☑

Information Flow Information Flow

For life's functions to proceed in an orderly manner, information must be received, transmitted, and used. Such information flow is apparent at all levels of biological organization. At the microscopic scale, every cell contains information in the form of **genes**, hereditary units of information consisting of specific sequences of DNA passed on from the previous generation. At the organismal level, as every multicellular organism develops from an embryo, information exchanged among cells enables the overall body plan to take shape in an organized fashion. Once the organism is mature, information about the internal conditions of its body is used to keep those conditions within a range that allows for life.

Although bacteria and humans inherit different genes, that information is encoded in an identical chemical language common to all organisms. In fact, the language of life has an alphabet of just four letters. The chemical names of DNA's four molecular building blocks

14

are abbreviated as A, G, C, and T **(Figure 17)**. A typical gene is hundreds to thousands of chemical "letters" in length. A gene's meaning to a cell is encoded in its specific sequence of these letters, just as the message of this sentence is encoded in its arrangement of the 26 letters of the English alphabet.

The entire set of genetic information that an organism inherits is called its **genome**. The nucleus of each human cell contains a genome that is about 3 billion chemical letters long. In recent years, scientists have tabulated virtually the entire sequence of the genome from humans and hundreds of other organisms. As this work progresses, biologists will continue to learn the functions of the genes and how their activities are coordinated in the development and functioning of an organism. The emerging field of genomics—a branch of biology that studies whole genomes—is a striking example of how the flow of information can inform our study of life at its many levels.

How is all this information used within your body? At any given moment, your genes are producing thousands of different proteins that control your body's processes. Food is broken down, new body tissues are built,

► Figure 17 **The language of DNA.** Every molecule of DNA is constructed from four kinds of chemical building blocks that are chained together, shown here as simple shapes and letters.

The four chemical building blocks of DNA

A DNA molecule

▲ Figure 18 **Biotechnology.** Since the 1970s, applications of biology have revolutionized medicine.

cells divide, signals are sent—all under the control of proteins, all of which are built from information stored in your DNA. For example, structures within your body assess the amount of glucose in your blood and, in response, secrete varying amounts of hormones that keep blood glucose levels within acceptable values. The information in one of your genes translates to "Make insulin." Insulin, produced by cells within the pancreas, is a chemical that helps regulate your body's use of glucose as a fuel.

People with type 1 diabetes often have a mutation (error) in a different gene that causes the body's immune cells to attack and destroy the insulin-producing pancreas cells. The breakdown of the normal flow of information within the body leads to disease. Some people with diabetes regulate their sugar levels by injecting themselves with insulin produced by genetically engineered bacteria. These bacteria can make insulin because the human gene has been transplanted into them. This example of genetic engineering was one of the earliest successes of biotechnology, a field that has transformed the pharmaceutical industry and extended millions of lives **(Figure 18)**. And biotechnology is only possible because biological information, written in the universal chemical language of DNA, is used in a similar manner by all life on Earth. ☑

Energy Transformations Pathways that Transform Energy and Matter

Movement, growth, reproduction, and the various cellular activities of life are work, and work requires energy. The input of energy, primarily from the sun, and the

☑ **CHECKPOINT**

Which is bigger: gene or genome?

Answer: genome (because your genome consists of all your genes)

transformation of energy from one form to another make life possible (Figure 19). At their source, most ecosystems are solar powered. The energy that enters an ecosystem as sunlight is captured by plants and other photosynthetic organisms (producers) that absorb the sun's energy and convert it, storing it as chemical bonds within sugars and other complex molecules. These molecules then become food for a series of consumers, such as animals, that feed on producers. Consumers can use the food as a source of energy by breaking chemical bonds or as building blocks for making molecules needed by the organism. In other words, the molecules consumed can be used as both a source of energy and a source of matter. In the process of these energy conversions between and within organisms, some energy is converted to heat, which is then lost from the ecosystem. Thus, energy flows through an ecosystem, entering as light and exiting as heat. This is represented by wavy lines in Figure 19.

Every object in the universe, both living and nonliving, is composed of matter. In contrast to energy flowing through an ecosystem, matter is recycled within an ecosystem. This is represented by the blue circle in Figure 19. For example, minerals that plants absorb from the soil can eventually be recycled back into to the soil when plants are decomposed by microorganisms. Decomposers, such as fungi and many bacteria, break down waste products and the remains of dead organisms, changing complex molecules into simple nutrients. The action of decomposers ensures that nutrients are

available to be taken up from the soil by plants again, thereby completing the cycle.

Within all living cells, a vast network of interconnected chemical reactions (collectively referred to as metabolism) continually converts energy from one form to another as matter is recycled. For example, as food molecules are broken down into simpler molecules, energy stored in the chemical bonds is released. This energy can be captured and used by the body (to power muscle contractions, for example). The atoms that made up the food can then be recycled (to build new muscle tissue, for example). Within all living organisms—there is a never-ending "chemical square dance" in which molecules swap chemical partners as they receive, convert, and release matter and energy. The importance of energy and matter transformations is made clear by examining what happens when they are disrupted. Cyanide is one of the deadliest known poisons. Ingesting just 200 milligrams (about half the size of a tablet of aspirin) causes death in humans. Cyanide is so toxic because it blocks an essential step within the metabolic pathway that harvests energy from glucose. When even a single protein within this pathway becomes inhibited, cells lose the ability to extract the energy stored in the chemical bonds of glucose. The rapid death that follows is a macabre illustration of the importance of energy and matter transformations to life. Throughout your study of biology, you will see more examples of the how living organisms regulate the transformation of energy and matter, from microscopic cellular processes such as photosynthesis and cellular respiration, to ecosystem-wide cycles of carbon and other nutrients, to global cycles of water across the planet. ☑

☑ CHECKPOINT

What is the key difference between how energy and matter move in ecosystems?

Answer: Energy moves through an ecosystem (entering and exiting), whereas matter is recycled within an ecosystem.

▼ Figure 19 **Nutrient and energy flow in an ecosystem.** Nutrients are recycled within an ecosystem, whereas energy flows into and then out of an ecosystem.

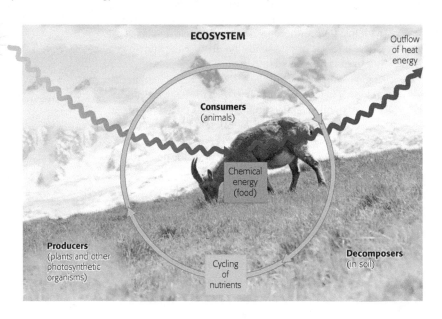

Inflow of light energy

ECOSYSTEM

Outflow of heat energy

Consumers (animals)

Chemical energy (food)

Producers (plants and other photosynthetic organisms)

Cycling of nutrients

Decomposers (in soil)

Interconnections within Systems

Interconnections within Biological Systems

The study of life extends from the microscopic scale of the molecules and cells that make up organisms to the global scale of the entire living planet. We can divide this enormous range into different levels of biological organization. There are many interconnections within and between these levels of biological systems.

Imagine zooming in from space to take a closer and closer look at life on Earth. Figure 20 takes you on a tour that spans the full scope of life. The top of the figure shows the global scale of the entire **biosphere**, which

▼ **Figure 20 Zooming in on life.**

2 Ecosystems
An ecosystem consists of all living organisms in a particular area and all the nonliving components of the environment with which life interacts, such as soil, water, and light.

3 Communities
All organisms in an ecosystem (such as the iguanas, crabs, seaweed, and even bacteria in this ecosystem) are collectively called a community.

1 Biosphere
Earth's biosphere includes all life and all the places where life exists.

4 Populations
Within communities are various populations, groups of interacting individuals of one species, such as a group of iguanas.

5 Organisms
An organism is an individual living thing, like this iguana.

6 Organ Systems and Organs
An organism's body consists of several organ systems, each of which contains two or more organs. For example, the iguana's circulatory system includes its heart and blood vessels.

10 Molecules and Atoms
Finally, we reach molecules, the chemical level in the hierarchy. Molecules are clusters of even smaller chemical units called atoms. Each cell consists of an enormous number of chemicals that function together to give the cell the properties we recognize as life. DNA, the molecule of inheritance and the substance of genes, is shown here as a computer graphic. Each sphere in the DNA model represents a single atom.

← Atom

9 Organelles
Organelles are functional components of cells, such as the nucleus that houses the DNA.

Nucleus →

Colorized LM 60x

8 Cells
The cell is the smallest unit that can display all the characteristics of life.

7 Tissues
Each organ is made up of several different tissues, such as the heart muscle tissue shown here. A tissue consists of a group of similar cells performing a specific function.

consists of all the environments on Earth that support life—including soil; oceans, lakes, and other bodies of water; and the lower atmosphere. At the other extreme of biological size and complexity are microscopic molecules such as DNA, the chemical responsible for

inheritance. Zooming outward from bottom to top in the figure, you can see that it takes many molecules to build a cell, many cells to make a tissue, multiple tissues to make an organ, and so on. At each new level, novel properties emerge that are absent from the preceding one. These emergent properties are due to the specific arrangement and interactions of parts in an increasingly complex system. Such properties are called emergent because they emerge as complexity increases. For example, life emerges at the level of the cell; a test tube full of molecules is not alive. The saying "the whole is greater than the sum of its parts" captures this idea. Emergent properties are not unique to life. A box of camera parts won't do anything, but if the parts are arranged and interact in a certain way, you can capture photographs. Add structures from a phone, and your camera and phone can interact to gain the ability to send photos to friends instantly. New properties emerge as the complexity increases. Compared to such nonliving examples, however, the unrivaled complexity of biological systems makes the emergent properties of life especially fascinating to study.

Consider another example of interconnectedness within biological systems, one that operates on a much larger scale: global climate. As the composition of the atmosphere changes, patterns of temperature are changing across the planet. This affects the makeup of ecosystems by changing patterns of weather and availability of

water. In turn, biological communities and populations are altered. For example, because of changing weather patterns and water levels, the range of several species of disease-causing mosquitoes has drifted north, bringing illnesses (such as malaria) to areas not previously affected by them. When someone is bit by a malaria-carrying mosquito, his or her body will be affected by an illness that occurs at a cellular level. Throughout our study of life, we will see countless interconnections that operate within and between every level of the biological hierarchy shown in Figure 20.

From the interactions within the biosphere to the molecular machinery within cells, biologists are investigating life at its many levels. Zooming in at ever-finer resolution illustrates the principle of reductionism—the approach of reducing complex systems to simpler components that are more manageable to study. Reductionism is a powerful strategy in biology. For example, by studying the molecular structure of DNA that had been extracted from cells, James Watson and Francis Crick inferred the chemical basis of biological inheritance. In this reductionist spirit, we will begin our investigation of biology by studying the chemistry of life. ☑

☑ **CHECKPOINT**

What is the smallest level of biological organization that can display all the characteristics of life?

Answer: a cell

Chapter Review

▊ SUMMARY OF KEY CONCEPTS

The Scientific Study of Life

Biology is the scientific study of life. It is important to distinguish scientific investigations from other ways of thinking, and to distinguish living objects from nonliving ones.

The Process of Science

Only scientific means of investigating life qualify as biology.

Discovery Science

Describing the natural world with verifiable data is the hallmark of discovery science.

Hypothesis-Driven Science

A scientist formulates a hypothesis (tentative explanation) to account for observations of the natural world. The hypothesis may then be tested via the steps of the scientific method:

Theories in Science

A theory is a broad and comprehensive statement about the world that is supported by the accumulation of a great deal of verifiable evidence.

The Nature of Life

The Properties of Life

All life displays a common set of characteristics:

Order   Regulation   Growth and development   Energy processing

Response to the environment   Reproduction   Evolution

Life in Its Diverse Forms

Biologists organize living organisms into three domains. The domain Eukarya is further divided into three kingdoms (distinguished partly by their means of obtaining food) and one catch-all group:

Life			
Prokaryotes		**Eukaryotes**	
		Plantae Fungi Animalia Protists (all other eukaryotes) Three kingdoms	
Domain Bacteria	**Domain Archaea**	**Domain Eukarya**	

Major Themes in Biology

Throughout your study of biology, you will frequently come upon examples of five unifying themes: evolution, the relationship of structure to function, the flow of information through biological systems, energy transformations, and interconnections with biological systems.

MAJOR THEMES IN BIOLOGY				
Evolution	**Structure/ Function**	**Information Flow**	**Energy Transformations**	**Interconnections within Systems**

Evolution

Charles Darwin established the ideas of evolution ("descent with modification") via natural selection (unequal reproductive success) in his 1859 publication *The Origin of Species*. Natural selection leads to adaptations to the environment, which—when passed from generation to generation—is the mechanism of evolution.

The Relationship of Structure to Function

At all levels of biology, structure and function are related. Changing structure often results in an altered function, and learning about a component's function will often give insight into its structure.

Information Flow

Throughout living systems, information is stored, transmitted, and used. Within your body, genes provide instructions for building proteins, which perform many of life's tasks.

Pathways That Transform Energy and Matter

 Within ecosystems, nutrients are recycled, but energy flows through.

Interconnections within Biological Systems

 Life can be studied on many scales, from molecules to the entire biosphere. As complexity increases, novel properties emerge. For example, the cell is the smallest unit that can possibly display all of the characteristics of life.

MasteringBiology®

For practice quizzes, BioFlix animations, MP3 tutorials, video tutors, and more study tools designed for this text, go to MasteringBiology®

SELF-QUIZ

1. Which of the following is *not* a characteristic of all living organisms?
   a. capable of self-reproduction
   b. composed of multiple cells
   c. complex yet organized
   d. uses energy

2. Place the following levels of biological organization in order from smallest to largest: atom, biosphere, cell, ecosystem, molecule, organ, organism, population, tissue. Which is the smallest level capable of demonstrating all of the characteristics of life?

3. Plants use the process of photosynthesis to convert the energy in sunlight to chemical energy in the form of sugar. While doing so, they consume carbon dioxide and water and release oxygen. Explain how this process functions in both the cycling of chemical nutrients and the flow of energy through an ecosystem.

4. For each of the following organisms, match its description to its most likely domain and/or kingdom:
   a. A foot-tall organism capable of producing its own food from sunlight
   b. A microscopic, simple, nucleus-free organism found living in a riverbed
   c. An inch-tall organism growing on the forest floor that consumes material from dead leaves
   d. A thimble-sized organism that feeds on algae growing in a pond

   1. Bacteria
   2. Eukarya/Animalia
   3. Eukarya/Fungi
   4. Eukarya/Plantae

5. How does natural selection cause a population to become adapted to its environment over time?

6. Which of the following statements best describes the logic of the scientific method?
   a. If I generate a testable hypothesis, tests and observations will support it.
   b. If my prediction is correct, it will lead to a testable hypothesis.
   c. If my observations are accurate, they will support my hypothesis.
   d. If my hypothesis is correct, I can expect certain test results.

7. Which of the following statements best distinguishes hypotheses from theories in science?
   a. Theories are hypotheses that have been proved.
   b. Hypotheses are tentative guesses; theories are correct answers to questions about nature.
   c. Hypotheses usually are narrow in scope; theories have broad explanatory power.
   d. Hypotheses and theories mean essentially the same thing in science.

8. _____ is the core idea that unifies all areas of biology.

9. Match each of the following terms to the phrase that best describes it.
   a. Natural selection   1. A testable idea
   b. Evolution   2. Descent with modification
   c. Hypothesis   3. Unequal reproductive success
   d. Biosphere   4. All life-supporting environments on Earth

THE PROCESS OF SCIENCE

10. The fruits of wild species of tomato are tiny compared with the giant beefsteak tomatoes available today. This difference in fruit size is almost entirely due to the larger number of cells in the domesticated fruits. Plant biologists have recently discovered genes that are responsible for controlling cell division in tomatoes. Why would such a discovery be important to producers of other kinds of fruits and vegetables? To the study of human development and disease? To our basic understanding of biology?

11. **Interpreting Data** Trans fats are a form of dietary fat that can have significant health consequences. The graph below represents data from a 2004 study that compared the amount of trans fats found in adipose tissue (body fat) of 79 heart attack patients and 167 people who did not have a heart attack. Write a one-sentence summary of the results presented in the graph.

Data from: P. M. Clifton et al., *Trans* fatty acids in adipose tissue and the food supply are associated with myocardial infarction. *Journal of Nutrition* 134: 874–879 (2004).

BIOLOGY AND SOCIETY

12. The news media and popular magazines frequently report stories that are connected to biology. In the next 24 hours, record all such stories you hear or read about from three different sources and briefly describe the biological connections you perceive in each story.

13. If you pay attention, you will find yourself conducting many hypothesis-driven experiments each day. Over the next day, try to think of a good example where you performed a simple experiment to test a hypothesis about some observation. Write the experience out as a story, and then rewrite it using the steps of the scientific method (observation, question, hypothesis, prediction, and so on).

Glossary

biology
The scientific study of life.

biosphere
The global ecosystem; the entire portion of Earth inhabited by life; all of life and where it lives.

data
Recorded verifiable observations.

discovery science
The process of scientific inquiry that focuses on using observations to describe nature. *See also* hypothesis, science.

genome
The genetic material of an organism or virus; the complete complement of an organism's or virus's genes along with its noncoding nucleic acid sequences.

hypothesis (*hī-poth'-uh-sis*)
(plural, **hypotheses**) A tentative explanation that a scientist proposes for a specific phenomenon that has been observed.

life
Defined by the set of common characteristics that distinguish living organisms from nonliving matter, including such properties and processes as order, regulation, growth and development, energy use, response to the environment, reproduction, and the capacity to evolve over time.

natural selection
A process in which organisms with certain inherited characteristics are more likely to survive and reproduce than are organisms with other characteristics; unequal reproductive success.

science
Any method of learning about the natural world that follows the scientific method. *See also* discovery science; hypothesis.

scientific method
Scientific investigation involving the observation of phenomena, the formulation of a hypothesis concerning the phenomena, experimentation to demonstrate the truth or falseness of the hypothesis, and results that validate or modify the hypothesis.

species
A group of populations whose members possess similar anatomical characteristics and have the ability to interbreed. The definition of a species as a population or group of populations whose members have the potential in nature to interbreed and produce fertile offspring.

taxonomy
The branch of biology concerned with identifying, naming, and classifying species.

theory
A widely accepted explanatory idea that is broader in scope than a hypothesis, generates new hypotheses, and is supported by a large body of evidence.

Credits

Self-Quiz Answers

1. b (some living organisms are single-celled)
2. atom, molecule, cell, tissue, organ, organism, population, ecosystem, biosphere; the cell
3. Photosynthesis cycles nutrients by converting the carbon in carbon dioxide to sugar, which is then consumed by other organisms. Additionally, the oxygen in water is released as oxygen gas. Photosynthesis contributes to energy flow by converting sunlight to chemical energy, which is then also consumed by other organisms, and by producing heat.
4. a4, b1, c3, d2
5. On average, those individuals with heritable traits best suited to the local environment produce the greatest number of offspring that survive and reproduce. This increases the frequency of those traits in the population over time. The result is the accumulation of evolutionary adaptations.
6. d
7. c
8. evolution
9. a3, b2, c1, d4

Cellular Reproduction: Cells from Cells

From Chapter 8 of *Campbell Essential Biology with Physiology*, Fifth Edition. Eric J. Simon, Jean L. Dickey, Kelly A. Hogan, Jane B. Reece. Copyright © 2016 by Pearson Education, Inc. All rights reserved.

Cellular Reproduction: Cells from Cells

Why Cellular Reproduction Matters

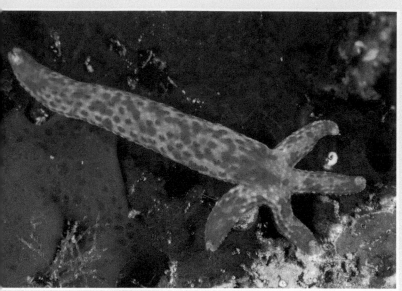

◄ In certain species of sea star, a severed arm may be able to regrow a whole new body.

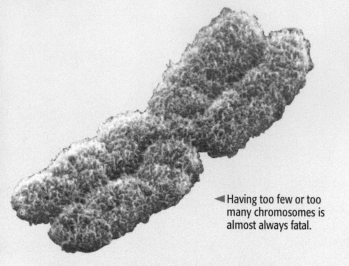

◄ Having too few or too many chromosomes is almost always fatal.

If stretched out, the DNA ► in any one of your cells would be taller than you.

▲ Every tumor is the result of a malfunction in cell division.

Life with and without Sex BIOLOGY AND SOCIETY

Virgin Birth of a Dragon

Zookeepers at the Chester Zoo in England were startled to discover that Flora, a female Komodo dragon—*Varanus komodoensis*, the largest living species of lizard, capable of growing up to 10 feet long—had laid a clutch of 25 eggs. It wasn't surprising that a captive Komodo dragon would breed. In fact, Flora was at the zoo for that very reason: She was one of two female Komodo dragons that were part of a captive breeding program intended to help repopulate the species. What made Flora's clutch of eggs so remarkable is that she had not yet been in the company of a male, let alone mated with one. As far as anyone knew, Komodo dragons, like the vast majority of animal species, create offspring only through sexual reproduction involving the union of a male's sperm and a female's egg. But despite Flora's virginity, eight of her eggs developed normally and hatched into live, healthy Komodo dragons.

DNA analysis confirmed that Flora's offspring derived their genes solely from her. The new dragons must have resulted from parthenogenesis, the production of offspring by a female without involvement of a male. Parthenogenesis is one form of asexual reproduction, the creation of a new generation without participation of sperm and egg. Parthenogenesis is rare among vertebrates (animals with backbones), although it has been documented in species as diverse as sharks (including the hammerhead), domesticated birds, and now Komodo dragons. Soon, zoologists identified a second Komodo at a different zoo who had also borne young by parthenogenesis. This same Komodo dragon later had additional offspring via sexual reproduction—indicating that this species is capable of switching between two reproductive modes. Biologists are investigating the evolutionary basis of this phenomenon and considering what implications it may have on efforts to repopulate this rare species.

The Komodo dragon. The Komodo is the world's largest lizard and is found in the wild only on three islands in Indonesia.

The ability of organisms to procreate is the one characteristic that best distinguishes living things from nonliving matter. All organisms—from bacteria to lizards to you—are the result of repeated cell divisions. The perpetuation of life therefore depends on cell division, the production of new cells. In this chapter, we'll look at how individual cells are copied and then see how cell reproduction underlies the process of sexual reproduction. Throughout our discussion, we'll consider examples of asexual and sexual reproduction among both plants and animals.

What Cell Reproduction Accomplishes

When you hear the word *reproduction*, you probably think of the birth of new organisms. But reproduction actually occurs much more often at the cellular level. Consider the skin on your arm. Skin cells are constantly reproducing themselves and moving outward toward the surface, replacing dead cells that have rubbed off. This renewal of your skin goes on throughout your life. And when your skin is injured, additional cell reproduction helps heal the wound.

When a cell undergoes reproduction, or **cell division**, the two "daughter" cells that result are genetically identical to each other and to the original "parent" cell. (Biologists traditionally use the word *daughter* in this context to refer to offspring cells, but of course cells lack gender.) Before the parent cell splits into two, it duplicates its **chromosomes**, the structures that contain most of the cell's DNA. Then, during cell division, each daughter cell receives one identical set of chromosomes from the original parent cell.

As summarized in **Figure 1**, cell division plays several important roles in the lives of organisms. For example, within your body, millions of cells must divide every second to replace damaged or lost cells. Another function of cell division is growth. All of the trillions of cells in your body are the result of repeated cell divisions that began in your mother's body with a single fertilized egg cell.

Another vital function of cell division is reproduction. Many single-celled organisms, such as amoebas,

In certain species of sea star, a severed arm may be able to regrow a whole new body.

reproduce by dividing in half, and the offspring are genetic replicas of the parent. Because it does not involve fertilization of an egg by a sperm, this type of reproduction is called **asexual reproduction**. Offspring produced by asexual reproduction inherit all of their chromosomes from a single parent and are thus genetic duplicates.

Many multicellular organisms can reproduce asexually as well. For example, some sea star species have the ability to grow new individuals from fragmented pieces. And if you've ever grown a houseplant from a clipping, you've observed asexual reproduction in plants. In asexual reproduction, there is one simple principle of inheritance: The lone parent and each of its offspring have identical genes. The type of cell division responsible for asexual reproduction and for the growth and maintenance of multicellular organisms is called mitosis.

Sexual reproduction is different; it requires fertilization of an egg by a sperm. The production of **gametes**—egg and sperm—involves a special type of cell division called meiosis, which occurs only in reproductive organs. As we'll discuss later, a gamete has only half as many chromosomes as the parent cell that gave rise to it.

In summary, two kinds of cell division are involved in the lives of sexually reproducing organisms: mitosis for growth and maintenance and meiosis for reproduction. The remainder of the chapter is divided into two main sections, one devoted to each type of cell division. ✓

✓ CHECKPOINT

Ordinary cell division produces two daughter cells that are genetically identical. Name three functions of this type of cell division. Which of these functions occur in your body?

Answer: cell replacement, growth of an organism, asexual reproduction of an organism; only the first two occur in your body

▶ **Figure 1** **Three functions of cell division by mitosis.**

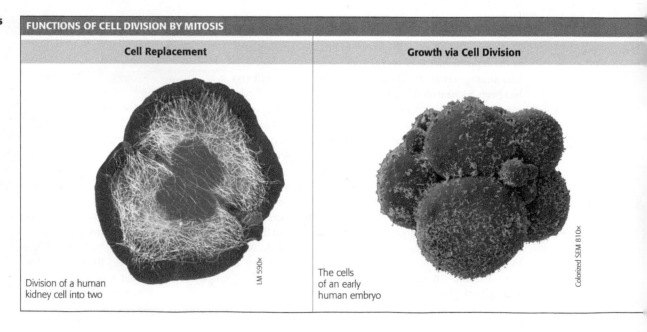

FUNCTIONS OF CELL DIVISION BY MITOSIS

Cell Replacement	Growth via Cell Division

Division of a human kidney cell into two

LM 590x

The cells of an early human embryo

Colorized SEM 810x

The Cell Cycle and Mitosis

Almost all of the genes of a eukaryotic cell—around 21,000 in humans—are located on chromosomes in the cell nucleus. (The main exceptions are genes on small DNA molecules found in mitochondria and chloroplasts.) Because chromosomes are the lead players in cell division, we'll focus on them before turning our attention to the cell as a whole.

If stretched out, the DNA in any one of your cells would be taller than you.

Most of the time, the chromosomes exist as thin fibers that are much longer than the nucleus they are stored in. In fact, if fully extended, the DNA in just one of your cells would be more than 6 feet long! Chromatin in this state is too thin to be seen using a light microscope. As a cell

Eukaryotic Chromosomes

Each eukaryotic chromosome contains one very long DNA molecule, typically bearing thousands of genes. The number of chromosomes in a eukaryotic cell depends on the species **(Figure 2)**. For example, human body cells have 46 chromosomes, while the body cells of a dog have 78 and those of a koala bear have 16. Chromosomes are made up of a material called **chromatin**, fibers composed of roughly equal amounts of DNA and protein molecules. The protein molecules help organize the chromatin and help control the activity of its genes.

▶ **Figure 2 The number of chromosomes in the cells of selected mammals.** Notice that humans have 46 chromosomes and that the number of chromosomes does not correspond to the size or complexity of an organism.

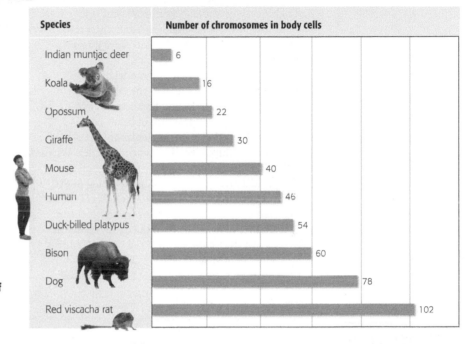

Species	Number of chromosomes in body cells
Indian muntjac deer	6
Koala	16
Opossum	22
Giraffe	30
Mouse	40
Human	46
Duck-billed platypus	54
Bison	60
Dog	78
Red viscacha rat	102

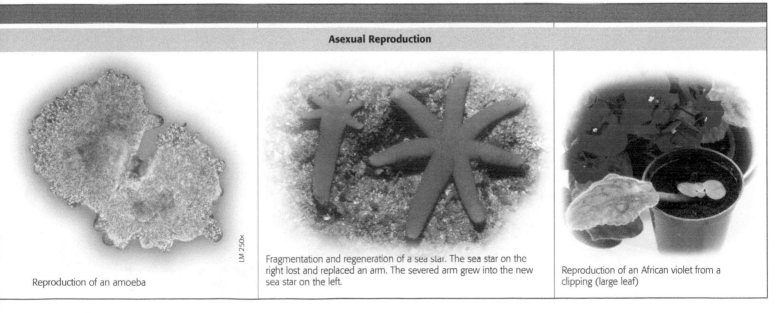

Asexual Reproduction

LM 250x

Reproduction of an amoeba

Fragmentation and regeneration of a sea star. The sea star on the right lost and replaced an arm. The severed arm grew into the new sea star on the left.

Reproduction of an African violet from a clipping (large leaf)

prepares to divide, its chromatin fibers coil up, forming compact chromosomes that become visible under a light microscope (Figure 3).

Such long molecules of DNA can fit into the tiny nucleus because within each chromosome the DNA is packed into an elaborate, multilevel system of coiling and folding. A crucial aspect of DNA packing is the association of the DNA with small proteins called **histones**. Why is it necessary for a cell's chromosomes to be compacted in this way? Imagine that your belongings are spread out around your room. If you had to move, you would gather up all your things and put them in small containers. Similarly, a cell must compact its DNA before it can move it to a new cell.

Figure 4 presents a simplified model of DNA packing. First, histones attach to the DNA. In electron micrographs, the combination of DNA and histones has the appearance of beads on a string. Each "bead," called a **nucleosome**, consists of DNA wound around several histone molecules. When not dividing, the DNA of active genes takes on this lightly packed arrangement. When preparing to divide, chromosomes condense even more: the beaded string itself wraps, loops, and folds into a tight, compact structure, as you can see in the chromosome at the bottom of the figure. Viewed as a whole, Figure 4 gives a sense of how successive levels of coiling and folding enable a huge amount of DNA to fit into a cell's tiny nucleus. Think of a DNA as a length of yarn; a chromosome is then like a skein of yarn, one very long piece that is folded into a tight package for easier handling.

▼ **Figure 4 DNA packing in a eukaryotic chromosome.** Successive levels of coiling of DNA and associated proteins ultimately result in highly compacted chromosomes. The fuzzy appearance of the final chromosome at the bottom arises from the intricate twists and folds of the chromatin fibers.

DNA double helix

Histones

"Beads on a string"

TEM 130,000×

Nucleosome

Duplicated chromosomes (sister chromatids)

Centromere

TEM 9,000×

▼ **Figure 3 A plant cell just before division, with chromosomes colored by stains.**

LM 1,400×

Chromosomes

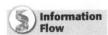

Information Flow

Duplicating Chromosomes

Think of the chromosomes as being like a detailed instruction manual on how to run a cell; during division, the original cell must pass on a copy of the manual to the new cell while also retaining a copy for itself. Before a cell begins the division process, it must therefore duplicate all of its chromosomes. The DNA molecule of each chromosome is copied through the process of DNA replication, and new histone protein molecules attach as needed. The result is that—at this point—each chromosome consists of two copies called **sister chromatids**, which contain identical genes. At the bottom of Figure 4, the two sister chromatids are joined together most tightly at a narrow "waist" called the **centromere**.

When the cell divides, the sister chromatids of a duplicated chromosome separate from each other (**Figure 5**). Once separated from its sister, each chromatid is considered a full-fledged chromosome, and it is identical to the original chromosome. One of the new chromosomes goes to one daughter cell, and the other goes to the other daughter cell. In this way, each daughter cell receives a complete and identical set of chromosomes. A dividing human skin cell, for example, has 46 duplicated chromosomes, and each of the two daughter cells that result from it has 46 single chromosomes.

The Cell Cycle

The rate at which a cell divides depends on its role within the organism's body. Some cells divide once a day, others less often, and some highly specialized cells, such as mature muscle cells, do not divide at all.

The **cell cycle** is the ordered sequence of events that extends from the time a cell is first formed from a dividing parent cell until its own division into two cells. Think of the cell cycle as the "lifetime" of a cell, from its "birth" to its own reproduction. As **Figure 6** shows, most of the cell cycle is spent in **interphase**. Interphase is a time when a cell goes about its usual business, performing its normal functions within the organism. For example,

Chromosome duplication

Sister chromatids

Chromosome distribution to daughter cells

▲ **Figure 5 Duplication and distribution of a single chromosome.** During cell reproduction, the cell duplicates each chromosome and distributes the two copies to the daughter cells.

during interphase a cell in your stomach lining might make and release enzyme molecules that aid in digestion. While in interphase, a cell roughly doubles everything in its cytoplasm. It increases its supply of proteins, increases the number of many of its organelles (such as mitochondria and ribosomes), and grows in size. Typically, interphase lasts for at least 90% of the cell cycle.

From the standpoint of cell reproduction, the most important event of interphase is chromosome duplication, when the DNA in the nucleus is precisely doubled. The period when this occurs is called the S phase (for DNA *synthesis*). The interphase periods before and after the S phase are called the G_1 and G_2 phases, respectively (G stands for *gap*). During G_1, each chromosome is single, and the cell performs its normal functions. During G_2 (after DNA duplication during the S phase), each chromosome in the cell consists of two identical sister chromatids, and the cell prepares to divide.

The part of the cell cycle when the cell is actually dividing is called the **mitotic (M) phase**. It includes two overlapping stages, mitosis and cytokinesis. In **mitosis**, the nucleus and its contents, most importantly the duplicated chromosomes, divide and are evenly distributed, forming two daughter nuclei. During **cytokinesis**, the cytoplasm (along with all the organelles) is divided in two. The combination of mitosis and cytokinesis produces two genetically identical daughter cells, each fully equipped with a nucleus, cytoplasm, organelles, and plasma membrane. ☑

☑ CHECKPOINT

1. A duplicated chromosome consists of two sister _____ joined together at the _____.
2. What are the two broadest divisions of the cell cycle? What two processes are involved in the actual duplication of the cell?

Answers: **1.** *chromatids; centromere* **2.** *interphase and the mitotic phase; mitosis and cytokinesis*

▼ **Figure 6 The eukaryotic cell cycle.** The cell cycle extends from the "birth" of a cell (just after the point indicated by the dark blue arrow at the bottom of the cycle), resulting from cell reproduction, to the time the cell itself divides in two. (During interphase, the chromosomes are diffuse masses of thin fibers; they do not actually appear in the rodlike form you see here.)

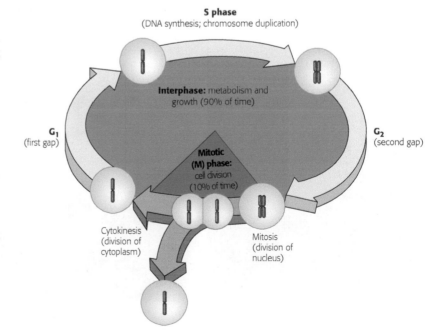

S phase
(DNA synthesis; chromosome duplication)

Interphase: metabolism and growth (90% of time)

G_1 (first gap)

G_2 (second gap)

Mitotic (M) phase: cell division (10% of time)

Cytokinesis (division of cytoplasm)

Mitosis (division of nucleus)

Mitosis and Cytokinesis

Figure 7 illustrates the cell cycle for an animal cell using drawings, descriptions, and photomicrographs. The micrographs running along the bottom row of the page show dividing cells from a salamander, with chromosomes depicted in blue. The drawings in the top row include details that are not visible in the micrographs. In these cells, we illustrate just four chromosomes to keep the process a bit simpler to follow; remember that one of your cells actually contains 46 chromosomes. The text within the figure describes

▼ **Figure 7 Cell reproduction: A dance of the chromosomes.** After the chromosomes duplicate during interphase, the elaborately choreographed stages of mitosis—prophase, metaphase, anaphase, and telophase—distribute the duplicate sets of chromosomes to two separate nuclei. Cytokinesis then divides the cytoplasm, yielding two genetically identical daughter cells.

INTERPHASE	PROPHASE

INTERPHASE

Centrosomes · Uncondensed chromosome · Nuclear envelope · Plasma membrane

Interphase is the period of cell growth when the cell makes new molecules and organelles. At the point shown here, late interphase (G_2), the cytoplasm contains two centrosomes. Within the nucleus, the chromosomes are duplicated, but they cannot be distinguished individually because they are still in the form of loosely packed chromatin fibers.

PROPHASE

Mitotic spindle forming · Centromere · Duplicated chromosome, consisting of two sister chromatids

During prophase, changes occur in both nucleus and cytoplasm. In the nucleus, the chromatin fibers coil, so that the chromosomes become thick enough to be seen individually with a light microscope. Each chromosome exists as two identical sister chromatids joined together at the narrow "waist" of the

Fragments of nuclear envelope · Condensed chromosome · Spindle tracks

centromere. In the cytoplasm, the mitotic spindle begins to form. Late in prophase, the nuclear envelope breaks into pieces. The spindle tracks attach to the centromeres of the chromosomes and move the chromosomes toward the center of the cell.

LM 375x

the events occurring at each stage. Study this figure carefully (it has a lot of information and it's important!) and notice the striking changes in the nucleus and other cellular structures.

Biologists distinguish four main stages of mitosis: **prophase**, **metaphase**, **anaphase**, and **telophase**. The timing of these stages is not precise, and they overlap a bit. Think of stages in your own life—infancy, childhood, adulthood, old age—and you'll realize that the stages run into each other and vary from individual to individual; so it is with the stages of mitosis.

The chromosomes are the stars of the mitotic drama, and their movements depend on the **mitotic spindle**, a football-shaped structure of microtubule tracks (colored green in the figure) that guides the separation of the two sets of daughter chromosomes. The tracks of spindle microtubules grow from structures within the cytoplasm called centrosomes.

METAPHASE	ANAPHASE	TELOPHASE

Condensed chromosomes align

Separated chromosomes

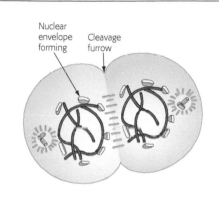

Nuclear envelope forming   Cleavage furrow

The mitotic spindle is now fully formed. The centromeres of all the chromosomes line up between the two poles of the spindle. For each chromosome, the tracks of the mitotic spindle attached to the two sister chromatids pull toward opposite poles. This tug of war keeps the chromosomes in the middle of the cell.

Anaphase begins suddenly when the sister chromatids of each chromosome separate. Each is now considered a full-fledged (daughter) chromosome. The chromosomes move toward opposite poles of the cell as the spindle tracks shorten. Simultaneously, the tracks not attached to chromosomes lengthen, pushing the poles farther apart and elongating the cell.

Telophase begins when the two groups of chromosomes have reached opposite ends of the cell. Telophase is the reverse of prophase: Nuclear envelopes form, the chromosomes uncoil, and the spindle disappears. Mitosis, the division of one nucleus into two genetically identical daughter nuclei, is now finished. Cytokinesis, the division of the cytoplasm, usually occurs with telophase. In animals, a cleavage furrow pinches the cell in two, producing two daughter cells.

▼ Figure 8 **Cytokinesis in animal and plant cells.**

(a) Animal cell cytokinesis

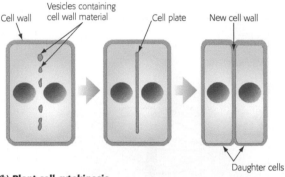

(b) Plant cell cytokinesis

Cytokinesis, the division of the cytoplasm into two cells, usually begins during telophase, overlapping the end of mitosis. In animal cells, the cytokinesis process is known as **cleavage**. The first sign of cleavage is the appearance of a cleavage furrow, an indentation at the equator of the cell. A ring of microfilaments in the cytoplasm just under the plasma membrane contracts, like the pulling of a drawstring on a hooded sweatshirt, deepening the furrow and pinching the parent cell in two **(Figure 8a)**.

Cytokinesis in a plant cell occurs differently. Vesicles containing cell wall material collect at the middle of the cell. The vesicles fuse, forming a membranous disk called the **cell plate**. The cell plate grows outward, accumulating more cell wall material as more vesicles join it. Eventually, the membrane of the cell plate fuses with the plasma membrane, and the cell plate's contents join the parental cell wall. The result is two daughter cells **(Figure 8b)**. ☑

Cancer Cells: Dividing Out of Control

For a plant or animal to grow and maintain its tissues normally, it must be able to control the timing of cell division—speeding up, slowing down, or turning the process off/on as needed. The sequential events of the cell cycle are directed by a **cell cycle control system** that consists of specialized proteins within the cell. These proteins integrate information from the environment and from other body cells and send "stop" and "go-ahead" signals at certain key points during the cell cycle. For example, the cell cycle normally halts within the G_1 phase of interphase unless the cell receives a go-ahead signal via certain control proteins. If that signal never arrives,

Every tumor is the result of a malfunction in cell division.

the cell will switch into a permanently nondividing state. Some of your nerve and muscle cells, for example, are arrested this way. If the go-ahead signal is received and the G_1 checkpoint is passed, the cell will usually complete the rest of the cycle.

What Is Cancer?

Cancer, which currently claims the lives of one out of every five people in the United States and other industrialized nations, is a disease of the cell cycle. Cancer cells do not respond normally to the cell cycle control system; they divide excessively and may invade other tissues of the body. If unchecked, cancer cells may continue to divide until they kill the host. Cancer cells are thus referred to as "immortal" since, unlike other human cells, they will never cease dividing. In fact, thousands of laboratories around the world today use HeLa cells, a laboratory strain of human cells that were originally obtained from a woman named Henrietta Lacks, who died of cervical cancer in 1951.

The abnormal behavior of cancer cells begins when a single cell undergoes genetic changes (mutations) in one or more genes that encode for proteins in the cell cycle control system. These changes cause the cell to grow abnormally. The immune system generally recognizes and destroys such cells. However, if the cell evades destruction, it may proliferate to form a **tumor**, an abnormally growing mass of body cells. If the abnormal cells remain at the original site, the lump is called a **benign tumor**. Benign tumors can cause problems if they grow large and disrupt certain organs, such as the brain, but often they can be completely removed by surgery and are rarely deadly.

In contrast, a **malignant tumor** is one that has the potential to spread into neighboring tissues and other parts of the body, forming new tumors (**Figure 9**). A malignant tumor may or may not have actually begun to spread, but once it does, it will soon displace normal tissue and interrupt organ function. An individual with a malignant tumor is said to have **cancer**. The spread of cancer cells beyond their original site is called **metastasis**. Cancers are named according to where they originate. Liver cancer, for example, always begins in liver tissue and may spread from there.

Cancer Treatment

Once a tumor starts growing in the body, how can it be treated? There are three main types of cancer treatment. Surgery to remove a tumor is usually the first step. For many benign tumors, surgery may be sufficient. If it is not, doctors turn to treatments that attempt to stop cancer cells from dividing. In **radiation therapy**, parts of the body that have cancerous tumors are exposed to concentrated beams of high-energy radiation, which often harm cancer cells more than normal cells. Radiation therapy is often effective against malignant tumors that have not yet spread. However, there is sometimes enough damage to normal body cells to produce side effects, such as nausea and hair loss.

Chemotherapy, the use of drugs to disrupt cell division, is used to treat widespread or metastatic tumors. Chemotherapy drugs work in a variety of ways. Some prevent cell division by interfering with the mitotic spindle. For example, paclitaxel (trade name Taxol) freezes the spindle after it forms, keeping it from functioning. Paclitaxel is made from a chemical discovered in the bark of the Pacific yew, a tree found mainly in the northwestern United States. It has fewer side effects than many other anticancer drugs and seems to be effective against some hard-to-treat cancers of the ovary and breast. Another drug, vinblastine, prevents the mitotic spindle from forming in the first place. Vinblastine was first obtained from the periwinkle plant, which is native to the tropical rain forests of Madagascar. Given these examples, preserving biodiversity may be the key to discovering the next generation of lifesaving anticancer drugs.

Cancer Prevention and Survival

Although cancer can strike anyone, there are certain lifestyle changes you can make to reduce your chances of developing cancer or increase your chances of surviving it. Not smoking, exercising adequately (usually defined as at least 150 minutes of moderate exercise each week), avoiding overexposure to the sun, and eating a high-fiber, low-fat diet can all help reduce the likelihood of getting cancer. Seven types of cancer can be easily detected: skin and oral (via physical exam), breast (via self-exams or mammograms for higher-risk women and women 50 and older), prostate (via rectal exam), cervical (via Pap smear), testicular (via self-exam), and colon (via colonoscopy). Regular visits to the doctor can help identify tumors early, which is the best way to increase the chance of successful treatment. ☑

▼ Figure 9 **Growth and metastasis of a malignant tumor of the breast.**

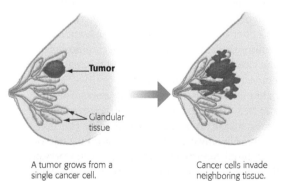

A tumor grows from a single cancer cell.

Cancer cells invade neighboring tissue.

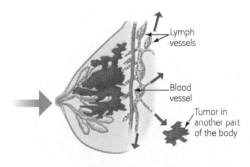

Lymph vessels

Blood vessel

Tumor in another part of the body

Metastasis: Cancer cells spread through lymph and blood vessels to other parts of the body.

Meiosis, the Basis of Sexual Reproduction

Only maple trees produce more maple trees, only goldfish make more goldfish, and only people make more people. These simple facts of life have been recognized for thousands of years and are reflected in the age-old saying, "Like begets like." But in a strict sense, "Like begets like" applies only to asexual reproduction, where offspring inherit all their DNA from a single parent. Asexual offspring are exact genetic replicas of that one parent and of each other, and their appearances are very similar.

The family photo in **Figure 10** makes the point that in a sexually reproducing species, like does not exactly beget like. You probably resemble your biological parents more closely than you resemble strangers, but you do not look exactly like your parents or your siblings—unless you are an identical twin. Each offspring of sexual reproduction inherits a unique combination of genes from its two parents, and this combined set of genes programs a unique combination of traits. As a result, sexual reproduction can produce tremendous variety among offspring.

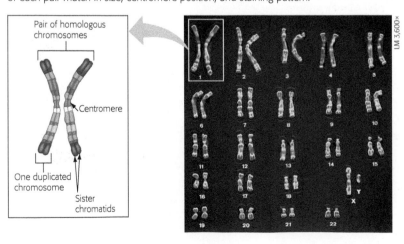

▲ **Figure 10 The varied products of sexual reproduction.** Every child inherits a unique combination of genes from his or her parents and displays a unique combination of traits.

Sexual reproduction depends on the cellular processes of meiosis and fertilization. But before discussing these processes, we need to return to chromosomes and the role they play in the life cycle of sexually reproducing organisms.

Homologous Chromosomes

If we examine cells from different individuals of a single species—sticking to one sex, for now—we find that they have the same number and types of chromosomes. Viewed with a microscope, your chromosomes would look exactly like those of Angelina Jolie (if you're a woman) or Brad Pitt (if you're a man).

A typical body cell, called a **somatic cell**, has 46 chromosomes in humans. A technician can break open a human cell in metaphase of mitosis, stain the chromosomes with dyes, take a picture with the aid of a microscope, and arrange the chromosomes in matching pairs by size. The resulting display is called a **karyotype (Figure 11)**. Notice in the figure that each chromosome is duplicated, with two sister chromatids joined along their length; within the white box, for example, the left "stick" is actually a pair of sister chromatids stuck together (as shown in the drawing to the left). Notice also that almost every chromosome has a twin that resembles it in length and centromere position; in the figure, the white box surrounds one set of twin chromosomes. The two chromosomes of such a matching pair, called **homologous chromosomes**, carry genes controlling the same inherited characteristics. For example, if a gene influencing freckles is located at a particular place on one chromosome—within the yellow band in the drawing in Figure 11, for instance—then the homologous chromosome has that same gene in the same location. However, the two homologous chromosomes may have different versions of the same gene. Let's restate this concept because it often confuses students: A pair of homologous chromosomes has two nearly identical chromosomes, each of which consists of two identical sister chromatids after chromosome duplication.

In human females, the 46 chromosomes fall neatly into 23 homologous pairs. For a male, however, the chromosomes in one pair do not look alike. This non-matching pair, only partly homologous, is the male's sex chromosomes. **Sex chromosomes** determine a person's sex (male versus female). In mammals, males have one X chromosome and one Y chromosome. Females have

▼ **Figure 11 Pairs of homologous chromosomes in a human male karyotype.** This karyotype shows 22 completely homologous pairs (autosomes) and a 23rd pair that consists of an X chromosome and a Y chromosome (sex chromosomes). With the exception of X and Y, the homologous chromosomes of each pair match in size, centromere position, and staining pattern.

Pair of homologous chromosomes

Centromere

One duplicated chromosome

Sister chromatids

LM 3,600×

two X chromosomes. (Other organisms have different systems; in this chapter, we focus on humans.) The remaining chromosomes (44 in humans), found in both males and females, are called **autosomes**. For both autosomes and sex chromosomes, you inherited one chromosome of each pair from your mother and the other from your father.

Gametes and the Life Cycle of a Sexual Organism

The **life cycle** of a multicellular organism is the sequence of stages leading from the adults of one generation to the adults of the next. Having two sets of chromosomes, one inherited from each parent, is a key factor in the life cycle of humans and all other species that reproduce sexually. **Figure 12** shows the human life cycle, emphasizing the number of chromosomes.

Humans (as well as most other animals and many plants) are **diploid** organisms because all body cells contain pairs of homologous chromosomes. In other words, all your chromosomes come in matching sets. This is similar to shoes in your closet: You may have 46 shoes, but they are organized as 23 pairs, with the members of each pair being nearly identical to each other. The total number of chromosomes, 46 in humans, is the diploid number (abbreviated 2*n*). The gametes, egg and sperm cells, are not diploid. Made by meiosis in an ovary or testis, each gamete has a single set of chromosomes: 22 autosomes plus a sex chromosome, either X or Y. A cell with a single chromosome set is called a **haploid** cell; it has only one member of each pair of homologous chromosomes. To visualize the haploid state, imagine your closet containing only one shoe from each pair. For humans, the haploid number, *n*, is 23.

In the human life cycle, a haploid sperm fuses with a haploid egg in a process called **fertilization**. The resulting fertilized egg, called a **zygote**, is diploid. It has two sets of chromosomes, one set from each parent. The life cycle is completed as a sexually mature adult develops from the zygote. Mitotic cell division ensures that all somatic cells of the human body receive a copy of all of the zygote's 46 chromosomes. Thus, every one of the trillions of cells in your body can trace its ancestry back through mitotic divisions to the single zygote produced when your father's sperm and your mother's egg fused about nine months before you were born (although you probably don't want to dwell on those details!).

◄ **Figure 12 The human life cycle.** In each generation, the doubling of chromosome number that results from fertilization is offset by the halving of chromosome number during meiosis.

Producing haploid gametes by meiosis keeps the chromosome number from doubling in every generation. To illustrate, **Figure 13** tracks one pair of homologous chromosomes. **1** Each of the chromosomes is duplicated during interphase (before mitosis). **2** The first division, meiosis I, segregates the two chromosomes of the homologous pair, packaging them in separate (haploid) daughter cells. But each chromosome is still doubled. **3** Meiosis II separates the sister chromatids. Each of the four daughter cells is haploid and contains only a single chromosome from the pair of homologous chromosomes.

▼ **Figure 13 How meiosis halves chromosome number.**

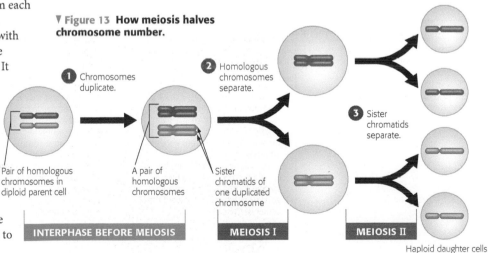

The Process of Meiosis

Meiosis, the process of cell division that produces haploid gametes in diploid organisms, resembles mitosis, but with two important differences. The first difference is that, during meiosis, the number of chromosomes is cut in half. In meiosis, a cell that has duplicated its chromosomes undergoes two consecutive divisions, called meiosis I and meiosis II. Because one duplication of the chromosomes is followed by two divisions, each of the four daughter cells resulting from meiosis has a haploid set of chromosomes—half as many chromosomes as the starting cell.

The second difference of meiosis compared with mitosis is an exchange of genetic material—pieces of chromosomes—between homologous chromosomes. This exchange, called crossing over, occurs during the first prophase of meiosis. We'll look more closely at crossing over later. For now, study **Figure 14,** including the text below it, which describes the stages of meiosis in detail for a hypothetical animal cell containing four chromosomes.

As you go through Figure 14, keep in mind the difference between homologous chromosomes and sister chromatids: The two chromosomes of a homologous pair are individual chromosomes that were inherited

▼ Figure 14 **The stages of meiosis.**

	MEIOSIS I: HOMOLOGOUS CHROMOSOMES SEPARATE

INTERPHASE	PROPHASE I	METAPHASE I	ANAPHASE I
Chromosomes duplicate.	**Homologous chromosomes pair up and exchange segments.**	**Pairs of homologous chromosomes line up.**	**Pairs of homologous chromosomes split up.**

As with mitosis, meiosis is preceded by an interphase during which the chromosomes duplicate. Each chromosome then consists of two identical sister chromatids. The chromosomes consist of uncondensed chromatin fibers.

Prophase I As the chromosomes coil up, special proteins cause the homologous chromosomes to stick together in pairs. The resulting structure has four chromatids. Within each set, chromatids of the homologous chromosomes exchange corresponding segments—they "cross over." Crossing over rearranges genetic information.

As prophase I continues, the chromosomes coil up further, a spindle forms, and the homologous pairs are moved toward the center of the cell.

Metaphase I At metaphase I, the homologous pairs are aligned in the middle of the cell. The sister chromatids of each chromosome are still attached at their centromeres, where they are anchored to spindle tracks. Notice that for each chromosome pair, the spindle tracks attached to one homologous chromosome come from one pole of the cell, and the tracks attached to the other chromosome come from the opposite pole. With this arrangement, the homologous chromosomes are poised to move toward opposite poles of the cell.

Anaphase I The attachment between the homologous chromosomes of each pair breaks, and the chromosomes now migrate toward the poles of the cell. *In contrast to mitosis, the sister chromatids migrate as a pair instead of splitting up.* They are separated not from each other but from their homologous partners.

from different parents, one from the mother and one from the father. The members of a pair of homologous chromosomes in Figure 14 (and later figures) are identical in size and shape but colored in the illustrations differently (red versus blue) to remind you that they differ in this way. In the interphase just before meiosis, each chromosome duplicates to form sister chromatids that remain together until anaphase of meiosis II. Before crossing over occurs, sister chromatids are identical and carry the same versions of all their genes. ✔

LM 900x

Meiosis II in a lily cell

MEIOSIS II: SISTER CHROMATIDS SEPARATE

TELOPHASE I AND CYTOKINESIS	PROPHASE II	METAPHASE II	ANAPHASE II	TELOPHASE II AND CYTOKINESIS

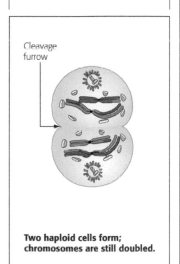

Cleavage furrow

Two haploid cells form; chromosomes are still doubled.

Sister chromatids separate

Haploid daughter cells forming

During another round of cell division, the sister chromatids finally separate; four haploid daughter cells result, containing single chromosomes.

Telophase I and Cytokinesis In telophase I, the chromosomes arrive at the poles of the cell. When they finish their journey, each pole has a haploid chromosome set, although each chromosome is still in duplicate form. Usually, cytokinesis occurs along with telophase I, and two haploid daughter cells are formed.

The Process of Meiosis II Meiosis II is essentially the same as mitosis. The important difference is that meiosis II starts with a haploid cell that has *not* undergone chromosome duplication during the preceding interphase.

During prophase II, a spindle forms and moves the chromosomes toward the middle of the cell. During metaphase II, the chromosomes are aligned as they are in mitosis, with the tracks attached to the sister chromatids of each chromosome coming from opposite poles.

In anaphase II, the centromeres of sister chromatids separate, and the sister chromatids of each pair move toward opposite poles of the cell. In telophase II, nuclei form at the cell poles, and cytokinesis occurs at the same time. There are now four haploid daughter cells, each with single chromosomes.

Review: Comparing Mitosis and Meiosis

You have now learned the two ways that cells of eukaryotic organisms divide (Figure 15). Mitosis—which provides for growth, tissue repair, and asexual reproduction—produces daughter cells that are genetically identical to the parent cell. Meiosis, needed for sexual reproduction, yields genetically unique haploid daughter cells—cells with only one member of each homologous chromosome pair.

For both mitosis and meiosis, the chromosomes duplicate only once, in the preceding interphase. Mitosis involves one division of the nucleus and cytoplasm (duplication, then division in half), producing two

▶ Figure 15 **Comparing mitosis and meiosis.** The events unique to meiosis occur during meiosis I: In prophase I, duplicated homologous chromosomes pair along their lengths, and crossing over occurs between homologous (nonsister) chromatids. In metaphase I, pairs of homologous chromosomes (rather than individual chromosomes) are aligned at the center of the cell. During anaphase I, sister chromatids of each chromosome stay together and go to the same pole of the cell as homologous chromosomes separate. At the end of meiosis I, there are two haploid cells, but each chromosome still has two sister chromatids.

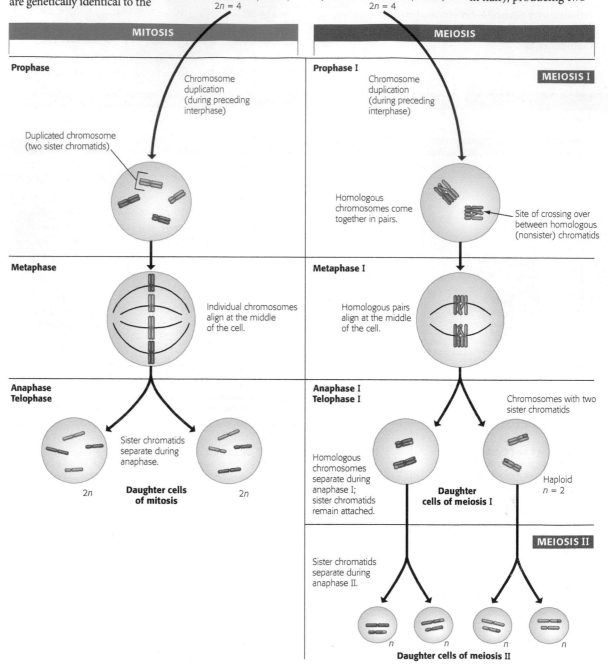

MITOSIS

MEIOSIS

Parent cell
(before chromosome duplication)
$2n = 4$

Parent cell
(before chromosome duplication)
$2n = 4$

Prophase

Chromosome duplication (during preceding interphase)

Duplicated chromosome (two sister chromatids)

Prophase I

MEIOSIS I

Chromosome duplication (during preceding interphase)

Homologous chromosomes come together in pairs.

Site of crossing over between homologous (nonsister) chromatids

Metaphase

Individual chromosomes align at the middle of the cell.

Metaphase I

Homologous pairs align at the middle of the cell.

Anaphase Telophase

Sister chromatids separate during anaphase.

$2n$

Daughter cells of mitosis

$2n$

Anaphase I Telophase I

Chromosomes with two sister chromatids

Homologous chromosomes separate during anaphase I; sister chromatids remain attached.

Daughter cells of meiosis I

Haploid $n = 2$

MEIOSIS II

Sister chromatids separate during anaphase II.

n n n n

Daughter cells of meiosis II

diploid cells. Meiosis entails two nuclear and cytoplasmic divisions (duplication, division in half, then division in half again), yielding four haploid cells.

Figure 15 compares mitosis and meiosis, tracing these two processes for a diploid parent cell with four chromosomes. As before, homologous chromosomes are those matching in size. (Imagine that the red chromosomes were inherited from the mother and the blue chromosomes from the father.) Notice that all the events unique to meiosis occur during meiosis I. Meiosis II is virtually identical to mitosis in that it separates sister chromatids. But unlike mitosis, meiosis II yields daughter cells with a haploid set of chromosomes. ☑

The Origins of Genetic Variation

As we discussed earlier, offspring that result from sexual reproduction are genetically different from their parents and from one another. How does meiosis produce such genetic variation?

Independent Assortment of Chromosomes

Figure 16 illustrates one way in which meiosis contributes to genetic variety. The figure shows how the arrangement of homologous chromosomes at metaphase

of meiosis I affects the resulting gametes. Once again, our example is from a hypothetical diploid organism with four chromosomes (two pairs of homologous chromosomes), with colors used to differentiate homologous chromosomes (red for chromosomes inherited from the mother and blue for chromosomes from the father).

When aligned during metaphase I, the side-by-side orientation of each homologous pair of chromosomes is a matter of chance—either the red or blue chromosome may be on the left or right. Thus, in this example, there are two possible ways that the chromosome pairs can align during metaphase I. In possibility 1, the chromosome pairs are oriented with both red chromosomes on the same side (blue/red and blue/red). In this case, each of the gametes produced at the end of meiosis II has only red or only blue chromosomes (combinations a and b). In possibility 2, the chromosome pairs are oriented differently (blue/red and red/blue). This arrangement produces gametes with one red and one blue chromosome (combinations c and d). Thus, with the two possible arrangements shown in this example, the organism will produce gametes with four different combinations of chromosomes. For a species with more than two pairs of chromosomes, such as humans, every chromosome pair orients independently of all the others at metaphase I. (Chromosomes X and Y behave as a homologous pair in meiosis.)

☑ **CHECKPOINT**
True or false: Both mitosis and meiosis are preceded by chromosome duplication.

Answer: true

◄ **Figure 16 Results of alternative arrangements of chromosomes at metaphase of meiosis I.** The arrangement of chromosomes at metaphase I determines which chromosomes will be packaged together in the haploid gametes.

POSSIBILITY 1 | POSSIBILITY 2

Two equally probable arrangements of chromosomes at metaphase of meiosis I

Metaphase of meiosis II

Gametes

Combination a | Combination b | Combination c | Combination d

Because possibilities 1 and 2 are equally likely, the four possible types of gametes will be made in approximately equal numbers.

For any species, the total number of chromosome combinations that can appear in gametes is 2^n, where n represents the haploid number. For the hypothetical organism in Figure 16, $n = 2$, so the number of chromosome combinations is 2^2, or 4. For a human ($n = 23$), there are 2^{23}, or about 8 million, possible chromosome combinations! This means that every gamete a person produces contains one of about 8 million possible combinations of maternal and paternal chromosomes. When you consider that a human egg cell with about 8 million possibilities is fertilized at random by a human sperm cell with about 8 million possibilities (**Figure 17**), you can see that a single man and a single woman can produce zygotes with 64 trillion combinations of chromosomes!

Crossing Over

So far, we have focused on genetic variety in gametes and zygotes at the whole-chromosome level. We'll now take a closer look at **crossing over**, the exchange of corresponding segments between nonsister chromatids of homologous chromosomes, which occurs during prophase I of meiosis. **Figure 18** shows crossing over between two homologous chromosomes and the resulting gametes. At the time that crossing over begins very early in prophase I, homologous chromosomes are closely paired all along their lengths, with a precise gene-by-gene alignment.

The exchange of segments between nonsister chromatids—one maternal chromatid and one paternal chromatid of a homologous pair—adds to the genetic variety resulting from sexual reproduction. In Figure 18, if there were no crossing over, meiosis could produce only two types of gametes: the ones ending up with chromosomes that exactly match the parents' chromosomes, either all blue or all red (as in Figure 16). With crossing over, gametes arise

▼ **Figure 17 The process of fertilization: a close-up view.** Here you see many human sperm contacting an egg. Only one sperm can add its chromosomes to produce a zygote.

Colorized LM 1320×

▼ **Figure 18 The results of crossing over during meiosis for a single pair of homologous chromosomes.** A real cell has multiple pairs of homologous chromosomes that produce a huge variety of recombinant chromosomes in the gametes.

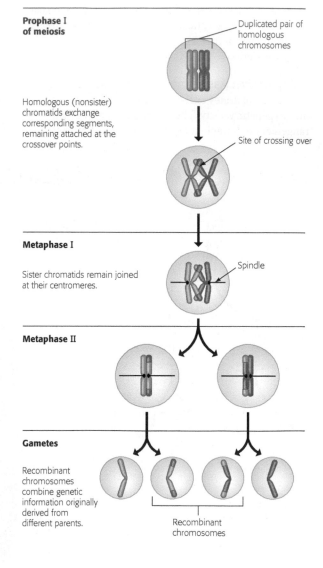

Prophase I of meiosis

Homologous (nonsister) chromatids exchange corresponding segments, remaining attached at the crossover points.

Duplicated pair of homologous chromosomes

Site of crossing over

Metaphase I

Sister chromatids remain joined at their centromeres.

Spindle

Metaphase II

Gametes

Recombinant chromosomes combine genetic information originally derived from different parents.

Recombinant chromosomes

with chromosomes that are partly from the mother and partly from the father. These chromosomes are called "recombinant" because they result from genetic recombination, the production of gene combinations different from those carried by the parental chromosomes.

Because most chromosomes contain thousands of genes, a single crossover event can affect many genes. When we also consider that multiple crossovers can occur in each pair of homologous chromosomes, it's not surprising that gametes and the offspring that result from them are so incredibly varied. ☑

Life with and without Sex THE PROCESS OF SCIENCE

Do All Animals Have Sex?

As discussed in the Biology and Society section, some species such as Komodo dragons can reproduce via both sexual and asexual routes. Although some animal species can reproduce asexually, very few animals reproduce *only* asexually. In fact, evolutionary biologists have traditionally considered asexual reproduction an evolutionary dead end (for reasons we'll discuss in the Evolution Connection section at the end of the chapter).

To investigate a case in which asexual reproduction seemed to be the norm, researchers from Harvard University studied a group of animals called bdelloid rotifers (Figure 19). This class of nearly microscopic freshwater invertebrates includes more than 300 known species. Despite hundreds of years of **observations**, no one had ever found bdelloid rotifer males or evidence of sexual reproduction. But the possibility remained that bdelloids had sex very infrequently or that the males were impossible to recognize by appearance. Thus, the Harvard research team posed the following **question**: Does this entire class of animals reproduce solely by asexual means?

The researchers formed the **hypothesis** that bdelloid rotifers have indeed thrived for millions of years without sexually reproducing. But how could this hypothesis be tested? In most species, the two versions of a gene in a pair of homologous chromosomes are very similar due to the constant trading of genes during sexual reproduction. If a species has survived without sex for millions of years, the researchers reasoned, then changes in the DNA sequences of homologous genes should accumulate independently, and the two versions of the genes should have significantly diverged from each other over time. This led to the **prediction** that bdelloid rotifers would display much more variation in their pairs of homologous genes than most organisms.

In a simple but elegant **experiment**, the researchers compared the sequences of a particular gene in bdelloid and non-bdelloid rotifers. Their **results** were striking. Among non-bdelloid rotifers that reproduce sexually, the two homologous versions of the gene were nearly identical, differing by only 0.5% on average. In contrast, the two versions of the same gene in bdelloid rotifers differed by 3.5–54%. These data provided strong evidence that bdelloid rotifers have evolved for millions of years without any sexual reproduction.

▶ Figure 19
A bdelloid rotifer.

When Meiosis Goes Awry

So far, our discussion of meiosis has focused on the process as it normally and correctly occurs. But what happens when there is an error in the process? Such a mistake can result in genetic abnormalities that range from mild to severe to fatal.

How Accidents during Meiosis Can Alter Chromosome Number

Within the human body, meiosis occurs repeatedly as the testes or ovaries produce gametes. Almost always, chromosomes are distributed to daughter cells without any errors. But occasionally there is a mishap, called a **nondisjunction**, in which the members of a chromosome pair fail to separate at anaphase. Nondisjunction can occur during meiosis I or II (Figure 20). In either case, gametes with abnormal numbers of chromosomes are the result.

Figure 21 shows what can happen when an abnormal gamete produced by nondisjunction unites with a normal gamete during fertilization. When a normal sperm fertilizes an egg cell with an extra chromosome,

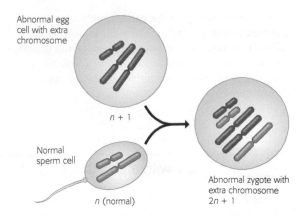

▲ Figure 21 **Fertilization after nondisjunction in the mother.**

the result is a zygote with a total of $2n + 1$ chromosomes. Because mitosis duplicates the chromosomes as they are, the abnormality will be passed to all embryonic cells. If the organism survives, it will have an abnormal karyotype and probably a medical disorder caused by the abnormal number of genes. ✔

✔ **CHECKPOINT**

Explain how nondisjunction in meiosis could result in a diploid gamete.

Answer: A diploid gamete would result if there were nondisjunction of all the chromosomes during meiosis I or II.

▼ Figure 20 **Two types of nondisjunction.** In both examples in the figure, the cell at the top is diploid ($2n$), with two pairs of homologous chromosomes.

NONDISJUNCTION IN MEIOSIS I	NONDISJUNCTION IN MEIOSIS II

Meiosis I

Nondisjunction: Pair of homologous chromosomes fails to separate.

Meiosis II

Nondisjunction: Sister chromatids fail to separate.

Gametes

Number of chromosomes

$n + 1$	$n + 1$	$n - 1$	$n - 1$		$n + 1$	$n - 1$	n	n
Abnormal gametes					**Abnormal gametes**		**Normal gametes**	

Down Syndrome: An Extra Chromosome 21

Figure 11 showed a normal human comple ment of 23 pairs of chromosomes. Compare it with the karyotype in **Figure 22**; besides having two X chromosomes (because it's from a female), the karyotype in Figure 22 has three number 21 chromosomes. Because this person is triploid for chromosome 21 (instead of the usual diploid condition),

Having too few or too many chromosomes is almost always fatal.

▼ **Figure 22 Trisomy 21 and Down syndrome.** This child displays the characteristic facial features of Down syndrome. The karyotype (bottom) shows trisomy 21; notice the three copies of chromosome 21.

LM 4,000×

Trisomy 21

they have 47 chromosomes in total. This condition is called **trisomy 21**.

In most cases, a human embryo with an atypical number of chromosomes is spontaneously aborted (miscarried) long before birth, often before the woman is even aware that she is pregnant. In fact, some doctors speculate that miscarriages due to genetic defects occur in nearly one-quarter of all pregnancies, although this number is difficult to verify. However, some aberrations in chromosome number seem to upset the genetic balance less drastically, and individuals with such abnormalities can survive. These people usually have a characteristic set of symptoms, called a syndrome. A person with trisomy 21 has a condition called **Down syndrome** (named after John Langdon Down, an English physician who first described this condition in 1866).

Affecting about 1 out of every 700 children, trisomy 21 is the most common chromosome number abnormality and the most common serious birth defect in the United States. Down syndrome includes characteristic facial features—frequently a fold of skin at the inner corner of the eye, a round face, and a flattened nose—as well as short stature, heart defects, and susceptibility to leukemia and Alzheimer's disease. People with Down syndrome usually have a life span shorter than normal. They also exhibit varying degrees of developmental delays. However, some individuals with the syndrome may live to middle age or beyond, and many are socially adept and can function well within society. Although no one is sure why, the risk of Down syndrome increases with the age of the mother, climbing to about 1% risk for mothers at age 40. The fetuses of pregnant women age 35 and older are therefore candidates for chromosomal prenatal screenings. ☑

Abnormal Numbers of Sex Chromosomes

Trisomy 21 is an autosomal nondisjunction. Nondisjunction in meiosis can also lead to abnormal numbers of sex chromosomes, X and Y. Unusual numbers of sex chromosomes seem to upset the genetic balance less than unusual numbers of autosomes. This may be because the Y chromosome is very small and carries relatively few genes. Furthermore, mammalian cells normally operate with only one functioning X chromosome because other copies of the chromosome become inactivated in each cell.

Table 1 lists the most common human sex chromosome abnormalities. An extra X chromosome in a male,

Table 1	Abnormalities of Sex Chromosome Number in Humans		
Sex Chromosomes	**Syndrome**	**Origins of Nondisjunction**	**Frequency in Population**
XXY	Klinefelter syndrome (male)	Meiosis in egg or sperm formation	$\frac{1}{2,000}$
XYY	None (normal male)	Meiosis in sperm formation	$\frac{1}{2,000}$
XXX	None (normal female)	Meiosis in egg or sperm formation	$\frac{1}{1,000}$
XO	Turner syndrome (female)	Meiosis in egg or sperm formation	$\frac{1}{5,000}$

making him XXY, produces a condition called Klinefelter syndrome. If untreated, men with this disorder have male sex organs, but the testes are abnormally small, the individual is sterile, and he often has breast enlargement and other feminine body contours. These symptoms can be reduced through administration of the sex hormone testosterone. Klinefelter syndrome is also found in individuals with more than three sex chromosomes, such as XXYY, XXXY, or XXXXY. These abnormal numbers of sex chromosomes result from multiple nondisjunctions.

Human males with a single extra Y chromosome (XYY) do not have any well-defined syndrome, although they tend to be taller than average. Females with an extra X chromosome (XXX) cannot be distinguished from XX females except by karyotype.

Females who are lacking an X chromosome are designated XO; the O indicates the absence of a second sex chromosome. These women have Turner syndrome. They have a characteristic appearance, including short stature and often a web of skin extending between the neck and shoulders. Women with Turner syndrome are of normal intelligence, but are sterile. If left untreated, they have poor development of breasts and other secondary sex characteristics. Administration of estrogen can alleviate those symptoms. The XO condition is the sole known case where having only 45 chromosomes is not fatal in humans.

Notice the crucial role of the Y chromosome in determining a person's sex. In general, a single Y chromosome is enough to produce biological maleness, regardless of the number of X chromosomes. The absence of a Y chromosome results in biological femaleness. ☑

Life with and without Sex EVOLUTION CONNECTION

▼ Figure 23 **Sexual and asexual reproduction.** Many plants, such as this strawberry, have the ability to reproduce both sexually (via flowers that produce fruit) and asexually (via runners).

Runner →

The Advantages of Sex

Throughout this chapter, we've examined cell division within the context of reproduction. Like the Komodo dragon discussed in the Biology and Society section, many species (including a few dozen animal species, but many more among the plant kingdom) can reproduce both sexually and asexually (Figure 23). An important advantage of asexual reproduction is that there is no need for a partner. Asexual reproduction may thus confer an evolutionary advantage when organisms are sparsely distributed (on an isolated island, for example) and unlikely to meet a mate. Furthermore, if an organism is superbly suited to a stable environment, asexual reproduction has the advantage of passing on its entire genetic legacy intact. Asexual reproduction also eliminates the need to expend energy forming gametes and copulating with a partner.

In contrast to plants, the vast majority of animals reproduce by sexual means. There are exceptions, such as the few species that can reproduce via parthenogenesis and the bdelloid rotifers discussed in the Process of Science section. But most animals reproduce only through sex. Therefore, sex must enhance evolutionary fitness. But how? The answer remains elusive. Most hypotheses focus on the unique combinations of genes formed during meiosis and fertilization. By producing offspring of varied genetic makeup, sexual reproduction may enhance survival by speeding adaptation to a changing environment. Another idea is that shuffling genes during sexual reproduction might reduce the incidence of harmful genes more rapidly. But for now, one of biology's most basic questions—Why have sex?—remains a hotly debated topic that is the focus of much ongoing research.

Chapter Review

SUMMARY OF KEY CONCEPTS

What Cell Reproduction Accomplishes

Cell reproduction, also called cell division, produces genetically identical daughter cells:

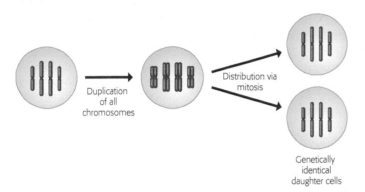

Some organisms use mitosis (ordinary cell division) to reproduce. This is called asexual reproduction, and it results in offspring that are genetically identical to the lone parent and to each other. Mitosis also enables multicellular organisms to grow and develop and to replace damaged or lost cells. Organisms that reproduce sexually, by the union of a sperm with an egg cell, carry out meiosis, a type of cell division that yields gametes with only half as many chromosomes as body (somatic) cells.

The Cell Cycle and Mitosis

Eukaryotic Chromosomes

The genes of a eukaryotic genome are grouped into multiple chromosomes in the nucleus. Each chromosome contains one very long DNA molecule, with many genes, that is wrapped around histone proteins. Individual chromosomes are coiled up and therefore visible with a light microscope only when the cell is in the process of dividing; otherwise, they are in the form of thin, loosely packed chromatin fibers.

Information Flow: Duplicating Chromosomes

Because chromosomes contain the information needed to control cellular processes, they must be copied and distributed to daughter cells. Before a cell starts dividing, the chromosomes duplicate, producing sister chromatids (containing identical DNA) joined together at the centromere.

The Cell Cycle

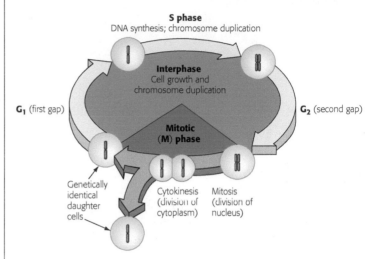

Mitosis and Cytokinesis

Mitosis is divided into four phases: prophase, metaphase, anaphase, and telophase. At the start of mitosis, the chromosomes coil up and the nuclear envelope breaks down (prophase). Next, a mitotic spindle made of microtubule tracks moves the chromosomes to the middle of the cell (metaphase). The sister chromatids then separate and are moved to opposite poles of the cell (anaphase), where two new nuclei form (telophase). Cytokinesis overlaps the end of mitosis. In animals, cytokinesis occurs by cleavage, which pinches the cell in two. In plants, a membranous cell plate divides the cell in two. Mitosis and cytokinesis produce genetically identical cells.

Cancer Cells: Dividing Out of Control

When the cell cycle control system malfunctions, a cell may divide excessively and form a tumor. Cancer cells may grow to form malignant tumors, invade other tissues (metastasize), and even kill the host. Surgery can remove tumors, and radiation and chemotherapy are effective as treatments because they interfere with cell division. You can increase the likelihood of surviving some forms of cancer through lifestyle changes and regular screenings.

Meiosis, the Basis of Sexual Reproduction

Homologous Chromosomes

The somatic cells (body cells) of each species contain a specific number of chromosomes; human cells have 46, made up of 23 pairs of homologous chromosomes. The chromosomes of a homologous pair carry genes for the same characteristics at the same places. Mammalian males have X and Y sex chromosomes (only partly homologous), and females have two X chromosomes.

Gametes and the Life Cycle of a Sexual Organism

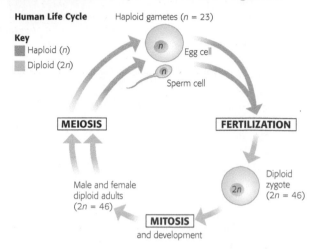

Human Life Cycle

Key
- ■ Haploid (*n*)
- ■ Diploid (2*n*)

Haploid gametes (*n* = 23)

n Egg cell

n Sperm cell

MEIOSIS

FERTILIZATION

Diploid zygote (2*n* = 46)

Male and female diploid adults (2*n* = 46)

MITOSIS
and development

The Process of Meiosis

Meiosis, like mitosis, is preceded by chromosome duplication. But in meiosis, the cell divides twice to form four daughter cells. The first division, meiosis I, starts with the pairing of homologous chromosomes. In crossing over, homologous chromosomes exchange corresponding segments. Meiosis I separates the members of the homologous pairs and produces two daughter cells, each with one set of (duplicated) chromosomes. Meiosis II is essentially the same as mitosis; in each of the cells, the sister chromatids of each chromosome separate.

Review: Comparing Mitosis and Meiosis

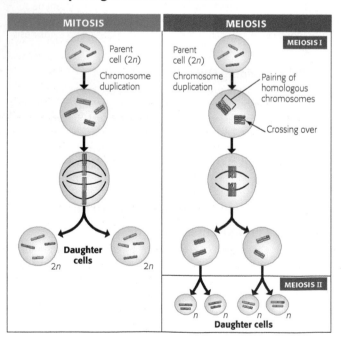

MITOSIS

Parent cell (2*n*)

Chromosome duplication

Daughter cells
2*n*   2*n*

MEIOSIS

MEIOSIS I

Parent cell (2*n*)

Chromosome duplication

Pairing of homologous chromosomes

Crossing over

MEIOSIS II

Daughter cells
n   *n*   *n*   *n*

The Origins of Genetic Variation

Because the chromosomes of a homologous pair come from different parents, they carry different versions of many of their genes. The large number of possible arrangements of chromosome pairs at metaphase of meiosis I leads to many different combinations of chromosomes in eggs and sperm. Random fertilization of eggs by sperm greatly increases the variation. Crossing over during prophase of meiosis I increases variation still further.

When Meiosis Goes Awry

Sometimes a person has an abnormal number of chromosomes, which causes problems. Down syndrome is caused by an extra copy of chromosome 21. The abnormal chromosome count is a product of nondisjunction, the failure of a pair of homologous chromosomes to separate during meiosis I or of sister chromatids to separate during meiosis II. Nondisjunction can also produce gametes with extra or missing sex chromosomes, which lead to varying degrees of malfunction but do not usually affect survival.

MasteringBiology®

For practice quizzes, BioFlix animations, MP3 tutorials, video tutors, and more study tools designed for this text, go to MasteringBiology®

■ SELF-QUIZ

1. Which of the following is not a function of mitosis in humans?
   a. repair of wounds
   b. growth
   c. production of gametes from diploid cells
   d. replacement of lost or damaged cells

2. In what sense are the two daughter cells produced by mitosis identical?

3. Why is it difficult to observe individual chromosomes during interphase?

4. A biochemist measures the amount of DNA in cells growing in the laboratory. The quantity of DNA in a cell would be found to double
   a. between prophase and anaphase of mitosis.
   b. between the G_1 and G_2 phases of the cell cycle.
   c. during the M phase of the cell cycle.
   d. between prophase I and prophase II of meiosis.

5. Which two phases of mitosis are essentially opposites in terms of changes in the nucleus?

6. Complete the following table to compare mitosis and meiosis:

	Mitosis	Meiosis
a. Number of chromosomal duplications		
b. Number of cell divisions		
c. Number of daughter cells produced		
d. Number of chromosomes in daughter cells		
e. How chromosomes line up during metaphase		
f. Genetic relationship of daughter cells to parent cells		
g. Functions performed in the human body		

7. If an intestinal cell in a dog contains 78 chromosomes, a dog sperm cell would contain _____ chromosomes.

8. A micrograph of a dividing cell from a mouse shows 19 chromosomes, each consisting of two sister chromatids. During which stage of meiosis could this micrograph have been taken? (Explain your answer.)

9. Tumors that remain at their site of origin are called _____, and tumors that have cells that can migrate to other body tissues are called _____.

10. A diploid body (somatic) cell from a fruit fly contains eight chromosomes. This means that _____ different combinations of chromosomes are possible in its gametes.

11. Although nondisjunction is a random event, there are many more individuals with an extra chromosome 21, which causes Down syndrome, than individuals with an extra chromosome 3 or chromosome 16. Propose an explanation for this.

THE PROCESS OF SCIENCE

12. A mule is the offspring of a horse and a donkey. A donkey sperm contains 31 chromosomes and a horse egg has 32 chromosomes, so the zygote contains a total of 63 chromosomes. The zygote develops normally. The combined set of chromosomes is not a problem in mitosis, and the mule combines some of the best characteristics of horses and donkeys. However, a mule is sterile; meiosis cannot occur normally in its testes or ovaries. Explain why mitosis is normal in cells containing both horse and donkey chromosomes but the mixed set of chromosomes interferes with meiosis.

13. You prepare a slide with a thin slice of an onion root tip. You see the following view in a light microscope. Identify the stage of mitosis for each of the outlined cells, a–d.

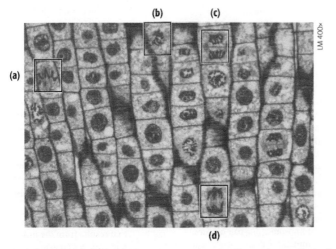

14. **Interpreting Data** The graph in the right hand column shows the incidence of Down syndrome in the offspring of normal parents as the age of the mother increases. For women under the age of 30, how many infants with Down syndrome are born per 1,000 births? How many for women at age 40? At age 50? How many times more likely is a 50-year-old woman to give birth to a baby with Down syndrome than a 30-year-old woman?

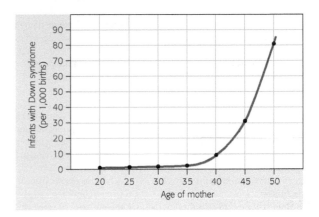

BIOLOGY AND SOCIETY

15. As described in the Biology and Society section, some species (including some endangered species) have been shown to be capable of reproduction via parthenogenesis, without participation of a mate. What implications might this have on efforts to repopulate endangered species? What drawbacks might a parthenogenesis program have on the well-being of the species it targets?

16. Every year, about a million Americans are diagnosed with cancer. This means that about 75 million Americans now living will eventually have cancer, and one in five will die of the disease. There are many kinds of cancers and many causes of the disease. For example, smoking causes most lung cancers. Overexposure to ultraviolet rays in sunlight causes most skin cancers. There is evidence that a high-fat, low-fiber diet is a factor in breast, colon, and prostate cancers. And agents in the workplace, such as asbestos and vinyl chloride, are also implicated as causes of cancer. Hundreds of millions of dollars are spent each year in the search for effective treatments for cancer, yet far less money is spent on preventing cancer. Why might this be true? What kinds of lifestyle changes can you make to help reduce your risk of cancer? What kinds of prevention programs could be initiated or strengthened to encourage these changes? What factors might impede such changes and programs? Should we devote more of our resources to treating cancer or to preventing it? Defend your position.

17. The practice of buying and selling gametes, particularly eggs from fertile women, is becoming increasingly common in the United States and some other industrialized countries. Do you have any objections to this type of transaction? Would you be willing to sell your gametes? At any price? Whether you are willing to do so or not, do you think that other people should be restricted from doing so?

Glossary

anaphase
The third stage of mitosis, beginning when sister chromatids separate from each other and ending when a complete set of daughter chromosomes has arrived at each of the two poles of the cell.

asexual reproduction
The creation of genetically identical offspring by a single parent, without the participation of gametes (sperm and egg).

autosome
A chromosome not directly involved in determining the sex of an organism; in mammals, for example, any chromosome other than X or Y.

benign tumor
An abnormal mass of cells that remains at its original site in the body.

cancer
A malignant growth or tumor caused by abnormal and uncontrolled cell division.

cell cycle control system
A cyclically operating set of proteins that triggers and coordinates events in the eukaryotic cell cycle.

cell division
The reproduction of a cell.

cell plate
A membranous disk that forms across the midline of a dividing plant cell. During cytokinesis, the cell plate grows outward, accumulating more cell wall material and eventually fusing into a new cell wall.

centromere (sen'-trō-mer)
The region of a chromosome where two sister chromatids are joined and where spindle microtubules attach during mitosis and meiosis. The centromere divides at the onset of anaphase during mitosis and anaphase II of meiosis.

chemotherapy (kē'-mō-ther'-uh-pē)
Treatment for cancer in which drugs are administered to disrupt cell division of the cancer cells.

cleavage
The process of cytokinesis in animal cells, characterized by pinching of the plasma membrane.

crossing over
The exchange of segments between chromatids of homologous chromosomes during prophase I of meiosis.

cytokinesis (sī'-tō-kuh-nē'-sis)
The division of the cytoplasm to form two separate daughter cells. Cytokinesis usually occurs during telophase of mitosis, and the two processes (mitosis and cytokinesis) make up the mitotic (M) phase of the cell cycle.

diploid (dip'-loid)
Containing two sets of chromosomes (pairs of homologous chromosomes) in each cell, one set inherited from each parent; referring to a 2n cell.

Down syndrome
A human genetic disorder resulting from a condition called trisomy 21, the presence of an extra chromosome 21; characterized by heart and respiratory defects and varying degrees of developmental disability.

fertilization
The union of a haploid sperm cell with a haploid egg cell, producing a zygote.

gamete (gam'-ēt)
A sex cell; a haploid egg or sperm. The union of two gametes of opposite sex (fertilization) produces a zygote.

haploid
Containing a single set of chromosomes; referring to an n cell.

histone (his'-tōn)
A small protein molecule associated with DNA and important in DNA packing in the eukaryotic chromosome.

homologous chromosomes (hō-mol'-uh-gus)
The two chromosomes that make up a matched pair in a diploid cell. Homologous chromosomes are of the same length, centromere position, and staining pattern and possess genes for the same characteristics at corresponding loci. One homologous chromosome is inherited from the organism's father, the other from the mother.

interphase
The phase in the eukaryotic cell cycle when the cell is not actually dividing. During interphase, cellular metabolic activity is high, chromosomes and organelles are duplicated, and cell size may increase. Interphase accounts for 90% of the cell cycle. *See also* mitosis.

karyotype (kār'-ē-ō-tīp)
A display of micrographs of the metaphase chromosomes of a cell, arranged by size and centromere position.

life cycle
The entire sequence of stages in the life of an organism, from the adults of one generation to the adults of the next.

malignant tumor
An abnormal tissue mass that spreads into neighboring tissue and to other parts of the body; a cancerous tumor.

meiosis (mī-ō'-sis)
In a sexually reproducing organism, the process of cell division that produces haploid gametes from diploid cells within the reproductive organs.

metaphase (met'-eh-fāz)
The second stage of mitosis. During metaphase, the centromeres of all the cell's duplicated chromosomes are lined up along the center line of the cell.

metastasis (muh-tas'-tuh-sis)
The spread of cancer cells beyond their original site.

mitosis (mī-tō'-sis)
The division of a single nucleus into two genetically identical daughter nuclei. Mitosis and cytokinesis make up the mitotic (M) phase of the cell cycle.

mitotic (M) phase
The phase of the cell cycle when mitosis divides the nucleus and distributes its chromosomes to the daughter nuclei and cytokinesis divides the cytoplasm, producing two daughter cells.

mitotic spindle
A spindle-shaped structure formed of microtubules and associated proteins that is involved in the movement of chromosomes during mitosis and meiosis. (A spindle is shaped roughly like a football.)

nondisjunction
An accident of meiosis or mitosis in which a pair of homologous chromosomes or a pair of sister chromatids fails to separate at anaphase.

nucleosome (nū'-klē-ō-sōm)
The bead-like unit of DNA packing in a eukaryotic cell; consists of DNA wound around a protein core made up of eight histone molecules.

prophase
The first stage of mitosis. During prophase, duplicated chromosomes condense to form structures visible with a light microscope, and the mitotic spindle forms and begins moving the chromosomes toward the center of the cell.

radiation therapy
Treatment for cancer in which parts of the body that have cancerous tumors are exposed to high-energy radiation to disrupt cell division of the cancer cells.

sex chromosome
A chromosome that determines whether an individual is male or female; in mammals, for example, the X or Y chromosome.

sexual reproduction
The creation of genetically distinct offspring by the fusion of two haploid sex cells (gametes: sperm and egg), forming a diploid zygote.

sister chromatid (krō'-muh-tid)
One of the two identical parts of a duplicated chromosome. While joined, two sister chromatids make up one chromosome; chromatids are eventually separated during mitosis or meiosis II.

somatic cell (sō-mat'-ik)
Any cell in a multicellular organism except a sperm or egg cell or a cell that develops into a sperm or egg; a body cell.

telophase
The fourth and final stage of mitosis, during which daughter nuclei form at the two poles of a cell. Telophase usually occurs together with cytokinesis.

trisomy 21
See Down syndrome.

tumor
An abnormal mass of cells that forms within otherwise normal tissue.

zygote (zī'-gōt)
The fertilized egg, which is diploid, that results from the union of haploid gametes (sperm and egg) during fertilization.

Credits

Credits are listed in the order of appearance.

Self-Quiz Answers

1. c
2. They have identical genes (DNA).
3. They are in the form of very long, thin strands.
4. b
5. prophase and telophase
6. a. 1, 1; b. 1, 2; c. 2, 4; d. $2n$, n; e. individually, by homologous pair; f. identical, unique; g. repair, growth, asexual reproduction; gamete formation
7. 39
8. Prophase II or metaphase II; it cannot be during meiosis I because then you would see an even number of chromosomes; it cannot be during a later stage of meiosis II because then you would see the sister chromatids separated.
9. benign; malignant
10. 16 ($2n = 8$, so $n = 4$ and $2^n = 2^4 = 16$)
11. Nondisjunction would create just as many gametes with an extra copy of chromosome 3 or 16, but extra copies of chromosome 3 or 16 are probably fatal.

Patterns of Inheritance

From Chapter 9 of *Campbell Essential Biology with Physiology*, Fifth Edition. Eric J. Simon, Jean L. Dickey, Kelly A. Hogan, Jane B. Reece. Copyright © 2016 by Pearson Education, Inc. All rights reserved.

Patterns of Inheritance

Hemophilia is more prevalent among European royalty than commoners because of past intermarriage. ▼

▲ Your mother's genes had no role in determining your sex.

Because the ► environment helps shape your appearance, identical twins aren't identical in every way.

Dog Breeding BIOLOGY AND SOCIETY

Our Longest-Running Genetic Experiment

The adorable canine in the photo to the right is a purebred Cavalier King Charles Spaniel. If you were to mate two purebred "Cavs," you'd expect the offspring to display the traits that distinguish this breed, such as a silky coat, long elegant ears, and gentle eyes. This is a reasonable expectation because each purebred dog has a well-documented pedigree that includes several generations of ancestors with similar genetic makeup and appearance. But similarities among purebred Cavaliers extend beyond mere appearance: Cavs are generally energetic, obedient, sweet, and gentle—traits that make these dogs particularly well suited to act as companion or therapy dogs. Such behavioral similarities suggest that dog breeders can select for personality as well as physical traits. Cavaliers have four standard coat types—Blenheim (chestnut brown on white, seen at right, named after Blenheim Palace in England, where such dogs were first bred), black and tan, ruby, and tricolor (black, white, and tan)—reminding us that even within a purebred line, there remains significant variation of certain traits.

Purebred pooches are living proof that dogs are more than man's best friend: They are also one of our longest-running genetic experiments. Evidence (which we'll explore at the end of this chapter) suggests that people have selected and mated dogs with preferred traits for more than 15,000 years. Nearly every modern Cavalier, for example, can trace its ancestry back to a single pair that were brought to America by a breeder in 1952. These original dogs were chosen due to their desired shape and temperament. Similar choices were made for every modern dog breed. Over thousands of years, such genetic tinkering has led to the incredible variety of body types and behaviors we have today, from huge, docile Great Danes to tiny, spunky Chihuahuas.

Breeding a best friend. Dogs, such as this Cavalier King Charles Spaniel, are one of humankind's longest running genetic experiments.

Although people have been applying genetics for thousands of years—by breeding food crops (such as wheat, rice, and corn) as well as domesticated animals (such as cows, sheep, and goats)—the biological principles underlying genetics have only recently been understood. In this chapter, you will learn the basic rules of how genetic traits are passed from generation to generation and how the behavior of chromosomes accounts for these rules. In the process, you will learn how to predict the ratios of offspring with particular traits. At several points in the chapter, we'll return to the subject of dog breeding to help illustrate genetic principles.

Genetics and Heredity

Heredity is the transmission of traits from one generation to the next. **Genetics**, the scientific study of heredity, began in the 1860s, when an Augustinian monk named Gregor Mendel (**Figure 1**) deduced its fundamental principles by breeding garden peas. Mendel lived and worked in an abbey in Brunn, Austria (now Brno, in the Czech Republic). Strongly influenced by his study of physics, mathematics, and chemistry at the University of Vienna, his research was both experimentally and mathematically rigorous, and these qualities were largely responsible for his success.

In a paper published in 1866, Mendel correctly argued that parents pass on to their offspring discrete genes (which he termed "heritable factors") that are responsible for inherited traits, such as purple flowers or round seeds in pea plants. (It is interesting to note that Mendel's publication came just seven years after Darwin's 1859 publication of *On the Origin of Species*, making the 1860s a banner decade in the advent of modern biology.) In his paper, Mendel stressed that genes retain their individual identities generation after generation, no matter how they are mixed up or temporarily masked.

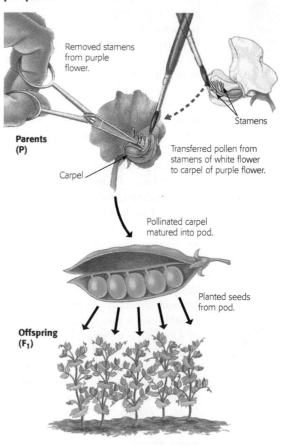

▲ Figure 1
Gregor Mendel.

reach the carpel. When he wanted to fertilize one plant with pollen from a different plant, he pollinated the plants by hand, as shown in **Figure 3**. Thus, Mendel was always sure of the parentage of his new plants.

Each of the characters Mendel chose to study, such as flower color, occurred in two distinct traits. Mendel worked with his plants until he was sure he had purebred varieties—that is, varieties for which self-fertilization produced offspring all identical to the parent. For instance, he identified a purple-flowered variety that, when self-fertilized, always produced offspring plants that had all purple flowers.

Next Mendel was ready to ask what would happen when he crossed different purebred varieties with each other. For example, what offspring would result if plants with purple flowers and plants with white flowers were

▼ Figure 3 **Mendel's technique for cross-fertilizing pea plants.**

Removed stamens from purple flower.

Parents (P)

Carpel

Stamens

Transferred pollen from stamens of white flower to carpel of purple flower.

Pollinated carpel matured into pod.

Planted seeds from pod.

Offspring (F_1)

In an Abbey Garden

Mendel probably chose to study garden peas because they were easy to grow and they came in many readily distinguishable varieties. For example, one variety has purple flowers and another variety has white flowers. A heritable feature that varies among individuals, such as flower color, is called a **character**. Each variant of a character, such as purple or white flowers, is called a **trait**.

Perhaps the most important advantage of pea plants as an experimental model was that Mendel could strictly control their reproduction. The petals of a pea flower (**Figure 2**) almost completely enclose the egg-producing organ (the carpel) and the sperm-producing organs (the stamens). Consequently, in nature, pea plants usually self-fertilize because sperm-carrying pollen grains released from the stamens land on the tip of the egg-containing carpel of the same flower. Mendel could ensure self-fertilization by covering a flower with a small bag so that no pollen from another plant could

▼ Figure 2 **The structure of a pea flower.** To reveal the reproductive organs—the stamens and carpel—one of the petals has been removed in this drawing.

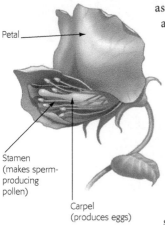

Petal

Stamen (makes sperm-producing pollen)

Carpel (produces eggs)

cross-fertilized as shown in Figure 3? The offspring of two different purebred varieties are called **hybrids**, and the cross-fertilization itself is referred to as a genetic **cross**. The parental plants are called the **P generation**, and their hybrid offspring are the **F₁ generation** (F for *filial*, from the Latin for "son" or "daughter"). When F₁ plants self-fertilize or fertilize each other, their offspring are the **F₂ generation**. ☑

Mendel's Law of Segregation

Mendel performed many experiments in which he tracked the inheritance of characters, such as flower color, that occur as two alternative traits (Figure 4). The results led him to formulate several hypotheses about inheritance. Let's look at some of his experiments and follow the reasoning that led to his hypotheses.

▼ **Figure 4 The seven characters of pea plants studied by Mendel.** Each character comes in the two alternative traits shown here.

	Dominant	Recessive
Flower color	Purple	White
Flower position	Axial	Terminal
Seed color	Yellow	Green
Seed shape	Round	Wrinkled
Pod shape	Inflated	Constricted
Pod color	Green	Yellow
Stem length	Tall	Dwarf

Monohybrid Crosses

Figure 5 shows a cross between a purebred pea plant with purple flowers and a purebred pea plant with white flowers. This is called a **monohybrid cross** because only one character is being studied—flower color in this case. Mendel saw that the F_1 plants all had purple flowers. Was the factor responsible for inheritance of white flowers now lost as a result of the cross? By mating the F_1 plants with each other, Mendel found the answer to this question to be no. Of the 929 F_2 plants he bred, about three-fourths (705) had purple flowers and one-fourth (224) had white flowers; that is, there were about three purple F_2 plants for every white plant, or a 3:1 ratio of purple to white. Mendel figured out that the gene for white flowers did not disappear in the F_1 plants but was somehow hidden or masked when the purple-flower factor was present. He also deduced that the F_1 plants must have carried two factors for the flower-color character, one for purple and one for white. From these results and others, Mendel developed four hypotheses:

1. *There are alternative versions of genes that account for variations in inherited characters.* For example, the gene for flower color in pea plants exists in one form for purple and another for white. The alternative versions of a gene are called **alleles**.

2. *For each inherited character, an organism inherits two alleles, one from each parent.* These alleles may be the same or different. An organism that has two identical alleles for a gene is said to be **homozygous** for that gene (and is called a homozygote). An organism that has two different alleles for a gene is said to be **heterozygous** for that gene (and is called a heterozygote).

3. *If the two alleles of an inherited pair differ, then one determines the organism's appearance and is called the **dominant allele**; the other has no noticeable effect on the organism's appearance and is called the **recessive allele**.* Geneticists use uppercase italic letters (such as *P*) to represent dominant alleles and lowercase italic letters (such as *p*) to represent recessive alleles.

4. *A sperm or egg carries only one allele for each inherited character because the two alleles for a character segregate (separate) from each other during the production of gametes.* This statement is called the **law of segregation**. When sperm and egg unite at fertilization, each contributes its alleles, restoring the paired condition in the offspring.

Figure 6 illustrates Mendel's law of segregation, which explains the inheritance pattern shown in Figure 5. Mendel's hypotheses predict that when alleles segregate during gamete formation in the F_1 plants, half the gametes will receive a purple-flower allele (*P*) and the other half a white-flower allele (*p*). During pollination among the F_1 plants, the gametes unite randomly. An egg with a purple-flower allele has an equal chance of being fertilized by a sperm with a purple-flower allele or one with a white-flower allele (that is, a *P* egg may fuse with a *P* sperm or a *p* sperm). Because the same is true for an egg with a white-flower allele (a *p* egg with a *P* sperm or *p* sperm), there are a total of four equally likely combinations of sperm and egg.

The diagram at the bottom of Figure 6, called a **Punnett square**, repeats the cross shown in Figure 5 in a way that highlights the four possible combinations of gametes and the resulting four possible offspring in the F_2 generation. Each square represents an equally probable product of fertilization. For example, the box in the upper right corner of the Punnett square shows the genetic combination resulting from a *p* sperm fertilizing a *P* egg.

According to the Punnett square, what will be the physical appearance of these F_2 offspring? One-fourth of the plants have two alleles specifying purple flowers (*PP*); clearly, these plants will have purple flowers. One-half (two-fourths) of the F_2 offspring have inherited one

▼ **Figure 5 Mendel's cross tracking one character (flower color).** Note the 3:1 ratio of purple flowers to white flowers in the F_2 generation.

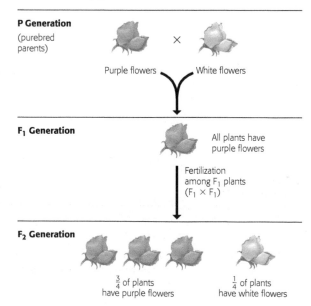

P Generation
(purebred parents)

×

Purple flowers   White flowers

F_1 Generation

All plants have purple flowers

Fertilization among F_1 plants ($F_1 \times F_1$)

F_2 Generation

$\frac{3}{4}$ of plants have purple flowers

$\frac{1}{4}$ of plants have white flowers

▼ Figure 6 **The law of segregation.**

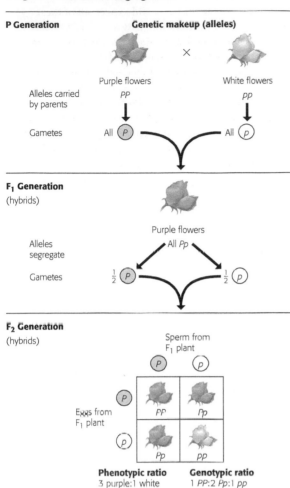

Mendel found that each of the seven characters he studied had the same inheritance pattern: A parental trait disappeared in the F_1 generation, only to reappear in one-fourth of the F_2 offspring. The underlying mechanism is explained by Mendel's law of segregation: Pairs of alleles segregate (separate) during gamete formation; the fusion of gametes at fertilization creates allele pairs again. Research since Mendel's day has established that the law of segregation applies to all sexually reproducing organisms, including people.

Genetic Alleles and Homologous Chromosomes

Before continuing with Mendel's experiments, let's consider how an understanding of chromosomes fits with what we've said about genetics so far. The diagram in **Figure 7** shows a pair of homologous chromosomes—chromosomes that carry alleles of the same genes. Recall that every diploid cell, whether from a pea plant or a person, has pairs of homologous chromosomes. One member of each pair comes from the organism's female parent and the other member of each pair comes from the male parent. Each labeled band on the chromosomes in the figure represents a gene **locus** (plural, *loci*), a specific location of a gene along the chromosome. You can see the connection between Mendel's law of segregation and homologous chromosomes: Alleles (alternative versions) of a gene reside at the same locus on homologous chromosomes. However, the two chromosomes may bear either identical alleles or different ones at any one locus. In other words, the organisms may be homozygous or heterozygous for the gene at that locus. We will return to the chromosomal basis of Mendel's law later in the chapter. ☑

☑ **CHECKPOINT**

1. Genes come in different versions called _____. What term describes the condition where the two copies are identical? What term describes the condition where the two copies are different?
2. If two plants have the same genotype, must they have the same phenotype? If two plants have the same phenotype, must they have the same genotype?
3. You carry two alleles for every trait. Where did these alleles come from?

Answers: 1. alleles; homozygous; heterozygous. 2. Yes; No: One could be homozygous for the dominant allele whereas the other is heterozygous. 3. One is from your father via his sperm and one is from your mother via her egg.

allele for purple flowers and one allele for white flowers (*Pp*); like the F_1 plants, these plants will also have purple flowers, the dominant trait. (Note that *Pp* and *pP* are equivalent and usually written as *Pp*.) Finally, one-fourth of the F_2 plants have inherited two alleles specifying white flowers (*pp*) and will express this recessive trait. Thus, Mendel's model accounts for the 3:1 ratio that he observed in the F_2 generation.

Geneticists distinguish between an organism's physical appearance, called its **phenotype** (such as purple or white flowers), and its genetic makeup, called its **genotype** (such as *PP*, *Pp*, or *pp*). Now we can see that Figure 5 shows only the phenotypes and Figure 6 both the genotypes and phenotypes in our sample cross. For the F_2 plants, the ratio of plants with purple flowers to those with white flowers (3:1) is called the phenotypic ratio. The genotypic ratio is 1(*PP*):2(*Pp*):1(*pp*).

▼ Figure 7 **The relationship between alleles and homologous chromosomes.** The matching colors of corresponding loci highlight the fact that homologous chromosomes carry alleles for the same genes at the same positions along their lengths.

Mendel's Law of Independent Assortment

In addition to flower color, Mendel studied two other pea plant characters: seed shape (round versus wrinkled) and seed color (yellow versus green). From tracking these characters one at a time in monohybrid crosses, Mendel knew that the allele for round shape (designated R) was dominant to the allele for wrinkled shape (r) and that the allele for yellow seed color (Y) was dominant to the allele for green seed color (y). What would result from a **dihybrid cross**, the mating of parental varieties differing in two characters? Mendel crossed homozygous plants having round-yellow seeds (genotype $RRYY$) with plants having wrinkled-green seeds ($rryy$). As shown in **Figure 8**, the union of RY and ry gametes from the P generation yielded

hybrids heterozygous for both characters ($RrYy$)—that is, dihybrids. As we would expect, all of these offspring, the F_1 generation, had round-yellow seeds (the two dominant traits). But were the two characters transmitted from parents to offspring as a package, or was each character inherited independently of the other?

The question was answered when Mendel crossed the F_1 plants with each other. If the genes for the two characters were inherited together (Figure 8a), then the F_1 hybrids would produce only the same two kinds of gametes that they received from their parents. In that case, the F_2 generation would show a 3:1 phenotypic ratio (three plants with round-yellow seeds for every one with wrinkled-green seeds), as in the Punnett square in Figure 8a. If, however, the two seed characters sorted independently, then the F_1 generation would produce four gamete genotypes—RY, rY, Ry, and ry—in equal

▼ **Figure 8 Testing alternative hypotheses for gene assortment in a dihybrid cross.** Only hypothesis B was supported by Mendel's data.

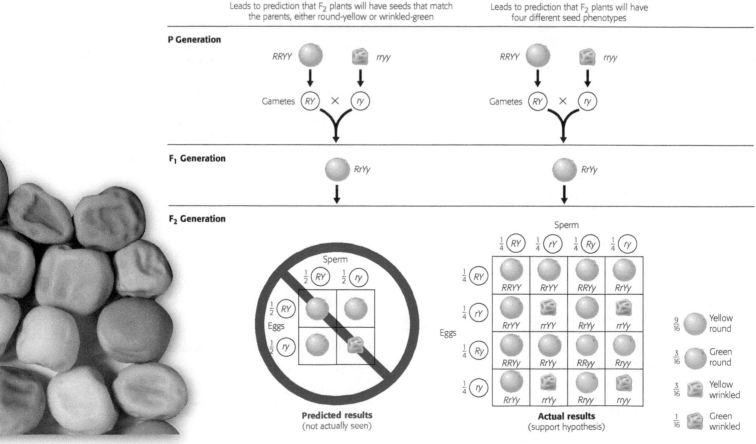

quantities. The Punnett square in Figure 8b shows all possible combinations of alleles that can result in the F$_2$ generation from the union of four kinds of sperm with four kinds of eggs. If you study the Punnett square, you'll see that it predicts nine different genotypes in the F$_2$ generation. These nine genotypes will produce four different phenotypes in a ratio of 9:3:3:1.

The Punnett square in Figure 8b also reveals that a dihybrid cross is equivalent to two monohybrid crosses occurring simultaneously. From the 9:3:3:1 ratio, we can see that there are 12 plants in the F$_2$ generation with round seeds compared to 4 with wrinkled seeds, and 12 yellow-seeded plants compared to four green-seeded ones. These 12:4 ratios each reduce to 3:1, which is the F$_2$ ratio for a monohybrid cross. Mendel tried his seven pea characters in various dihybrid combinations and always observed a 9:3:3:1 ratio (or two simultaneous 3:1 ratios) of phenotypes in the F$_2$ generation. These results supported the hypothesis that *each pair of alleles segregates independently of the other pairs of alleles during gamete formation*. In other words, the inheritance of one character has no effect on the inheritance of another. This is called Mendel's **law of independent assortment**.

For another application of the law of independent assortment, examine the dog breeding experiment described in **Figure 9**. The inheritance of two characters in Labrador retrievers is controlled by separate genes: black versus chocolate coat color, and normal vision versus the eye disorder progressive retinal atrophy (PRA). Black Labs have at least one copy of an allele called *B*. The *B* allele is dominant to *b*, so only the coats of dogs with genotype *bb* are chocolate in color. The allele that causes PRA, called *n*, is recessive to allele *N*, which is necessary for normal vision. Thus, only dogs of genotype *nn* become blind from PRA. If you mate two doubly heterozygous (*BbNn*) Labs (bottom of Figure 9), the phenotypic ratio of the offspring (F$_2$) is 9:3:3:1. These results resemble the F$_2$ results in Figure 8, demonstrating that the coat color and PRA genes are inherited independently. ☑

☑ CHECKPOINT

Looking at Figure 9, what is the ratio of black coat to chocolate coat in Labs? Of normal vision to blindness?

Answer: 3:1; 3:1

▼ **Figure 9 Independent assortment of genes in Labrador retrievers.**
Blanks in the genotypes indicate alleles that can be either dominant or recessive.

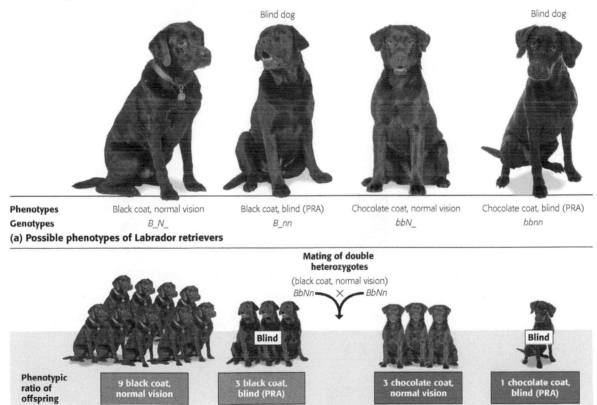

Phenotypes	Black coat, normal vision	Black coat, blind (PRA)	Chocolate coat, normal vision	Chocolate coat, blind (PRA)
Genotypes	*B_N_*	*B_nn*	*bbN_*	*bbnn*

(a) Possible phenotypes of Labrador retrievers

Mating of double heterozygotes
(black coat, normal vision)
BbNn —— × —— *BbNn*

Phenotypic ratio of offspring	9 black coat, normal vision	3 black coat, blind (PRA)	3 chocolate coat, normal vision	1 chocolate coat, blind (PRA)

(b) A Labrador dihybrid cross

Using a Testcross to Determine an Unknown Genotype

Suppose you have a Labrador retriever with a chocolate coat. Consulting Figure 9, you can tell that its genotype must be *bb*, the only combination of alleles that produces the chocolate-coat phenotype. But what if you have a black Lab? It could have one of two possible genotypes—*BB* or *Bb*—and there is no way to tell which genotype is the correct one by looking at the dog. To determine your dog's genotype, you could perform a **testcross**, a mating between an individual of dominant phenotype but unknown genotype (your black Lab) and a homozygous recessive individual—in this case, a *bb* chocolate Lab.

Figure 10 shows the offspring that could result from such a mating. If, as shown on the left, the black Lab parent's genotype is *BB*, we would expect all the offspring to be black, because a cross between genotypes *BB* and *bb* can produce only *Bb* offspring. On the other hand, if the black Lab parent is *Bb*, we would expect both black (*Bb*) and chocolate (*bb*) offspring. Thus, the appearance of the offspring may reveal the original black dog's genotype. ☑

▼ **Figure 10 A Labrador retriever testcross.** To determine the genotype of a black Lab, it can be crossed with a chocolate Lab (homozygous recessive, *bb*). If all the offspring are black, the black parent most likely had genotype *BB*. If any of the offspring are chocolate, the black parent must be heterozygous (*Bb*).

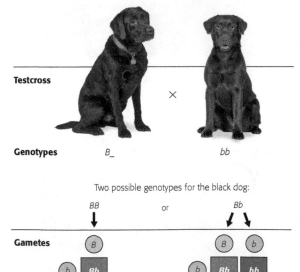

The Rules of Probability

Mendel's strong background in mathematics served him well in his studies of inheritance. For instance, he understood that genetic crosses obey the rules of probability—the same rules that apply when tossing coins, rolling dice, or drawing cards. An important lesson we can learn from tossing coins is that for each and every toss, the probability of heads is $\frac{1}{2}$. Even if heads has landed five times in a row, the probability of the next toss coming up heads is still $\frac{1}{2}$. In other words, the outcome of any particular toss is unaffected by what has happened on previous attempts. Each toss is an independent event.

If two coins are tossed simultaneously, the outcome for each coin is an independent event, unaffected by the other coin. What is the chance that both coins will land heads-up? The probability of such a dual event is the product of the separate probabilities of the independent events—for the coins, $\frac{1}{2} \times \frac{1}{2} = \frac{1}{4}$. This is called the **rule of multiplication**, and it holds true for independent events that occur in genetics as well as coin tosses, as shown in **Figure 11**. In our dihybrid cross of Labradors (see Figure 9), the genotype of the F_1 dogs

▼ **Figure 11 Segregation of alleles and fertilization as chance events.** When heterozygotes (*Bb*) form gametes, segregation of alleles during sperm and egg formation is like two separately tossed coins (that is, two independent events).

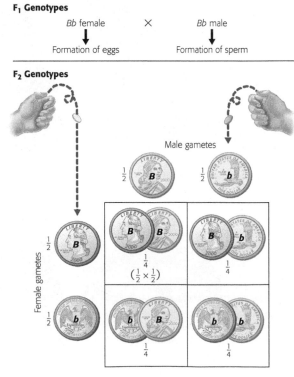

for coat color was *Bb*. What is the probability that a particular F_2 dog will have the *bb* genotype? To produce a *bb* offspring, both egg and sperm must carry the *b* allele. The probability that an egg from a *Bb* dog will have the *b* allele is $\frac{1}{2}$, and the probability that a sperm will have the *b* allele is also $\frac{1}{2}$. By the rule of multiplication, the probability that two *b* alleles will come together at fertilization is $\frac{1}{2} \times \frac{1}{2} = \frac{1}{4}$. This is exactly the answer given by the Punnett square in Figure 11. If we know the genotypes of the parents, we can predict the probability for any genotype among the offspring. By applying the rules of probability to segregation and independent assortment, we can solve some rather complex genetics problems. ☑

Family Pedigrees

Mendel's laws apply to the inheritance of many human traits. **Figure 12** illustrates alternative forms of three human characters that are each thought to be determined by simple dominant-recessive inheritance of one gene. (The genetic basis of many other human characters—such as eye and hair color—is much more complex and poorly understood.) If we call the dominant allele of any such gene *A*, the dominant phenotype results from either the homozygous genotype *AA* or the heterozygous genotype *Aa*. Recessive phenotypes result only from the homozygous genotype *aa*. In genetics, the word *dominant* does not imply that a phenotype is either normal or more common than a recessive phenotype; **wild-type traits** (those seen most often in nature) are not necessarily specified by dominant alleles. In genetics, dominance means that a heterozygote (*Aa*), carrying only a single copy of a dominant allele, displays the dominant phenotype. By contrast, the phenotype of the corresponding recessive allele is seen only in a homozygote (*aa*). Recessive traits may in fact be more common in the population than dominant ones. For example, the absence of freckles (*ff*) is more common than their presence (*FF* or *Ff*).

How can human genetics be studied? Researchers working with pea plants or Labrador retrievers can perform testcrosses. But geneticists who study people obviously cannot control the mating of their research participants. Instead, they must analyze the results of matings that have already occurred. First, the geneticist collects as much information as possible about a family's history for a trait. Then the researcher assembles this information into a family tree, called a **pedigree**. (You may associate pedigrees with purebred animals such as racehorses and champion dogs, but they can be used to represent human matings just as well.) To analyze a pedigree, the geneticist applies logic and Mendel's laws.

☑ CHECKPOINT

Using a standard 52-card deck, what is the probability of being dealt an ace? What about being dealt an ace or a king? What about being dealt an ace and then another ace?

Answer: $\frac{1}{13}$ (4 aces/52 cards); $\frac{4}{13}(\frac{8}{52}) \times \frac{3}{51}$ (because there are 3 aces left in a deck with 51 cards remaining) = 0.0045, or $\frac{1}{221}$

Freckles

Widow's peak

Free earlobe

No freckles

Straight hairline

Attached earlobe

DOMINANT TRAITS

RECESSIVE TRAITS

◀ Figure 12 **Examples of inherited human traits thought to be controlled by a single gene.**

Let's apply this approach to the example in **Figure 13**, a pedigree tracing the incidence of free versus attached earlobes. The letter *F* stands for the dominant allele for free earlobes, and *f* symbolizes the recessive allele for attached earlobes. In the pedigree, □ represents a male, ○ represents a female, colored symbols (■ and ●) indicate that the person has the trait being investigated (in this case, attached earlobes), and an unshaded symbol represents a person who does not have the trait (that person has free earlobes). The earliest (oldest) generation is at the top of the pedigree, and the most recent generation is at the bottom.

By applying Mendel's laws, we can deduce that the attached allele is recessive because that is the only way that Kevin can have attached earlobes when neither of his parents (Hal and Ina) do. We can therefore label all the individuals with attached earlobes in the pedigree (that is, all those with colored circles or squares) as homozygous recessive (*ff*).

Mendel's laws enable us to deduce the genotypes for most of the people in the pedigree. For example, Hal and Ina must have carried the *f* allele (which they passed on to Kevin) along with the *F* allele that gave them free earlobes. The same must be true of Aaron and Betty because they both have free earlobes but Fred and Gabe have attached earlobes. For each of these cases, Mendel's laws and simple logic allow us to definitively assign a genotype.

Notice that we cannot deduce the genotype of every member of the pedigree. For example, Lisa must have at least one *F* allele, but she could be *FF* or *Ff*. We cannot distinguish between these two possibilities using the available data. Perhaps future generations will provide the data that solve this mystery. ✓

Human Disorders Controlled by a Single Gene

The human genetic disorders listed in **Table 1** are known to be inherited as dominant or recessive traits controlled by a single gene. These disorders therefore show simple inheritance patterns like the ones Mendel studied in pea plants. The genes involved are all located on autosomes, chromosomes other than the sex chromosomes X and Y.

Recessive Disorders

Most human genetic disorders are recessive. They range in severity from harmless to life-threatening. Most people who have recessive disorders are born to normal parents who are both heterozygotes—that is, parents who are **carriers** of the recessive allele for the disorder but appear normal themselves.

Using Mendel's laws, we can predict the fraction of affected offspring that is likely to result from a marriage between two carriers. Consider a form of inherited deafness caused by a recessive allele. Suppose two heterozygous carriers (*Dd*) have a child. What is the probability that the child will be deaf? As the Punnett square

▼ Figure 13 **A family pedigree showing inheritance of free versus attached earlobes.**

First generation
(grandparents)

Aaron *Ff* — Betty *Ff*   Cletus *ff* — Debbie *Ff*

Second generation
(parents, aunts, and uncles)

Evelyn *FF or Ff*   Fred *ff*   Gabe *ff*   Hal *Ff*   Ina *Ff*   Julia *ff*

Third generation
(brother and sister)

Kevin *ff*   Lisa *FF or Ff*

Female   Male
● □ Attached
○ □ Free

Table 1	Some Autosomal Disorders in People
Disorder	**Major Symptoms**
Recessive Disorders	
Albinism	Lack of pigment in skin, hair, and eyes
Cystic fibrosis	Excess mucus in lungs, digestive tract, liver; increased susceptibility to infections; death in early childhood unless treated
Phenylketonuria (PKU)	Accumulation of phenylalanine in blood; lack of normal skin pigment; mental retardation unless treated
Sickle-cell disease	Sickled red blood cells; damage to many tissues
Tay-Sachs disease	Lipid accumulation in brain cells; mental deficiency; blindness; death in childhood
Dominant Disorders	
Achondroplasia	Dwarfism
Alzheimer's disease (one type)	Mental deterioration; usually strikes late in life
Huntington's disease	Mental deterioration and uncontrollable movements; strikes in middle age
Hypercholesterolemia	Excess cholesterol in blood; heart disease

in **Figure 14** shows, each child of two carriers has a $\frac{1}{4}$ chance of inheriting two recessive alleles. Thus, we can say that about one-fourth of the children of this couple are likely to be deaf. We can also say that a hearing child from such a family has a $\frac{2}{3}$ chance of being a carrier (that is, on average, two out of three of the offspring with the hearing phenotype will be *Dd*). We can apply this same method of pedigree analysis and prediction to any genetic trait controlled by a single gene.

The most common lethal genetic disease in the United States is **cystic fibrosis (CF)**. Affecting about 30,000 Americans, the recessive CF allele is carried by about 1 in 31 Americans. A person with two copies of this allele has cystic fibrosis, which is characterized by an excessive secretion of very thick mucus from the lungs, pancreas, and other organs. This mucus can interfere with breathing, digestion, and liver function and makes the person vulnerable to recurrent bacterial infections. Although there is no cure for this fatal disease, a special diet, antibiotics to prevent infection, frequent pounding of the chest and back to clear the lungs, and other treatments can greatly extend life. Once invariably fatal in childhood, advances in CF treatment have raised the median survival age of Americans with CF to 37. ☑

Dominant Disorders

A number of human disorders are caused by dominant alleles. Some are harmless, such as extra fingers and toes or digits that are webbed. A serious but nonlethal disorder caused by a dominant allele is achondroplasia, a form of dwarfism in which the head and torso develop

▼ **Figure 14** **Predicted offspring when both parents are carriers for a recessive disorder.**

Parents

Hearing *Dd* × Hearing *Dd*

Offspring

Sperm: *D*, *d*
Eggs: *D*, *d*

	D Sperm	*d*
D	DD Hearing	Dd Hearing (carrier)
d	Dd Hearing (carrier)	dd Deaf

☑ Checkpoint
A man and a woman who are both carriers of cystic fibrosis have had three children without cystic fibrosis. If the couple has a fourth child, what is the probability that the child will have the disorder?

Answers: $\frac{1}{4}$ (The genotypes and phenotypes of their other children are irrelevant.)

normally but the arms and legs are short. The homozygous dominant genotype (*AA*) causes death of the embryo, and therefore only heterozygotes (*Aa*), individuals with a single copy of the defective allele, have this disorder. This also means that a person with achondroplasia has a 50% chance of passing the condition on to any children (**Figure 15**). Therefore, all those who do not have achondroplasia, more than 99.99% of the population, are homozygous for the recessive allele (*aa*). This example makes it clear that a dominant allele is not necessarily more common in a population than the corresponding recessive allele.

Dominant alleles that cause lethal disorders are much less common than lethal recessive alleles. One example is the allele that causes Huntington's disease, a degeneration of the nervous system that usually does not begin until middle age. Once the deterioration of the nervous system begins, it is irreversible and inevitably fatal. Because the allele for Huntington's disease is dominant, any child born to a parent with the allele has a 50% chance of inheriting the allele and the disorder. This example makes it clear that a dominant allele is not necessarily "better" than the corresponding recessive allele.

One way that geneticists study human traits is to find similar genes in animals, which can then be studied in greater detail through controlled matings and other experiments. Let's return to the chapter thread—dog breeding—to investigate the furry coats of man's best friend.

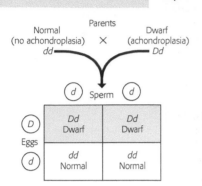

▲ Figure 15 **A Punnett square illustrating a family with and without achondroplasia.**

Dog Breeding THE PROCESS OF SCIENCE

What Is the Genetic Basis of Coat Variation in Dogs?

You've probably made the **observation** that compared with most mammals, dogs come in a wide variety of physical types. For instance, dog coats can be short or long, straight or curly or wire-haired (having a "moustache" and "eyebrows"). Sometimes a single breed, such as the fox terrier, may display two or more of these variations (**Figure 16**).

In 2005, the complete genome of a dog—the sequence of all the DNA of a female boxer named Tasha—was published. Since that time, canine geneticists have added a wealth of data from other breeds. In 2009, an international group of researchers set out to investigate the **question** of the genetic basis for canine coats. They proposed the **hypothesis** that a comparison of genes from a wide variety of dogs with different coats would identify the genes responsible. They made the **prediction** that mutations in just a few genes could account for the coat appearance. Their **experiment** compared DNA sequences in 622 dogs from dozens of breeds. Their **results** identified three genes that in different combinations produced seven different coat appearances, from very short hair to full, thick, wired hair. The difference between the two dogs in the photo, for example, is due to a change in a single gene that regulates keratin, a protein that is one of the primary structural components of hair.

This experiment shows how the extreme range of phenotypes in dogs combined with the availability of genome sequences can be used to provide insight into interesting genetic questions. Indeed, similar research has uncovered the genetic basis of other dog traits, such as body size, hairlessness, and coat color.

▼ Figure 16 **Smooth versus wired fox terrier.** The fox terrier, like several other breeds, comes in smooth (left) and wired (right) coats.

Genetic Testing

Until relatively recently, the onset of symptoms was the only way to know if a person had inherited an allele that might lead to disease. Today, there are many tests that can detect the presence of disease-causing alleles in an individual's genome.

Most genetic tests are performed during pregnancy if the prospective parents are aware that they have an increased risk of having a baby with a genetic disease. Genetic testing before birth usually requires the collection of fetal cells. In amniocentesis, a physician uses a needle to extract about 2 teaspoons of the fluid that bathes the developing fetus (Figure 17). In chorionic villus sampling, a physician inserts a narrow, flexible tube through the mother's vagina and into her uterus, removing some placental tissue. Once cells are obtained, they can be screened for genetic diseases.

Because amniocentesis and chorionic villus sampling have risks of complications, these techniques are usually reserved for situations in which the possibility of a genetic disease is high. Alternatively, blood tests on the mother at 15 to 20 weeks of pregnancy can help identify fetuses at risk for certain birth defects. The most widely used blood test measures levels of a protein called AFP in the mother's blood; abnormally high levels may indicate developmental defects in the fetus, while abnormally low levels may indicate Down syndrome. For a more complete risk profile, a woman's doctor may order a "triple screen test," which measures AFP as well as two other hormones produced by the placenta. Abnormal levels of these substances in the maternal blood may also point to a risk of Down syndrome. Newer genetic screening procedures involve isolating tiny amounts of fetal cells or DNA released into the mother's bloodstream. Because they are more accurate and can be performed earlier and more safely than other tests, these newer technologies are gradually replacing more invasive screening methods.

As genetic testing becomes more routine, geneticists are working to make sure that the tests do not cause more problems than they solve. Geneticists stress that patients seeking genetic testing should receive counseling both before and after to explain the test and to help them cope with the results. Identifying a genetic disease early can give families time to prepare—emotionally, medically, and financially. Advances in biotechnology offer possibilities for reducing human suffering, but not before key ethical issues are resolved. The dilemmas posed by human genetics reinforce one of this text's themes: the immense social implications of biology. ☑

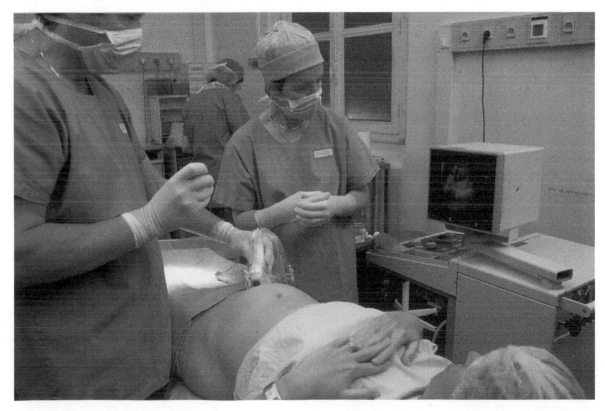

◄ Figure 17
Amniocentesis. A doctor uses a sonogram to help guide the removal of fetal cells for genetic testing.

Variations on Mendel's Laws

Mendel's two laws explain inheritance in terms of genes that are passed along from generation to generation according to simple rules of probability. These laws are valid for all sexually reproducing organisms, including garden peas, Labrador retrievers, and people. But just as the basic rules of musical harmony cannot account for all the rich sounds of a symphony, Mendel's laws stop short of explaining some patterns of genetic inheritance. In fact, for most sexually reproducing organisms, cases in which Mendel's rules can strictly account for the patterns of inheritance are relatively rare. More often, the observed inheritance patterns are more complex. Next, we'll look at several extensions to Mendel's laws that help account for this complexity.

Incomplete Dominance in Plants and People

The F_1 offspring of Mendel's pea crosses always looked like one of the two parent plants. In such situations, the dominant allele has the same effect on the phenotype whether present in one or two copies. But for some characters, the appearance of F_1 hybrids falls between the phenotypes of the two parents, an effect called **incomplete dominance**. For instance, when red snapdragons are crossed with white snapdragons, all the F_1 hybrids have pink flowers **(Figure 18)**. And in the F_2 generation, the genotypic ratio and the phenotypic ratio are the same: 1:2:1.

We also see examples of incomplete dominance in people. One case involves a recessive allele (h) that causes hypercholesterolemia, dangerously high levels of cholesterol in the blood. Normal individuals are homozygous dominant, HH. Heterozygotes (Hh) have blood cholesterol levels about twice what is normal. Such heterozygotes are very prone to cholesterol buildup in artery walls and may have heart attacks from blocked heart arteries by their mid-30s. Hypercholesterolemia is even more serious in homozygous individuals (hh). Homozygotes have about five times the normal amount of blood cholesterol and may have heart attacks as early as age 2. If we look at the molecular basis for hypercholesterolemia, we can understand the intermediate phenotype of heterozygotes **(Figure 19)**. The H allele specifies a cell-surface receptor protein that liver cells use to mop up excess low-density lipoprotein (LDL, or "bad cholesterol") from the blood. With only half as many receptors as HH individuals, heterozygotes can remove much less excess cholesterol.

▼ Figure 18 Incomplete dominance in snapdragons.
Compare this diagram with Figure 6, where one of the alleles displays complete dominance.

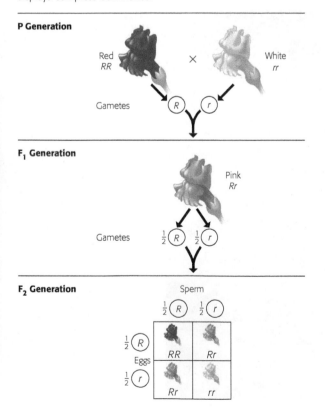

▼ Figure 19 Incomplete dominance in human hypercholesterolemia.
LDL receptors on liver cells promote the breakdown of cholesterol carried in the bloodstream by LDL (low-density lipoprotein). This process helps prevent the accumulation of cholesterol in the arteries. Having too few receptors allows dangerous levels of LDL to build up in the blood.

ABO Blood Groups: An Example of Multiple Alleles and Codominance

So far, we have discussed inheritance patterns involving only two alleles per gene (H versus h, for example). But most genes can be found in populations in more than two forms, known as multiple alleles. Although each individual carries, at most, two different alleles for a particular gene, in cases of multiple alleles, more than two possible alleles exist in the population.

The **ABO blood groups** in humans involve three alleles of a single gene. Various combinations of these three alleles produce four phenotypes: A person's blood type may be A, B, AB, or O. These letters refer to two carbohydrates, designated A and B, that may be found on the surface of red blood cells **(Figure 20)**. A person's red blood cells may be coated with carbohydrate A (giving them type A blood), carbohydrate B (type B), both (type AB), or neither (type O). (In case you are wondering, the "positive" and "negative" notations associated with blood types—referred to as the Rh blood group system—are due to inheritance of a separate, unrelated gene.)

Matching compatible blood groups is critical for safe blood transfusions. If a donor's blood cells have a carbohydrate (A or B) that is foreign to the recipient, then the recipient's immune system produces blood proteins called antibodies that bind to the foreign carbohydrates and cause the donor blood cells to clump together, potentially killing the recipient.

The four blood groups result from various combinations of the three different alleles: I^A (for the ability to make substance A), I^B (for B), and i (for neither A nor B). Each person inherits one of these alleles from each parent. Because there are three alleles, there are six possible genotypes, as listed in Figure 21. Both the I^A and I^B alleles are dominant to the i allele. Thus, $I^A I^A$ and $I^A i$ people have type A blood, and $I^B I^B$ and $I^B i$ people have type B. Recessive homozygotes (ii) have type O blood with neither carbohydrate. Finally, people of genotype $I^A I^B$ make *both* carbohydrates. In other words, the I^A and I^B alleles are **codominant**, meaning that both alleles are expressed in heterozygous individuals ($I^A I^B$) who have type AB blood. Notice that type O blood reacts with no others, making such a person a universal donor. A person with type AB blood is a universal receiver. Be careful to distinguish codominance (the expression of both alleles) from incomplete dominance (the expression of one intermediate trait). ☑

▼ **Figure 20 Multiple alleles for the ABO blood groups.** The three versions of the gene responsible for blood type may produce carbohydrate A (allele I^A), carbohydrate B (allele I^B), or neither carbohydrate (allele i). Because each person carries two alleles, six genotypes are possible that result in four different phenotypes. The clumping reaction that occurs between antibodies and foreign blood cells is the basis of blood-typing (shown in the photograph at right) and of the adverse reaction that occurs when someone receives a transfusion of incompatible blood.

Blood Group (Phenotype)	Genotypes	Red Blood Cells	Antibodies Present in Blood	Reactions When Blood from Groups Below Is Mixed with Antibodies from Groups at Left			
				O	A	B	AB
A	$I^A I^A$ or $I^A i$	Carbohydrate A	Anti-B				
B	$I^B I^B$ or $I^B i$	Carbohydrate B	Anti-A				
AB	$I^A I^B$		—				
O	ii		Anti-A Anti-B				

Pleiotropy and Sickle-Cell Disease

Structure/Function

Our genetic examples to this point have been cases in which each gene specifies only one hereditary character. But in many cases, one gene influences several characters, a property called **pleiotropy**.

An example of pleiotropy in humans is sickle-cell disease (sometimes called sickle-cell anemia), a disorder characterized by a diverse set of symptoms. The direct effect of the sickle-cell allele is to make red blood cells produce abnormal hemoglobin proteins. These abnormal molecules tend to link together and crystallize, especially when the oxygen content of the blood is lower than usual because of high altitude, overexertion, or respiratory ailments. As the hemoglobin crystallizes, the normally disk-shaped red blood cells deform to a sickle shape with jagged edges (**Figure 21**). As is so often the case in biology, altering structure affects function. Because of their shape, sickled cells do not flow smoothly in the blood and tend to accumulate and clog tiny blood vessels. Blood flow to body parts is reduced, resulting in periodic fever, severe pain, and damage to the heart, brain, and kidneys. The abnormal sickled cells are destroyed by the body, causing anemia and general weakness. Blood transfusions and drugs may relieve some of the symptoms, but there is no cure, and sickle-cell disease kills about 100,000 people in the world annually. ☑

▼ **Figure 21 Sickle-cell disease: multiple effects of a single human gene.**

Individual homozygous for sickle-cell allele

Sickle-cell (abnormal) hemoglobin

Abnormal hemoglobin crystallizes into long, flexible chains, causing red blood cells to become sickle-shaped.

Colorized SEM 4,000×

Sickled cells can lead to a cascade of symptoms, such as weakness, pain, organ damage, and paralysis.

Polygenic Inheritance

Mendel studied genetic characters that could be classified on an either-or basis, such as purple or white flower color. However, many characters, such as human skin color and height, vary along a continuum in a population. Many such features result from **polygenic inheritance**, the additive effects of two or more genes on a single phenotypic character. (This is the logical opposite of pleiotropy, in which one gene affects several characters.)

There is evidence that height in people is controlled by several genes that are inherited separately. (In actuality, human height is probably affected by a great number of genes, but we'll simplify here.) Let's consider three genes, with a tall allele for each (*A*, *B*, and *C*) contributing one "unit" of tallness to the phenotype and being incompletely dominant to the other alleles (*a*, *b*, and *c*).

o = short allele
● = tall allele

P Generation

aabbcc (very short) × *AABBCC* (very tall)

F₁ Generation

AaBbCc (medium height) × *AaBbCc* (medium height)

F₂ Generation

Sperm

Eggs

$\frac{1}{64}$ $\frac{6}{64}$ $\frac{15}{64}$ $\frac{20}{64}$ $\frac{15}{64}$ $\frac{6}{64}$ $\frac{1}{64}$

Fraction of population

Very short ← Adult height → Very tall

▲ **Figure 22 A model for polygenic inheritance of height.**

A person who is *AABBCC* would be very tall, while an *aabbcc* individual would be very short. An *AaBbCc* person would be of intermediate height. Because the alleles have an additive effect, the genotype *AaBbCc* would produce the same height as any other genotype with just three tallness alleles, such as *AABbcc*. The Punnett square in **Figure 22** shows all possible genotypes from a mating of two triple heterozygotes (*AaBbCd*). The row of figures below the Punnett square shows the seven height phenotypes that would theoretically result. This hypothetical example shows how inheritance of three genes could lead to seven different versions of a trait at the frequencies indicated by the bars in the graph at the bottom of the figure.

Epigenetics and the Role of Environment

If we examine a real human population for height, we would see more height phenotypes than just seven. The true range might be similar to the entire distribution of height under the bell-shaped curve in Figure 22. In fact, no matter how carefully we characterize the genes for height, a purely genetic description will always be incomplete. This is because height is also influenced by environmental factors, such as nutrition and exercise.

Because the environment helps shape your appearance, identical twins aren't identical in every way.

Many phenotypic characters result from a combination of heredity and environment. For example, the leaves of a tree all have the same genotype, but they vary in size, shape, and color, depending on exposure to wind and sun and the tree's nutritional state. For people, exercise alters build; experience improves performance on intelligence tests; and social and cultural factors can greatly affect appearance. As geneticists learn more and more about our genes, it's becoming clear that many human characters—such as risk of heart disease, cancer, alcoholism, and schizophrenia—are influenced by both genes *and* environment.

Whether human characters are more influenced by genes or by the environment—nature or nurture—is a very old and hotly contested issue. For some characters, such as the ABO blood group, a given genotype mandates an exact phenotype, and the environment plays no role whatsoever. In contrast, the number of blood cells in a drop of your blood varies quite a bit, depending on such factors as the altitude, your physical activity, and whether or not you have a cold.

Spending time with identical twins will convince anyone that environment, and not just genes, affects a person's traits (**Figure 23**). In general, only genetic influences are inherited, and any effects of the environment are not usually passed to the next generation. In recent years, however, biologists have begun to recognize the importance of **epigenetic inheritance**, the transmission of traits by mechanisms not directly involving DNA sequence. For example, DNA and/or protein components of chromosomes can be chemically modified by adding or removing chemical groups. Over a lifetime, the environment plays a role in these changes, which may explain how one identical twin can suffer from a genetically based disease whereas the other twin does not, despite their identical genomes. Recent research has shown that young identical twins are essentially indistinguishable in terms of their epigenetic markers, but epigenetic differences accumulate as they age, resulting in substantial differences in gene expression between older twins. Epigenetic modifications—and the changes in gene activity that result—may even be carried on to the next generation. For example, some research suggests that epigenetic changes may underlie certain instincts in animals, allowing behaviors learned by one generation (such as avoiding certain stimuli) to be passed on to the next generation via chromosomal modifications.

Unlike alterations to the DNA sequence, chemical changes to the chromosomes can be reversed (by processes that are not yet fully understood). Research into the importance of epigenetic inheritance is a very active area of biology, and new discoveries that alter our understanding of genetics are sure to follow. ☑

The Chromosomal Basis of Inheritance

It was not until many years after Mendel's death that biologists understood the significance of his work. Cell biologists worked out the processes of mitosis and meiosis in the late 1800s. Then, around 1900, researchers began to notice parallels between the behavior of chromosomes and the behavior of genes. One of biology's most important concepts began to emerge.

The **chromosome theory of inheritance** states that genes are located at specific positions (loci) on chromosomes and that the behavior of chromosomes during meiosis and fertilization accounts for inheritance patterns. Indeed, it is chromosomes that undergo segregation and independent assortment during meiosis and thus account for Mendel's laws. **Figure 24** correlates the results of the dihybrid cross in Figure 8b with the movement of chromosomes through meiosis. Starting with two purebred parental plants, the diagram follows two genes on different chromosomes—one for seed shape (alleles R and r) and one for seed color (alleles Y and y)—through the F_1 and F_2 generations. ☑

Linked Genes

Realizing that genes are on chromosomes when they segregate leads to some important conclusions about the ways genes can be inherited. The number of genes in a cell is far

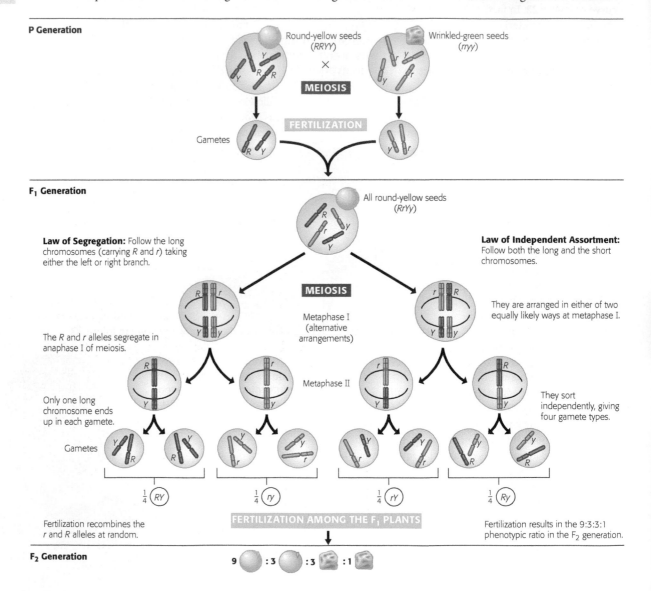

► Figure 24 **The chromosomal basis of Mendel's laws.**

P Generation

Round-yellow seeds (*RRYY*)   ×   Wrinkled-green seeds (*rryy*)

MEIOSIS

FERTILIZATION

Gametes

F₁ Generation

All round-yellow seeds (*RrYy*)

Law of Segregation: Follow the long chromosomes (carrying *R* and *r*) taking either the left or right branch.

Law of Independent Assortment: Follow both the long and the short chromosomes.

MEIOSIS

Metaphase I (alternative arrangements)

They are arranged in either of two equally likely ways at metaphase I.

The *R* and *r* alleles segregate in anaphase I of meiosis.

Metaphase II

Only one long chromosome ends up in each gamete.

They sort independently, giving four gamete types.

Gametes

$\frac{1}{4}$ (*RY*) $\frac{1}{4}$ (*rY*) $\frac{1}{4}$ (*rY*) $\frac{1}{4}$ (*RY*)

Fertilization recombines the *r* and *R* alleles at random.

FERTILIZATION AMONG THE F₁ PLANTS

Fertilization results in the 9:3:3:1 phenotypic ratio in the F₂ generation.

F₂ Generation   9 : 3 : 3 : 1

greater than the number of chromosomes; each chromosome therefore carries hundreds or thousands of genes. Genes located near each other on the same chromosome, called **linked genes**, tend to travel together during meiosis and fertilization. Such genes are often inherited as a set and therefore often do not follow Mendel's law of independent assortment. For closely linked genes, the inheritance of one does in fact correlate with the inheritance of the other, producing results that do not follow the standard ratios predicted by Punnett squares. In contrast, genes located far apart on the same chromosome usually do sort independently because of crossing over.

The patterns of genetic inheritance we've discussed so far have always involved genes located on autosomes, not on the sex chromosomes. We're now ready to look at the role of sex chromosomes and the inheritance patterns exhibited by the characters they control. As you'll see, genes located on sex chromosomes produce some unusual patterns of inheritance. ☑

Sex Determination in Humans

Many animals, including all mammals, have a pair of sex chromosomes—designated X and Y—that determine an individual's sex (Figure 25). Individuals with one X chromosome and one Y chromosome are males; XX individuals are females. Human males and females both have 44 autosomes (chromosomes other than sex chromosomes). As a result of chromosome segregation during

Your mother's genes had no role in determining your sex.

meiosis, each gamete contains one sex chromosome and a haploid set of autosomes (22 in humans). All eggs contain a single X chromosome. Of the sperm cells, half contain an X chromosome and half contain a Y chromosome. An offspring's sex depends on whether the sperm cell that fertilizes the egg bears an X or a Y.

Sex-Linked Genes

Besides bearing genes that determine sex, the sex chromosomes also contain genes for characters unrelated to maleness or femaleness. A gene located on a sex chromosome is called a **sex-linked gene**. The human X chromosome contains approximately 1,100 genes, whereas the Y chromosome contains genes that encode for only about 25 proteins (most of which affect only the testes); therefore, most sex-linked genes are found on the X chromosome.

A number of human conditions, including red-green colorblindness, hemophilia, and a type of muscular dystrophy, result from sex-linked recessive alleles. Red-green colorblindness is a common sex-linked disorder that is caused by a malfunction of light-sensitive cells in the eyes. (Colorblindness is actually a large class of disorders involving several sex-linked genes, but we will focus on just one specific type of colorblindness here.) A person with normal color vision can see more than 150 colors. In contrast, someone with red-green colorblindness can see fewer than 25. Figure 26 shows a simple test for red-green

☑ **CHECKPOINT**

What are linked genes? Why do they often disobey Mendel's law of independent assortment?

Answer: Genes located near each other on the same chromosome. Because they often travel together during meiosis and fertilization, linked genes tend to be inherited together rather than independently.

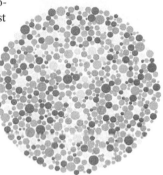

▲ Figure 26 **A test for red-green colorblindness.** Can you see a green numeral 7 against the reddish background? If not, you probably have some form of red-green colorblindness, a sex-linked trait.

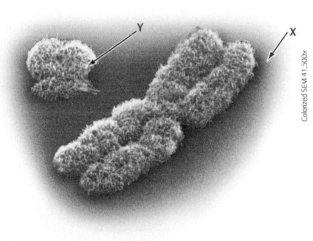

▲ Figure 25 **The chromosomal basis of sex determination in humans.** The micrograph above shows human X and Y chromosomes in a duplicated state.

Colonized SEM 41,500x

colorblindness. Mostly males are affected, but heterozygous females have some defects, too.

Queen Victoria — Albert

Alice — Louis

Alexandra — Czar Nicholas II of Russia

Alexis

Because they are located on the sex chromosomes, sex-linked genes exhibit unusual inheritance patterns. **Figure 27a** (below) illustrates what happens when a colorblind male has offspring with a homozygous female with normal color vision. All the children have normal color vision, suggesting that the allele for wild-type (normal) color vision is dominant. If a female carrier mates with a male who has normal color vision, the classic 3:1 phenotypic ratio of normal color vision to colorblindness appears among the children **(Figure 27b)**. However, there is a surprising twist: The colorblind trait shows up only in males. All the females have normal vision, while half the males are colorblind and half are normal. This is because the gene involved in this inheritance pattern is located exclusively on the X chromosome; there is no corresponding locus on the Y. Thus, females (XX) carry two copies of the gene for this character, and males (XY) carry only one. Because the colorblindness allele is recessive, a female will be colorblind only if she receives that allele on both X chromosomes **(Figure 27c)**. For a male, however, a single copy of the recessive allele confers colorblindness. For this reason, recessive sex-linked traits are expressed much more frequently in men than in women. For example, colorblindness is about 20-fold more common among males than among females. This inheritance pattern is why people often say that certain genes "skip a generation"— because they are passed from a male (in generation 1) to a female carrier (who does not express it in generation 2) back to a male (in generation 3).

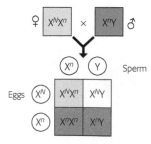

▲ **Figure 28 Hemophilia in the royal family of Russia.** The photograph shows Queen Victoria's granddaughter Alexandra, her husband Nicholas, who was the last czar of Russia, their son Alexis, and their daughters. In the pedigree, half-colored symbols represent heterozygous carriers of the hemophilia allele and fully colored symbols represent a person with hemophilia.

Hemophilia is a sex-linked recessive trait with a long, well-documented history. Hemophiliacs bleed excessively when injured because they have inherited an abnormal allele for a factor involved in blood clotting. The most seriously affected individuals may bleed to death after relatively minor bruises or cuts. A high incidence of hemophilia plagued the royal families of Europe. Queen Victoria (1819–1901) of England was a carrier of the hemophilia allele. She passed it on to one of her sons and two of her daughters. Through marriage, her daughters then introduced the disease into the royal families of Prussia, Russia, and Spain. In this way, the former practice of strengthening international alliances by marriage effectively spread hemophilia through the royal families of several nations **(Figure 28).**

Hemophilia is more prevalent among European royalty than commoners because of past intermarriage.

▼ **Figure 27 Inheritance of colorblindness, a sex-linked recessive trait.** We use an uppercase *N* for the dominant, normal color-vision allele and *n* for the recessive, colorblind allele. To indicate that these alleles are on the X chromosome, we show them as superscripts to the letter X. The Y chromosome does not have a gene locus for vision; therefore, the male's phenotype results entirely from the sex-linked gene on his single X chromosome.

Key
- Unaffected individual
- Carrier
- Colorblind individual

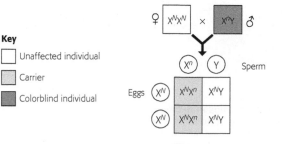

(a) Normal female ✕ colorblind male

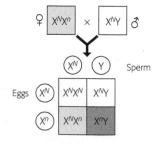

(b) Carrier female ✕ normal male

(c) Carrier female ✕ colorblind male

Dog Breeding EVOLUTION CONNECTION

Barking Up the Evolutionary Tree

As we've seen throughout this chapter, dogs are more than man's best friend: They are also one of our longest-running genetic experiments. About 15,000 years ago, in East Asia, people began to cohabit with ancestral canines that were predecessors of both modern wolves and dogs. As people moved into permanent, geographically isolated settlements, populations of canines were separated from one another and eventually became inbred.

Different groups of people chose dogs with different traits. A 2010 study indicated that small dogs were first bred within early agricultural settlements of the Middle East around 12,000 years ago. Elsewhere, herders selected dogs for controlling flocks while hunters chose dogs for retrieving prey. Continued over millennia, such genetic tinkering has resulted in a diverse array of dog body types and behaviors. In each breed, a distinct genetic makeup results in a distinct set of physical and behavioral traits.

As discussed in the Process of Science section, our understanding of canine evolution took a big leap forward when researchers sequenced the complete genome of a dog. Using the genome sequence and other data, canine geneticists produced an evolutionary tree based on a genetic analysis of 85 breeds (Figure 29). The analysis shows that the canine family tree includes a series of well-defined branch points. Each fork represents a purposeful selection by people that produced a genetically distinct subpopulation with specific desired traits.

The genetic tree shows that the most ancient breeds, those most closely related to the wolf, are Asian species such as the shar-pei and Akita. Subsequent genetic splits created distinct breeds in Africa (basenji), the Arctic (Alaskan malamute and Siberian husky), and the Middle East (Afghan hound and saluki). The remaining breeds, primarily of European ancestry, were developed most recently and can be grouped by genetic makeup into those bred for guarding (for example, the rottweiler), herding (such as sheepdogs), and hunting (including the Labrador retriever and beagle). The formulation of an evolutionary tree for the domestic dog shows that new technologies can provide important insights into genetic and evolutionary questions about life on Earth.

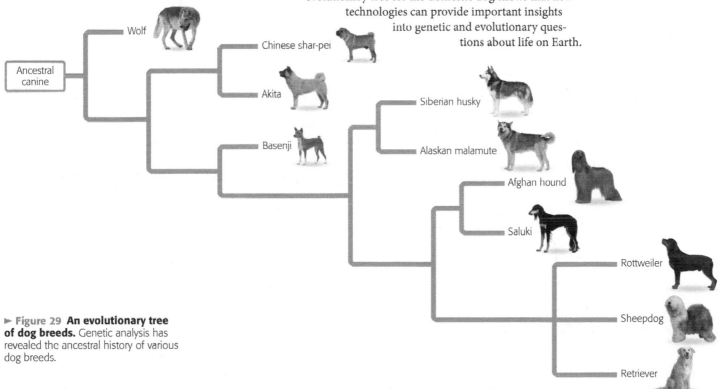

► Figure 29 **An evolutionary tree of dog breeds.** Genetic analysis has revealed the ancestral history of various dog breeds.

Chapter Review

SUMMARY OF KEY CONCEPTS

Genetics and Heredity

Gregor Mendel, the first to study the science of heredity by analyzing patterns of inheritance, emphasized that genes retain permanent identities.

In an Abbey Garden

Mendel started with purebred varieties of pea plants representing two alternative variants of a hereditary character. He then crossed the different varieties and traced the inheritance of traits from generation to generation.

Mendel's Law of Segregation

Pairs of alleles separate during gamete formation; fertilization restores the pairs.

If an individual's genotype (genetic makeup) has two different alleles for a gene and only one influences the organism's phenotype (appearance), that allele is said to be dominant and the other allele recessive. Alleles of a gene reside at the same locus, or position, on homologous chromosomes. When the allele pair matches, the organism is homozygous; when the alleles are different, the organism is heterozygous.

Mendel's Law of Independent Assortment

By following two characters at once, Mendel found that the alleles of a pair segregate independently of other allele pairs during gamete formation.

Using a Testcross to Determine an Unknown Genotype

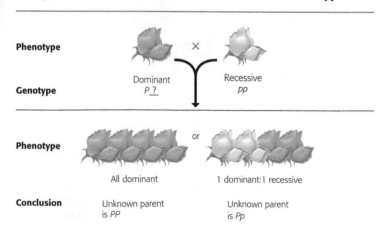

The Rules of Probability

Inheritance follows the rules of probability. The chance of inheriting a recessive allele from a heterozygous parent is $\frac{1}{2}$. The chance of inheriting it from both of two heterozygous parents is $\frac{1}{2} \times \frac{1}{2} = \frac{1}{4}$, illustrating the rule of multiplication for calculating the probability of two independent events.

Family Pedigrees

The inheritance of many human traits, from freckles to genetic diseases, follows Mendel's laws and the rules of probability. Geneticists can use family pedigrees to determine patterns of inheritance and individual genotypes.

Human Disorders Controlled by a Single Gene

For traits that vary within a population, the one most commonly found in nature is called the wild type. Many inherited disorders in humans are controlled by a single gene with two alleles. Most of these disorders, such as cystic fibrosis, are caused by autosomal recessive alleles. A few, such as Huntington's disease, are caused by dominant alleles.

Variations on Mendel's Laws

Incomplete Dominance in Plants and People

ABO Blood Groups: An Example of Multiple Alleles and Codominance

Within a population, there are often multiple kinds of alleles for a character, such as the three alleles for the ABO blood groups. The alleles determining blood groups are codominant; that is, both are expressed in a heterozygote.

Structure/Function: Pleiotropy and Sickle-Cell Disease

In pleiotropy, one gene (such as the sickle-cell disease gene) can affect many characters (such as the multiple symptoms of the disease).

Polygenic Inheritance

Epigenetics and the Role of Environment

Many phenotypic characters result from a combination of genetic and environmental effects, but only genetic influences are biologically heritable. Epigenetic inheritance, the transmission of traits from one generation to the next by means of chemical modifications to DNA and proteins, may explain how environmental factors can affect genetic traits.

The Chromosomal Basis of Inheritance

Genes are located on chromosomes. The behavior of chromosomes during meiosis and fertilization accounts for inheritance patterns.

Linked Genes

Certain genes are linked: They tend to be inherited as a set because they lie close together on the same chromosome.

Sex Determination in Humans

In humans, sex is determined by whether a Y chromosome is present. A person who inherits two X chromosomes develops as a female. A person who inherits one X and one Y chromosome develops as a male.

Male 44 + XY Somatic cells Female 44 + XX

Sex-Linked Genes

Their inheritance of genes on the X chromosome reflects the fact that females have two homologous X chromosomes, but males have only one. Most sex-linked human disorders, such as red-green colorblindness and hemophilia, are due to recessive alleles and are seen mostly in males. A male receiving a single sex-linked recessive allele from his mother will have the disorder; a female has to receive the allele from both parents to be affected.

Sex-Linked Traits				
Female: Two alleles	Genotype	$X^N X^N$	$X^N X^n$	$X^n X^n$
	Phenotype	Normal female	Carrier female	Affected female (rare)

Male: One allele	Genotype	$X^N Y$	$X^n Y$
	Phenotype	Normal male	Affected male

MasteringBiology®

For practice quizzes, BioFlix animations, MP3 tutorials, video tutors, and more study tools designed for this text, go to MasteringBiology®

SELF-QUIZ

1. The genetic makeup of an organism is called its _____, and the physical traits of an organism are called its _____.

2. Which of Mendel's laws is represented by each statement?
   a. Alleles of each pair of homologous chromosomes separate independently during gamete formation.
   b. Alleles segregate during gamete formation; fertilization creates pairs of alleles once again.

3. Edward was found to be heterozygous (Ss) for the sickle-cell trait. The alleles represented by the letters S and s are
   a. on the X and Y chromosomes.
   b. linked.
   c. on homologous chromosomes.
   d. both present in each of Edward's sperm cells.

4. Whether an allele is dominant or recessive depends on
   a. how common the allele is, relative to other alleles.
   b. whether it is inherited from the mother or the father.
   c. whether it or another allele determines the phenotype when both are present.
   d. whether or not it is linked to other genes.

5. Two fruit flies with eyes of the usual red color are crossed, and their offspring are as follows: 77 red-eyed males, 71 ruby-eyed males, 152 red-eyed females. The gene that controls whether eyes are red or ruby is _____, and the allele for ruby eyes is _____.
   a. autosomal (carried on an autosome); dominant
   b. autosomal; recessive
   c. sex-linked; dominant
   d. sex-linked; recessive

6. All the offspring of a white hen and a black rooster are gray. The simplest explanation for this pattern of inheritance is
   a. pleiotropy.
   b. sex linkage.
   c. codominance.
   d. incomplete dominance.

7. A man who has type B blood and a woman who has type A blood could have children of which of the following phenotypes? (Hint: Review Figure 20.)
   a. A, B, or O
   b. AB only
   c. AB or O
   d. A, B, AB, or O

8. Duchenne muscular dystrophy is a sex-linked recessive disorder characterized by a progressive loss of muscle tissue. Neither Rudy nor Carla has Duchenne muscular dystrophy, but their first son does have it. If the couple has a second child, what is the probability that he or she will also have the disease?

9. Adult height in people is at least partially hereditary; tall parents tend to have tall children. But people come in a range of sizes, not just tall or short. What extension of Mendel's model could produce this variation in height?

10. A purebred brown mouse is repeatedly mated with a purebred white mouse, and all their offspring are brown. If two of these brown offspring are mated, what fraction of the F_2 mice will be brown?

11. How could you determine the genotype of one of the brown F_2 mice in problem 10? How would you know whether a brown mouse is homozygous? Heterozygous?

12. Tim and Jan both have freckles (a dominant trait), but their son Michael does not. Show with a Punnett square how this is possible. If Tim and Jan have two more children, what is the probability that *both* of them will have freckles?

13. Incomplete dominance is seen in the inheritance of hypercholesterolemia. Mack and Toni are both heterozygous for this character, and both have elevated levels of cholesterol. Their daughter Katerina has a cholesterol level six times normal; she is apparently homozygous, *hh*. What fraction of Mack and Toni's children are likely to have elevated but not extreme levels of cholesterol, like their parents? If Mack and Toni have one more child, what is the probability that the child will suffer from the more serious form of hypercholesterolemia seen in Katerina?

14. Why was Henry VIII wrong to blame his wives for always producing daughters?

15. Both parents of a boy are phenotypically normal, but their son suffers from hemophilia, a sex-linked recessive disorder. Draw a pedigree that shows the genotypes of the three individuals. What fraction of the couple's children are likely to suffer from hemophilia? What fraction are likely to be carriers?

16. Heather was surprised to discover that she suffered from red-green colorblindness. She told her biology professor, who said, "Your father is colorblind, too, right?" How did her professor know this? Why did her professor not say the same thing to the colorblind males in the class?

17. In rabbits, black hair depends on a dominant allele, *B*, and brown hair on a recessive allele, *b*. Short hair is due to a dominant allele, *S*, and long hair to a recessive allele, *s*. If a true-breeding black short-haired male is mated with a brown long-haired female, describe their offspring. What will be the genotypes of the offspring? If two of these F_1 rabbits are mated, what phenotypes would you expect among their offspring? In what proportions?

THE PROCESS OF SCIENCE

18. In 1981, a stray cat with unusual curled-back ears was adopted by a family in Lakewood, California. Hundreds of descendants of this cat have since been born, and cat fanciers hope to develop the "curl" cat into a show breed. The curl allele is apparently dominant and carried on an autosome. Suppose you owned the first curl cat and wanted to develop a purebred variety. Describe tests that would determine whether the curl gene is dominant or recessive and whether it is autosomal or sex-linked.

19. **Interpreting Data** As shown in the Punnett square below, one variety of deafness is caused by an autosomal recessive allele. Two parents who do not show any signs of the disease but are carriers could therefore have a child who is deaf, because that child could inherit one recessive deafness-causing gene from each parent. Imagine that a deaf male mates with a hearing female. We know the deaf male must have the genotype *dd*, but the female could be either *Dd* or *DD*. Such a mating is essentially a testcross, like the one shown in Figure 10. If the parents' first child has hearing, can you say with certainty what the mother's genotype must be? What if the couple has four children (none twins), all with hearing—can you say with certainty the mother's genotype? What would it take for a definitive genotype to be assigned?

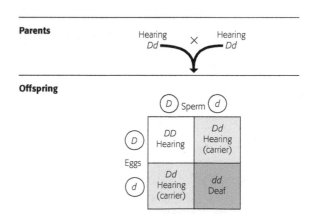

BIOLOGY AND SOCIETY

20. There are now nearly 200 recognized breeds of dog, from the Affenpinscher to the Yorkshire Terrier. But several of these suffer from medical problems due to the inbreeding required to establish the breed. For example, nearly every Cavalier King Charles (discussed in the Biology and Society essay) suffers from heart murmurs caused by a genetically defective heart valve. Such problems are likely to remain as long as the organizations that oversee dog breeding maintain strict pedigree requirements. Some people are suggesting that every breed be allowed to mix with others to help introduce new gene lines free of the congenital defects. Why do you think the governing societies are resistant to such cross-breed mixing? What would you do if you were in charge of addressing the genetic defects that currently plague some breeds?

21. Gregor Mendel never saw a gene, yet he concluded that some inherited factors were responsible for the patterns of inheritance he observed in peas. Similarly, maps of *Drosophila* chromosomes (and the very idea that genes are carried on chromosomes) were conceived by observing the patterns of inheritance of linked genes, not by observing the genes directly. Is it legitimate for biologists to claim the existence of objects and processes they cannot actually see? How do scientists know whether an explanation is correct?

22. Many infertile couples turn to in vitro fertilization to try to have a baby. In this technique, sperm and ova are collected and used to create eight-cell embryos for implantation into a woman's uterus. At the eight-cell stage, one of the fetal cells can be removed without causing harm to the developing fetus. Once removed, the cell can be genetically tested. Some couples may know that a particular genetic disease runs in their family. They might wish to avoid implanting any embryos with the disease-causing genes. Do you think this is an acceptable use of genetic testing? What if a couple wanted to use genetic testing to select embryos for traits unrelated to disease, such as freckles? Do you think that couples undergoing in vitro fertilization should be allowed to perform whatever genetic tests they wish? Or do you think that there should be limits on what tests can be performed? How do you draw the line between genetic tests that are acceptable and those that are not?

Glossary

ABO blood groups
Genetically determined classes of human blood that are based on the presence or absence of carbohydrates A and B on the surface of red blood cells. The ABO blood group phenotypes, also called blood types, are A, B, AB, and O.

allele (*uh-lē′-ul*)
An alternative version of a gene.

carrier
An individual who is heterozygous for a recessively inherited disorder and who therefore does not show symptoms of that disorder.

character
A heritable feature that varies among individuals within a population, such as flower color in pea plants or eye color in humans.

chromosome theory of inheritance
A basic principle in biology stating that genes are located on chromosomes and that the behavior of chromosomes during meiosis accounts for inheritance patterns.

codominant
Expressing two different alleles of a gene in a heterozygote.

cross
The cross-fertilization of two different varieties of an organism or of two different species; also called hybridization.

cystic fibrosis (CF)
A human genetic disorder caused by a recessive allele and characterized by an excessive secretion of mucus and consequent vulnerability to infection; fatal if untreated.

dihybrid cross (*dī′-hī′-brid*)
A mating of individuals differing at two genetic loci.

dominant allele
In a heterozygote, the allele that determines the phenotype with respect to a particular gene; the dominant version of a gene is usually represented with a capital italic letter (e.g., *F*).

epigenetic inheritance
Inheritance of traits transmitted by mechanisms not directly involving the nucleotide sequence of a genome; frequently involves chemical modification of DNA bases and/or histone proteins.

F_1 generation
The offspring of two parental (P generation) individuals. F_1 stands for first filial.

F_2 generation
The offspring of the F_1 generation. F_2 stands for second filial.

genetics
The scientific study of heredity (inheritance).

genotype (*jē′-nō-tīp*)
The genetic makeup of an organism.

heredity
The transmission of traits from one generation to the next.

heterozygous (*het′-er-ō-zī′-gus*)
Having two different alleles for a given gene.

homozygous (*hō′-mō-zī′-gus*)
Having two identical alleles for a given gene.

hybrid
The offspring of parents of two different species or of two different varieties of one species; the offspring of two parents that differ in one or more inherited traits; an individual that is heterozygous for one or more pairs of genes.

incomplete dominance
A type of inheritance in which the phenotype of a heterozygote (*Aa*) is intermediate between the phenotypes of the two types of homozygotes (*AA* and *aa*).

law of independent assortment
A general rule of inheritance, first proposed by Gregor Mendel, that states that when gametes form during meiosis, each pair of alleles for a particular character segregates (separates) independently of each other pair.

law of segregation
A general rule of inheritance, first proposed by Gregor Mendel, that states that the two alleles in a pair segregate (separate) into different gametes during meiosis.

linked genes
Genes located close enough together on a chromosome that they are usually inherited together.

locus
(plural, **loci**) The particular site where a gene is found on a chromosome. Homologous chromosomes have corresponding gene loci.

monohybrid cross
A mating of individuals differing at one genetic locus.

P generation
The parent individuals from which offspring are derived in studies of inheritance. P stands for parental.

pedigree
A family tree representing the occurrence of heritable traits in parents and offspring across a number of generations.

phenotype (*fē′-nō-tīp*)
The expressed traits of an organism.

pleiotropy (*plī′-uh-trō-pē*)
The control of more than one phenotypic character by a single gene.

polygenic inheritance (*pol′-ē-jen′-ik*)
The additive effect of two or more genes on a single phenotypic character.

Punnett square
A diagram used in the study of inheritance to show the results of random fertilization.

recessive allele
In heterozygotes, the allele that has no noticeable effect on the phenotype; the recessive version of a gene is usually represented with a lowercase italic letter (e.g., *f*).

rule of multiplication
A rule stating that the probability of a compound event is the product of the separate probabilities of the independent events.**sex-linked gene**
A gene located on a sex chromosome.

testcross
The mating between an individual of unknown genotype for a particular character and an individual that is homozygous recessive for that same character.

trait
A variant of a character found within a population, such as purple flowers in pea plants or blue eyes in people.

wild-type trait
The trait most commonly found in nature.

Credits

Credits are listed in the order of appearance.

PHOTO CREDITS

Self-Quiz Answers

1. genotype; phenotype
2. Statement **a.** is the law of independent assortment; statement **b.** is the law of segregation.
3. c
4. c
5. d
6. d
7. d
8. Rudy must be $X^D Y^0$. Carla must be $X^D X^d$ (because she had a son with the disease). There is a ¼ chance that their second child will be a male with the disease.
9. Height appears to result from polygenic inheritance, like human skin color. See Figure 9.22.
10. The brown allele appears to be dominant, the white allele recessive. The brown parent appears to be homozygous dominant, *BB*, and the white mouse is homozygous recessive, *bb*. The F_1 mice are all heterozygous, *Bb*. If two of the F_1 mice are mated, ¾ of the F_2 mice will be brown.
11. The best way to find out whether a brown F_2 mouse is homozygous dominant or heterozygous is to do a testcross: Mate the brown mouse with a white mouse. If the brown mouse is homozygous, all the offspring will be brown. If the brown mouse is heterozygous, you would expect half the offspring to be brown and half to be white.
12. Freckles are dominant, so Tim and Jan must both be heterozygous. There is a ¾ chance that they will produce a child with freckles and a ¼ chance that they will produce a child without freckles. The probability that the next two children will have freckles is $\frac{3}{4} \times \frac{3}{4} = \frac{9}{16}$.
13. According to the odds, half their children will be heterozygous and have elevated cholesterol levels. There is a ¼ chance that their next child will be homozygous, *hh,* and have an extremely high cholesterol level, like Katerina.
14. Because it is the father's sperm (that could carry either an X or a Y chromosome) that determines the sex of the offspring, not the mother's egg (which always carries an X).
15. The mother is a heterozygous carrier, and the father is normal. See the brown boxed area at the bottom of Figure 9.28 for a pedigree. One-quarter of their children will be boys suffering from hemophilia; ¼ will be female carriers.
16. For a woman to be colorblind, she must inherit X chromosomes bearing the colorblindness allele from both parents. Her father has only one X chromosome, which he passes on to all his daughters, so he must be colorblind. A male only needs to inherit the colorblindness allele from a carrier mother; both his parents are usually phenotypically normal.
17. The genotype of the black short-haired parent rabbit is *BBSS.* The genotype of the brown long-haired parent is *bbss.* The F_1 rabbits will all be black and short-haired, *BbSs.* The F_2 rabbits will be black short-haired, black long-haired, brown short-haired, and brown long-haired, in a proportion of 9:3:3:1.

The Structure and Function of DNA

From Chapter 10 of *Campbell Essential Biology with Physiology*, Fifth Edition. Eric J. Simon, Jean L. Dickey, Kelly A. Hogan, Jane B. Reece. Copyright © 2016 by Pearson Education, Inc. All rights reserved.

The Structure and Function of DNA

Why Molecular Biology Matters

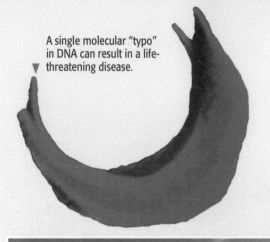

A single molecular "typo" in DNA can result in a life-threatening disease.

▲ Because all life on Earth shares a universal genetic code, your DNA could be used to genetically modify a monkey.

◄ Mad cow disease is caused by an abnormal molecule of protein.

◄ Enzymes help maintain the integrity of your DNA to greater than 99.999% accuracy.

The Deadliest Virus BIOLOGY AND SOCIETY

The First 21st-Century Pandemic

In 2009, a cluster of unusual flu cases was reported in and around Mexico City. Despite a near total shutdown of the city, the new flu virus, called 2009 H1N1, quickly spread to California and Texas. This strain was originally misnamed the "swine flu"; in fact, pigs had little impact on the spread of this virus, which, like most flu viruses, is passed from person to person through respiratory fluids. Nonetheless, the new strain received heavy media attention and caused considerable worry among the general public. In June 2009, the World Health Organization (WHO) declared H1N1 to be the first influenza pandemic (global epidemic) of the 21st century; the last flu pandemic was in 1968. In response, the WHO unveiled a comprehensive effort to contain H1N1, including increased surveillance, development of rapid testing procedures, the issuance of travel warnings, recommendations for increased sanitation (hand washing, etc.), and the production, stockpiling, and distribution of antiviral drugs. By 2010, cases of H1N1 had been confirmed in 214 countries.

The H1N1 influenza virus. Citizens of Russia try to protect themselves from H1N1 infection in late fall 2009.

Scientists soon determined that H1N1 was a hybrid flu strain, created when a previously known flu virus (which itself originated through a combination of viruses from birds, swine, and people) mixed with an Asian swine flu virus. This novel combination of genes produced some unusual features in the H1N1 strain. Most significantly, it infected young, healthy people, whereas the flu usually affects the elderly or people who are already sick. Many countries participated in the WHO-coordinated response, including widespread distribution of a new vaccine. As a result, the virus was contained, and WHO declared the pandemic over in August 2010. The WHO confirmed that this virus killed about 18,000 people, and estimates of the total number of unreported deaths topped 250,000.

You may wonder, What's the big deal about the flu? The flu is not merely a seasonal inconvenience. In fact, the influenza virus may be the deadliest pathogen known to science. In a typical year in the United States, more than 20,000 people die from influenza infection. And that is considered a good year. Once every few decades, a new flu strain explodes on the scene, causing pandemics and widespread death. H1N1 pales in comparison to the deadliest outbreak: the pandemic of 1918–1919, which in just 18 months killed 40 million people worldwide—that's more people than have died of AIDS since it was discovered more than 30 years ago. Given the nature of the threat, it's no surprise that health workers remain vigilant, always aware that a new and deadly flu virus may appear at any time.

The flu virus, like all viruses, consists of a relatively simple structure of nucleic acid (RNA in this case) and protein. Combating any virus requires a detailed understanding of life at the molecular level. In this chapter, we will explore the structure of DNA, how it replicates and mutates, and how it controls the cell by directing the synthesis of RNA and protein.

DNA: Structure and Replication

DNA was known to be a chemical component of cells by the late 1800s, but Gregor Mendel and other early geneticists did their work without any knowledge of DNA's role in heredity. By the late 1930s, experimental studies had convinced most biologists that one specific kind of molecule, rather than a complex chemical mixture, is the basis of inheritance. Attention focused on chromosomes, which were already known to carry genes. By the 1940s, scientists knew that chromosomes consist of two types of chemicals: DNA and protein. And by the early 1950s, a series of discoveries had convinced the scientific world that DNA was the molecule that acts as the hereditary material. This breakthrough ushered in the field of **molecular biology**, the study of heredity at the molecular level.

What came next was one of the most celebrated quests in the history of science: the effort to figure out the structure of DNA. A good deal was already known about DNA. Scientists had identified all its atoms and knew how they were bonded to one another. What was not understood was the specific three-dimensional arrangement of atoms that gives DNA its unique properties—the capacity to store genetic information, copy it, and pass it from

generation to generation. The race was on to discover the link between the structure and function of this important molecule. We will describe that momentous discovery shortly. First, let's review the underlying chemical structure of DNA and its chemical cousin RNA.

DNA and RNA Structure

Both DNA and RNA are nucleic acids, which consist of long chains (polymers) of chemical units (monomers) called **nucleotides**. A diagram of a nucleotide polymer, or **polynucleotide**, is shown in **Figure 1**. Polynucleotides can be very long and may have any sequence of the four different types of nucleotides (abbreviated A, C, T, and G), so a tremendous variety of polynucleotide chains is possible.

Nucleotides are joined together by covalent bonds between the sugar of one nucleotide and the phosphate of the next. This results in a repeating pattern of sugar-phosphate-sugar-phosphate, which is known as a **sugar-phosphate backbone**. The nitrogenous bases are arranged like ribs that project from this backbone. You can think of a polynucleotide as a long ladder split in half longwise, with rungs that come in four colors. The

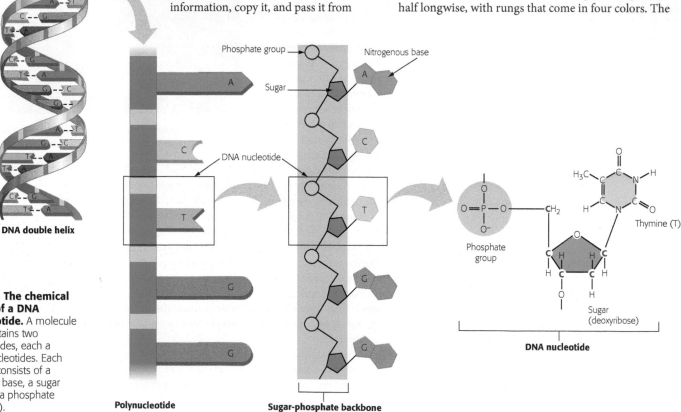

DNA double helix

▶ Figure 1 **The chemical structure of a DNA polynucleotide.** A molecule of DNA contains two polynucleotides, each a chain of nucleotides. Each nucleotide consists of a nitrogenous base, a sugar (blue), and a phosphate group (gold).

Polynucleotide

Sugar-phosphate backbone

Phosphate group

Nitrogenous base

Sugar

DNA nucleotide

Phosphate group

Thymine (T)

Sugar (deoxyribose)

DNA nucleotide

sugars and phosphates make up the side of the ladder, with the sugars acting as the half-rungs.

Moving from left to right across Figure 1, we can zoom in to see that each nucleotide consists of three components: a nitrogenous base, a sugar (blue), and a phosphate group (gold). Examining a single nucleotide even more closely, we see the chemical structure of its three components. The phosphate group, with a phosphorus atom (P) at its center, is the source of the *acid* in nucleic acid. Each phosphate has a negative charge on one of its oxygen atoms. The sugar has five carbon atoms (shown in red): four in its ring and one extending above the ring. The ring also includes an oxygen atom. The sugar is called *deoxyribose* because, compared with the sugar ribose, it is missing an oxygen atom. The full name for **DNA** is *deoxyribonucleic acid*, with *nucleic* referring to DNA's location in the nuclei of eukaryotic cells. The nitrogenous base (thymine, in our example) has a ring of nitrogen and carbon atoms with various chemical groups attached. Nitrogenous bases are basic (having a high pH, the opposite of acidic), hence their name.

The four nucleotides found in DNA differ only in their nitrogenous bases. The bases can be divided into two types. **Thymine (T)** and **cytosine (C)** are single-ring structures. **Adenine (A)** and **guanine (G)** are larger, double-ring structures. Instead of thymine, RNA has a similar base called **uracil (U)**. And RNA contains a slightly different sugar than DNA (ribose instead of deoxyribose, accounting for the names RNA vs. DNA). Other than that, RNA and DNA polynucleotides have the same chemical structure. **Figure 2** is a computer graphic of a piece of RNA polynucleotide about 20 nucleotides long. ☑

▶ **Figure 2 An RNA polynucleotide.** The yellow used for the phosphorus atoms and the blue of the sugar atoms make it easy to spot the sugar-phosphate backbone.

☑ **CHECKPOINT**

Compare and contrast the chemical components of DNA and RNA.

Answer: Both are polymers of nucleotides (a sugar + a nitrogenous base + a phosphate group). In RNA, the sugar is ribose; in DNA, it is deoxyribose. Both RNA and DNA have the bases A, G, and C, but DNA has T and RNA has U.

Watson and Crick's Discovery of the Double Helix

The celebrated partnership that solved the puzzle of DNA structure began soon after a 23-year-old newly minted American Ph.D. named James D. Watson journeyed to Cambridge University in England. There, a more senior scientist, Francis Crick, was studying protein structure with a technique called X-ray crystallography. While visiting the laboratory of Maurice Wilkins at King's College in London, Watson saw an X-ray image of DNA produced by Wilkins's colleague Rosalind Franklin. The data produced by Franklin turned out to be the key to the puzzle. A careful study of the image enabled Watson to figure out that the basic shape of DNA is a helix (spiral) with a uniform diameter. The thickness of the helix suggested that it was made up of two polynucleotide strands—in other words, a **double helix**. But how were the nucleotides arranged in the double helix?

Using wire models, Watson and Crick began trying to construct a double helix that conformed to all known data about DNA **(Figure 3)**. Watson placed the backbones on the outside of the model, forcing the nitrogenous bases to swivel to the interior of the molecule. As he did this, it occurred to him that the four kinds of bases must pair in a specific way. This idea of specific base pairing was a flash of inspiration that enabled Watson and Crick to solve the DNA puzzle.

▼ **Figure 3 Discoverers of the double helix.**

James Watson (left) and **Francis Crick**. The discoverers of the structure of DNA are shown in 1953 with their model of the double helix.

Rosalind Franklin Using X-rays, Franklin generated some of the key data that provided insight into the structure of DNA.

At first, Watson imagined that the bases paired like with like—for example, A with A, C with C. But that kind of pairing did not fit with the fact that the DNA molecule has a uniform diameter. An AA pair (made of two double-ringed bases) would be almost twice as wide as a CC pair (made of two single-ringed bases), resulting in an uneven molecule. It soon became apparent that a double-ringed base on one strand must always be paired with a single-ringed base on the opposite strand. Moreover, Watson and Crick realized that the chemical structure of each kind of base dictated the pairings even more specifically.

Each base has protruding chemical groups that can best form hydrogen bonds with just one appropriate partner. This would be like having four colors of snap-together puzzle pieces and realizing that only certain colors can snap together (e.g., red can only snap together with blue). Similarly, adenine can best form hydrogen bonds with thymine, and guanine with cytosine. In the biologist's shorthand: A pairs with T, and G pairs with C. A is also said to be "complementary" to T, and G to C.

If you imagine a polynucleotide strand as a half ladder, then you can picture the model of the DNA double helix proposed by Watson and Crick as a full ladder twisted into a spiral (**Figure 4**). Figure 5 shows three more detailed representations of the double helix. The ribbonlike diagram in **Figure 5a** symbolizes the bases with shapes that emphasize their complementarity. **Figure 5b** is a more chemically precise version showing only four base pairs, with the helix untwisted and the individual hydrogen bonds specified by dashed lines. **Figure 5c** is a computer model showing part of a double helix in detail.

Although the base-pairing rules dictate the side-by-side combinations of bases that form the rungs of the double helix, they place no restrictions on the sequence of nucleotides along the length of a DNA strand. In fact, the sequence of bases can vary in countless ways.

In 1953, Watson and Crick rocked the scientific world with a succinct paper proposing their molecular model for

► **Figure 4 A rope-ladder model of a double helix.** The ropes at the sides represent the sugar-phosphate backbones. Each rung stands for a pair of bases connected by hydrogen bonds.

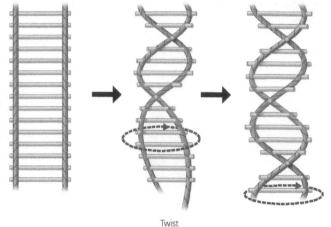

Twist

▼ **Figure 5 Three representations of DNA.**

Hydrogen bond

(a) Ribbon model. The sugar-phosphate backbones are blue ribbons, and the bases are complementary shapes in shades of green and orange.

(b) Atomic model. In this more chemically detailed structure, you can see the individual hydrogen bonds (dashed lines). You can also see that the strands run in opposite directions: Notice that the sugars on the two strands are upside down with respect to each other.

(c) Computer model. Each atom is shown as a sphere, creating a space-filling model.

DNA. Few milestones in the history of biology have had as broad an impact as their double helix, with its A-T and C-G base pairing. In 1962, Watson, Crick, and Wilkins received the Nobel Prize for their work. (Franklin deserved a share of the prize, but she had died from cancer in 1958, and Nobel prizes are never granted posthumously.)

In their 1953 paper, Watson and Crick wrote that the structure they proposed "immediately suggests a possible copying mechanism for the genetic material." In other words, the structure of DNA points toward a molecular explanation for life's unique properties of reproduction and inheritance. Understanding how the arrangement of parts within DNA affects it actions within a cell is an excellent example of biology's important theme of the relationship of structure to function, as we see next.

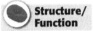 ## DNA Replication

Every cell contains a DNA "cookbook" that provides complete information on how to make and maintain that cell. When a cell reproduces, it must duplicate this information, providing one copy to the new offspring cell while keeping one copy for itself. Thus, each cell must have a means of copying the DNA instructions. In a clear demonstration of how the structure of a biological system can provide insight into its function, Watson and Crick's model of DNA suggests that each DNA strand serves as a mold, or template, to guide reproduction of the other strand. If you know the sequence of bases in one strand of the double helix, you can very easily determine the sequence of bases in the other strand by applying the base-pairing rules: A pairs with T (and T with A), and G pairs with C (and C with G). For example, if one polynucleotide has the sequence AGTC, then the complementary polynucleotide in that DNA molecule must have the sequence TCAG.

Figure 6 shows how this model can account for the direct copying of a piece of DNA. The two strands of parental DNA separate, and each becomes a template for the assembly of a complementary strand from a supply of free nucleotides. The nucleotides are lined up one at a time along the template strand in accordance with the base-pairing rules. Enzymes link the nucleotides to form new DNA strands. The completed new molecules, identical to the parental molecule, are known as daughter DNA molecules (no gender should be inferred from this name).

The process of DNA replication requires the cooperation of more than a dozen enzymes and other proteins. The enzymes that make the covalent bonds between the nucleotides of a new DNA strand are called **DNA polymerases**. As an incoming nucleotide

Enzymes help maintain the integrity of your DNA to greater than 99.999% accuracy.

base-pairs with its complement on the template strand, a DNA polymerase adds it to the end of the growing daughter strand. The process is both fast (a rate of 50 nucleotides per second is typical) and amazingly accurate, with fewer than one in a billion bases incorrectly paired. In addition to their roles in DNA replication, DNA polymerases and some of the associated proteins can repair DNA that has been damaged by toxic chemicals or high-energy radiation, such as X-rays and ultraviolet light.

DNA replication begins on a double helix at specific sites, called origins of replication. Replication then proceeds in both directions, creating what are called replication "bubbles" **(Figure 7)**. The parental DNA strands open up as daughter strands elongate on both sides of each bubble. The DNA molecule of a typical eukaryotic chromosome has many origins where replication can start simultaneously, shortening the total time needed for the process. Eventually, all the bubbles merge, yielding two completed double-stranded daughter DNA molecules.

DNA replication ensures that all the body cells in a multicellular organism carry the same genetic information. It is also the means by which genetic information is passed along to offspring. ☑

Parental (old) DNA molecule

Daughter (new) strand

Parental (old) strand

Daughter DNA molecules (double helices)

▲ **Figure 6 DNA replication.** Replication results in two daughter DNA molecules, each consisting of one old strand and one new strand. The parental DNA untwists as its strands separate, and the daughter DNA rewinds as it forms.

▼ **Figure 7 Multiple "bubbles" in replicating DNA.**

Origin of replication

Origin of replication

Parental strands

Origin of replication

Parental strand

Daughter strand

Bubble

Two daughter DNA molecules

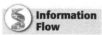 **Information Flow** # From DNA to RNA to Protein

Now that we've seen how the structure of DNA allows it to be copied, let's explore how DNA provides instructions to a cell and to an organism as a whole.

How an Organism's Genotype Determines Its Phenotype

We can now define genotype and phenotype with regard to the structure and function of DNA. An organism's *genotype*, its genetic makeup, is the heritable information contained in the sequence of nucleotide bases in its DNA. The *phenotype*, the organism's physical traits, arises from the actions of a wide variety of proteins. For example, structural proteins help make up the body of

an organism, and enzymes catalyze the chemical reactions that are necessary for life.

DNA specifies the synthesis of proteins. However, a gene does not build a protein directly. Instead, DNA dispatches instructions in the form of RNA, which in turn programs protein synthesis. This fundamental concept in biology is summarized in **Figure 8**. The molecular "chain of command" is from DNA in the nucleus (purple area in the figure) to RNA to protein synthesis in the cytoplasm (blue area). The two stages are **transcription**, the transfer of genetic information from DNA into an RNA molecule, and **translation**, the transfer of the information from RNA into a polypeptide (protein strand). The relationship between genes and proteins is thus one of information flow: The function of a DNA gene is to dictate the production of a polypeptide. ☑

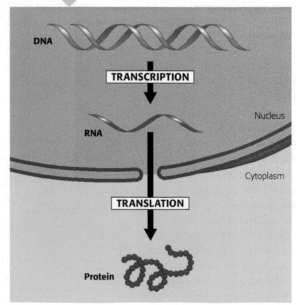

▼ Figure 8 **The flow of genetic information in a eukaryotic cell.** A sequence of nucleotides in the DNA is transcribed into a molecule of RNA in the cell's nucleus. The RNA travels to the cytoplasm, where it is translated into the specific amino acid sequence of a protein.

From Nucleotides to Amino Acids: An Overview

Genetic information in DNA is transcribed into RNA and then translated into polypeptides, which then fold into proteins. But how do these processes occur? Transcription and translation are linguistic terms, and it is useful to think of nucleic acids and proteins as having languages. To understand how genetic information passes from genotype to phenotype, we need to see how the chemical language of DNA is translated into the different chemical language of proteins.

What exactly is the language of nucleic acids? Both DNA and RNA are polymers made of nucleotide monomers strung together in specific sequences that convey information, much as specific sequences of letters convey information in English. In DNA, the monomers are the four types of nucleotides, which differ in their nitrogenous bases (A, T, C, and G). The same is true for RNA, although it has the base U instead of T.

The language of DNA is written as a linear sequence of nucleotide bases, such as the blue sequence you see on the enlarged DNA strand in **Figure 9**. Every gene is made up of a specific sequence of bases, with special sequences marking the beginning and the end. A typical gene is a few thousand nucleotides in length.

When a segment of DNA is transcribed, the result is an RNA molecule. The process is called transcription because the nucleic acid language of DNA has simply been rewritten (transcribed) as a sequence of bases of RNA; the language is still that of nucleic acids. The nucleotide bases of the RNA molecule are complementary to those on the DNA strand. As you will soon see, this is because the RNA was synthesized using the DNA as a template.

Translation is the conversion of the nucleic acid language to the polypeptide language. Like nucleic acids, polypeptides are straight polymers, but the monomers that make them up—the letters of the polypeptide alphabet—are the 20 amino acids common to all organisms (represented as purple shapes in Figure 9). The sequence of nucleotides of the RNA molecule dictates the sequence of amino acids of the polypeptide. But remember, RNA is only a messenger; the genetic information that dictates the amino acid sequence originates in DNA.

What are the rules for translating the RNA message into a polypeptide? In other words, what is the correspondence between the nucleotides of an RNA molecule and the amino acids of

a polypeptide? Keep in mind that there are only four different kinds of nucleotides in DNA (A, G, C, T) and RNA (A, G, C, U). During translation, these four must somehow specify 20 amino acids. If each nucleotide base coded for one amino acid, only 4 of the 20 amino acids could be accounted for. In fact, triplets of bases are the smallest "words" of uniform length that can specify all the amino acids. There can be 64 (that is, 4^3) possible code words of this type—more than enough to specify the 20 amino acids. Indeed, there are enough triplets to allow more than one coding for each amino acid. For example, the base triplets AAA and AAG both code for the same amino acid.

Experiments have verified that the flow of information from gene to protein is based on a triplet code. The genetic instructions for the amino acid sequence of a polypeptide chain are written in DNA and RNA as a series of three-base words called **codons**. Three-base codons in the DNA are transcribed into complementary three-base codons in the RNA, and then the RNA codons are translated into amino acids that form a polypeptide. As summarized in Figure 9, one DNA codon (three nucleotides) → one RNA codon (three nucleotides) → one amino acid. Next we turn to the codons themselves. ☑

☑ **CHECKPOINT**

How many nucleotides are necessary to code for a polypeptide that is 100 amino acids long?

Answer: 300

▼ **Figure 9 Transcription of DNA and translation of codons.** This figure focuses on a small region of one of the genes carried by a DNA molecule. The enlarged segment from one strand of gene 3 shows its specific sequence of bases. The red strand and purple chain represent the results of transcription and translation, respectively.

89

The Genetic Code

The **genetic code** is the set of rules that convert a nucleotide sequence in RNA to an amino acid sequence. As **Figure 10** shows, 61 of the 64 triplets code for amino acids. The triplet AUG has a dual function: It codes for the amino acid methionine (abbreviated Met) and can also provide a signal for the start of a polypeptide chain. Three codons (UAA, UAG, and UGA) do not designate amino acids. They are the stop codons that instruct the ribosomes to end the polypeptide.

Notice in Figure 10 that a given RNA triplet always specifies a given amino acid. For example, although codons UUU and UUC both specify phenylalanine (Phe), neither of them ever represents any other amino acid. The codons in the figure are the triplets found in RNA. They have a straightforward, complementary relationship to the codons in DNA. The nucleotides making up the codons occur in a linear order along the DNA and RNA, with no gaps separating the codons.

The genetic code is nearly universal, shared by organisms from the simplest bacteria to the most complex plants and animals. The universality of the genetic vocabulary suggests that it arose very early in evolution and was passed on over the eons to all the organisms living on Earth today. In fact, such universality is the key to modern DNA technologies. Because diverse organisms share a common genetic code, it is possible to program one species to produce a protein from another species by transplanting DNA (**Figure 11**). This allows scientists to mix and match genes from various species—a procedure with many useful genetic engineering applications in agriculture, medicine, and research. Besides having practical purposes, a shared genetic vocabulary also reminds us of the evolutionary kinship that connects all life on Earth. ☑

> Because all life on Earth shares a universal genetic code, your DNA could be used to genetically modify a monkey.

▼ Figure 11 **A pig expressing a foreign gene.** The glowing porker in the middle was created when researchers incorporated a jelly (jellyfish) gene for a protein called green fluorescent protein (GFP) into the DNA of a standard pig.

Second base of RNA codon

	U	C	A	G	
U	UUU UUC Phenylalanine (Phe) / UUA UUG Leucine (Leu)	UCU UCC UCA UCG Serine (Ser)	UAU UAC Tyrosine (Tyr) / UAA Stop / UAG Stop	UGU UGC Cysteine (Cys) / UGA Stop / UGG Tryptophan (Trp)	U C A G
C	CUU CUC CUA CUG Leucine (Leu)	CCU CCC CCA CCG Proline (Pro)	CAU CAC Histidine (His) / CAA CAG Glutamine (Gln)	CGU CGC CGA CGG Arginine (Arg)	U C A G
A	AUU AUC AUA Isoleucine (Ile) / AUG Met or start	ACU ACC ACA ACG Threonine (Thr)	AAU AAC Asparagine (Asn) / AAA AAG Lysine (Lys)	AGU AGC Serine (Ser) / AGA AGG Arginine (Arg)	U C A G
G	GUU GUC GUA GUG Valine (Val)	GCU GCC GCA GCG Alanine (Ala)	GAU GAC Aspartic acid (Asp) / GAA GAG Glutamic acid (Glu)	GGU GGC GGA GGG Glycine (Gly)	U C A G

First base of RNA codon · *Third base of RNA codon*

▲ Figure 10 **The dictionary of the genetic code, listed by RNA codons.** Practice using this dictionary by finding the codon UGG. (It is the only codon for the amino acid tryptophan, Trp.) Notice that the codon AUG (highlighted in green) not only stands for the amino acid methionine (Met), but also functions as a signal to "start" translating the RNA at that place. Three of the 64 codons (highlighted in red) function as "stop" signals that mark the end of a genetic message, but do not encode any amino acids.

☑ **CHECKPOINT**

An RNA molecule contains the nucleotide sequence CCAUUUACG. Using Figure 10, translate this sequence into the corresponding amino acid sequence.

Answer: Pro-Phe-Thr

Transcription: From DNA to RNA

Let's look more closely at transcription, the transfer of genetic information from DNA to RNA. If you think of your DNA as a cookbook, then transcription is the process of copying one recipe onto an index card (a molecule of RNA) for immediate use. **Figure 12a** is a close-up view of this process. As with DNA replication, the two DNA strands must first separate at the place where the process will start. In transcription, however, only one of the DNA strands serves as a template for the newly forming RNA molecule; the other strand is unused. The nucleotides that make up the new RNA molecule take their place one at a time along the DNA template strand by forming hydrogen bonds with the nucleotide bases there. Notice that the RNA nucleotides follow the usual base-pairing rules, except that U, rather than T, pairs with A. The RNA nucleotides are linked by the transcription enzyme **RNA polymerase**.

Figure 12b is an overview of the transcription of an entire gene. Special sequences of DNA nucleotides tell the RNA polymerase where to start and where to stop the transcribing process.

① Initiation of Transcription

The "start transcribing" signal is a nucleotide sequence called a **promoter**, which is located in the DNA at the beginning of the gene. A promoter is a specific place where RNA polymerase attaches. The first phase of transcription, called initiation, is the attachment of RNA polymerase to the promoter and the start of RNA synthesis. For any gene, the promoter dictates which of the two DNA strands is to be transcribed (the particular strand varies from gene to gene).

② RNA Elongation

During the second phase of transcription, elongation, the RNA grows longer. As RNA synthesis continues, the RNA strand peels away from its DNA template, allowing the two separated DNA strands to come back together in the region already transcribed.

③ Termination of Transcription

In the third phase, termination, the RNA polymerase reaches a special sequence of bases in the DNA template called a **terminator**. This sequence signals the end of the gene. At this point, the polymerase molecule detaches from the RNA molecule and the gene, and the DNA strands rejoin.

In addition to producing RNA that encodes amino acid sequences, transcription makes two other kinds of RNA that are involved in building polypeptides. We discuss these kinds of RNA a little later. ☑

▼ **Figure 12 Transcription.**

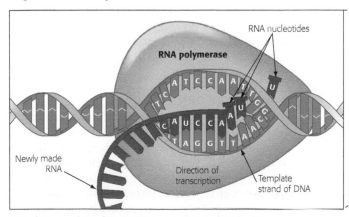

(a) A close-up view of transcription. As RNA nucleotides base-pair one by one with DNA bases on one DNA strand (called the template strand), the enzyme RNA polymerase (orange) links the RNA nucleotides into an RNA chain.

(b) Transcription of a gene. The transcription of an entire gene occurs in three phases: initiation, elongation, and termination of the RNA. The section of DNA where the RNA polymerase starts is called the promoter; the place where it stops is called the terminator.

The Processing of Eukaryotic RNA

In the cells of prokaryotes, which lack nuclei, the RNA transcribed from a gene immediately functions as **messenger RNA (mRNA)**, the molecule that is translated into protein. But this is not the case in eukaryotic cells. The eukaryotic cell not only localizes transcription in the nucleus but also modifies, or processes, the RNA transcripts there before they move to the cytoplasm for translation by the ribosomes.

One kind of RNA processing is the addition of extra nucleotides to the ends of the RNA transcript. These additions, called the **cap** and **tail**, protect the RNA from attack by cellular enzymes and help ribosomes recognize the RNA as mRNA.

Another type of RNA processing is made necessary in eukaryotes by noncoding stretches of nucleotides that interrupt the nucleotides that actually code for amino acids. It is as if nonsense words were randomly interspersed within a recipe that you copied. Most genes of plants and animals, it turns out, include such internal noncoding regions, which are called **introns**. The coding regions—the parts of a gene that are expressed—are called **exons**. As **Figure 13** illustrates, both exons and introns are transcribed from DNA into RNA. However, before the RNA leaves the nucleus, the introns are removed, and the exons are joined to produce an mRNA molecule with a continuous coding sequence. This process is called **RNA splicing**. RNA splicing is believed to play a significant role in humans in allowing our approximately 21,000 genes to produce many thousands more

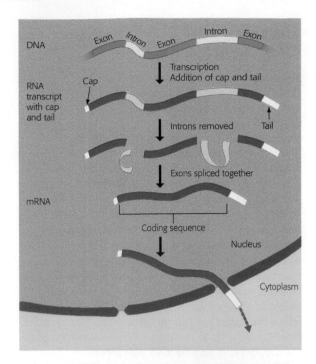

▲ Figure 13 **The production of messenger RNA (mRNA) in a eukaryotic cell.** Note that the molecule of mRNA that leaves the nucleus is substantially different from the molecule of RNA that was first transcribed from the gene. In the cytoplasm, the coding sequence of the final mRNA will be translated.

polypeptides. This is accomplished by varying the exons that are included in the final mRNA.

With capping, tailing, and splicing completed, the "final draft" of eukaryotic mRNA is ready for translation. ☑

✅ **CHECKPOINT**

Why is a final mRNA often shorter than the DNA gene that coded for it?

Answer: because introns are removed from the RNA

Translation: The Players

As we have already discussed, translation is a conversion between different languages—from the nucleic acid language to the protein language—and it involves more elaborate machinery than transcription.

Messenger RNA (mRNA)

The first important ingredient required for translation is the mRNA produced by transcription. Once it is present, the machinery used to translate mRNA requires

enzymes and sources of chemical energy, such as ATP. In addition, translation requires two other important components: ribosomes and a kind of RNA called transfer RNA.

Transfer RNA (tRNA)

Translation of any language into another requires an interpreter, someone or something that can recognize the words of one language and convert them to the other. Translation of the genetic message carried in mRNA into the amino acid language of proteins also requires an interpreter. To convert the three-letter words (codons) of nucleic acids to the amino acid words of proteins, a cell uses a molecular interpreter, a type of RNA called **transfer RNA (tRNA)**, depicted in **Figure 14**.

▼ **Figure 14 The structure of tRNA.** At one end of the tRNA is the site where an amino acid will attach (purple), and at the other end is the three-nucleotide anticodon where the mRNA will attach (light green).

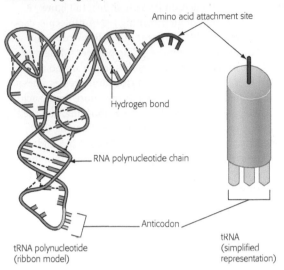

Amino acid attachment site

Hydrogen bond

RNA polynucleotide chain

Anticodon

tRNA polynucleotide
(ribbon model)

tRNA
(simplified
representation)

Ribosomes

Ribosomes are the organelles in the cytoplasm that coordinate the functioning of mRNA and tRNA and actually make polypeptides. As you can see in **Figure 15a**, a ribosome consists of two subunits. Each subunit is made up of proteins and a considerable amount of yet another kind of RNA, **ribosomal RNA (rRNA)**. A fully assembled ribosome has a binding site for mRNA on its small subunit and binding sites for tRNA on its large subunit. **Figure 15b** shows how two tRNA molecules get together with an mRNA molecule on a ribosome. One of the tRNA binding sites, the P site, holds the tRNA carrying the growing polypeptide chain, while another, the A site, holds a tRNA carrying the next amino acid to be added to the chain. The anticodon on each tRNA base-pairs with a codon on the mRNA. The subunits of the ribosome act like a vise, holding the tRNA and mRNA molecules close together. The ribosome can then connect the amino acid from the tRNA in the A site to the growing polypeptide. ☑

A cell that is producing proteins has in its cytoplasm a supply of amino acids. But amino acids themselves cannot recognize the codons arranged in sequence along messenger RNA. It is up to the cell's molecular interpreters, tRNA molecules, to match amino acids to the appropriate codons to form the new polypeptide. To perform this task, tRNA molecules must carry out two distinct functions: (1) pick up the appropriate amino acids and (2) recognize the appropriate codons in the mRNA. The unique structure of tRNA molecules enables them to perform both tasks.

As shown on the left in Figure 14, a tRNA molecule is made of a single strand of RNA—one polynucleotide chain—consisting of about 80 nucleotides. The chain twists and folds upon itself, forming several double-stranded regions in which short stretches of RNA base-pair with other stretches. At one end of the folded molecule is a special triplet of bases called an **anticodon**. The anticodon triplet is complementary to a codon triplet on mRNA. During translation, the anticodon on the tRNA recognizes a particular codon on the mRNA by using base-pairing rules. At the other end of the tRNA molecule is a site where one specific kind of amino acid attaches. Although all tRNA molecules are similar, there are slightly different versions of tRNA for each amino acid.

▼ **Figure 15 The ribosome.**

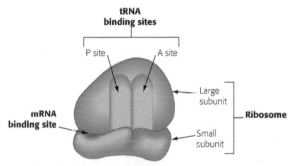

tRNA
binding sites

P site | A site

Large
subunit

Ribosome

**mRNA
binding site**

Small
subunit

(a) A simplified diagram of a ribosome. Notice the two subunits and sites where mRNA and tRNA molecules bind.

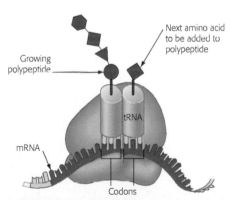

Next amino acid
to be added to
polypeptide

Growing
polypeptide

tRNA

mRNA

Codons

(b) The "players" of translation. When functioning in polypeptide synthesis, a ribosome holds one molecule of mRNA and two molecules of tRNA. The growing polypeptide is attached to one of the tRNAs.

Translation: The Process

Translation is divided into the same three phases as transcription: initiation, elongation, and termination.

Initiation

This first phase brings together the mRNA, the first amino acid with its attached tRNA, and the two subunits of a ribosome. An mRNA molecule, even after splicing, is longer than the genetic message it carries (**Figure 16**). Nucleotide sequences at either end of the molecule (pink) are not part of the message, but along with the cap and tail in eukaryotes, they help the mRNA bind to the ribosome. The initiation process determines exactly where translation will begin so that the mRNA codons will be translated into the correct sequence of amino acids. Initiation occurs in two steps, as shown in **Figure 17** ❶. An mRNA molecule binds to a small ribosomal subunit. A special initiator tRNA then binds to the **start codon**, where translation is to begin on the mRNA. The initiator tRNA carries the amino acid methionine (Met); its anticodon, UAC, binds to the start codon, AUG ❷. A large ribosomal subunit binds to the small one, creating a functional ribosome. The initiator tRNA fits into the P site on the ribosome.

Elongation

Once initiation is complete, amino acids are added one by one to the first amino acid. Each addition occurs in the three-step elongation process shown in **Figure 18**. ❶ The anticodon of an incoming tRNA molecule, carrying its amino acid, pairs with the mRNA codon in the A site of the ribosome. ❷ The polypeptide leaves the tRNA in the P site and attaches to the amino acid on the tRNA in the A site. The ribosome creates a new peptide bond. Now the chain has one more amino acid. ❸ The P site tRNA now leaves the ribosome, and the ribosome moves the remaining tRNA, carrying the growing polypeptide, to the P site. The mRNA and tRNA move as a unit. This movement brings into the A site the next mRNA codon to be translated, and the process can start again with step 1.

Termination

Elongation continues until a **stop codon** reaches the ribosome's A site. Stop codons—UAA, UAG, and UGA—do not code for amino acids but instead tell translation to stop. The completed polypeptide, typically several hundred amino acids long, is freed, and the ribosome splits back into its subunits. ☑

▼ **Figure 16 A molecule of mRNA.**

Cap

Start of genetic message

End

Tail

☑ **CHECKPOINT**

Which of the following does not participate directly in translation: ribosomes, transfer RNA, messenger RNA, DNA?

Answer: DNA

▼ **Figure 17 The initiation of translation.**

Met

Initiator tRNA

mRNA

❶

Start codon

Small ribosomal subunit

P site

Large ribosomal subunit

A site

❷

Polypeptide

P site

mRNA

Amino acid

tRNA

Anticodon

A site

Codons

① **Codon recognition**

ELONGATION

New peptide bond

② **Peptide bond formation**

mRNA movement

③ **Translocation**

► **Figure 18 The elongation of a polypeptide.** The dashed red arrows indicate movement.

Review: DNA → RNA → Protein

Figure 19 reviews the flow of genetic information in the cell, from DNA to RNA to protein. In eukaryotic cells, transcription (DNA → RNA) occurs in the nucleus, and the RNA is processed before it enters the cytoplasm. Translation (RNA → protein) is rapid; a single ribosome can make an average-sized polypeptide in less than a minute. As it is made, a polypeptide coils and folds, assuming its final three-dimensional shape.

What is the overall significance of transcription and translation? These are the processes whereby genes control the structures and activities of cells—or, more broadly, the way the genotype produces the phenotype. The flow of information originates with the specific sequence of nucleotides in a DNA gene. The gene dictates the transcription of a complementary sequence of nucleotides in mRNA. In turn, the information within the mRNA specifies the sequence of amino acids in a polypeptide. Finally, the proteins that form from the polypeptides determine the appearance and capabilities of the cell and organism.

For decades, the DNA → RNA → protein pathway was believed to be the sole means by which genetic information controls traits. In recent years, however, this notion has been challenged by discoveries that point to more complex roles for RNA. ☑

▼ Figure 19 A summary of transcription and translation. This figure summarizes the main stages in the flow of genetic information from DNA to protein in a eukaryotic cell.

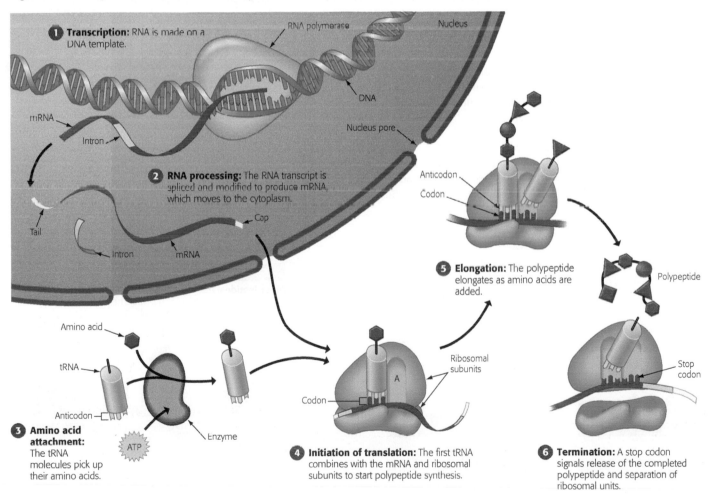

① **Transcription:** RNA is made on a DNA template.

RNA polymerase

Nucleus

DNA

Nucleus pore

mRNA

Intron

Tail

Intron

mRNA

Cap

② **RNA processing:** The RNA transcript is spliced and modified to produce mRNA, which moves to the cytoplasm.

Anticodon

Codon

Amino acid

tRNA

Anticodon

ATP

Enzyme

③ **Amino acid attachment:** The tRNA molecules pick up their amino acids.

Codon

A

Ribosomal subunits

④ **Initiation of translation:** The first tRNA combines with the mRNA and ribosomal subunits to start polypeptide synthesis.

⑤ **Elongation:** The polypeptide elongates as amino acids are added.

Polypeptide

Stop codon

⑥ **Termination:** A stop codon signals release of the completed polypeptide and separation of ribosomal units.

Mutations

Since discovering how genes are translated into proteins, scientists have been able to describe many heritable differences in molecular terms. For instance, sickle-cell disease can be traced to a change in a single amino acid in one of the polypeptides in the hemoglobin protein. This difference is caused by a single nucleotide difference in the DNA coding for that polypeptide (Figure 20).

> A single molecular "typo" in DNA can result in a life-threatening disease.

Any change in the nucleotide sequence of a cell's DNA is called a **mutation**. Mutations can involve large regions of a chromosome or just a single nucleotide pair, as in sickle-cell disease. Occasionally, a base substitution leads to an improved protein or one with new capabilities that enhance the success of the mutant organism and its descendants. Much more often, though, mutations are harmful. Think of a mutation as a typo in a recipe; occasionally, such a typo might lead to an improved recipe, but much more often it will be neutral, mildly bad, or disastrous. Let's consider how mutations involving only one or a few nucleotide pairs can affect gene translation.

Types of Mutations

Mutations within a gene can be divided into two general categories: nucleotide substitutions and nucleotide insertions or deletions (Figure 21). A substitution is the replacement of one nucleotide and its base-pairing partner with another nucleotide pair. For example, in the second row in Figure 21, A replaces G in the fourth codon of the mRNA. What effect can a substitution have? Because the genetic code is redundant, some substitution

mutations have no effect at all. For example, if a mutation causes an mRNA codon to change from GAA to GAG, no change in the protein product would result because GAA and GAG both code for the same amino acid (Glu). Such a change is called a silent mutation. In our recipe example, changing "1¼ cup sugar" to "1¼ cup sugor" would probably be translated the same way, just like

▼ **Figure 21 Three types of mutations and their effects.** Mutations are changes in DNA, but they are shown here in mRNA and the polypeptide product.

mRNA and protein from a normal gene

(a) Base substitution. Here, an A replaces a G in the fourth codon of the mRNA. The result in the polypeptide is a serine (Ser) instead of a glycine (Gly). This amino acid substitution may or may not affect the protein's function.

(b) Nucleotide deletion. When a nucleotide is deleted, all the codons from that point on are misread. The resulting polypeptide is likely to be completely nonfunctional.

(c) Nucleotide insertion. As with a deletion, inserting one nucleotide disrupts all codons that follow, most likely producing a nonfunctional polypeptide.

▼ **Figure 20 The molecular basis of sickle-cell disease.** The sickle-cell allele differs from its normal counterpart, a gene for hemoglobin, by only one nucleotide (orange). This difference changes the mRNA codon from one that codes for the amino acid glutamic acid (Glu) to one that codes for valine (Val).

Normal hemoglobin DNA

Mutant hemoglobin DNA

mRNA

mRNA

Normal hemoglobin

| Glu |

Sickle-cell hemoglobin

| Val |

the translation of a silent mutation does not change the meaning of the message.

Other substitutions involving a single nucleotide do change the amino acid coding. Such mutations are called missense mutations. For example, if a mutation causes an mRNA codon to change from GGC to AGC, the resulting protein will have a serine (Ser) instead of a glycine (Gly) at this position. Some missense mutations have little or no effect on the shape or function of the resulting protein; imagine changing a recipe from "1¼ cups sugar" to "1⅓ cups sugar"—this will probably have a negligible effect on your final product. However, other substitutions, as we saw in the sickle-cell case, cause changes in the protein that prevent it from performing normally. This would be like changing "1¼ cups sugar" to "6¼ cups sugar"—this one change is enough to ruin the recipe.

Some substitutions, called nonsense mutations, change an amino acid codon into a stop codon. For example, if an AGA (Arg) codon is mutated to a UGA (stop) codon, the result will be a prematurely terminated protein, which probably will not function properly. In our recipe analogy, this would be like stopping food preparation before the end of the recipe, which is almost certainly going to ruin the dish.

Mutations involving the deletion or insertion of one or more nucleotides in a gene, called frameshift mutations, often have disastrous effects (see Figure 21b and c). Because mRNA is read as a series of nucleotide triplets during translation, adding or subtracting nucleotides may alter the triplet grouping of the genetic message. All the nucleotides after the insertion or deletion will be regrouped into different codons. Consider this recipe example: Add one cup egg nog. Deleting the second letter produces an entirely nonsensical message—ado nec upe ggn og—which will not produce a useful product. Similarly, a frameshift mutation most often produces a nonfunctioning polypeptide.

Mutagens

Mutations can occur in a number of ways. Spontaneous mutations result from random errors during DNA replication or recombination. Other sources of mutation are physical and chemical agents called **mutagens**. The most common physical mutagen is high-energy radiation, such as X-rays and ultraviolet (UV) light. Chemical mutagens are of various types. One type, for example, consists of chemicals that are similar to normal DNA bases but that base-pair incorrectly when incorporated into DNA.

Because many mutagens can act as carcinogens, agents that cause cancer, you would do well to avoid them as much as possible. What can you do to avoid exposure to mutagens? Several lifestyle practices can help, including not smoking and wearing protective clothing and sunscreen to minimize direct exposure to the sun's UV rays. But such precautions are not foolproof, and it is not possible to avoid mutagens (such as UV radiation and secondhand smoke) entirely.

Although mutations are often harmful, they can also be beneficial, both in nature and in the laboratory. Mutations are one source of the rich diversity of genes in the living world, a diversity that makes evolution by natural selection possible (**Figure 22**). Mutations are also essential tools for geneticists. Whether naturally occurring or created in the laboratory, mutations are responsible for the different alleles needed for genetic research. ☑

▼ **Figure 22 Mutations and diversity.** Mutations are one source of the diversity of life visible in this scene from the Isle of Staffa, in the North Atlantic.

Viruses and Other Noncellular Infectious Agents

Viruses share some of the characteristics of living organisms, such as having genetic material in the form of nucleic acid packaged within a highly organized structure. A virus is generally not considered alive, however, because it is not cellular and cannot reproduce on its own. A **virus** is an infectious particle consisting of little more than "genes in a box": a bit of nucleic acid wrapped in a protein coat and, in some cases, an envelope of membrane **(Figure 23)**. A virus cannot reproduce on its own, and thus it can multiply only by infecting a living cell and directing the cell's molecular machinery to make more viruses. In this section, we'll look at viruses that infect different types of host organisms, starting with bacteria.

Bacteriophages

Viruses that attack bacteria are called **bacteriophages** ("bacteria-eaters"), or **phages** for short. **Figure 24** shows a micrograph of a bacteriophage called T4 infecting an *Escherichia coli* bacterium. The phage consists of a molecule of DNA enclosed within an elaborate structure made of proteins. The "legs" of the phage bend when they touch the cell surface. The tail is a hollow rod enclosed in a springlike sheath. As the legs bend, the spring compresses, the bottom of the rod punctures the cell membrane, and the viral DNA passes from inside the head of the virus into the cell.

Once they infect a bacterium, most phages enter a reproductive cycle called the **lytic cycle**. The lytic cycle gets its name from the fact that after many copies of the phage are produced within the bacterial cell, the bacterium lyses (breaks open). Some viruses can also reproduce by an alternative route—the **lysogenic cycle**. During a lysogenic cycle, viral DNA replication occurs without phage production or the death of the cell.

Protein coat — DNA

▲ **Figure 23 Adenovirus.** A virus that infects the human respiratory system, an adenovirus consists of DNA enclosed in a protein coat shaped like a 20-sided polyhedron, shown here in a computer-generated model that is magnified approximately 500,000 times the actual size. At each corner of the polyhedron is a protein spike, which helps the virus attach to a susceptible cell.

▼ **Figure 24 Bacteriophages (viruses) infecting a bacterial cell.**

Head

Bacteriophage
(200 nm tall)

Tail

Bacterial cell

DNA
of virus

Colorized TEM 225,000×

Figure 25 illustrates the two kinds of cycles for a phage named lambda that can infect *E. coli* bacteria. At the start of infection, ❶ lambda binds to the outside of a bacterium and injects its DNA inside. ❷ The injected lambda DNA forms a circle. In the lytic cycle, this DNA immediately turns the cell into a virus-producing factory. ❸ The cell's own machinery for DNA replication, transcription, and translation is hijacked by the virus and used to produce copies of the virus. ❹ The cell lyses, releasing the new phages.

In the lysogenic cycle, ❺ the viral DNA is inserted into the bacterial chromosome. Once there, the phage DNA is referred to as a **prophage**, and most of its genes

are inactive. Survival of the prophage depends on the reproduction of the cell where it resides. ❻ The host cell replicates the prophage DNA along with its cellular DNA and then, upon dividing, passes on both the prophage and the cellular DNA to its two daughter cells. A single infected bacterium can quickly give rise to a large population of bacteria that all carry prophages. The prophages may remain in the bacterial cells indefinitely. ❼ Occasionally, however, a prophage leaves its chromosome; this event may be triggered by environmental conditions such as exposure to a mutagen. Once separate, the lambda DNA usually switches to the lytic cycle, which results in the production of many copies of the virus and lysing of the host cell.

Sometimes the few prophage genes active in a lysogenic bacterial cell can cause medical problems. For example, the bacteria that cause diphtheria, botulism, and scarlet fever would be harmless to people if it were not for the prophage genes they carry. Certain of these genes direct the bacteria to produce toxins that make people ill. ☑

☑ CHECKPOINT

Describe one way some viruses can perpetuate their genes without immediately destroying the cells they infect.

Answer: Some viruses can insert their DNA into the DNA of the cell they infect (the lysogenic cycle). The viral DNA is replicated along with the cell's DNA every time the cell divides.

▼ **Figure 25 Alternative phage reproductive cycles.** Certain phages can undergo alternative reproductive cycles. After entering the bacterial cell, the phage DNA can either integrate into the bacterial chromosome (lysogenic cycle) or immediately start the production of progeny phages (lytic cycle), destroying the cell. Once it enters a lysogenic cycle, the phage's DNA may be carried in the host cell's chromosome for many generations.

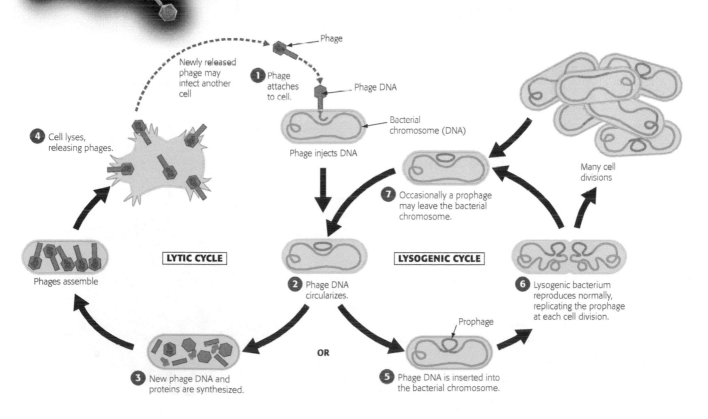

Plant Viruses

Viruses that infect plant cells can stunt plant growth and diminish crop yields. Most known plant viruses have RNA rather than DNA as their genetic material. Many of them, like the tobacco mosaic virus (TMV) shown in **Figure 26**, are rod-shaped with a spiral arrangement of proteins surrounding the nucleic acid. TMV, which infects tobacco and related plants, causing discolored spots on the leaves, was the first virus ever discovered (in 1930).

To infect a plant, a virus must first get past the plant's epidermis, an outer protective layer of cells. For this reason, a plant damaged by wind, chilling, injury, or insects is more susceptible to infection than a healthy plant. Some insects carry and transmit plant viruses, and farmers and gardeners may unwittingly spread plant viruses through the use of pruning shears and other tools.

There is no cure for most viral plant diseases, and agricultural scientists focus on preventing infection and on breeding or genetically engineering varieties of crop plants that resist viral infection. In Hawaii, for example, the spread of papaya ringspot potyvirus (PRSV) by aphids wiped out the native papaya (Hawaii's second largest crop) in certain island regions. But since 1998, farmers have been able to plant a genetically engineered PRSV-resistant strain of papaya, and papayas have been reintroduced into their old habitats. ☑

☑ CHECKPOINT

What are three ways that viruses can get into a plant?

Answer: through lesions caused by injuries, transfer by insects that feed on the plant, and contaminated farming or gardening tools

▼ **Figure 26 Tobacco mosaic virus.** The photo shows the mottling of leaves in tobacco mosaic disease. The rod-shaped virus causing the disease has RNA as its genetic material.

RNA

Protein

Tobacco mosaic virus

Animal Viruses

Viruses that infect animal cells are common causes of disease. As discussed in the Biology and Society section, no virus is a greater human health threat than the influenza (flu) virus **(Figure 27)**. Like many animal viruses, this one has an outer envelope made of phospholipid membrane, with projecting spikes of protein. The envelope enables the virus to enter and leave a host cell. Many viruses, including those that cause the flu, common cold, measles, mumps, AIDS, and polio, have RNA as their genetic material. Diseases caused by DNA viruses include hepatitis, chicken pox, and herpes infections.

► **Figure 27 An influenza virus.** The genetic material of this virus consists of eight separate molecules of RNA, each wrapped in a protein coat.

Membranous envelope

Protein spike

RNA

Protein coat

Figure 28 shows the reproductive cycle of the mumps virus, a typical RNA virus. Once a common childhood disease characterized by fever and swelling of the salivary glands, mumps has become quite rare in industrialized nations due to widespread vaccination. When the virus contacts a susceptible cell, protein spikes on its outer surface attach to receptor proteins on the cell's plasma membrane. ❶ The viral envelope fuses with the cell's membrane, allowing the protein-coated RNA to enter the cytoplasm. ❷ Enzymes then remove the protein coat. ❸ An enzyme that entered the cell as part of the virus uses the virus's RNA genome as a template for making complementary strands of RNA. The new strands have two functions: ❹ They serve as mRNA for the synthesis of new viral proteins, and ❺ they serve as templates for synthesizing new viral genome RNA. ❻ The new coat proteins assemble around the new viral RNA. ❼ Finally, the viruses leave the cell by cloaking themselves in plasma membrane. In other words, the virus obtains its envelope from the cell, budding off the cell without necessarily rupturing it.

Not all animal viruses reproduce in the cytoplasm. For example, herpesviruses—which cause chicken pox, shingles, cold sores, and genital herpes—are enveloped DNA viruses that reproduce in a host cell's nucleus, and they get their envelopes from the cell's nuclear membrane. Copies of the herpesvirus DNA usually remain behind in the nuclei of certain nerve cells. There they remain dormant until some sort of stress, such as a cold, sunburn, or emotional stress, triggers virus production, resulting in unpleasant symptoms. Once acquired, herpes infections may flare up repeatedly throughout a person's life. More than 75% of American adults carry herpes simplex 1 (which causes cold sores), and more than 20% carry herpes simplex 2 (which causes genital herpes).

The amount of damage a virus causes the body depends partly on how quickly the immune system responds to fight the infection and partly on the ability of the infected tissue to repair itself. We usually recover completely from colds because our respiratory tract tissue can efficiently replace damaged cells. In contrast, the poliovirus attacks nerve cells, which are not usually replaceable. The damage to such cells by polio is permanent. In such cases, the only medical option is to prevent the disease with vaccines.

How effective are vaccines? We'll examine this question next using the example of the flu vaccine. ☑

▼ Figure 28 **The reproductive cycle of an enveloped virus.** This virus is the one that causes mumps. Like the flu virus, it has a membranous envelope with protein spikes, but its genome is a single molecule of RNA.

Mumps virus

Colorized TEM 294,000×

☑ **CHECKPOINT**

Why is infection by herpesvirus permanent?

Answer: because herpesvirus leaves viral DNA in the nuclei of nerve cells

The Deadliest Virus THE PROCESS OF SCIENCE

Do Flu Vaccines Protect the Elderly?

Yearly flu vaccinations are recommended for nearly all people over the age of six months. But how can we be sure they are effective? Because elderly people often have weaker immune systems than younger people and because the elderly account for a significant slice of total health-care spending, they are an important population for vaccination efforts. Epidemiologists (scientists who study the distribution, causes, and control of diseases in populations) have made the **observation** that vaccination rates among the elderly rose from 15% in 1980 to 65% in 1996. This observation has led them to ask an important and basic **question:** Do flu vaccines decrease the mortality rate as a result of the flu among those elderly people who receive them? To find out, researchers

investigated data from the general population. Their **hypothesis** was that elderly people who were immunized would have fewer hospital stays and deaths during the winter after vaccination. Their **experiment** followed tens of thousands of people over the age of 65 during the ten flu seasons of the 1990s. The **results** are summarized in **Figure 29**. People who were vaccinated had a 27% less chance of being hospitalized during the next flu season and a 48% less chance of dying. But could some factor other than flu shots be at play? For example, maybe people who choose to be vaccinated are healthier for other reasons. As a control, the researchers examined health data for the summer (when flu is not a factor). During these months, there was no difference in the hospitalization rates and only 16% fewer deaths for the immunized, suggesting that flu vaccines provide a significant health benefit among the elderly during the flu season.

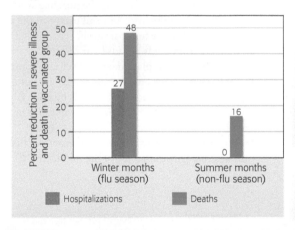

► Figure 29 **The effect of flu vaccines on the elderly.** Receiving a flu vaccine greatly reduced the risk of hospitalization and death in the flu season following the shot. The reduction was much smaller or nonexistent in later summer months.

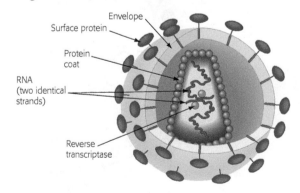

HIV, the AIDS Virus

The devastating disease **AIDS** (a̲cquired i̲mmuno̲d̲efi̲ciency s̲yndrome) is caused by **HIV** (h̲uman i̲mmuno̲deficiency v̲irus), an RNA virus with some nasty twists. In outward appearance, HIV **(Figure 30)** resembles the mumps virus. Its envelope enables HIV to enter and leave a cell much the way the mumps virus does. But HIV has a different mode of reproduction. It is a **retrovirus**, an RNA virus that reproduces by means of a DNA molecule, the reverse of the usual DNA → RNA flow of genetic information. These viruses carry molecules of an enzyme called **reverse transcriptase**, which catalyzes reverse transcription: the synthesis of DNA on an RNA template.

▼ Figure 30 **HIV, the AIDS virus.**

Envelope
Surface protein
Protein coat
RNA (two identical strands)
Reverse transcriptase

Figure 31 illustrates what happens after HIV RNA is uncoated in the cytoplasm of a cell. The reverse transcriptase (green) ❶ uses the RNA as a template to make a DNA strand and then ❷ adds a second, complementary DNA strand. ❸ The resulting double-stranded viral DNA then enters the cell nucleus and inserts itself into the chromosomal DNA, becoming a **provirus.** Occasionally, the provirus is ❹ transcribed into RNA ❺ and translated into viral proteins. ❻ New viruses assembled from these components eventually leave the cell and can then infect other cells. This is the standard reproductive cycle for retroviruses.

HIV infects and eventually kills several kinds of white blood cells that are important in the body's immune system. The loss of such cells causes the body to become susceptible to other infections that it would normally be able to fight off. Such secondary infections cause the syndrome (a collection of symptoms) that eventually

▼ **Figure 31 The behavior of HIV nucleic acid in an infected cell.**

HIV (red dots) infecting a white blood cell

kills AIDS patients. Since it was first recognized in 1981, HIV has infected tens of millions of people worldwide, resulting in millions of deaths.

Although there is as yet no cure for AIDS, its progression can be slowed by two categories of anti-HIV drugs. Both types of medicine interfere with the reproduction of the virus. The first type inhibits the action of enzymes called proteases, which help produce the final versions of HIV proteins. The second type, which includes the drug AZT, inhibits the action of the HIV enzyme reverse transcriptase. The key to AZT's effectiveness is its shape. The shape of a molecule of AZT is very similar to the shape of part of the T (thymine) nucleotide **(Figure 32).** In fact, AZT's shape is so similar to the T nucleotide that AZT can bind to reverse transcriptase, essentially taking the place of T. But unlike thymine, AZT cannot be incorporated into a growing DNA chain. Thus, AZT "gums up the works," interfering with the synthesis of HIV DNA. Because this synthesis is an essential step in the reproductive cycle of HIV, AZT may block the spread of the virus within the body.

Many HIV-infected people in the United States and other industrialized countries take a "drug cocktail" that contains both reverse transcriptase inhibitors and protease inhibitors, and the combination seems to be much more effective than the individual drugs in keeping the virus at bay and extending patients' lives. In fact, the death rate from HIV infection can be lowered by 80% with proper treatment. However, even in combination, the drugs do not completely rid the body of the virus. Typically, HIV reproduction and the symptoms of AIDS return if a patient discontinues the medications. Because AIDS has no cure yet, prevention (namely, avoiding unprotected sex, and staying away from needle sharing) is the only healthy option. ☑

☑ **CHECKPOINT**

Why is HIV called a retrovirus?

Answer: Because it synthesizes DNA from its RNA genome. This is the reverse ("retro") of the usual DNA → RNA information flow.

▼ **Figure 32 AZT and the T nucleotide.** The anti-HIV drug AZT (right) has a chemical shape very similar to part of the T (thymine) nucleotide of DNA.

Viroids and Prions

Viruses may be small and simple, but they are giants compared to two other classes of pathogens: viroids and prions. Viroids are small, circular RNA molecules that infect plants. Viroids do not encode proteins but can nonetheless replicate in host plant cells using cellular enzymes. These small RNA molecules may cause disease by interfering with the regulatory systems that control plant growth.

Even stranger are infectious proteins called **prions**. Prions cause a number of brain diseases in various animal species, including scrapie in sheep and goats, chronic wasting disease in deer and elk, and mad cow disease (formally called bovine spongiform encephalopathy, or BSE), which infected more than

Mad cow disease is caused by an abnormal molecule of protein.

2 million cattle in the United Kingdom in the 1980s. In humans, prions cause Creutzfeldt-Jakob disease, an extremely rare, incurable, and inevitably fatal deterioration of the brain.

How can a protein cause disease? A prion is thought to be a misfolded form of a protein normally present in brain cells. When a prion enters a cell containing the normal form of protein, the prion somehow converts the normal protein molecules to the misfolded prion version. The abnormal proteins clump together, which may lead to loss of brain tissue (although how this occurs is the subject of much debate and ongoing research). To date, there is no known cure for prion diseases, so hope rests on understanding and preventing the process of infection. ☑

The Deadliest Virus EVOLUTION CONNECTION

Emerging Viruses

Viruses that suddenly come to the attention of medical scientists are called **emerging viruses**. H1N1 (discussed in the Biology and Society section) is one example; another is West Nile virus, which appeared in North America in 1999 and has since spread to all 48 contiguous U.S. states. West Nile virus is spread primarily by mosquitoes, which carry the virus in blood sucked from one victim and can transfer it to another victim. West Nile virus cases surged in 2012, especially in Texas, claiming nearly 300 lives **(Figure 33)**.

How do such viruses burst on the human scene, giving rise to new diseases? One way is by the mutation of existing viruses. RNA viruses tend to have unusually high rates of mutation because errors in replicating their RNA genomes are not subject to proofreading mechanisms that help reduce errors during DNA replication. Some mutations enable existing viruses to evolve into new strains that can cause disease in individuals who have developed resistance to the ancestral virus. This is why we need yearly flu vaccines: Mutations create new influenza virus strains to which people have no immunity.

New viral diseases also arise from the spread of existing viruses from one host species to another. Scientists estimate that about three-quarters of new human diseases originated in other animals. The spread of a viral disease from a small, isolated population can also lead to widespread epidemics. For instance, AIDS went unnamed and virtually unnoticed for decades before it began to spread around the world. In this case, technological and social factors, including affordable international travel, blood transfusions, sexual activity, and the abuse of intravenous drugs, allowed a previously rare human disease to become a global scourge.

Acknowledging the persistent threat that viruses pose to human health, Nobel Prize winner Joshua Lederberg once warned: "We live in evolutionary competition with microbes. There is no guarantee that we will be the survivors." If we someday manage to control HIV, influenza, and other emerging viruses, this success will likely arise from our understanding of molecular biology.

► **Figure 33 Mapping the West Nile virus outbreak of 2012.**

Incidence per 100,000

- 0.00
- 0.01–0.024
- 0.25–0.49
- 0.50–0.99
- ≥1.00

Chapter Review

◼ SUMMARY OF KEY CONCEPTS

DNA: Structure and Replication

DNA and RNA Structure

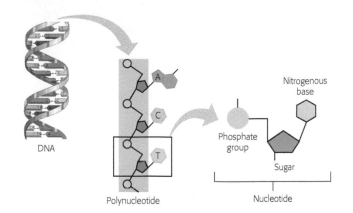

	DNA	RNA
Nitrogenous base	C G A T	C G A U
Sugar	Deoxy-ribose	Ribose
Number of strands	2	1

Structure/Function: Watson and Crick's Discovery of the Double Helix

Watson and Crick worked out the three-dimensional structure of DNA: two polynucleotide strands wrapped around each other in a double helix. Hydrogen bonds between bases hold the strands together. Each base pairs with a complementary partner: A with T, and G with C.

DNA Replication

The structure of DNA, with its complementary base pairing, allows it to function as the molecule of heredity through DNA replication.

Information Flow: From DNA to RNA to Protein

How an Organism's Genotype Determines Its Phenotype

The information constituting an organism's genotype is carried in the sequence of its DNA bases. The genotype controls phenotype through the expression of proteins.

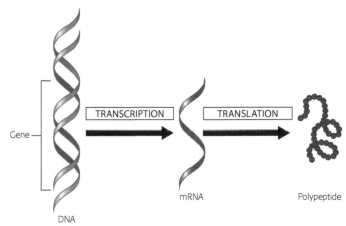

From Nucleotides to Amino Acids: An Overview

The DNA of a gene is transcribed into RNA using the usual base-pairing rules, except that an A in DNA pairs with U in RNA. In the translation of a genetic message, each triplet of nucleotide bases in the RNA, called a codon, specifies one amino acid in the polypeptide.

The Genetic Code

In addition to codons that specify amino acids, the genetic code has one codon that is a start signal and three that are stop signals for translation. The genetic code is redundant: There is more than one codon for most amino acids.

Transcription: From DNA to RNA

In transcription, RNA polymerase binds to the promoter of a gene, opens the DNA double helix there, and catalyzes the synthesis of an RNA molecule using one DNA strand as a template. As the single-stranded RNA transcript peels away from the gene, the DNA strands rejoin.

The Processing of Eukaryotic RNA

The RNA transcribed from a eukaryotic gene is processed before leaving the nucleus to serve as messenger RNA (mRNA). Introns are spliced out, and a cap and tail are added.

Translation: The Players

Translation: The Process

In initiation, a ribosome assembles with the mRNA and the initiator tRNA bearing the first amino acid. Beginning at the start codon, the codons of the mRNA are recognized one by one by tRNAs bearing succeeding amino acids. The ribosome bonds the amino acids together. With each addition, the mRNA moves by one codon through the ribosome. When a stop codon is reached, the completed polypeptide is released.

Review: DNA → RNA → Protein

The sequence of codons in DNA, via the sequence of codons in mRNA, spells out the primary structure of a polypeptide.

Mutations

Mutations are changes in the DNA base sequence, caused by errors in DNA replication or recombination or by mutagens. Substituting, deleting, or inserting nucleotides in a gene has varying effects on the polypeptide and organism.

Type of Mutation	Effect
Substitution of one DNA base for another	**Silent** mutations result in no change to amino acids.
	Missense mutations swap one amino acid for another.
	Nonsense mutations change an amino acid codon to a stop codon.
Insertions or **deletions** of DNA nucleotides	Frameshift mutations can alter the triplet grouping of codons and greatly change the amino acid sequence.

Viruses and Other Noncellular Infectious Agents

Viruses are infectious particles consisting of genes packaged in protein.

Bacteriophages

When phage DNA enters a lytic cycle inside a bacterium, it is replicated, transcribed, and translated. The new viral DNA and protein molecules then assemble into new phages, which burst from the cell. In the lysogenic cycle, phage DNA inserts into the cell's chromosome and is passed on to generations of daughter cells. Much later, it may initiate phage production.

Plant Viruses

Viruses that infect plants can be a serious agricultural problem. Most have RNA genomes. Viruses enter plants via breaks in the plant's outer layers.

Animal Viruses

Many animal viruses, such as flu viruses, have RNA genomes; others, such as hepatitis viruses, have DNA. Some animal viruses "steal" a bit of cell membrane as a protective envelope. Some, such as the herpesvirus, can remain latent inside cells for long periods.

HIV, the AIDS Virus

HIV is a retrovirus. Inside a cell it uses its RNA as a template for making DNA, which is then inserted into a chromosome.

Viroids and Prions

Even smaller than viruses, viroids are small molecules of RNA that can infect plants. Prions are infectious proteins that cause a number of degenerative brain diseases in humans and other animals.

MasteringBiology®

For practice quizzes, BioFlix animations, MP3 tutorials, video tutors, and more study tools designed for this text, go to MasteringBiology®

SELF-QUIZ

1. A molecule of DNA contains two polymer strands called _____, made by bonding together many monomers called _____.

2. Name the three parts of every nucleotide.

3. Which of the following correctly ranks nucleic acid structures in order of size, from largest to smallest?
   a. gene, chromosome, nucleotide, codon
   b. chromosome, gene, codon, nucleotide
   c. nucleotide, chromosome, gene, codon
   d. chromosome, nucleotide, gene, codon

4. A scientist inserts a radioactively labeled DNA molecule into a bacterium. The bacterium replicates this DNA molecule and distributes one daughter molecule (double helix) to each of two daughter cells. How much radioactivity will the DNA in each of the two daughter cells contain? Why?

5. The nucleotide sequence of a DNA codon is GTA. What would be the nucleotide sequence of an mRNA molecule transcribed from this DNA? In the process of protein synthesis, a tRNA pairs with the mRNA codon. What is the nucleotide sequence of the tRNA anticodon that corresponds to this mRNA codon? What amino acid is attached to the tRNA (see Figure 10)?

6. Describe the process by which the information in a gene is transcribed and translated into a protein. Correctly use these terms in your description: tRNA, amino acid, start codon, transcription, mRNA, gene, codon, RNA polymerase, ribosome, translation, anticodon, peptide bond, stop codon.

7. Match the following molecules with the cellular process or processes in which they are primarily involved.

   a. ribosomes
   b. tRNA
   c. DNA polymerases
   d. RNA polymerase
   e. mRNA

   1. DNA replication
   2. transcription
   3. translation

8. A geneticist finds that a particular mutation has no effect on the polypeptide encoded by the gene. This mutation probably involves
   a. deletion of one nucleotide.
   b. alteration of the start codon.
   c. insertion of one nucleotide.
   d. substitution of one nucleotide.

9. Scientists have discovered how to put together a bacteriophage with the protein coat of phage A and the DNA of phage B. If this composite phage were allowed to infect a bacterium, the phages produced in the cell would have
   a. the protein of A and the DNA of B.
   b. the protein of B and the DNA of A.
   c. the protein and DNA of A.
   d. the protein and DNA of B.

10. How do some viruses reproduce without ever having DNA?

11. HIV requires an enzyme called _____ to convert its RNA genome to a DNA version. Why is this enzyme a particularly good target for anti-AIDS drugs? (*Hint*: Would you expect such a drug to harm the human host?)

THE PROCESS OF SCIENCE

12. A cell containing a single chromosome is placed in a medium containing radioactive phosphate, making any new DNA strands formed by DNA replication radioactive. The cell replicates its DNA and divides. Then the daughter cells (still in the radioactive medium) replicate their DNA and divide, resulting in a total of four cells. Sketch the DNA molecules in all four cells, showing a normal (nonradioactive) DNA strand as a solid line and a radioactive DNA strand as a dashed line.

13. In a classic 1952 experiment, biologists Alfred Hershey and Martha Chase labeled two batches of bacteriophages, one with radioactive sulfur (which only tags protein) and the other with radioactive phosphorus (which only tags DNA). In separate test tubes, they allowed each batch of phages to bind to nonradioactive bacteria and inject its DNA. After a few minutes, they separated the bacterial cells from the viral parts that remained outside the bacterial cells and measured the radioactivity of both portions. What results do you think they obtained? How would these results help them to determine which viral component—DNA or protein—was the infectious portion?

14. **Interpreting Data** The graph below summarizes the number of children who died of all strains of flu from 2007 until 2013. Each bar represents the number of child deaths occurring in one week. Why does the graph have the shape it does, with a series of peaks and valleys? Looking over the Biology and Society section at the start of the chapter, why does the graph reach its highest points near the middle? Based on these data, when does flu season begin and end in a typical year?

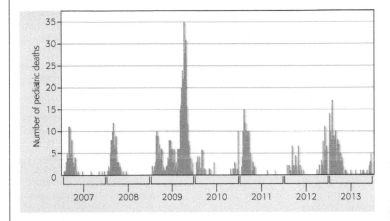

BIOLOGY AND SOCIETY

15. Scientists at the National Institutes of Health (NIH) have worked out thousands of sequences of genes and the proteins they encode, and similar analyses are being carried out at universities and private companies. Knowledge of the nucleotide sequences of genes might be used to treat genetic defects or produce lifesaving medicines. NIH and some U.S. biotechnology companies have applied for patents on their discoveries. In Britain, the courts have ruled that a naturally occurring gene cannot be patented. Do you think individuals and companies should be able to patent genes and gene products? Before answering, consider the following: What are the purposes of a patent? How might the discoverer of a gene benefit from a patent? How might the public benefit? What negative effects might result from patenting genes?

16. Your college roommate seeks to improve her appearance by visiting a tanning salon. How would you explain the dangers of this to her?

17. Flu vaccines have been shown to be safe, are very reliable at reducing the risk of hospitalization or death from influenza, and are inexpensive. Should children be required to obtain a flu vaccine before going to school? What about hospital workers before reporting to work? Defend your answers to these questions.

Glossary

adenine (A) (*ad'-uh-nēn*)
A double-ring nitrogenous base found in DNA and RNA.

AIDS
Acquired immunodeficiency syndrome; the late stages of HIV infection, characterized by a reduced number of T cells; usually results in death caused by infections that would be defeated by a properly functioning immune system.

anticodon (*an'-tī-kō'-don*)
On a tRNA molecule, a specific sequence of three nucleotides that is complementary to a codon triplet on mRNA.

bacteriophage (*bak-tēr'-ē-ō-fāj*)
A virus that infects bacteria; also called a phage.

cap
Extra nucleotides added to the beginning of an RNA transcript in the nucleus of a eukaryotic cell.

codon (*kō'-don*)
A three-nucleotide sequence in mRNA that specifies a particular amino acid or polypeptide termination signal; the basic unit of the genetic code.

cytosine (C) (*sī'-tuh-sēn*)
A single-ring nitrogenous base found in DNA and RNA.

emerging virus
A virus that has appeared suddenly or has recently come to the attention of medical scientists.

exon (*ek'-son*)
In eukaryotes, a coding portion of a gene. *See also* intron.

genetic code
The set of rules giving the correspondence between nucleotide triplets (codons) in mRNA and amino acids in protein.

guanine (G) (*gwa'-nēn*)
A double-ring nitrogenous base found in DNA and RNA.

HIV
Human immunodeficiency virus; the retrovirus that attacks the human immune system and causes AIDS.

intron (*in'-tron*)
In eukaryotes, a nonexpressed (noncoding) portion of a gene that is excised from the RNA transcript. *See also* exon.

lysogenic cycle (*lī-sō-jen'-ik*)
A bacteriophage reproductive cycle in which the viral genome is incorporated into the bacterial host chromosome as a prophage. New phages are not produced, and the host cell is not killed or lysed unless the viral genome leaves the host chromosome.

lytic cycle (*lit'-ik*)
A viral reproductive cycle resulting in the release of new viruses by lysis (breaking open) of the host cell.**messenger RNA (mRNA)**
The type of ribonucleic acid that encodes genetic information from DNA and conveys it to ribosomes, where the information is translated into amino acid sequences.

molecular biology
The study of the molecular basis of heredity.

mutagen (*myū'-tuh-jen*)
A chemical or physical agent that interacts with DNA and causes a mutation.

mutation
A change in the nucleotide sequence of DNA; a major source of genetic diversity.

phage (*fāj*)
See bacteriophage.

polynucleotide (*pol'-ē-nū'-klē-ō-tīd*)
A polymer made up of many nucleotides covalently bonded together.

prion (*prī'on*)
An infectious form of protein that may multiply by converting related proteins to more prions. Prions cause several related diseases in different animals, including scrapie in sheep, mad cow disease, and Creutzfeldt-Jakob disease in humans.

promoter
A specific nucleotide sequence in DNA, located at the start of a gene, that is the binding site for RNA polymerase and the place where transcription begins.

prophage (*prō'-fāj*)
Phage DNA that has inserted into the DNA of a prokaryotic chromosome.

provirus
Viral DNA that inserts into a host genome.

retrovirus
An RNA virus that reproduces by means of a DNA molecule. It reverse-transcribes its RNA into DNA, inserts the DNA into a cellular chromosome, and then transcribes more copies of the RNA from the viral DNA. HIV and a number of cancer-causing viruses are retroviruses.

reverse transcriptase (*tran-skrip'-tās*)
An enzyme that catalyzes the synthesis of DNA on an RNA template.

ribosomal RNA (rRNA)
(*rī'-buh-sōm'-ul*)
The type of ribonucleic acid that, together with proteins, makes up ribosomes.

RNA splicing
The removal of introns and joining of exons in eukaryotic RNA, forming an mRNA molecule with a continuous coding sequence; occurs before mRNA leaves the nucleus.

start codon (*kō'-don*)
On mRNA, the specific three-nucleotide sequence (AUG) to which an initiator tRNA molecule binds, starting translation of genetic information.

stop codon (*kō'-don*)
In mRNA, one of three triplets (UAG, UAA, UGA) that signal gene translation to stop.

tail
Extra nucleotides added at the end of an RNA transcript in the nucleus of a eukaryotic cell.

terminator
A special sequence of nucleotides in DNA that marks the end of a gene. It signals RNA polymerase to release the newly made RNA molecule, which then departs from the gene.

thymine (T) (*thī'-mēn*)
A single-ring nitrogenous base found in DNA.

transcription
The synthesis of RNA on a DNA template.

transfer RNA (tRNA)
A type of ribonucleic acid that functions as an interpreter in translation. Each tRNA molecule has a specific anticodon, picks up a specific amino acid, and conveys the amino acid to the appropriate codon on mRNA.

translation
The synthesis of a polypeptide using the genetic information encoded in an mRNA molecule. There is a change of "language" from nucleotides to amino acids. *See also* genetic code.

uracil (U) (*yū'-ruh-sil*)
A single-ring nitrogenous base found in RNA.

virus
A microscopic particle capable of infecting cells of living organisms and inserting its genetic material. Viruses have a very simple structure and are generally not considered to be alive because they do not display all of the characteristics associated with life.

Credits

Credits are listed in the order of appearance.

PHOTO CREDITS

ILLUSTRATION AND TEXT CREDITS

Self-Quiz Answers

1. polynucleotides; nucleotides
2. sugar (deoxyribose), phosphate, nitrogenous base
3. b
4. Each daughter DNA molecule will have half the radioactivity of the parent molecule, because one polynucleotide from the original parental DNA molecule winds up in each daughter DNA molecule.
5. CAU; GUA; histidine (His)
6. A gene is the polynucleotide sequence with information for making one polypeptide. Each codon—a triplet of bases in DNA or RNA—codes for one amino acid. Transcription occurs when RNA polymerase produces mRNA using one strand of DNA as a template. A ribosome is the site of translation, or polypeptide synthesis, and tRNA molecules serve as interpreters of the genetic code. Each tRNA molecule has an amino acid attached at one end and a three-base anticodon at the other end. Beginning at the start codon, mRNA moves relative to the ribosome a codon at a time. A tRNA with a complementary anticodon pairs with each codon, adding its amino acid to the polypeptide chain. The amino acids are linked by peptide bonds. Translation stops at a stop codon, and the finished polypeptide is released. The polypeptide folds to form a functional protein, sometimes in combination with other polypeptides.

7. a3, b3, c1, d2, e2 and 3
8. d
9. d
10. The genetic material of these viruses is RNA, which is replicated inside the infected cell by special enzymes encoded by the virus. The viral genome (or its complement) serves as mRNA for the synthesis of viral proteins.
11. reverse transcriptase; The process of reverse transcription occurs only in infections by RNA-containing retroviruses like HIV. Cells do not require reverse transcriptase (their RNA molecules do not undergo reverse transcription), so reverse transcriptase can be knocked out without harming the human host.

How Genes Are Controlled

From Chapter 11 of *Campbell Essential Biology with Physiology*, Fifth Edition. Eric J. Simon, Jean L. Dickey, Kelly A. Hogan, Jane B. Reece. Copyright © 2016 by Pearson Education, Inc. All rights reserved.

How Genes Are Controlled

Why Gene Regulation Matters

Someday a DNA chip might report on the activities of all your genes. ►

▼ Cloning may help save the giant panda from extinction.

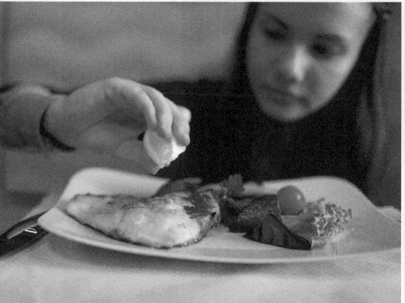

▲ Lifestyle choices you make can dramatically affect your risk of cancer.

Cancer BIOLOGY AND SOCIETY

Tobacco's Smoking Gun

When European explorers returned from their first voyages to the Americas, they brought back tobacco, a common trade item among Native Americans. The novelty of smoking tobacco quickly spread through Europe. To keep up with demand, the southern United States soon became a major tobacco producer. Over time, smoking increased in popularity around the world, and by the 1950s, about half of all Americans smoked more than a pack of cigarettes each day. In these early days, little attention was paid to purported health risks; in fact, cigarette advertising often touted the "health benefits" of tobacco, claiming that use of the product had a soothing effect on the throat and helped the smoker remain calm and lose weight.

By the 1960s, however, doctors began to notice a disturbing trend: The rate of lung cancer had increased dramatically. Although the disease was rare in 1930, by 1955 it had become the deadliest form of cancer among American men. In fact, by 1990, lung cancer was killing more than twice as many men each year as any other type of cancer. But a few vocal skeptics, mostly tied to groups with an economic interest in the tobacco industry, doubted the link between smoking and cancer. They pointed out that the evidence was purely statistical or based on animal studies; no direct proof, they said, had been found that tobacco smoke causes cancer in humans.

The "smoking gun" of proof was found in 1996 when researchers added one component of tobacco smoke, called BPDE, to human lung cells growing in the lab. The researchers showed that BPDE binds to a gene within these cells called *p53*. That gene codes for a protein that helps suppress the formation of tumors. The researchers showed that BPDE causes mutations in the *p53* gene that deactivate the protein; with this important tumor-suppressor protein deactivated, tumors grow. This work directly linked a chemical in tobacco smoke to the formation of human lung tumors. Since that time, a mountain of experimental data and statistical studies has removed any scientific doubt of the link between smoking and cancer.

How can a mutation in a gene lead to cancer? It turns out that many cancer-associated genes encode proteins that turn other genes on or off. When these proteins malfunction, the cell may become cancerous. In fact, the ability to properly control which genes are active at any given time is crucial to normal cell function. How genes are controlled and how the regulation of genes affects cells and organisms—including ways this topic affects your own life—are the subjects of this chapter.

Colorized SEM 450x

Human cancer cells. These tumor cells have lost the ability to control their growth.

How and Why Genes Are Regulated

Every cell in your body—and, indeed, all the cells in the body of every sexually reproducing organism—was produced through successive rounds of mitosis starting from the zygote, the original cell that formed after fusion of sperm and egg. Mitosis exactly duplicates the chromosomes. Therefore, every cell in your body has the same DNA as the zygote. To put it another way: Every somatic (body) cell contains every gene. However, the cells in your body are specialized in structure and function; a neuron, for example, looks and acts nothing like a red blood cell. But if every cell contains identical genetic instructions, how do cells develop differently from one another? To help you understand this idea, imagine that every restaurant in your hometown uses the same cookbook. If that were the case, how could each restaurant develop a unique menu? The answer is obvious: Even though each restaurant has the same cookbook, different restaurants pick and choose different recipes from this book to prepare. Similarly, cells with the same genetic information can develop into different types of cells through **gene regulation**, mechanisms that turn on certain genes while other genes remain turned off. Regulating gene activity allows for specialization of cells within the body, just as regulating which recipes are used allows for varying menus in multiple restaurants.

As an example of gene regulation, consider the development of a unicellular zygote into a multicellular organism. During embryonic growth, groups of cells follow different paths, and each group becomes a particular kind of tissue. In the mature organism, each cell type—neuron or red blood cell, for instance—has a different pattern of turned-on genes.

What does it mean to say that genes are turned on or off? Genes determine the nucleotide sequence of specific mRNA molecules, and mRNA in turn determines the sequence of amino acids in proteins (in summary: DNA → RNA → protein). A gene that is turned on is being transcribed into mRNA, and that message is being translated into specific proteins. The overall process by which genetic information flows from genes to proteins is called **gene expression**.

As an illustration of this principle, **Figure 1** shows the patterns of gene expression for four genes in three different specialized cells of an adult human. Note that the genes for "housekeeping" enzymes, such as those that provide energy via glycolysis, are "on" in all the cells. In contrast, the genes for some proteins, such as insulin and hemoglobin, are expressed only by particular kinds of cells. One protein, hemoglobin, is not expressed in any of the cell types shown in the figure. ☑

Gene Regulation in Bacteria

To understand how a cell can regulate gene expression, consider the relatively simple case of bacteria. In the course of their lives, bacteria must regulate their genes in response to environmental changes. For example,

► Figure 1 **Patterns of gene expression in three types of human cells.** Different types of cells express different combinations of genes. The specialized proteins whose genes are represented here are an enzyme involved in glucose digestion; an antibody, which aids in fighting infection; insulin, a hormone made in the pancreas; and the oxygen transport protein hemoglobin, which is expressed only in red blood cells.

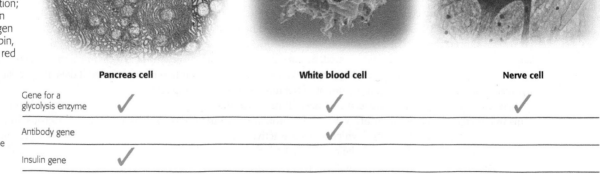

Colorized TEM 2,200x   Colorized SEM 2,500x   Colorized TEM 1,800x

	Pancreas cell	White blood cell	Nerve cell
Gene for a glycolysis enzyme	✓	✓	✓
Antibody gene		✓	
Insulin gene	✓		
Hemoglobin gene			

Key

✓ = Active gene

when a nutrient is plentiful, bacteria do not squander valuable resources to make the nutrient from scratch. Bacterial cells that can conserve resources and energy have a survival advantage over cells that are unable to do so. Thus, natural selection has favored bacteria that express only the genes whose products are needed by the cell.

Imagine an *Escherichia coli* bacterium living in your intestines. It will be bathed in various nutrients, depending on what you eat. If you drink a milk shake, for example, there will be a sudden rush of the sugar lactose. In response, *E. coli* will express three genes for enzymes that enable the bacterium to absorb and digest this sugar. After the lactose is gone, these genes are turned off; the bacterium does not waste its energy continuing to produce these enzymes when they are not needed. Thus, a bacterium can adjust its gene expression to changes in the environment.

How does a bacterium "know" if lactose is present or not? In other words, how does the presence or absence of lactose influence the activity of the genes that code for the lactose enzymes? The key is the way the three lactose-digesting genes are organized: They are adjacent in the DNA and turned on and off as a single unit. This regulation is achieved through short stretches of DNA that help turn all three genes on and off at once, coordinating their expression. Such a cluster of related genes and sequences that control them is called an **operon** (Figure 2). The operon considered here, the *lac* (short for lactose) operon, illustrates principles of gene regulation that apply to a wide variety of prokaryotic genes.

How do DNA control sequences turn genes on or off? One control sequence, called a **promoter** (green in the figure), is the site where the enzyme RNA polymerase attaches and initiates transcription—in our example, transcription of the genes for lactose-digesting enzymes. Between the promoter and the enzyme genes, a DNA segment called an **operator** (yellow) acts as a switch that is turned on or off, depending on whether a specific protein is bound there. The operator and protein together determine whether RNA polymerase can attach to the promoter and start transcribing the genes (light blue). In the *lac* operon, when the operator switch is turned on, all the enzymes needed to metabolize lactose are made at once.

The top half of Figure 2 shows the *lac* operon in "off" mode, its status when there is no lactose available. Transcription is turned off because ❶ a protein called a **repressor** ( ) binds to the operator ( ) and ❷ physically blocks the attachment of RNA polymerase ( ) to the promoter ( ).

The bottom half of Figure 2 shows the operon in "on" mode, when lactose is present. The lactose ( )

interferes with attachment of the *lac* repressor to the operator by ❶ binding to the repressor and ❷ changing the repressor's shape. In its new shape ( ), the repressor cannot bind to the operator, and the operator switch remains on. ❸ RNA polymerase is no longer blocked, so it can now bind to the promoter and from there ❹ transcribe the genes for the lactose enzymes into mRNA. ❺ Translation produces all three lactose enzymes (purple).

Many operons have been identified in bacteria. Some are quite similar to the *lac* operon, whereas others have somewhat different mechanisms of control. For example, operons that control amino acid synthesis cause bacteria to stop making these molecules when they are already present in the environment, saving materials and energy for the cells. In these cases, the amino acid *activates* the repressor. Armed with a variety of operons, *E. coli* and other prokaryotes can thrive in frequently changing environments. ☑

☑ **CHECKPOINT**

A mutation in *E. coli* makes the *lac* operator unable to bind the active repressor. How would this mutation affect the cell? Why would this effect be a disadvantage?

Answer: The cell would wastefully produce the enzymes for lactose metabolism continuously, even in the absence of lactose.

▼ Figure 2 **The *lac* operon of *E. coli.***

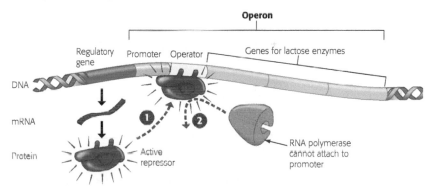

Operon turned off (lactose absent)

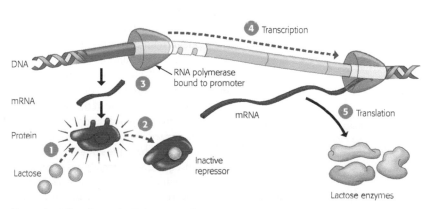

Operon turned on (lactose inactivates repressor)

Gene Regulation in Eukaryotic Cells

Eukaryotes, especially multicellular ones, have more sophisticated mechanisms than bacteria for regulating the expression of their genes. This is not surprising because a prokaryote, being a single cell, does not require the elaborate regulation of gene expression that leads to cell specialization in multicellular eukaryotic organisms. A bacterium does not have neurons that need to be different from blood cells, for example.

The pathway from gene to protein in eukaryotic cells is a long one, providing a number of points where the process can be turned on or off, speeded up or slowed down. Picture the series of pipes that carry water from your local reservoir to a faucet in your home. At various points, valves control the flow of water. We use this analogy in **Figure 3** to illustrate the flow of genetic information from a eukaryotic chromosome—a reservoir of genetic information—to an active protein that has been made in the cell's cytoplasm. The multiple mechanisms that control gene expression are analogous to the control valves in your water pipes. In the figure, each control knob indicates a gene expression "valve." All these knobs represent possible control points, although only one or a few control points are likely to be important for a typical protein.

Using a reduced version of Figure 3 as a guide, we will explore several ways that eukaryotes can control gene expression, starting within the nucleus.

The Regulation of DNA Packing

Eukaryotic chromosomes may be in a more or less condensed state, with the DNA and accompanying proteins more or less tightly wrapped together . DNA packing tends to prevent gene expression by preventing RNA polymerase and other transcription proteins from binding to the DNA.

Cells may use DNA packing for the long-term inactivation of genes. One intriguing case is seen in female mammals, where one X chromosome in each somatic cell is highly compacted and almost entirely inactive. This **X chromosome inactivation** first takes place early in embryonic development, when one of the two X chromosomes in each cell is inactivated at random. After one X chromosome is inactivated in each embryonic cell, all of that cell's descendants will have the same X chromosome turned off. Consequently, if a female has different versions of a gene on each of her X chromosomes, about half of her cells will express one version, while the other half will express the alternate version (**Figure 4**). ☑

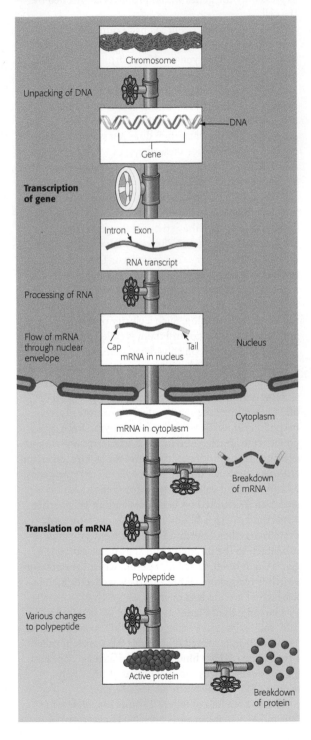

▼ **Figure 3 The gene expression "pipeline" in a eukaryotic cell.** Each valve in the pipeline represents a stage at which the pathway from chromosome to functioning protein can be regulated, turned on or off, or speeded up or slowed down. Throughout this discussion we will use a miniature version of this figure to keep track of the stages as they are discussed.

Chromosome

Unpacking of DNA

DNA

Gene

Transcription of gene

Intron Exon

RNA transcript

Processing of RNA

Flow of mRNA through nuclear envelope

Cap   Tail
mRNA in nucleus

Nucleus

mRNA in cytoplasm

Cytoplasm

Breakdown of mRNA

Translation of mRNA

Polypeptide

Various changes to polypeptide

Active protein

Breakdown of protein

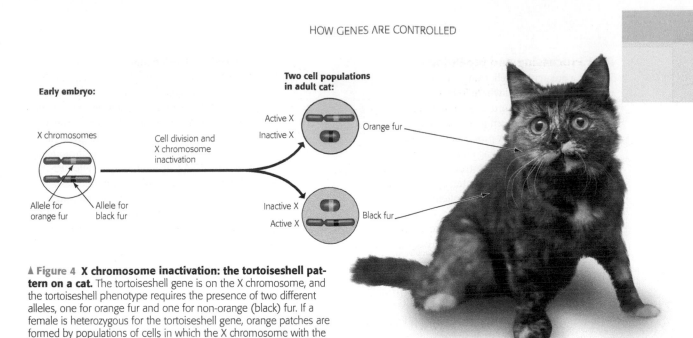

▲ Figure 4 X chromosome inactivation: the tortoiseshell pattern on a cat. The tortoiseshell gene is on the X chromosome, and the tortoiseshell phenotype requires the presence of two different alleles, one for orange fur and one for non-orange (black) fur. If a female is heterozygous for the tortoiseshell gene, orange patches are formed by populations of cells in which the X chromosome with the orange allele is active; black patches have cells in which the X chromosome with the non-orange allele is active.

The Initiation of Transcription

The initiation of transcription (whether transcription starts or not) is the most important stage for regulating gene expression. In both prokaryotes and eukaryotes, regulatory proteins bind to DNA and turn the transcription of genes on and off. Unlike prokaryotic genes, however, most eukaryotic genes are not grouped into operons. Instead, each eukaryotic gene usually has its own promoter and other control sequences.

As illustrated in **Figure 5**, transcriptional regulation in eukaryotes is complex, typically involving many proteins (collectively called **transcription factors;** shown in purple in the figure) acting in concert to bind to DNA sequences called **enhancers** (yellow) and to the promoter (green). The DNA-protein assembly promotes the binding of RNA polymerase (orange) to the promoter. Genes coding for related enzymes, such as those in a metabolic pathway, may share a specific kind of enhancer (or collection of enhancers), allowing these genes to be activated at the same time. Not shown in the figure are repressor proteins, which may bind to DNA sequences called **silencers**, inhibiting the start of transcription.

In fact, repressor proteins that turn genes off are less common in eukaryotes than **activators**, proteins that turn genes on by binding to DNA. Activators act by making it easier for RNA polymerase to bind to the promoter. The use of activators is efficient because a typical animal or plant cell needs to turn on (transcribe) only a small percentage of its genes, those required for the cell's specialized structure and function. The "default" state for most genes in multicellular eukaryotes seems to be off, with the exception of "housekeeping" genes for routine activities such as the digestion of glucose. ☑

☑ CHECKPOINT

Of all the control points of DNA expression shown in Figure 3, which is under the tightest regulation?

Answer: the initiation of transcription

▼ Figure 5 A model for turning on a eukaryotic gene. A large assembly of transcription factors (proteins shown in purple) and several control sequences in the DNA are involved in initiating the transcription of a eukaryotic gene.

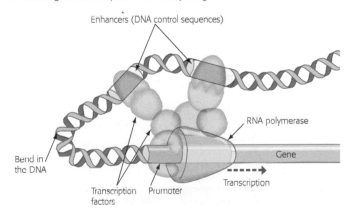

Enhancers (DNA control sequences)

Bend in the DNA

Transcription factors

Promoter

RNA polymerase

Gene

Transcription

RNA Processing and Breakdown

Within a eukaryotic cell, transcription occurs in the nucleus, where RNA transcripts are processed into mRNA before moving to the cytoplasm for translation by the ribosomes. RNA processing includes the addition of a cap and a tail, as well as the removal of any introns—noncoding DNA segments that interrupt the genetic message—and the splicing together of the remaining exons.

Within a cell, exon splicing can occur in more than one way, generating different mRNA molecules from the same starting RNA molecule. Notice in **Figure 6**, for example, that one mRNA ends up with the green exon and the other with the brown exon. With this sort of **alternative RNA splicing**, an organism can produce more than one type of polypeptide from a single gene. A typical human gene contains about ten exons; nearly all genes are spliced in at least two different ways, and some are spliced hundreds of different ways.

After an mRNA is produced in its final form, its "lifetime" can be highly variable, from hours to weeks to months. Controlling the timing of mRNA breakdown provides another opportunity for regulation. But all mRNAs are eventually broken down and their parts recycled.

microRNAs

Recent research has established an important role for a variety of small single-stranded RNA molecules, called microRNAs (miRNAs), that can bind to complementary sequences on mRNA molecules in the cytoplasm. After binding, some miRNAs trigger breakdown of their target mRNA, whereas others block translation. It has been estimated that miRNAs may regulate the expression of one half of all human genes, a striking figure given that miRNAs were unknown 20 years ago. New techniques attempt to exploit miRNAs via a technique called RNA interference, the injection of small RNA molecules into a cell to turn off specific genes. By understanding the natural process of information flow through a cell, biologists may soon be able to artificially control gene expression in humans.

The Initiation of Translation

The process of translation—in which an mRNA is used to make a protein—offers additional opportunities for control by regulatory molecules. Red blood cells, for instance, have a protein that prevents the translation of hemoglobin mRNA unless the cell has a supply of heme, an iron-containing chemical group essential for hemoglobin function.

Protein Activation and Breakdown

The final opportunities for regulating gene expression occur after translation. For example, the hormone insulin is synthesized as one long, inactive polypeptide that must be chopped into pieces before it comes active **(Figure 7)**. Other proteins require chemical modification before they become active.

Another control mechanism operating after translation is the selective breakdown of proteins. Some proteins that trigger metabolic changes in cells are broken down within a few minutes or hours. This regulation allows a cell to adjust the kinds and amounts of its proteins in response to changes in its environment. ☑

☑ CHECKPOINT

After a gene is transcribed in the nucleus, how is the transcript modified to become mRNA? After the mRNA reaches the cytoplasm, what are four control mechanisms that can regulate the amount of active protein in the cell?

Answer: by RNA processing, including the addition of cap and tail and RNA splicing; control by microRNAs, initiation of translation, activation of the protein, and breakdown of the protein

▼ **Figure 6 Alternative RNA splicing: producing multiple mRNAs from the same gene.** Two different cells can use the same DNA gene to synthesize different mRNAs and proteins. In this example, one mRNA has ended up with exon 3 (brown) and the other with exon 4 (green). These mRNAs, which are just two of many possible outcomes, can then be translated into different proteins.

▼ **Figure 7 The formation of an active insulin molecule.** Only in its final form, with a central region removed, does insulin act as a hormone.

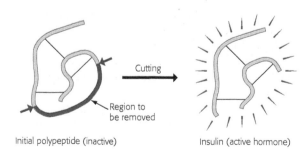

Cell Signaling

Information Flow

The control of gene expression is a good example of one of biology's important themes: information flow. Through regulation, a cell can alter its activities in response to signals from the environment. So far, we have considered gene regulation only within a single cell. In a multicellular organism, the process can cross cell boundaries, allowing information to be communicated between and among cells. For example, a cell can produce and secrete chemicals, such as hormones, that affect gene regulation in another cell. Consider an analogy from your own experience: In grade school, did you ever station a classmate near the door to signal the teacher's return? Information from outside the room (the teacher's approach) was used to alter behavior within the classroom (stop messing around!). In a similar way, cells use protein "lookouts" to convey information into the cell, resulting in changes to cellular functions.

A signal molecule can act by binding to a receptor protein and initiating a **signal transduction pathway**, a series of molecular changes that converts a signal received outside a cell to a specific response inside the target cell. **Figure 8** shows an example of cell-to-cell signaling in which the target cell's response is the transcription (turning on) of a gene. ❶ First, the signaling cell secretes the signal molecule (⬤). ❷ This molecule binds to a specific receptor protein (⬤) embedded in the target cell's plasma membrane. ❸ The binding activates a signal transduction pathway consisting of a series of relay proteins (green) within the target cell. Each relay molecule activates the next. ❹ The last relay molecule in the series activates a transcription factor (⬤) that ❺ triggers the transcription of a specific gene. ❻ Translation of the mRNA produces a protein that can then perform the function originally called for by the signal. ☑

Homeotic Genes

Cell-to-cell signaling and the control of gene expression are particularly important during early embryonic development, when a single-celled zygote develops into a multicellular organism. Master control genes called **homeotic genes** regulate groups of other genes that determine what body parts will develop in which locations. For example, one set of homeotic genes in fruit flies instructs cells in the midbody to form legs. Elsewhere, these homeotic genes remain turned off, while others are turned on. Mutations in homeotic genes can produce bizarre effects. For example, fruit flies with mutations in homeotic genes may have extra sets of legs growing from their head **(Figure 9)**.

CHECKPOINT

How can a signal molecule from one cell alter gene expression in a target cell without entering the target cell?

Answer: by binding to a receptor protein in the membrane of the target cell and triggering a signal transduction pathway that activates transcription factors

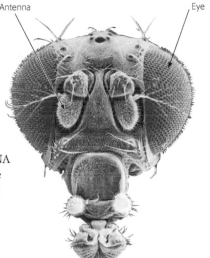

Normal head due to presence of normal homeotic gene

Antenna   Eye

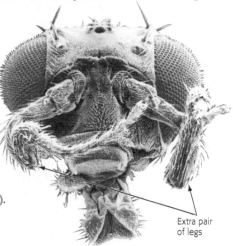

Extra pair of legs

Head with extra legs growing due to presence of mutant homeotic gene

▲ **Figure 8 A cell-signaling pathway that turns on a gene.** The coordination of cellular activities in a multicellular organism depends on cell-to-cell signaling that helps regulate genes.

Signaling cell diagram labels: SIGNALING CELL, Signal molecule, Plasma membrane, Receptor protein, TARGET CELL, Relay proteins, Transcription factor (activated), Nucleus, Transcription, mRNA, New protein, Translation

▶ **Figure 9 The effect of homeotic genes.** The strange mutant fruit fly shown at the bottom results from a mutation in a homeotic (master control) gene.

119

One of the most significant biological discoveries in recent years uncovered the fact that similar homeotic genes help direct embryonic development in nearly every eukaryotic organism examined so far, including yeasts, plants, earthworms, frogs, chickens, mice, and humans. These similarities suggest that these homeotic genes arose very early in the history of life and that the genes have remained remarkably unchanged over eons of animal evolution. ☑

Someday a DNA chip might report on the activities of all your genes.

which genes were being transcribed in the starting cells. Researchers can thus learn which genes are active in different tissues, at different times, or in tissues from individuals in different states of health. Such information may contribute to a better understanding of diseases and suggest new therapies. For example, comparing patterns of gene expression in breast cancer tumors with noncancerous breast tissue has resulted in more effective treatment protocols.

DNA Microarrays: Visualizing Gene Expression

Scientists who study gene regulation often want to determine which genes are switched on or off in a particular cell. A **DNA microarray** is a slide with thousands of different kinds of single-stranded DNA fragments attached in a tightly spaced array (grid). Each DNA fragment is obtained from a particular gene; a single microarray thus carries DNA from thousands of genes, perhaps even all the genes of an organism.

Figure 10 outlines how microarrays are used. ❶ A researcher collects all of the mRNA transcribed in a particular type of cell at a given moment. This collection of mRNA is mixed with reverse transcriptase, a viral enzyme that ❷ produces DNA that is complementary to each mRNA sequence. This **complementary DNA (cDNA)** is synthesized using nucleotides that have been modified to fluoresce (glow). The fluorescent cDNA collection thus represents all of the genes being actively transcribed in the cell. ❸ A small amount of the fluorescently labeled cDNA mixture is added to the DNA fragments of the microarray. If a molecule in the cDNA mixture is complementary to a DNA fragment at a particular location on the grid, the cDNA molecule binds to it, becoming fixed there. ❹ After unbound cDNA is rinsed away, the remaining cDNA glows in the microarray. The pattern of glowing spots enables the researcher to determine

❶ mRNA isolated

Reverse transcriptase combined with fluorescent DNA nucleotides

❷ cDNA made from mRNA

Fluorescent cDNA

DNA microarray (each spot contains DNA from a particular gene)

❸ cDNA mixture added to spots

❹ Unbound cDNA rinsed away

Nonfluorescent spot

Fluorescent spot

Fluorescent cDNA

DNA of an expressed gene

DNA of an unexpressed gene

DNA microarray, actual size (6,400 genes)

▲ Figure 10 **Visualizing gene expression using a DNA microarray.**

Cloning Plants and Animals

Now that we have examined how gene expression is regulated, we will devote the rest of this chapter to discussing how gene regulation affects two important processes: cloning and cancer.

The Genetic Potential of Cells

One of the most important take-home lessons from this chapter is that all body cells contain a complete complement of genes, even if they are not expressing all of them. If you've ever grown a plant from a small cutting, you've seen evidence of this yourself: A single differentiated plant cell can undergo cell division and give rise to a complete adult plant. On a larger scale, the technique described in **Figure 11** can be used to produce hundreds or thousands of genetically identical organisms—clones—from the cells of a single plant.

Plant cloning is now used extensively in agriculture. For some plants, such as orchids, cloning is the only commercially practical means of reproducing plants. In other cases, cloning has been used to reproduce a plant with specific desirable traits, such as high fruit yield or resistance to disease. Seedless plants (such as seedless grapes, watermelons, and oranges) cannot reproduce sexually, leaving cloning as the sole means of mass-producing these common foods.

Is this sort of cloning possible in animals? A good indication that some animal cells can also tap into their full genetic potential is **regeneration**, the regrowth of lost body parts. When a salamander loses a tail, for example, certain cells in the tail stump reverse their differentiated state, divide, and then differentiate again to give rise to a new tail. Many other animals, especially among the invertebrates (sea stars and sponges, for example), can regenerate lost parts, and isolated pieces of a few relatively simple animals can dedifferentiate and then develop into an entirely new organism.

▶ **Figure 11 Test-tube cloning of an orchid.** Tissue removed from the stem of an orchid plant and placed in growth medium may begin dividing and eventually grow into an adult plant. The new plant is a genetic duplicate of the parent plant. This process proves that mature plant cells can reverse their differentiation and develop into all the specialized cells of an adult plant.

Cells removed from orchid plant

Cells in growth medium

Single cell

Cell division in culture

Young plant

Adult plant

Reproductive Cloning of Animals

Animal cloning is achieved through a procedure called **nuclear transplantation** (Figure 12). First performed in the 1950s on frog embryos and in the 1990s on adult mammals, nuclear transplantation involves replacing the nucleus of an egg cell or a zygote with a nucleus removed from an adult body cell. If properly stimulated, the recipient cell may then begin to divide. Repeated cell divisions form a hollow ball of about 100 cells. At this point, the cells may be used for different purposes, as indicated by the two branches in Figure 12.

If the animal to be cloned is a mammal, further development requires implanting the early embryo into the uterus of a surrogate mother (Figure 12, upper branch). The resulting animal will be a "clone" (genetic copy) of the donor. This type of cloning is called **reproductive cloning** because it results in the birth of a new animal.

In 1996, researchers used reproductive cloning to produce the first mammal cloned from an adult cell, a sheep named Dolly. The researchers fused specially treated sheep cells with eggs from which they had removed the nuclei. After several days of growth, the resulting embryos were implanted in the uteruses of surrogate mothers. One of the embryos developed into Dolly—and, as expected, Dolly resembled the nucleus donor, not the egg donor or the surrogate mother.

Practical Applications of Reproductive Cloning

Since the first success in 1996, researchers have cloned many species of mammals, including mice, horses, dogs, mules, cows, pigs, rabbits, ferrets, camels, goats, and cats (Figure 13a). Why would anyone want to do this? In agriculture, farm animals with specific sets of desirable traits might be cloned to produce identical herds. In research, genetically identical animals can provide perfect "control animals" for experiments. The pharmaceutical industry is experimenting with cloning animals for potential medical use (Figure 13b). For example, researchers have produced pig clones that lack a gene for a protein that can cause immune system rejection in humans. Organs from such pigs may one day be used in human patients who require life-saving transplants.

Perhaps the most intriguing use of reproductive cloning is to restock populations of endangered animals. Among the rare animals that have been cloned are a wild mouflon (a small European sheep), a gaur (an Asian ox), and gray wolves (Figure 13c), and many others are being attempted. In 2003, a banteng (a Javanese cow whose numbers have dwindled to just a few in the wild) was cloned using frozen cells from a zoo-raised banteng that had died 23 years prior. Scientists obtained banteng skin tissue from "The Frozen Zoo," a facility in San Diego, California, where samples from rare or endangered animals are stored for conservation. The scientists transplanted nuclei from the frozen cells

> Cloning may help save the giant panda from extinction.

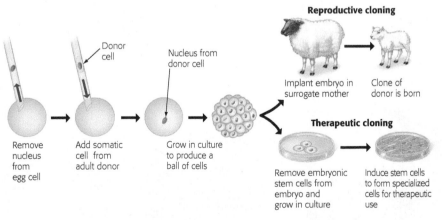

▲ Figure 12 Cloning by nuclear transplantation. In nuclear transplantation, a nucleus from an adult body cell is injected into a nucleus-free egg cell. The resulting embryo may then be used to produce a new organism (reproductive cloning, shown in the upper branch) or to provide stem cells (therapeutic cloning, lower branch).

into nucleus-free eggs from dairy cows. The resulting embryos were implanted into surrogate cows, leading to the birth of a healthy baby banteng. This success shows that it is possible to produce a baby even when a female of the donor species is unavailable. Scientists may someday be able to use similar cross-species methods to clone an animal from a recently extinct species.

The use of cloning to repopulate endangered species holds tremendous promise. However, cloning may also create new problems. Conservationists argue that cloning may detract from efforts to preserve natural habitats. They correctly point out that cloning does not increase genetic diversity and is therefore not as beneficial to endangered species as natural reproduction. In addition, an increasing body of evidence suggests that cloned animals are less healthy than animals produced via fertilization: Many cloned animals exhibit defects such as susceptibility to obesity, pneumonia, liver failure, and premature death. Dolly the cloned

sheep, for example, was euthanized in 2003 after suffering complications from a lung disease usually seen only in much older sheep. She was 6 years old, while her breed has a life expectancy of 12 years. Some evidence suggests that chromosomal changes in the cloned animals are the cause, but the effects of cloning on animal health are still being investigated.

Human Cloning

The cloning of various mammals has heightened speculation that humans could be cloned. Critics point out the many practical and ethical objections to human cloning. Practically, cloning of mammals is extremely difficult and inefficient. Only a small percentage of cloned embryos (usually less than 10%) develop normally, and they appear less healthy than naturally born kin. Ethically, the discussion about whether or not people should be cloned—and if so, under what circumstances—is far from settled. Meanwhile, the research and the debate continue. ☑

▼ Figure 13 **Reproductive cloning of mammals.**

(a) The first clone. Dolly the sheep, shown in 1996 with her lone parent, was the first mammal cloned from an adult cell.

(b) Cloning for medical use. These piglets are clones of a pig that was genetically modified to lack a protein that causes transplant rejection in humans.

(c) Clones of endangered animals

Mouflon lamb with mother

Banteng

Gaur

Therapeutic Cloning and Stem Cells

The lower branch of Figure 12 shows the process of **therapeutic cloning**. The purpose of this procedure is not to produce a living organism but rather to produce embryonic stem cells.

Embryonic Stem Cells

In mammals, **embryonic stem cells (ES cells)** are obtained by removing cells from an early embryo and growing them in laboratory culture. Embryonic stem cells can divide indefinitely, and under the right conditions—such as the presence of certain growth-stimulating proteins—can (hypothetically) develop into a wide variety of different specialized cells **(Figure 14)**. If scientists can discover the right conditions, they may be able to grow cells for the repair of injured or diseased organs. Some people speculate, for example, that ES cells may one day be used to replace cells damaged by spinal cord injuries or heart attacks. The use of embryonic stem cells in therapeutic cloning is controversial, however, because the removal of ES cells destroys the embryo.

Umbilical Cord Blood Banking

Another source of stem cells is blood collected from the umbilical cord and placenta at birth **(Figure 15)**. Such stem cells appear to be partially differentiated. In 2005, doctors reported that an infusion of umbilical cord blood stem cells appeared to cure some babies of Krabbe disease, a fatal inherited disorder of the nervous system. Other people have received cord blood as a treatment for leukemia. To date, however, most attempts at umbilical cord blood therapy have not been successful. At present, the American Academy of Pediatrics recommends cord blood banking only for babies born into families with a known genetic risk.

Adult Stem Cells

Embryonic stem cells are not the only stem cells available to researchers. **Adult stem cells** can also generate replacements for some of the body's cells. Adult stem cells are further along the road to differentiation than ES cells and can therefore give rise to only a few related types of specialized cells. For example, stem cells in bone marrow generate different kinds of blood cells. Adult stem cells from donor bone marrow have long been used as a source of immune system cells in patients whose own immune systems have been destroyed by disease or cancer treatments.

Because no embryonic tissue is involved in their harvest, adult stem cells are less ethically problematic than ES cells. However, many researchers hypothesize that only the more versatile ES cells are likely to lead to groundbreaking advances in human health. Recent research has shown that some adult cells, such as human skin cells, may be reprogrammed to act like ES cells. In the near future, such cells may prove to be both therapeutically useful and ethically clear. ☑

✅ **CHECKPOINT**

How do the results of reproductive cloning and therapeutic cloning differ?

Answer: Reproductive cloning results in the production of a live individual; therapeutic cloning produces stem cells.

▼ Figure 14 **Differentiation of embryonic stem cells in culture.** Scientists hope to someday discover growth conditions that will stimulate cultured stem cells to differentiate into specialized cells.

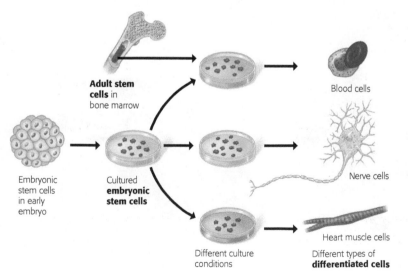

Adult stem cells in bone marrow

Embryonic stem cells in early embryo

Cultured **embryonic stem cells**

Different culture conditions

Blood cells

Nerve cells

Heart muscle cells

Different types of **differentiated cells**

▼ Figure 15 **Umbilical cord blood banking.** Just after birth, a doctor inserts a needle into the umbilical cord and extracts ¼ to ½ cup of blood. The umbilical cord blood (inset), rich in stem cells, is frozen and kept in a blood bank, where it is available if needed for medical treatment.

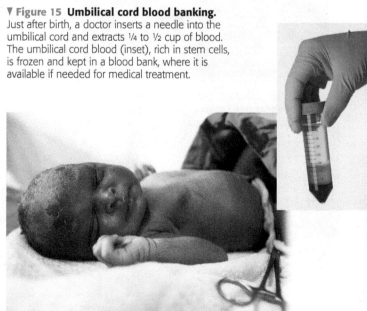

The Genetic Basis of Cancer

Cancer includes a variety of diseases in which cells escape from the control mechanisms that normally limit their growth and division. This escape involves changes in gene expression.

Genes That Cause Cancer

One of the earliest clues to the role of genes in cancer was the discovery in 1911 of a virus that causes cancer in chickens. Viruses that cause cancer can become permanent residents in host cells by inserting their nucleic acid into the DNA of host chromosomes. Over the last century, researchers have identified a number of viruses that harbor cancer-causing genes. One example is the human papillomavirus (HPV), which can be transmitted through sexual contact and is associated with several types of cancer, including cervical cancer.

Oncogenes and Tumor-Suppressor Genes

In 1976, American molecular biologists J. Michael Bishop, Harold Varmus, and their colleagues made a startling discovery. They found that a cancer-causing chicken virus contains a cancer-causing gene that is an altered version of a normal chicken gene. A gene that causes cancer is called an **oncogene** ("tumor gene"). Subsequent research has shown that the chromosomes of many animals, including humans, contain genes that can be converted to oncogenes. A normal gene with the potential to become an oncogene is called a **proto-oncogene**. (These terms can be confusing, so let's repeat them: A *proto-oncogene* is a normal, healthy gene that, if changed, can become a cancer-causing *oncogene*.) A cell can acquire an oncogene from a virus or from the mutation of one of its own proto-oncogenes.

How can a change in a gene cause cancer? Searching for the normal roles of proto-oncogenes in the cell, researchers found that many of these genes code for **growth factors**—proteins that stimulate cell division—or for other proteins that affect the cell cycle. When all these proteins are functioning normally, in the right amounts at the right times, they help keep the rate of cell division at an appropriate level. When they malfunction—if a growth factor becomes hyperactive, for example—cancer (uncontrolled cell growth) may result.

For a proto-oncogene to become an oncogene, a mutation must occur in the cell's DNA. **Figure 16** illustrates three kinds of changes in DNA that can produce active oncogenes. In all three cases, abnormal gene expression stimulates the cell to divide excessively.

Changes in genes whose products inhibit cell division are also involved in cancer. These genes are called **tumor-suppressor genes** because the proteins they encode normally help prevent uncontrolled cell growth (**Figure 17**). Any mutation that keeps a growth-inhibiting protein from being made or from functioning may contribute to the development of cancer. Researchers have identified many mutations in both tumor-suppressor and growth factor genes that are associated with cancer, as we'll discuss next.

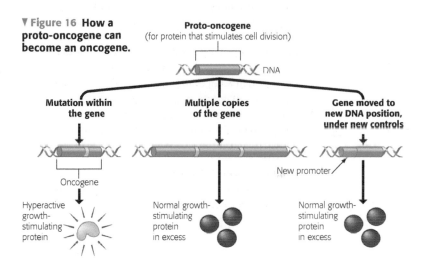

▼ **Figure 16 How a proto-oncogene can become an oncogene.**

▼ **Figure 17 Tumor-suppressor genes.**

(a) Normal cell growth. A tumor-suppressor gene normally codes for a protein that inhibits cell growth and division. Such genes help prevent cancerous tumors from arising or spreading.

(b) Uncontrolled cell growth (cancer). When a mutation in a tumor-suppressor gene makes its protein defective, cells that are usually under the control of the normal protein may divide excessively, forming a tumor.

Cancer THE PROCESS OF SCIENCE

Are Childhood Tumors Different?

Medical researchers have made many **observations** of specific mutations that can lead to cancer. They therefore **question** whether different kinds of cancers are associated with specific mutations. A large research team led by the Johns Hopkins Kimmel Cancer Center in Baltimore formed the **hypothesis** that young patients with medulloblastoma (MB)—the most common pediatric brain cancer and the deadliest form of childhood cancer (**Figure 18**)—harbor unique mutations. They made the **prediction** that a genetic map of MB cells from childhood tumors would have cancer-associated mutations not found in adult brain cancer tissue.

The **experiment** involved sequencing all the genes in tumors removed from 22 pediatric MB patients and comparing them with normal tissue from these same patients. Their **results** showed that each tumor had an average of 11 mutations. Although this may seem like a lot, it is actually five to ten times fewer than the number of mutations associated with MB in adult patients. Young MB patients therefore seem to have fewer, but deadlier,

mutations. When they investigated the role that the mutated genes play, the research team found that some help control DNA packing, whereas others play a role in the development of organs. The researchers hope that this new knowledge about the genetic basis of MB may be used to develop new therapies for this often fatal disease.

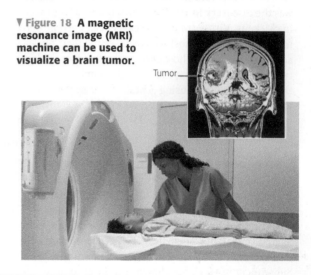

▼ Figure 18 **A magnetic resonance image (MRI) machine can be used to visualize a brain tumor.**

Tumor

The Progression of a Cancer

Nearly 150,000 Americans will be stricken by cancer of the colon (the main part of the large intestine) this year. One of the best-understood types of human cancer, colon cancer illustrates an important principle about how cancer develops: Although we still don't know exactly how a particular cell becomes a cancer cell, we do know that more than one mutation is needed to produce a full-fledged cancer cell. As in many cancers, the development of colon cancer is a gradual process.

As shown in **Figure 19**, ❶ colon cancer begins when an oncogene arises through mutation, causing unusually frequent division of normal-looking cells in the colon lining. ❷ Later, additional DNA mutations (such as the inactivation of a tumor-suppressor gene) cause the growth of a small benign tumor (called a polyp) in the colon wall. The cells of the polyp look normal, although they divide unusually frequently. If detected during a colonoscopy, suspicious polyps can usually be removed before they become a serious risk. ❸ Further mutations

▼ Figure 19 **Stepwise development of colon cancer.**

Colon wall

Colon wall

Cellular changes: Increased cell division   Growth of benign tumor   Growth of malignant tumor

DNA changes: Oncogene activated   Tumor-suppressor gene inactivated   Second tumor-suppressor gene inactivated eventually lead to formation of a malignant tumor—a tumor that has the potential to metastasize (spread). It typically takes at least six DNA mutations (usually creating at least one active oncogene and disabling at least one tumor-suppressor gene) before a cell becomes fully cancerous.

The development of a malignant tumor is accompanied by a gradual accumulation of mutations that convert proto-oncogenes to oncogenes and knock out tumor-suppressor genes (Figure 20). The requirement for several DNA mutations—usually four or more—explains why cancers can take a long time to develop. This requirement may also help explain why the incidence of cancer increases with age; the longer we live, the more likely we are to accumulate mutations that cause cancer.

Inherited Cancer

The fact that multiple genetic changes are required to produce a cancer cell helps explain the observation that cancers can run in families. An individual inheriting an oncogene or a mutant version of a tumor-suppressor gene is one step closer to accumulating the necessary mutations for cancer to develop than is an individual without any such mutations. Geneticists are therefore devoting much effort to identifying inherited cancer mutations so that predisposition to certain cancers can be detected early in life.

About 15% of colorectal cancers, for example, involve inherited mutations. There is also evidence that inheritance plays a role in 5–10% of patients with breast cancer, a disease that strikes one out of every ten American women (Figure 21). Mutations in either or both of two genes—called *BRCA1* (pronounced "braca-1") and *BRCA2*—are found in at least half of inherited breast cancers. Both *BRCA1* and *BRCA2* are considered tumor-suppressor genes because the normal versions protect against breast cancer. A woman who inherits one mutant

▲ Figure 21 **Breast cancer.** In 2013, at age 37, the actress Angelina Jolie underwent a preventive double mastectomy after learning she had a mutant *BRCA1* gene. Jolie's mother, grandmother, and aunt all died young from breast or ovarian cancer.

BRCA1 allele has a 60% probability of developing breast cancer before the age of 50, compared with only a 2% probability for an individual lacking the mutations. Tests using DNA sequencing can now detect these mutations. Unfortunately, these tests are of limited use because surgical removal of the breasts and/or ovaries is the only preventive option currently available to women who carry the mutant genes. ☑

☑ **CHECKPOINT**

How can a mutation in a tumor-suppressor gene contribute to the development of cancer?

Answer: A mutated tumor-suppressor gene may produce a defective protein that normally inhibits cell division and therefore normally suppresses tumors.

▼ Figure 20 **Accumulation of mutations in the development of a cancer cell.**
Mutations leading to cancer accumulate in a lineage of cells. In this figure, colors distinguish the normal cells from cells with one or more mutations, leading to increased cell division and cancer. Once a cancer-promoting mutation occurs (orange band on chromosome), it is passed to all the descendants of the cell carrying it.

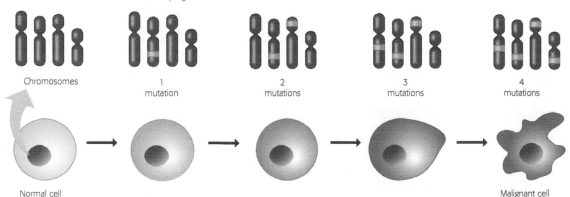

| Chromosomes | 1 mutation | 2 mutations | 3 mutations | 4 mutations |

Normal cell

Malignant cell

Cancer Risk and Prevention

Cancer is the second-leading cause of death (after heart disease) in most industrialized countries. Death rates due to certain forms of cancer have decreased in recent years, but the overall cancer death rate is still on the rise, currently increasing at about 1% per decade.

Although some cancers occur spontaneously, most cancers arise from mutations that are caused by **carcinogens**, cancer-causing agents found in the environment. Mutations often result from decades of exposure to carcinogens. One of the most potent carcinogens is ultraviolet (UV) radiation. Excessive exposure to UV radiation from the sun can cause skin cancer, including a deadly type called melanoma. You can decrease your risk by using sun protection (clothing, lotion, hats, etc.).

The one substance known to cause more cases and types of cancer than any other is tobacco. By a wide margin, more people die from lung cancer (nearly 160,000 Americans in 2014) than from any other form of cancer. Most tobacco-related cancers are due to smoking cigarettes, but smoking cigars, inhaling secondhand smoke, and smokeless tobacco also pose risks. As **Table 1** indicates, tobacco use, sometimes in combination with alcohol consumption, causes several types of cancer. Exposure to some of the most lethal carcinogens is often a matter of individual choice: Tobacco use, the consumption of alcohol, and excessive time spent in the sun are all avoidable behaviors that affect cancer risk.

Some food choices significantly reduce a person's odds of developing cancer. For instance, eating 20–30 g of plant fiber daily (about the amount found in seven apples), while eating less animal fat may help prevent colon cancer. There is also evidence that certain substances in fruits and vegetables, including vitamins C and E and certain compounds related to vitamin A, may help protect against a variety of cancers. Cabbage and its relatives, such as broccoli and cauliflower, are thought to be especially rich in substances that help prevent cancer, although some of the specific substances have not yet been identified. Determining how diet influences cancer has become an important focus of nutrition research.

The battle against cancer is being waged on many fronts, and there is reason for optimism in the progress being made. It is especially encouraging that we can help reduce our risk of acquiring some of the most common forms of cancer by the choices we make in our daily lives. ☑

> Lifestyle choices you make can dramatically affect your risk of cancer.

☑ CHECKPOINT

Of all known behavioral factors, which one causes the most cancer cases and deaths?

Answer: tobacco use

Table 1	Cancer in the United States (Ranked by Number of Cases)		
Cancer	**Known or Likely Carcinogens or Factors**	**Estimated Cases (2014)**	**Estimated Deaths (2014)**
Breast	Estrogen; possibly dietary fat	235,000	40,400
Prostate	Testosterone; possibly dietary fat	233,000	29,500
Lung	Cigarette smoke	224,000	159,000
Colon and rectum	High dietary fat; low dietary fiber	136,800	50,310
Skin	Ultraviolet light	81,200	13,000
Lymphomas	Viruses (for some types)	80,000	20,100
Bladder	Cigarette smoke	74,700	15,600
Uterus	Estrogen	65,000	12,600
Kidney	Cigarette smoke	63,900	13,900
Leukemias	X-rays; benzene; viruses (for some types)	52,400	24,100
Pancreas	Cigarette smoke	46,400	39,600
Liver	Alcohol; hepatitis viruses	33,200	23,000
Brain and nerve	Trauma; X-rays	23,400	14,300
Stomach	Table salt; cigarette smoke	22,200	11,000
Ovary	Large number of ovulation cycles	22,000	14,300
Cervix	Viruses; cigarette smoke	12,400	4,000
All other types		259,940	101,010
Total		1,665,540	585,720

Data from: Cancer Facts and Figures 2014 (American Cancer Society Inc.).

Cancer EVOLUTION CONNECTION

The Evolution of Cancer in the Body

The theory of evolution describes natural selection acting on populations. Recently, medical researchers have been using an evolutionary perspective to gain insight into the development of tumors, such as the bone tumor shown in **Figure 22**. Evolution drives the growth of a tumor—which can be thought of as a population of cancer cells—and also affects how those cells respond to cancer treatments.

Recall that there are several assumptions behind Darwin's theory of natural selection. Let's consider how each one can be applied to cancer. First, all evolving populations have the potential to produce more offspring than can be supported by the environment. Cancer cells, with their uncontrolled growth, clearly demonstrate overproduction. Second, there must be variation among individuals of the population. Studies of tumor cell DNA, like the one described in the Process of Science section, show genetic variability within tumors. Third, variations in the population must affect survival and reproductive success. Indeed, the accumulation of mutations in cancer cells renders them less susceptible to normal mechanisms of reproductive control. Mutations that enhance survival of malignant cancer cells are passed on to that cell's descendants. In short, a tumor evolves.

Viewing the progression of cancer through the lens of evolution helps explain why there is no easy "cure" for cancer but may also pave the way for novel therapies. For example, some researchers are attempting to "prime" tumors for treatment by increasing the reproductive success of only those cells that will be susceptible to a chemotherapy drug. Our understanding of cancer, like all other aspects of biology, benefits from an evolutionary perspective.

▼ **Figure 22** **X-ray of shoulder and upper arm, revealing a large bone tumor.**

Chapter Review

■ SUMMARY OF KEY CONCEPTS

How and Why Genes Are Regulated

The various types of cells in a multicellular organism owe their distinctiveness to different combinations of genes being turned on and off via gene regulation in each cell type.

Gene Regulation in Bacteria

An operon is a cluster of genes with related functions together with their promoter and other DNA sequences that control their transcription. For example, the *lac* operon allows *E. coli* to produce enzymes for lactose use only when the sugar is present.

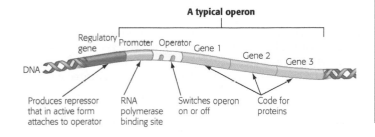

A typical operon

Regulatory gene — Promoter — Operator — Gene 1 — Gene 2 — Gene 3

DNA

Produces repressor that in active form attaches to operator | RNA polymerase binding site | Switches operon on or off | Code for proteins

Gene Regulation in Eukaryotic Cells

In the nucleus of eukaryotic cells, there are several possible control points in the pathway of gene expression.

- DNA packing tends to block gene expression by preventing access of transcription proteins to the DNA. An extreme example is X chromosome inactivation in the cells of female mammals.

- The most important control point in both eukaryotes and prokaryotes is at gene transcription. Various regulatory proteins interact with DNA and with each other to turn the transcription of eukaryotic genes on or off.

- There are also opportunities for the control of eukaryotic gene expression after transcription, when introns are cut out of the RNA and a cap and tail are added to process RNA transcripts into mRNA.

- In the cytoplasm, presence of microRNAs may block the translation of an mRNA, and various proteins may regulate the start of translation.

- Finally, the cell may activate the finished protein in various ways (for instance, by cutting out portions or chemical modification). Eventually, the protein may be selectively broken down.

DNA unpacking
Transcription
RNA processing
RNA transport
mRNA breakdown
Translation
Protein activation
Protein breakdown

Information Flow: Cell Signaling

Cell-to-cell signaling is key to the development and function-ing of multicellular organisms. Signal transduction pathways convert molecular messages to cell responses, such as the transcription of particular genes.

Homeotic Genes

Evidence for the evolutionary importance of gene regulation is apparent in homeotic genes, master genes that regulate other genes that in turn control embryonic development.

DNA Microarrays: Visualizing Gene Expression

DNA microarrays can be used to determine which genes are turned on in a particular cell type.

Cloning Plants and Animals

The Genetic Potential of Cells

Most differentiated cells retain a complete set of genes, so an orchid plant, for example, can be made to grow from a single orchid cell. Under con-trolled conditions, animals can also be cloned.

Reproductive Cloning of Animals

Nuclear transplantation is a procedure whereby a donor cell nucleus is inserted into an egg from which the nucleus has been removed. First demonstrated in frogs in the 1950s, reproductive cloning was used in 1996 to clone a sheep from an adult cell and has since been used to create many other cloned animals.

Nucleus from donor cell → Early embryo resulting from nuclear transplantation → Embryo implanted in surrogate mother → Clone of nucleus donor

Therapeutic Cloning and Stem Cells

The purpose of therapeutic cloning is to produce embryonic stem cells for medical uses. Embryonic, umbilical cord, and adult stem cells all show promise for therapeutic uses.

Nucleus from donor cell → Early embryo resulting from nuclear transplantation → Embryonic stem cells in culture → Specialized cells

The Genetic Basis of Cancer

Genes That Cause Cancer

Cancer cells, which divide uncontrollably, can result from mutations in genes whose protein products regulate the cell cycle.

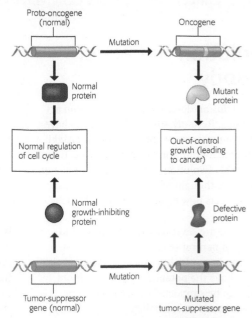

Many proto-oncogenes and tumor-suppressor genes code for proteins active in signal transduction pathways regulating cell division. Mutations of these genes cause malfunction of the pathways. Cancer results from a series of genetic changes in a cell lineage. Researchers have identified many genes that, when mutated, promote the development of cancer.

Cancer Risk and Prevention

Reducing exposure to carcinogens (which induce cancer-causing mutations) and making other healthful lifestyle choices can help reduce cancer risk.

MasteringBiology®

For practice quizzes, BioFlix animations, MP3 tutorials, video tutors, and more study tools designed for this text, go to MasteringBiology®

▮ SELF-QUIZ

1. Your bone cells, muscle cells, and skin cells look different because
   a. different kinds of genes are present in each kind of cell.
   b. they are present in different organs.
   c. different genes are active in each kind of cell.
   d. different mutations have occurred in each kind of cell.

2. A group of prokaryotic genes with related functions that are regulated as a single unit, along with the control sequences that perform this regulation, is called a(n) _____.

3. The regulation of gene expression must be more complex in multicellular eukaryotes than in prokaryotes because
   a. eukaryotic cells are much larger.
   b. in a multicellular eukaryote, different cells are specialized for different functions.
   c. prokaryotes are restricted to stable environments.
   d. eukaryotes have fewer genes, so each gene must do several jobs.

4. A eukaryotic gene was inserted into the DNA of a bacterium. The bacterium then transcribed this gene into mRNA and translated the mRNA into protein. The protein produced was useless and contained many more amino acids than the protein made by the eukaryotic cell. Why?
   a. The mRNA was not spliced as it is in eukaryotes.
   b. Eukaryotes and prokaryotes use different genetic codes.
   c. Repressor proteins interfered with transcription and translation.
   d. Ribosomes were not able to bind to tRNA.

5. How does dense packing of DNA in chromosomes prevent gene expression?

6. What evidence demonstrates that differentiated cells in a plant or animal retain their full genetic potential?

7. The most common procedure for cloning an animal is _____.

8. What is learned from a DNA microarray?

9. Which of the following is a substantial difference between embryonic stem cells and the stem cells found in adult tissues?
   a. In laboratory culture, only adult stem cells are immortal.
   b. In nature, only embryonic stem cells give rise to all the different types of cells in the organism.
   c. Only adult stem cells can be made to differentiate in the laboratory.
   d. Only embryonic stem cells are in every tissue of the adult body.

10. Name three potential sources of stem cells.

11. What is the difference between oncogenes and proto-oncogenes? How can one turn into the other? What function do proto-oncogenes serve?

12. A mutation in a single gene may cause a major change in the body of a fruit fly, such as an extra pair of legs or wings. Yet it takes many genes to produce a wing or leg. How can a change in just one gene cause such a big change in the body? What are such genes called?

THE PROCESS OF SCIENCE

13. Study the depiction of the *lac* operon in Figure 2. Normally, the genes are turned off when lactose is not present. Lactose activates the genes, which code for enzymes that enable the cell to use lactose. Mutations can alter the function of this operon. Predict how the following mutations would affect the function of the operon in the presence and absence of lactose:
    a. mutation of regulatory gene; repressor will not bind to lactose
    b. mutation of operator; repressor will not bind to operator
    c. mutation of regulatory gene; repressor will not bind to operator
    d. mutation of promoter; RNA polymerase will not attach to promoter

14. The human body has a far greater variety of proteins than genes, a fact that seems to highlight the importance of alternative RNA splicing, which allows several different mRNAs to be made from a single gene. Suppose you have samples of two types of adult cells from one person. Design an experiment using microarrays to determine whether or not the different gene expression is due to alternative RNA splicing.

15. Because a cat must have both orange and non-orange alleles to be tortoiseshell (see Figure 4), we would expect only female cats, which have two X chromosomes, to be tortoiseshell. Normal male cats (XY) can carry only one of the two alleles. Male tortoiseshell cats are rare and usually sterile. What might you guess their genotype to be?

16. Design a DNA microarray experiment that measures the difference in gene expression between normal colon cells and cells from a colon tumor.

17. **Interpreting Data** Review Table 1, which lists the number of diagnoses and the number of deaths for many types of cancer. We can estimate the deadliness of each type of cancer by dividing the number of deaths by the number of cases. (This is not accurate, however, because someone diagnosed during a particular year will not necessarily die during that same year, but it is a useful approximation.) If nearly everyone who received a diagnosis of one particular type of cancer dies, that ratio will be near 1 (or 100% deadly). If many more people receive diagnoses than die, the ratio will be near 0 (or near 0% deadly). Using this criteria, which two forms of cancer listed are the deadliest? The least deadly? What is the overall ratio for all types of cancer? What does this tell you about cancer survivability in general?

BIOLOGY AND SOCIETY

18. A chemical called dioxin is produced as a by-product of certain chemical manufacturing processes. Trace amounts of this substance were present in Agent Orange, a defoliant sprayed on vegetation during the Vietnam War. There has been a continuing controversy over its effects on soldiers exposed to Agent Orange during the war. Animal tests have suggested that dioxin can cause cancer, liver and thymus damage, immune system suppression, and birth defects; at high dosage it can be lethal. But such animal tests are inconclusive; a hamster is not affected by a dose that can kill a much larger guinea pig, for example. Researchers have discovered that dioxin enters a cell and binds to a protein that in turn attaches to the cell's DNA. How might this mechanism help explain the variety of dioxin's effects on different body systems and in different animals? How might you determine whether a particular individual became ill as a result of exposure to dioxin? Do you think this information is relevant in the lawsuits of soldiers suing over exposure to Agent Orange? Why or why not?

19. There are genetic tests available for several types of "inherited cancer." The results from these tests cannot usually predict that someone will get cancer within a particular amount of time. Rather, they indicate only that a person has an increased risk of developing cancer. For many of these cancers, lifestyle changes cannot decrease a person's risk. Therefore, some people consider the tests useless. If your close family had a history of cancer and a test were available, would you want to get screened? Why or why not? What would you do with this information? If a sibling decided to get screened, explain whether you would want to know the results.

Glossary

activator
A protein that switches on a gene or group of genes by binding to DNA.

adult stem cell
A cell present in adult tissues that generates replacements for nondividing differentiated cells.

alternative RNA splicing
A type of regulation at the RNA-processing level in which different mRNA molecules are produced from the same primary transcript, depending on which RNA segments are treated as exons and which as introns.

carcinogen (*kar-sin'-uh-jin*)
A cancer-causing agent, either high-energy radiation (such as X-rays or UV light) or a chemical.

complementary DNA (cDNA)
A DNA molecule made in vitro using mRNA as a template and the enzyme reverse transcriptase. A cDNA molecule therefore corresponds to a gene but lacks the introns present in the DNA of the genome.

DNA microarray
A glass slide containing thousands of different kinds of single-stranded DNA fragments arranged in an array (grid). Tiny amounts of DNA fragments, representing different genes, are attached to the glass slide. These fragments are tested for hybridization with various samples of cDNA molecules, thereby measuring the expression of thousands of genes at one time.

embryonic stem cell (ES cell)
Any of the cells in the early animal embryo that differentiate during development to give rise to all the kinds of specialized cells in the body.

enhancer
A eukaryotic DNA sequence that helps stimulate the transcription of a gene at some distance from it. An enhancer functions by means of a transcription factor called an activator, which binds to it and then to the rest of the transcription apparatus.

gene expression
The process whereby genetic information flows from genes to proteins; the flow of genetic information from the genotype to the phenotype: DNA → RNA → protein.

gene regulation
The turning on and off of specific genes within a living organism.

growth factor
A protein secreted by certain body cells that stimulates other cells to divide.

homeotic gene (*hō'-mē-ot'-ik*)
A master control gene that determines the identity of a body structure of a developing organism, presumably by controlling the developmental fate of groups of cells. (In plants, such genes are called organ identity genes.)

nuclear transplantation
A technique in which the nucleus of one cell is placed into another cell that already has a nucleus or in which the nucleus has been previously destroyed. The cell is then stimulated to grow, producing an embryo that is a genetic copy of the nucleus donor.

oncogene (*on'-kō-jēn*)
A cancer-causing gene; usually contributes to malignancy by abnormally enhancing the amount or activity of a growth factor made by the cell.

operator
In prokaryotic DNA, a sequence of nucleotides near the start of an operon to which an active repressor can attach. The binding of repressor prevents RNA polymerase from attaching to the promoter and transcribing the genes of the operon.

operon (*op'-er-on*)
A unit of genetic regulation common in prokaryotes; a cluster of genes with related functions, along with the promoter and operator that control their transcription.

proto-oncogene (*prō'-tō-on'-kō-jēn*)
A normal gene that can be converted to a cancer-causing gene.

regeneration
The regrowth of body parts from pieces of an organism.

repressor
A protein that blocks the transcription of a gene or operon.

reproductive cloning
Using a body cell from a multicellular organism to make one or more genetically identical individuals.

signal transduction pathway
A series of molecular changes that converts a signal received on a target cell's surface to a specific response inside the cell.

silencer
A eukaryotic DNA sequence that inhibits the start of gene transcription; may act analogously to an enhancer, binding a repressor.

therapeutic cloning
The cloning of human cells by nuclear transplantation for therapeutic purposes, such as the replacement of body cells that have been irreversibly damaged by disease or injury. *See also* nuclear transplantation; reproductive cloning.

transcription factor
In the eukaryotic cell, a protein that functions in initiating or regulating transcription. Transcription factors bind to DNA or to other proteins that bind to DNA.

tumor-suppressor gene
A gene whose product inhibits cell division, thereby preventing uncontrolled cell growth.

X chromosome inactivation
In female mammals, the inactivation of one X chromosome in each somatic cell. Once X inactivation occurs in a given cell (during embryonic development), all descendants of that cell will have the same copy of the X chromosome inactivated.

Self-Quiz Answers

1. c
2. operon
3. b
4. a
5. DNA polymerase and other proteins required for transcription do not have access to tightly packed DNA.

6. the ability of these cells to produce entire organisms through cloning
7. nuclear transplantation
8. which genes are active in a particular sample of cells
9. b

10. embryonic tissue (ES cells), umbilical cord blood, and bone marrow (adult stem cells)
11. Proto-oncogenes are normal genes involved in the control of the cell cycle. Mutation or viruses can cause them to be converted to oncogenes, or cancer-causing genes.

Proto-oncogenes are necessary for normal control of cell division.
12. Master control genes, called homeotic genes, regulate many other genes during development.

How Populations Evolve

From Chapter 13 of *Campbell Essential Biology with Physiology*, Fifth Edition. Eric J. Simon, Jean L. Dickey, Kelly A. Hogan, Jane B. Reece. Copyright © 2016 by Pearson Education, Inc. All rights reserved.

How Populations Evolve

Why Evolution Matters

If it weren't for artificial selection, you'd be eating tomatoes the size of blueberries.

Thanks to natural selection, populations of more than 500 insect species are invulnerable to the most widely used pesticides.

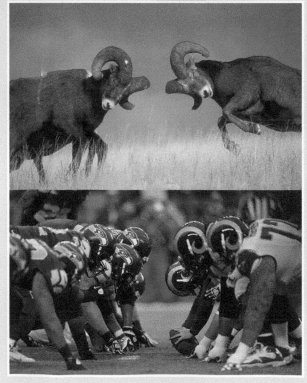

In some species, males engage in nonlethal combat in the hope of mating with females.

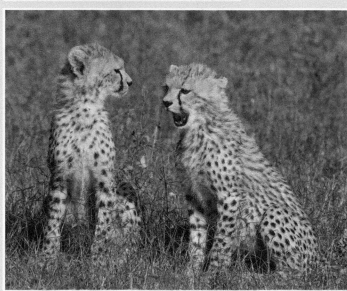

Populations of endangered species may be doomed by their lack of genetic diversity.

136

Evolution Past, Present, and Future BIOLOGY AND SOCIETY

Evolution Today

Life on Earth is gloriously diverse. More than 1.3 million species have been identified, and scientists estimate that several million more await discovery. How did Earth come to be populated by this abundance of diversity? The answer is evolution. In studying evolution, we reach hundreds of millions of years into the past to trace the history of life up until the present time. It isn't all about stones and bones, though. Evolution is happening right now, somewhere near you.

Consider the biological diversity in your surroundings. The organisms that are our closest neighbors are those that are best adapted to a human-dominated environment—the birds that feed on seeds and insects in suburban yards or city parks; the plants that thrive in vacant lots or sidewalk cracks; the insects and other pests that feast on our discarded food, our crops, and even our blood. Then there's the vast variety of microscopic life teeming everywhere, including both beneficial and disease-causing species that have adapted to the human body. All of these organisms are products of evolution, and they continue to evolve generation by generation in the present day. As you will learn in this chapter, the environment plays a powerful role in evolution. Human

White-tailed deer. Suburban landscapes often include patches of forest that provide food and shelter for deer, such as this one nibbling on garden plants.

activities—agriculture, mining, logging, development, the burning of fossil fuels, and the use of medicine, to name just a few—may alter the environments of organisms in ways that result in rapid, observable evolution. Evolutionary changes can also be studied in settings affected by natural environmental changes. Within a hundred thousand years, a blink of the eye in geologic time, lakes may appear or disappear; and newly minted volcanic islands can be clothed in plants and animals over a span of decades, centuries, or millennia, depending on the nearness of land.

An understanding of evolution informs all of biology, from exploring life's molecules to analyzing ecosystems. And applications of evolutionary biology are transforming medicine, agriculture, biotechnology, and conservation biology. In this chapter, you'll learn how the process of evolution works and read about verifiable, measurable examples of evolution that affect our world.

The Diversity of Life

For all of human history, people have named, described, and classified the inhabitants of the natural world. As trade and exploration connected all regions of the planet, these tasks became increasingly complex. For example, a scholar who sought to describe all the types of plants known to the Greeks in 300 B.C. had about 500 species to distinguish. Today, scientists recognize roughly 400,000 plant species.

By the 1700s, it was clear that a unified system of naming and classifying was needed. Agreement eventually coalesced around a scheme introduced by Carolus Linnaeus, a Swedish scientist. His system, which is still in use today, is the basis for **taxonomy**, the branch of biology concerned with identifying, naming, and classifying species. The Linnaean system includes a method of naming species and a hierarchical classification of species into broader groups of organisms.

Naming and Classifying the Diversity of Life

In the Linnaean system, each species is given a two-part Latinized name, or **binomial**. The first part of a binomial is the **genus** (plural, *genera*), a group of closely related species. For example, the genus of large cats is *Panthera*. The second part of a binomial is used to distinguish species within a genus. The two parts must be used together to name a species. Thus, the scientific name for the leopard is *Panthera pardus*. Notice that the first letter of the genus is capitalized and that the whole binomial is italicized. For instance, a newly discovered spider in the genus *Aptostichus* was named *Aptostichus stephencolberti*, after the television personality.

The Linnaean binomial solved the problem of the ambiguity of common names. Referring to an animal as a squirrel or a plant as a daisy is not specific—there are many species of squirrels and daisies. In addition, people in different regions may use the same common name for different species. For example, the flowers called bluebells in Scotland, England, Texas, and the eastern United States are actually four unrelated species.

Linnaeus also introduced a system for grouping species into a hierarchy of categories. The first step of this classification is built into the binomial. For example, the genus *Panthera* contains three other species: the lion (*Panthera leo*), the tiger (*Panthera tigris*), and the jaguar (*Panthera onca*). Beyond the grouping of species within genera, taxonomy extends to progressively broader categories of classification. It places similar genera in the same **family**, puts families into **orders**, orders into **classes**, classes into **phyla** (singular, *phylum*), phyla into **kingdoms**, and kingdoms into **domains**. Figure 1 places the leopard in this taxonomic scheme of groups within groups. The resulting classification of a particular organism is somewhat like a postal address identifying a person in a particular apartment, in a building with many apartments, on a street with many apartment buildings, in a city with many streets, and so on.

Grouping organisms into broader categories is a way to structure our understanding of the world. However, the criteria used to define more inclusive groups such as families, orders, and classes are ultimately arbitrary. After you learn about the processes by which the diversity of life evolved, we will introduce a classification system based on an understanding of evolutionary relationships. ☑

◄ **Figure 1 Hierarchical classification.**
Taxonomy classifies species—the least inclusive groups—into increasingly broad categories. *Panthera pardus* is one of four species (indicated here with yellow boxes) in the genus *Panthera*; *Panthera* is a genus (orange box) in the family Felidae, and so on.

Species: *Panthera pardus*

Genus: *Panthera*

Family: Felidae

Order: Carnivora

Class: Mammalia

Phylum: Chordata

Kingdom: Animalia

Bacteria   **Domain:** Eukarya   Archaea

Explaining the Diversity of Life

While early naturalists and philosophers sought to describe and organize the diversity of life, they also sought to explain its origin. The explanation accepted by present-day biologists is the evolutionary theory proposed by Charles Darwin in his best-known book, *On the Origin of Species by Means of Natural Selection*, published in 1859. Before we introduce Darwin's theory, however, let's take a brief look at the scientific and cultural context that made the theory of evolution such a radical idea in Darwin's time.

The Idea of Fixed Species

The Greek philosopher Aristotle, whose ideas had an enormous impact on Western culture, generally held the view that species are fixed, permanent forms that do not change over time. Judeo-Christian culture reinforced this idea with a literal interpretation of the biblical book of Genesis, which tells the story of each form of life being individually created in its present-day form. In the 1600s, religious scholars used biblical accounts to estimate the age of Earth at 6,000 years. Thus, the idea that all living species came into being relatively recently and are unchanging in form dominated the intellectual climate of the Western world for centuries.

At the same time, however, naturalists were also grappling with the interpretation of **fossils**—imprints or remains of organisms that lived in the past. Although fossils were thought to be the remains of living creatures, many were puzzling. For example, if "snakestones"

(Figure 2a) were the coiled bodies of snakes, then why were none ever found with an intact head? Could some fossils represent species that had become extinct? Stunning discoveries in the early 1800s, including fossilized skeletons of a gigantic sea creature dubbed an ichthyosaur, or fish-lizard (Figure 2b), convinced many naturalists that extinctions had indeed occurred.

Lamarck and Evolutionary Adaptations

Fossils told of other changes in the history of life, too. Naturalists compared fossil forms with living species and noted patterns of similarities and differences. In the early 1800s, French naturalist Jean-Baptiste de Lamarck suggested that the best explanation for these observations is that life evolves. Lamarck explained evolution as the refinement of traits that equip organisms to perform successfully in their environments. He proposed that by using or not using its body parts, an individual may develop certain traits that it passes on to its offspring. For example, some birds have powerful beaks that enable them to crack tough seeds. Lamarck suggested that these strong beaks are the cumulative result of ancestors exercising their beaks during feeding and passing that acquired beak power on to offspring. However, simple observations provide evidence against the inheritance of acquired traits: A carpenter who builds up strength and stamina through a lifetime of pounding nails with a heavy hammer will not pass enhanced biceps on to children. Although Lamarck's idea of how species evolve was mistaken, his proposal that species evolve as a result of interactions between organisms and their environments helped set the stage for Darwin. ☑

☑ CHECKPOINT

How do fossils contradict the idea of fixed species?

Answer: They don't match any living creature.

▼ Figure 2 **Fossils that perplexed naturalists in the 1800s.**

(a) **"Snakestone."** This fossil is actually a mollusc called an ammonite, an extinct relative of the present-day nautilus. Ammonites of this type ranged in size from about several inches to more than 7 feet in diameter.

(b) **Icthyosaur skull and paddle-like forelimb.** These marine reptiles—some more than 50 feet long—ruled the oceans for 155 million years before becoming extinct about 90 million years ago. The enormous eye is thought to be an adaptation to the dim light of the deep sea.

Charles Darwin and *The Origin of Species*

Although Charles Darwin was born more than 200 years ago—on the very same day as Abraham Lincoln—his work had such an extraordinary impact that many scientists mark his birthday with a celebration of his contributions to biology. How did Darwin become a rock star of science?

As a boy, Darwin was fascinated with nature. He loved collecting insects and fossils, as well as reading books about nature. His father, an eminent physician, could see no future for his son as a naturalist and sent him to medical school. But young Darwin, finding medicine boring and surgery before the days of anesthesia horrifying, quit medical school. His father then enrolled him at Cambridge University with the intention that he should become a clergyman. After college, however, Darwin returned to his childhood interests rather than following the career path mapped out by his father. At the age of 22, he began a sea voyage on the HMS *Beagle* that helped frame his theory of evolution.

Darwin's Journey

The *Beagle* was a survey ship. Although it stopped at many locations around the world, its main task was charting poorly known stretches of the South American coast (Figure 3). Darwin, a skilled naturalist, spent most of his time on shore doing what he enjoyed most—exploring the natural world. He collected thousands of specimens of fossils and living plants and animals. He also kept detailed journals of his observations. For a naturalist from a small, temperate country, seeing the glorious diversity of unfamiliar life-forms on other continents was a revelation. He carefully noted the characteristics of plants and animals that made them well suited to such diverse environments as the jungles of Brazil, the grasslands of Argentina, the towering peaks of the Andes, and the desolate and frigid lands at the southern tip of South America.

Observations

Many of Darwin's observations indicated that geographic proximity is a better predictor of relationships among organisms than similarity of environment. For example, the plants and animals living in temperate regions of South America more closely resembled species living in tropical regions of that continent than

▼ Figure 3 **The voyage of the *Beagle*.**

species living in similarly temperate regions of Europe. And the South American fossils Darwin found, though clearly examples of species different from living ones, were distinctly South American in their resemblance to the contemporary plants and animals of that continent. For instance, he collected fossilized armor plates resembling those of living armadillo species. Paleontologists later reconstructed the creature to which the armor belonged—which turned out to be an extinct armadillo the size of a Volkswagen Beetle.

Darwin was particularly intrigued by the geographic distribution of organisms on the Galápagos Islands. The Galápagos are relatively young volcanic islands about 900 kilometers (540 miles) off the Pacific coast of South America. Most of the animals that inhabit these remote islands are found nowhere else in the world, but they resemble South American species.

Darwin noticed that Galápagos marine iguanas—with a flattened tail that aids in swimming—are similar to, but distinct from, land-dwelling iguanas on the islands and on the South American mainland. Furthermore, each island had its own distinct variety of giant tortoise (Figure 4), the strikingly unique inhabitants for which the islands were named (*galápago* means "tortoise" in Spanish).

New Insights

While on his voyage, Darwin was strongly influenced by the newly published *Principles of Geology* by Scottish geologist Charles Lyell. The book presented the case for an ancient Earth sculpted over millions of years by gradual geological processes that continue today. Darwin witnessed the power of natural forces to change Earth's surface firsthand when he experienced an earthquake that raised part of the coastline of Chile almost a meter.

By the time Darwin returned to Great Britain five years after the *Beagle* first set sail, he had begun to seriously doubt that Earth and all its living organisms had been specially created only a few thousand years earlier. As he reflected on his observations, analyzed his specimen collections, and discussed his work with colleagues, he concluded that the evidence was better explained by the hypothesis that present-day species are the descendants of ancient ancestors that they still resemble in some ways. Over time, differences gradually accumulated by a process that Darwin called "descent with modification," his phrase to describe evolution. Unlike others who had explored the idea that organisms had changed over time, however, Darwin also proposed a scientific mechanism for *how* life evolves, a process he called natural selection. In **natural selection**, individuals with certain inherited traits are more likely to survive and reproduce than are individuals with other traits. He hypothesized that as the descendants of a remote ancestor spread into various habitats over millions and millions of years, natural selection resulted in diverse modifications, or **evolutionary adaptations**, that fit them to specific ways of life in their environment.

▼ Figure 4 **Two varieties of Galápagos tortoise.**

(a) The thick, domed shell and short neck and legs are characteristic of tortoises found on wetter islands that have more abundant, dense vegetation.

(b) Saddleback shells have an arch at the front, which allows the long neck to emerge. This, along with longer legs, enables the tortoise to stretch higher to reach the scarce vegetation on dry islands.

Darwin's Theory

Darwin spent the next two decades compiling and writing about evidence for evolution. He realized that his ideas would cause an uproar, however, and he delayed publishing. Meanwhile, Darwin learned that Alfred Russel Wallace, a British naturalist doing fieldwork in Indonesia, had conceived a hypothesis almost identical to Darwin's. Not wanting to have his life's work eclipsed by Wallace's, Darwin finally published *The Origin of Species*, a book that supported his hypothesis with immaculate logic and hundreds of pages of evidence drawn from observations and experiments in biology, geology, and paleontology. The hypothesis of evolution set forth in *The Origin*

of Species has since generated predictions that have been tested and verified by more than 150 years of research. Consequently, scientists regard Darwin's concept of evolution by means of natural selection as a **theory**—a widely accepted explanatory idea that is broader in scope than a hypothesis, generates new hypotheses, and is supported by a large body of evidence.

In the next several pages, we examine lines of evidence for Darwin's theory of **evolution**, the idea that living species are descendants of ancestral species that were different from present-day ones. Then we will return to natural selection as the mechanism for evolutionary change. With our current understanding of how this mechanism works, we extend Darwin's definition of evolution to include genetic changes in a population from generation to generation. ☑

CHECKPOINT

What was the most significant difference between Darwin's theory of evolution and the ideas about evolution that had been proposed previously?

Answer: Darwin also proposed a mechanism (natural selection) for how evolution occurs.

Evidence of Evolution

Evolution leaves observable signs. Such clues to the past are essential to any historical science. Historians of human civilization can study written records from earlier times. But they can also piece together the evolution of societies by recognizing vestiges of the past in modern cultures. Even if we did not know from written documents that Spaniards colonized the Americas, we would deduce this from the Hispanic stamp on Latin American culture. Similarly, biological evolution has left evidence in fossils, as well as in today's organisms.

Evidence from Fossils

Fossils—imprints or remains of organisms that lived in the past—document differences between past and present organisms and show that many species have become extinct. The soft parts of a dead organism usually decay rapidly, but the hard parts of an animal that are rich in minerals, such as the bones and teeth of vertebrates and the shells of clams and snails, may remain as fossils. **Figure 5** (facing page) illustrates some of the ways that organisms can fossilize.

Not all fossils are the actual remnants of organisms. Some, such as the ammonite in Figure 2a, are casts. A cast forms when a dead organism that was buried in sediment decomposes and leaves an empty "mold" that is later filled by minerals dissolved in water. The minerals harden within the mold, making a replica

of the organism. You may have seen crime scene investigators on TV shows use fast-acting plaster in the same way to make casts of footprints or tire tracks. Fossils may also be imprints, such as footprints or burrows, that remain after the organism decays. **Paleontologists** (scientists who study fossils) also eagerly examine coprolites—fossilized feces—for clues about the diets and digestive systems of extinct animals.

In rare instances, an entire organism, including its soft parts, is encased in a medium that prevents decomposition. Examples include insects trapped in amber (fossilized tree resin) and mammoths, bison, and even prehistoric humans frozen in ice or preserved in bogs.

Many fossils are found in fine-grained sedimentary rocks formed from the sand or mud that settles to the bottom of seas, lakes, swamps, and other aquatic habitats, covering dead organisms. Over millions of years, new layers of sediment are deposited atop older ones and compress them into layers of rock called strata (singular, *stratum*). Thus, the fossils in a particular stratum provide a glimpse of some of the organisms that lived in the area at the time the layer formed. Because younger strata are on top of older layers, the relative ages of fossils can be determined by the layer in which they are found. (Radiometric datingcan be used to determine the approximate ages of fossils.) As a result, the sequence in which fossils appear within layers of sedimentary rocks is a historical record of life on Earth. The **fossil record** is this ordered sequence of fossils as they appear in the rock layers, marking the passage of geologic time.

Of course, as Darwin acknowledged, the fossil record is incomplete. Many of Earth's organisms did not live in areas that favor fossilization. Many fossils that did form were in rocks later distorted or destroyed by geologic processes. Furthermore, not all fossils that have been preserved are accessible to paleontologists. Even with its limitations, however, the fossil record is remarkably detailed. And although the incompleteness of the fossil record may seem frustrating (wouldn't it be nice to have all our questions answered!), it makes paleontology an unexpectedly thrilling occupation. Like a mystery series in which new clues are uncovered in each episode, the thousands of fossils newly discovered each year give paleontologists new opportunities to test hypotheses about how the diversity of life evolved. In the next section, you'll learn how fossils are revealing answers to a very old puzzle. ☑

☑ **CHECKPOINT**
Why are older fossils generally in deeper rock layers than younger fossils?

Answer: Sedimentation places younger rock layers on top of older ones.

▼ Figure 5 **A fossil gallery.**

Sedimentary fossils are formed when minerals seep into and replace organic matter. This petrified (stone) tree in Arizona's Petrified Forest National Park is about 190 million years old.

This 45-million-year-old insect is embedded in amber (hardened resin from a tree).

Sedimentary rocks are the richest hunting grounds for paleontologists, scientists who study fossils. This researcher is excavating a fossilized dinosaur skeleton from sandstone in Dinosaur National Monument, located in Utah and Colorado.

A dinosaur left these footprints 120 million years ago in what is now northern Spain. Biologists often study footprints to learn how extinct animals moved.

These tusks belong to a whole 23,000-year-old mammoth, which scientists discovered in Siberian ice in 1999.

Evolution Past, Present, and Future THE PROCESS OF SCIENCE

Did Whales Evolve from Land-Dwelling Mammals?

In *The Origin of Species*, Darwin predicted the existence of fossils of transitional forms linking very different groups of organisms. The first such fossil was discovered shortly after Darwin's book was published—the 150-million-year-old *Archaeopteryx*, a fossil that displayed a combination of reptilian and birdlike features. Thousands of fossil discoveries have since shed light on the evolutionary origin of birds from a lineage of dinosaurs, as well as the origins of many other groups of plants and animals, including the transition of fish to amphibian and the evolution of mammals from a reptilian ancestor.

The origin of whales is one of the most intriguing evolutionary transitions. Whales are cetaceans, a group that also includes dolphins and porpoises. As you probably know, cetaceans are mammals that are thoroughly adapted to their aquatic environment. For example, their ears are internal and highly specialized for underwater hearing. They have forelimbs in the form of flippers but lack hind limbs. Overall, cetaceans are so very different from other mammals that scientists have long puzzled over their origins. In the 1960s, **observations** of fossil teeth led paleontologists to form the **hypothesis** that whales were the descendants of primitive hoofed, wolflike carnivores. They made the **prediction** that transitional fossils would show reduced hind limb and pelvic bones as whales evolved from these terrestrial, four-limbed ancestors. Rather than a controlled **experiment**, paleontologists tested their hypothesis by making detailed measurements and other observations of fossils accumulated over 20 years of extraordinary discoveries in Pakistan and Egypt. The **results** supported their hypothesis. **Figure 6** illustrates the diminishing size of the hind limb and pelvic bones in a few of the specimens studied. As you will learn shortly, however, a different kind of evidence later called this conclusion into question.

Key

- Pelvis
- Femur
- Tibia
- Foot

Pakicetus

Rodhocetus

Dorudon

Living cetaceans

▲ Figure 6 **Transitional forms in the evolution of whales.**

Evidence from Homologies

A second type of evidence for evolution comes from analyzing similarities among different organisms. Evolution is a process of descent with modification—characteristics present in an ancestral organism are altered over time by natural selection as its descendants face different environmental conditions. In other words, evolution is a remodeling process. As a result, related species can have characteristics that have an underlying similarity yet function differently. Similarity resulting from common ancestry is known as **homology**.

Darwin cited the anatomical similarities among vertebrate forelimbs as evidence of common ancestry. As **Figure 7** shows, the same skeletal elements make up the forelimbs of humans, cats, whales, and bats. The functions of these forelimbs differ. A whale's flipper does not do the same job as a bat's wing, so if these structures had been uniquely engineered, then we would expect that their basic designs would be very different. The logical explanation instead is that the arms, forelegs, flippers, and wings of these different mammals are variations on an anatomical structure of an ancestral organism that over millions of years has become adapted to different functions. Biologists call such anatomical similarities in different organisms homologous structures—features that often have different functions but are structurally similar because of common ancestry.

As a result of advances in **molecular biology**, the study of the molecular basis of genes and gene expression, present-day scientists have a much deeper understanding of homologies than Darwin did. Just as your genetic background is recorded in the DNA you inherit from your parents, the evolutionary history of each

Human   **Cat**   **Whale**   **Bat**

▲ **Figure 7 Homologous structures: anatomical signs of descent with modification.**
The forelimbs of all mammals are constructed from the same skeletal elements. (Homologous bones in each of these four mammals are colored the same.) The hypothesis that all mammals descended from a common ancestor predicts that their forelimbs, though diversely adapted, would be variations on a common anatomical theme.

species is documented in the DNA inherited from its ancestral species. If two species have homologous genes with sequences that match closely, biologists conclude that these sequences must have been inherited from a relatively recent common ancestor. Conversely, the greater the number of sequence differences between species, the more distant is their last common ancestor. Molecular comparisons between diverse organisms have allowed biologists to develop and test hypotheses about the evolutionary divergence of major branches on the tree of life.

Darwin's boldest hypothesis was that all life-forms are related. Molecular biology provides strong evidence for this claim: All forms of life use the same genetic language of DNA and RNA, and the genetic code—how RNA triplets are translated into amino acids—is essentially universal. Thus, it is likely that all species descended from common ancestors that used this code. Because of these molecular homologies, bacteria engineered with human genes can produce human proteins such as insulin and human growth hormone. But molecular homologies go beyond a shared genetic code. For example, organisms as dissimilar as humans and bacteria share homologous genes inherited from a very distant common ancestor.

Geneticists have also uncovered hidden molecular homologies. Organisms may retain genes that have lost their function through mutations, even though homologous genes in related species are fully functional. Many of these inactive genes have been identified in humans. For example, one such gene encodes an enzyme known as GLO that is used in making vitamin C. Almost all mammals have a metabolic pathway to make this essential vitamin from glucose. Although humans and other primates have functional genes for the first three steps in the pathway, the inactive GLO gene prevents us from making vitamin C—we must get sufficient amounts in our diet to maintain health.

Some of the most interesting homologies are "left-over" structures that are of marginal or perhaps no importance to the organism. These **vestigial structures** are remnants of features that served important functions in the organism's ancestors. For example, the small pelvis and hind-leg bones of ancient whales are vestiges (traces) of their walking ancestors. The eye remnants that are buried under scales in blind species of cave fishes—a vestige of their sighted ancestors—are another example. Humans have vestigial structures, too. When we're cold or agitated, we often get goose bumps caused by small muscles under the skin that make the body hair stand on end. The same response is more visible (and more functional) in a bird that fluffs up its feathery insulation or a cat that bristles when threatened.

An understanding of homology can also explain observations about embryonic development that are otherwise puzzling. For example, comparing early stages of development in different animal species reveals similarities not visible in adult organisms (**Figure 8**). At some point in their development, all vertebrate embryos have a tail posterior to the anus, as well as structures called pharyngeal (throat) pouches. These pouches are homologous structures that ultimately develop to have very different functions, such as gills in fishes and parts of the ears and throat in humans.

Next we see how homologies help us trace evolutionary descent. ✓

Evolutionary Trees

Darwin was the first to visualize the history of life as a tree in which patterns of descent branch off from a common

trunk—the first organism—to the tips of millions of twigs representing the species living today. At each fork of the evolutionary tree is an ancestor common to all evolutionary branches extending from that fork. Closely related species share many traits because their lineage of common descent traces to a recent fork of the tree of life. Biologists illustrate these patterns of descent with an **evolutionary tree**, although today they often turn the trees sideways so they can be read from left to right.

Homologous structures, both anatomical and molecular, can be used to determine the branching sequence of an evolutionary tree. Some homologous characters, such as the genetic code, are shared by all species because they date to the deep ancestral past. In contrast, traits that evolved more recently are shared by smaller groups of organisms. For example, all tetrapods (from the Greek *tetra*, four, and *pod*, foot) have the same basic limb bone structure illustrated in Figure 7, but their ancestors do not.

Figure 9 is an evolutionary tree of tetrapods (amphibians, mammals, and reptiles, including birds) and their closest living relatives, the lungfishes. In this diagram, each branch point represents the common ancestor of all species that

▶ **Figure 8 Evolutionary signs from comparative embryology.** At the early stage of development shown here, the kinship of vertebrates is unmistakable. Notice, for example, the pharyngeal pouches and tails in both the chicken embryo and the human embryo.

Pharyngeal pouches

Post-anal tail

Chicken embryo   **Human embryo**

▼ **Figure 9** **An evolutionary tree of tetrapods (four-limbed animals).**

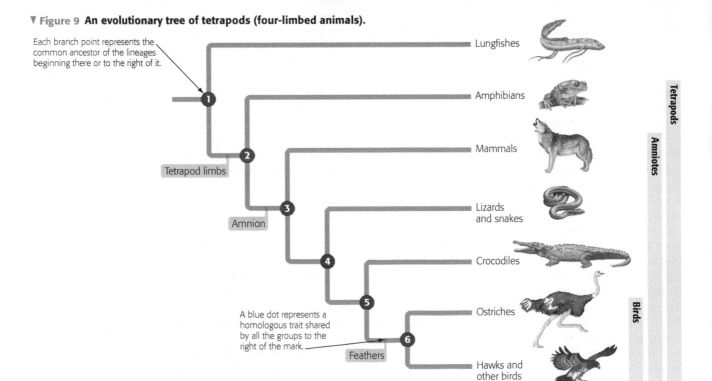

Each branch point represents the common ancestor of the lineages beginning there or to the right of it.

Tetrapod limbs

Amnion

A blue dot represents a homologous trait shared by all the groups to the right of the mark.

Feathers

Lungfishes

Amphibians

Mammals

Lizards and snakes

Crocodiles

Ostriches

Hawks and other birds

Tetrapods

Amniotes

Birds

descended from it. For example, lungfishes and all tetrapods descended from ancestor ❶. Three homologies are shown by the blue dots on the tree—tetrapod limbs, the amnion (a protective embryonic membrane), and feathers. Tetrapod limbs were present in common ancestor ❷ and hence are found in its descendants (the tetrapods). The amnion was present in ancestor ❸ and thus is shared only by mammals and reptiles, which are known as amniotes. Feathers were present only in ❻ ancestor and hence are found only in birds.

Evolutionary trees are hypotheses reflecting our current understanding of patterns of evolutionary descent. Some trees, such as the one in Figure 9, are based on a convincing combination of fossil, anatomical, and molecular data. Others are more speculative because sufficient data are not yet available. ☑

Whale Evolution Revisited

Now let's resume the story of whale evolution. As we discussed, beginning in the 1970s, paleontologists unearthed a remarkable series of transitional fossils that supported the hypothesis that whales evolved from hoofed, wolflike carnivores. However, molecular biologists using DNA analysis to infer relationships among living animals found a close relationship between whales and hippopotamuses, which are members of a group of mostly herbivorous, cloven-hoofed mammals that includes pigs, deer, and camels (Figure 10). Consequently, they proposed an alternative hypothesis of whale evolution: that whales and hippos are both descendants of a cloven-hoofed ancestor.

Paleontologists were taken aback by the contradictory results. Nevertheless, openness to new evidence is a hallmark of science, and the paleontologists had an idea

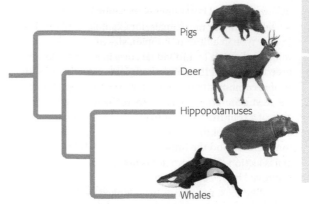

▲ Figure 10 **An evolutionary tree of present-day whales and herbivorous cloven-hoofed mammals.**
Data from: M. Nikaido et al., Phylogenetic relationships among Cetartiodactyls based on insertions of short and long interspersed elements: hippopotamuses are the closest extant relatives of whales. *Proceedings of the National Academy of Sciences USA* 96: 10261–10266 (1999).

☑ CHECKPOINT
In Figure 9, which number represents the most recent common ancestor of humans and canaries?

Answer: *The most recent ancestor of humans (mammals) and canaries (birds) is* ❺.

for resolving the issue. Cloven-hoofed mammals have a unique ankle bone. Like most fossilized skeletons, the specimens of early cetaceans that had been found were incomplete—none included an ankle bone. If the ancestor of whales was a wolflike carnivore, then the shape of its ankle bone would be similar to most present-day mammals. Two fossils discovered in 2001 provided the answer. Both *Pakicetus* and *Rodhocetus* (see Figure 6) had the distinctive ankle bone of a cloven-hoofed mammal, a result that supported the hypothesis based on the DNA analysis. Thus, as is often the case in science, scientists are becoming more certain about the evolutionary origin of whales as mounting evidence from different lines of inquiry converge.

Natural Selection as the Mechanism for Evolution

Now that you have learned about the lines of evidence supporting Darwin's theory of descent with modification, let's look at Darwin's explanation of *how* life evolves. Because he hypothesized that species formed gradually over long periods of time, Darwin knew that he would not be able to study the evolution of new species by direct observation. But he did have a way to gain insight into the process of incremental change: the practices used by plant and animal breeders.

All domesticated plants and animals are the products of selective breeding from wild ancestors. For example,

the baseball-sized tomatoes grown today are very different from their Peruvian ancestors, which were not much larger than blueberries. Having conceived the notion that **artificial selection**—the selective breeding of domesticated plants and animals to promote the occurrence of desirable traits in the offspring—was the key to understanding evolutionary change, Darwin bred pigeons to gain firsthand experience. He acquired further insight through conversations with farmers about livestock breeding. He learned that artificial selection

If it weren't for artificial selection, you'd be eating tomatoes the size of blueberries.

has two essential components: variation and heritability. Variation among individuals, for example, differences in coat type in a litter of puppies, size of corn ears, or milk production by individual cows in a herd, allows the breeder to select the animals or plants with the most desirable combination of characters as breeding stock for the next generation. Heritability refers to the transmission of a trait from parent to offspring. Despite their lack of knowledge of the underlying genetics, breeders had long understood the importance of heritability in artificial selection—if a character is not heritable, it cannot be improved by selective breeding.

Unlike most naturalists, who looked for consistency of traits as a way to classify organisms, Darwin was a careful observer of variations between individuals. He knew that individuals in natural populations have small but measurable differences, for example, variations in color and markings **(Figure 11)**. But what forces in nature determined which individuals became the breeding stock for the next generation?

Darwin found inspiration in an essay written by economist Thomas Malthus, who contended that much of human suffering—disease, famine, and war—was the consequence of human populations increasing faster than food supplies and other resources. Darwin applied Malthus's idea to populations of plants and animals, reasoning that the resources of any given environment are limited. The production of more individuals than the environment can support leads to a struggle for existence, with only some offspring surviving in each generation **(Figure 12)**. Of the many eggs laid, young born, and seeds spread, only a tiny fraction complete development and leave offspring themselves. The rest are eaten, starved, diseased, unmated, or unable to reproduce for other reasons. The essence of natural selection

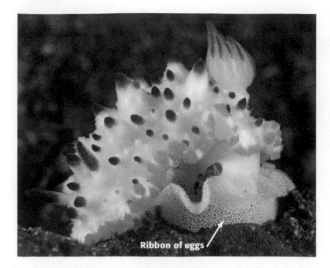

▲ **Figure 12 Overproduction of offspring.** This sea slug, a mollusc related to snails , is laying thousands of eggs embedded in the yellow ribbon around its body. Only a tiny fraction of the eggs will actually give rise to offspring that survive and reproduce.

is this unequal reproduction. In the process of natural selection, individuals whose traits better enable them to obtain food, escape predators, or tolerate physical conditions will survive and reproduce more successfully, passing these adaptive traits to their offspring.

Darwin reasoned that if artificial selection can bring about significant change in a relatively short period of time, then natural selection could modify species considerably over hundreds or thousands of generations. Over vast spans of time, many traits that adapt a population to its environment will accumulate. If the environment changes, however, or if individuals move to a new environment, natural selection will select for adaptations to these new conditions, sometimes producing changes that result in the origin of a completely new species.

Next, let's look at an example of how natural selection operates.

Natural Selection in Action

Look at any natural environment and you will see the products of natural selection—adaptations that suit organisms to their environment. But can we see natural selection in action? Yes, indeed! Biologists have documented evolutionary change in thousands of scientific studies.

An unsettling example of natural selection in action is the evolution of pesticide resistance in hundreds of insect species. Pesticides control insects and prevent them from eating crops or transmitting diseases. But whenever a new type of pesticide is used to control pests, the outcome

▼ **Figure 11 Color variation within a population of Asian lady beetles.**

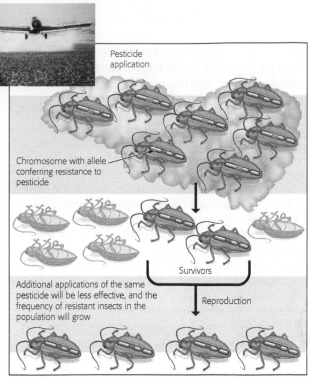

Pesticide application

Chromosome with allele conferring resistance to pesticide

Survivors

Additional applications of the same pesticide will be less effective, and the frequency of resistant insects in the population will grow

Reproduction

▲ **Figure 13 Evolution of pesticide resistance in insect populations.** By spraying crops with poisons to kill insect pests, people have unwittingly favored the reproductive success of insects with inherent resistance to the poisons.

is similar **(Figure 13)**: A relatively small amount of poison initially kills most of the insects, but subsequent applications are less and less effective. The few survivors of the first pesticide wave are individuals that are genetically resistant, carrying an allele (alternative form of a gene) that somehow enables them to survive the chemical attack. So the poison kills most members of the population, leaving the resistant survivors to reproduce and pass the alleles for pesticide resistance to their offspring. Thus, the proportion of pesticide-resistant individuals increases in each generation.

Key Points about Natural Selection

Before we move on, let's summarize how natural selection works in bringing about evolutionary change.

Natural selection affects individual organisms—in Figure 13, each insect either survived the pesticide or was killed by it. However, individuals do not evolve. Rather, it is the population—the group of organisms—that evolves over time as adaptive traits become more common in the group and other traits change or disappear. Thus, evolution refers to generation-to-generation changes in populations.

Natural selection can amplify or diminish only heritable traits. Although an organism may, during its lifetime, acquire characters that help it survive, such acquired characters cannot be passed on to offspring.

Natural selection is more an editing process than a creative mechanism. A pesticide does not create new alleles that allow insects to survive. Rather, the presence of the pesticide leads to natural selection for insects in the population that already have those alleles.

Natural selection is not goal-directed; it does not lead to perfectly adapted organisms. Whereas artificial selection is a deliberate attempt by humans to produce individuals with specific traits, natural selection is the result of environmental factors that vary from place to place and over time. A trait that is favorable in one situation may be useless—or even detrimental—in different circumstances. And, as you will see, some adaptations are compromises. ☑

> Thanks to natural selection, populations of more than 500 insect species are invulnerable to the most widely used pesticides.

☑ **CHECKPOINT**

Explain why the following statement is incorrect: "Pesticides cause pesticide resistance in insects."

Answer: An environmental factor does not create new traits such as pesticide resistance, but instead favors traits that are already represented in the population.

The Evolution of Populations

In *The Origin of Species*, Darwin provided evidence that life on Earth has evolved over time, and he proposed that natural selection, in favoring some heritable traits over others, was the primary mechanism for that change. But how do the variations that are the raw material for natural selection arise in a population? And how are these variations passed along from parents to offspring? Darwin did not know that Gregor Mendel had already answered these questions. Although both men lived and worked at around the same time, Mendel's work was largely ignored by the scientific community. Its rediscovery in 1900 set the stage for understanding the genetic differences on which evolution is based.

Sources of Genetic Variation

You have no trouble recognizing friends in a crowd. Each person has a unique genome, reflected in individual phenotypic variations such as appearance and other traits. Indeed, individual variation occurs in all species, as illustrated by the garter snakes in **Figure 14**. In addition to obvious physical differences, such as the snakes' colors and patterns, most populations have a great deal of phenotypic variation that can be observed only at the molecular level, such as an enzyme that detoxifies a pesticide. Of course, not all variation in a population is heritable. Phenotype—the expressed traits of an organism—results from a combination of the genotype, which is inherited, and many environmental influences. For instance, if you have dental work to straighten and whiten your teeth, you will not pass your environmentally produced smile to your offspring. Only the genetic component of variation is relevant to natural selection. Many of the characters that vary in a population result from the combined effect of several genes. Other features, such as Mendel's purple and white pea flowers or human blood types, are determined by a single gene locus, with different alleles producing distinct phenotypes. But where do these alleles come from?

Mutation

New alleles originate by mutation, a change in the nucleotide sequence of DNA. Thus, mutation is the ultimate

source of the genetic variation that serves as raw material for evolution. In multicellular organisms, however, only mutations in cells that produce gametes can be passed to offspring and affect a population's genetic variability.

A change as small as a single nucleotide in a protein-coding gene can have a significant effect on phenotype, as in sickle-cell disease. An organism is a refined product of thousands of generations of past selection, and a random change in its DNA is not likely to improve its genome any more than randomly changing some words on a page is likely to improve a story. In fact, mutation that affects a protein's function will probably be harmful. On rare occasions, however, a mutated allele may actually improve the adaptation of an individual to its environment and enhance its reproductive success. This kind of effect is more likely when the environment is changing in such a way that mutations that were once disadvantageous are favorable under the new conditions. For instance, mutations that endow houseflies with resistance to the pesticide DDT also reduce their growth rate. Before DDT was introduced, such mutations were a handicap to the flies that had them. But once DDT was part of the environment, the mutant alleles were advantageous, and natural selection increased their frequency in fly populations.

Chromosomal mutations that delete, disrupt, or rearrange many gene loci at once are almost certain to be harmful. But duplication of a gene or small pieces of DNA through errors in meiosis can provide an important source of genetic variation. If a repeated segment of DNA can persist over the generations, mutations may accumulate in the duplicate copies without affecting the function of the original gene, eventually leading to new genes with novel functions. This process may have played a major role in evolution. For example, the remote ancestors of mammals carried a single gene for detecting odors that has since been duplicated repeatedly. As a result, mice have about 1,300 different genes that encode smell receptors. It is likely that such dramatic increases helped early mammals by enabling them to distinguish among many different smells. And repeated duplications of genes that control development are linked to the origin of vertebrate animals from an invertebrate ancestor.

▼ **Figure 14 Variation in a garter snake population.** These four garter snakes, which belong to the same species, were all captured in one Oregon field. The behavior of each physical type is correlated with its coloration. When approached, spotted snakes, which blend in with their background, generally freeze. In contrast, snakes with stripes, which make it difficult to judge the speed of motion, usually flee rapidly when approached.

In prokaryotes, mutations can quickly generate genetic variation in a population. Because bacteria multiply so rapidly, a beneficial mutation can increase in frequency in a matter of hours or days. And because bacteria are haploid, with a single allele for each gene, a new allele can have an effect immediately. Mutation rates in animals and plants average about 1 in every 100,000 genes per generation. For these organisms, low mutation rates, long time spans between generations, and diploid genomes prevent most mutations from significantly affecting genetic variation from one generation to the next.

Sexual Reproduction

In organisms that reproduce sexually, most of the genetic variation in a population results from the unique combination of alleles that each individual inherits. (Of course, the origin of those allele variations is past mutations.)

Fresh assortments of existing alleles arise every generation from three random components of sexual reproduction: independent orientation of homologous chromosomes at metaphase I of meiosis, crossing over , and random fertilization. During meiosis, pairs of homologous chromosomes, one set inherited from each parent, trade some of their genes by crossing over. These homologous chromosomes separate into gametes independently of other chromosome pairs. Thus, gametes from any individual vary extensively in their genetic makeup. Finally, each zygote made by a mating pair has a unique assortment of alleles resulting from the random union of sperm and egg.

Populations as the Units of Evolution

One common misconception about evolution is that individual organisms evolve during their lifetimes. It is true that natural selection acts on individuals: Each individual's combination of traits affects its survival and reproductive success. But the evolutionary impact of natural selection is only apparent in the changes in a population of organisms over time.

A **population** is a group of individuals of the same species that live in the same area and interbreed. We can measure evolution as a change in the prevalence of certain heritable traits in a population over a span of generations. The increasing

proportion of resistant insects in areas sprayed with pesticide is one example. Natural selection favored insects with alleles for pesticide resistance. As a result, these insects left more offspring than nonresistant individuals, changing the genetic makeup of the next generation's population.

Different populations of the same species may be geographically isolated from each other to such an extent that an exchange of genetic material never or only rarely occurs. Such isolation is common in populations confined to different lakes **(Figure 15)** or islands. For example, each population of Galápagos tortoise is restricted to its own island. Not all populations have such sharp boundaries, however; members of a population typically breed with one another and are therefore more closely related to each other than they are to members of a different population.

In studying evolution at the population level, biologists focus on the **gene pool**, which consists of all copies of every type of allele at every locus in all members of the population. For many loci, there are two or more alleles in the gene pool. For example, in a housefly population, there may be two alleles relating to DDT breakdown, one that codes for an enzyme that breaks down DDT and one for a version of the enzyme that does not. In populations living in fields sprayed with DDT, the allele for the enzyme conferring resistance will

▼ **Figure 15 Isolated lakes in Denali National Park and Preserve, Alaska.**

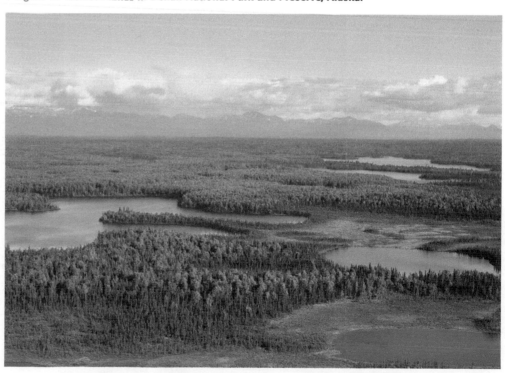

increase in frequency and the other allele will decrease in frequency. When the relative frequencies of alleles in a population change like this over a number of generations, evolution is taking place.

Next, we'll explore how to test whether evolution is occurring in a population. ✓

Analyzing Gene Pools

Imagine a wildflower population with two varieties of blooms that are different colors (Figure 16). An allele for red flowers, which we will symbolize by *R*, is dominant to an allele for white flowers, symbolized by *r*. These are the only two alleles for flower color in the gene pool of this hypothetical plant population. Now, let's say that 80%, or 0.8, of all flower-color loci in the gene pool have the *R* allele. We'll use the letter *p* to represent the relative frequency of the *R* allele in the population. Thus, $p = 0.8$. Because there are only two alleles in this example, the *r* allele must be present at the other 20% (0.2) of the gene pool's flower-color loci. (This accounts for 100% of the flower-color loci in the gene pool, or a relative frequency of 1.) Let's use the letter *q* for the frequency of the *r* allele in the population. For the wildflower population, $q = 0.2$. And since there are only two alleles for flower color, we can express their frequencies as follows:

$$p \quad + \quad q \quad = \quad 1$$

Frequency of one allele   Frequency of alternate allele

Notice that if we know the frequency of either allele in the gene pool, we can subtract it from 1 to calculate the frequency of the other allele.

From the frequencies of alleles, we can also calculate the frequencies of different genotypes in the population if the gene pool is completely stable (not evolving). In the wildflower population, what is the probability of producing an *RR* individual by "drawing" two *R* alleles from the pool of gametes? The probability of drawing an *R* sperm multiplied by the probability of drawing an *R* egg is $p \times p = p^2$, or $0.8 \times 0.8 = 0.64$. In other words, 64% of the plants in the population will have the *RR* genotype. Applying the same math, we also know the frequency of *rr* individuals in the population: $q^2 = 0.2 \times 0.2 = 0.04$. Thus, 4% of the plants are *rr*, giving them white flowers. Calculating the frequency of heterozygous individuals, *Rr*, is trickier. That's because the heterozygous genotype can form in two ways, depending on whether the sperm or egg supplies the dominant allele. So the frequency of the *Rr* genotype is $2pq$, which is $2 \times 0.8 \times 0.2 = 0.32$. In our imaginary wildflower population, 32% of the plants are *Rr*, with red flowers. Figure 17 reviews these calculations graphically.

Now we can write a general formula for calculating the frequencies of genotypes in a gene pool from the frequencies of alleles, and vice versa:

$$p^2 \quad + \quad 2pq \quad + \quad q^2 \quad = \quad 1$$

Frequency of homozygotes for one allele   Frequency of heterozygotes   Frequency of homozygotes for alternate allele

✓ CHECKPOINT

Which process, mutation or sexual reproduction, results in most of the generation-to-generation variability in human populations? Why?

Answer: sexual reproduction, because humans have a relatively long generation span and mutations have relatively little effect in a single generation

▼ Figure 16 **A population of wildflowers with two varieties of color.**

▼ Figure 17 **A mathematical swim in the gene pool.** Each of the four boxes in the Punnett square corresponds to a probable "draw" of alleles from the gene pool.

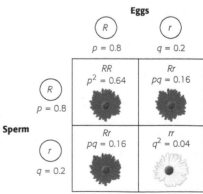

Allele frequencies $p = 0.8$ $q = 0.2$
               (*R*)   (*r*)

Eggs

    R   *r*
   $p = 0.8$ $q = 0.2$

Sperm

R $p = 0.8$:
   RR $p^2 = 0.64$ *Rr* $pq = 0.16$

r $q = 0.2$:
   Rr $pq = 0.16$ *rr* $q^2 = 0.04$

Genotype frequencies $p^2 = 0.64$ $2pq = 0.32$ $q^2 = 0.04$
                   (*RR*)   (*Rr*)   (*rr*)

Notice that the frequencies of all genotypes in the gene pool must add up to 1. This formula is called the Hardy-Weinberg equation, named for the two scientists who derived it.

Population Genetics and Health Science

Public health scientists use the Hardy-Weinberg equation to calculate the percentage of a human population that carries the allele for certain inherited diseases. Consider phenylketonuria (PKU), which is an inherited inability to break down the amino acid phenylalanine. If untreated, the disorder has serious effects on brain development. PKU occurs in about 1 out of 10,000 babies born in the United States. Newborn babies are now routinely tested for PKU, and symptoms can be prevented if individuals living with the disease follow a strict diet that limits phenylalanine. In addition to occurring naturally, phenylalanine is found in the widely used artificial sweetener aspartame (Figure 18).

PKU is caused by a recessive allele (that is, one that must be present in two copies to produce the phenotype). Thus, we can represent the frequency of individuals in the U.S. population born with PKU with the q^2 term in the Hardy-Weinberg formula. For one PKU occurrence per 10,000 births, $q^2 = 0.0001$. Therefore, q, the frequency of the recessive allele in the population,

equals the square root of 0.0001, or 0.01. And p, the frequency of the dominant allele, equals $1 - q$, or 0.99.

Now let's calculate the frequency of carriers, who are heterozygous individuals who carry the PKU allele in a single copy and may pass it on to offspring. Carriers are represented in the formula by $2pq$: $2 \times 0.99 \times 0.01$, or 0.0198. Thus, the Hardy-Weinberg formula tells us that about 2% of the U.S. population are carriers for the PKU allele. Estimating the frequency of a harmful allele is essential for any public health program dealing with genetic diseases.

Microevolution as Change in a Gene Pool

As stated earlier, evolution can be measured as changes in the genetic composition of a population over time. It helps, as a basis of comparison, to know what to expect if a population is not evolving. A nonevolving population is in genetic equilibrium, which is also known as **Hardy-Weinberg equilibrium**. The population's gene pool remains constant. From generation to generation, the frequencies of alleles (p and q) and genotypes (p^2, $2pq$, and q^2) are unchanged. Sexual shuffling of genes cannot by itself change a large gene pool. Because a generation-to-generation change in allele frequencies of a population is evolution viewed on the smallest scale, it is sometimes referred to as **microevolution**. ✓

▼ Figure 18
A warning to individuals with PKU.

INGREDIENTS: SORBITOL, MAGNESIUM STEARATE, ARTIFICIAL FLAVOR, **ASPARTAME† (SWEETENER)**, ARTIFICIAL COLOR (YELLOW 5 LAKE, BLUE 1 LAKE), ZINC GLUCONATE. **†PHENYLKETONURICS: CONTAINS PHENYLALANINE**

✓ CHECKPOINT

1. Which term in the Hardy-Weinberg formula ($p^2 + 2pq + q^2 = 1$) corresponds to the frequency of individuals with *no* alleles for the recessive disease PKU?
2. Define microevolution.

Answers: 1. p^2 2. Microevolution is a change in a population's frequencies of alleles.

Mechanisms That Alter Allele Frequencies in a Population

Now that we've defined microevolution as changes in a population's genetic makeup from generation to generation, we come to an obvious question: What mechanisms can change a gene pool? Natural selection is the most important, because it is the only process that promotes adaptation. We'll examine natural selection in more detail shortly. But first, we look at two other mechanisms of evolutionary change: genetic drift, which is due to chance, and gene flow, the exchange of alleles between neighboring populations.

Genetic Drift

Flip a coin 1,000 times, and a result of 700 heads and 300 tails would make you very suspicious about that coin.

But flip a coin 10 times, and an outcome of 7 heads and 3 tails would seem within reason. With a smaller sample, there is a greater chance of deviation from an idealized result—in this case, an equal number of heads and tails.

Let's apply this coin toss logic to a population's gene pool. If a new generation draws its alleles at random from the previous generation, then the larger the population (the sample size), the better the new generation will represent the gene pool of the previous generation. Thus, one requirement for a gene pool to maintain the status quo is a large population size. The gene pool of a small population may not be accurately represented in the next generation because of sampling error. The changed gene pool is analogous to the erratic outcome from a small sample of coin tosses.

Figure 19 applies this concept of sampling error to a small population of wildflowers. Chance causes the frequencies of the alleles for red (*R*) and white (*r*) flowers to change over the generations. And that fits our definition of microevolution. This evolutionary mechanism, a change in the gene pool of a population due to chance, is called **genetic drift**. But what would cause a population to shrink down to a size where there is genetic drift? Two ways this can occur are the bottleneck effect and the founder effect, both of which we explore next.

The Bottleneck Effect

Disasters such as earthquakes, floods, and fires may kill large numbers of individuals, producing a small surviving population that is unlikely to have the same genetic makeup as the original population. Again, the gene pool of the surviving population is a small sample of the genetic diversity originally present. By chance, certain alleles may be overrepresented among the survivors. Other alleles may be underrepresented. And some alleles may be eliminated. Chance may continue to change the gene pool for many generations until the population is again large enough for sampling errors to be insignificant.

The analogy illustrated in **Figure 20** shows why genetic drift due to a drastic reduction in population size is called the **bottleneck effect**.

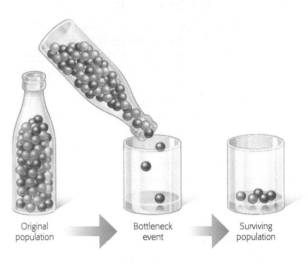

▼ Figure 20 The bottleneck effect. The colored marbles in this analogy represent three alleles in an imaginary population. Shaking just a few of the marbles through the bottleneck is like an environmental disaster that drastically reduces the size of a population. Compared with the predisaster population, purple marbles are overrepresented in the new population, green marbles are underrepresented, and orange marbles are absent—all by chance. Similarly, a population that passes through a "bottleneck" event emerges with reduced variability.

Original population → Bottleneck event → Surviving population

▼ Figure 19 Genetic drift. This hypothetical wildflower population consists of only ten plants. Due to random change over the generations, genetic drift can eliminate some alleles, as is the case for the *r* allele in generation 3 of this imaginary population.

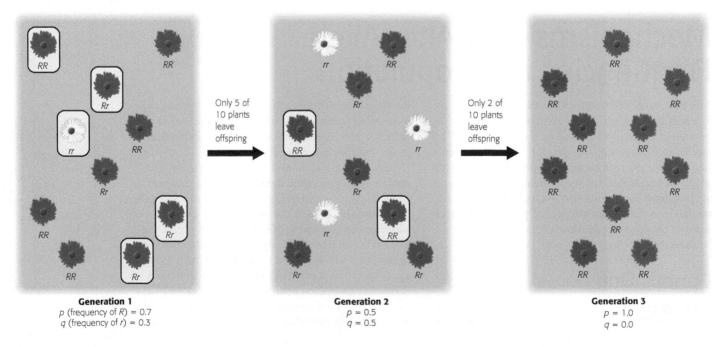

Generation 1
p (frequency of *R*) = 0.7
q (frequency of *r*) = 0.3

Only 5 of 10 plants leave offspring

Generation 2
p = 0.5
q = 0.5

Only 2 of 10 plants leave offspring

Generation 3
p = 1.0
q = 0.0

Passing through a "bottleneck"—a severe reduction in population size—decreases the overall genetic variability in a population because at least some alleles are likely to be lost from the gene pool. We can see this concept at work in the potential loss of individual variation, and hence adaptability, in drastically reduced populations of endangered species.

One such endangered species is the cheetah (**Figure 21**). The fastest of all running animals, cheetahs are magnificent cats that were once widespread in Africa and Asia. Like many African mammals, the number of cheetahs fell dramatically during the last ice age (around 10,000 years ago). At that time, the species suffered a severe bottleneck, possibly as a result of disease, human hunting, and periodic droughts. The South African cheetah population may have suffered a second bottleneck during the 1800s, when farmers hunted the animals to near extinction. Today, only a few small populations of cheetahs exist in the wild. Genetic variability in these populations is very low. In addition, the cheetahs remaining in Africa are being crowded into nature preserves and parks as human demands on the land increase. Along with crowding comes an increased potential for the spread of disease. With so little variability, the cheetah has a reduced capacity to adapt to such environmental challenges. Although captive breeding programs can boost cheetah population sizes, the species' pre-bottleneck genetic diversity can never be restored. ☑

The Founder Effect

When a few individuals colonize an isolated island, lake, or other new habitat, the genetic makeup of the colony is only a sample of the gene pool in the larger population. The smaller the colony (in other words, the smaller the sample size), the less likely it is to be representative of all the genetic diversity present in the population from which the colonists emigrated. If the colony succeeds, genetic drift will continue to change the frequency of alleles randomly until the population is large enough for genetic drift to be minimal. The type of genetic drift resulting from the establishment of a small, new population whose gene pool differs from that of the parent population is called the **founder effect**.

Numerous examples of the founder effect have been identified in geographically or socially isolated human populations. In such situations, disease-causing alleles that are rare in the larger population may became common in a small colony. For example, Amish and Mennonite communities in North America were founded by small numbers of European immigrants in the 1700s, and individuals within the community have since intermarried, remaining genetically separate from the larger population (**Figure 22**). Dozens of genetic diseases that are extremely rare elsewhere are relatively common in these communities. On the other hand, the high frequency of genetic diseases in populations has enabled genetic researchers to identify the mutation responsible for certain genetic disorders. In some cases, a disorder is treatable if detected early.

> Populations of endangered species may be doomed by their lack of genetic diversity.

▲ **Figure 22** **The founder effect.** Small, isolated populations often have high frequencies of alleles that are rare in large populations.

☑ **CHECKPOINT**

Would you expect modern cheetahs to have more genetic variation or less than cheetahs did 1,000 years ago?

Answer: less, because the bottleneck effect reduces genetic variability.

▼ **Figure 21** **Implications of the bottleneck effect in conservation biology.** Some endangered species, such as the cheetah, have low genetic variability. As a result, they are less adaptable to environmental changes, such as new diseases, than are species with a greater resource of genetic variation.

Gene Flow

Another source of evolutionary change is **gene flow**, which is genetic exchange with another population. A population may gain or lose alleles when fertile individuals move into or out of the population or when gametes (such as plant pollen) are transferred between populations **(Figure 23)**. For example, consider our hypothetical wildflower population in Figure 16. Suppose a neighboring population consists entirely of white-flowered individuals. A wind storm may blow pollen to our wildflowers from the neighboring population, resulting in a higher frequency of the white-flower allele in the next generation—a microevolutionary change.

Gene flow tends to reduce differences between populations. If it is extensive enough, gene flow can eventually join neighboring populations into a single population with a common gene pool. As people began to move about the world more freely, gene flow became an important agent of microevolutionary change in populations that were previously isolated. ☑

▲ **Figure 23 Gene flow.** The pollen of some plants can be carried by the wind for hundreds of miles, allowing gene flow to occur between distant populations.

☑ **CHECKPOINT**

Which mechanism of microevolution has been most affected by the increased ease of people traveling throughout the world?

Answer: gene flow

Natural Selection: A Closer Look

Genetic drift, gene flow, and even mutation can cause microevolution. But only by rare chance would these events result in improving a population's fit to its environment. In natural selection, on the other hand, only the events that produce genetic variation (mutation and sexual reproduction) are random. The process of natural selection, in which individuals better adapted to the environment are more likely to survive and reproduce, is *not* random. Consequently, only natural selection consistently leads to adaptive evolution—evolution that results in a better fit between organisms and their environment.

The adaptations of organisms include many striking examples. Consider the blue-footed booby **(Figure 24)**, one of the most memorable creatures that Darwin encountered on the Galápagos Islands. The bird's body and bill are streamlined like a torpedo, minimizing friction as it dives from heights up to 24 m (over 75 feet) into the shallow water below. To pull out of this high-speed dive once it hits the water, the booby uses its large tail as a brake. Those remarkable blue feet are an essential requirement for the male's reproductive success. Female boobies prefer males with the brightest blue feet. Thus, the male's courtship display is a dance that features frequent flashes of his colorful assets.

Such adaptations are the result of natural selection. By consistently favoring some alleles over others, natural

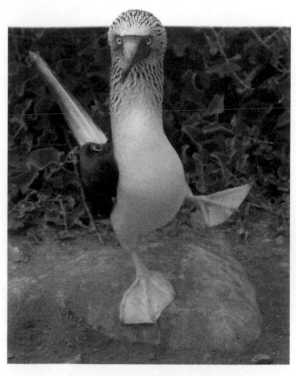

▲ **Figure 24 A blue-footed booby.** Although the booby's large, webbed feet are highly advantageous in the water, they are clumsy for walking on land.

selection improves the match between organisms and their environment. However, the environment may change over time. As a result, what constitutes a "good match" between an organism and its environment is a moving target, making adaptive evolution a continuous, dynamic process.

Evolutionary Fitness

The commonly used phrase "survival of the fittest" is misleading if we take it to mean head-to-head competition between individuals. Reproductive success, the key to evolutionary success, is generally more subtle and passive. In a varying population of moths, certain individuals may produce more offspring than others because their wing colors hide them from predators better. Plants in a wildflower population may differ in reproductive success because some attract more pollinators, owing to slight variations in flower color, shape, or fragrance. In a given environment, such traits can lead to greater **relative fitness**, the contribution an individual makes to the gene pool of the next generation *relative to* the contributions of other individuals. The fittest individuals in the context of evolution are those that produce the largest number of viable, fertile offspring and thus pass on the most genes to the next generation. ☑

☑ **CHECKPOINT**

What is the best measure of relative fitness?

Answer: the number of fertile offspring an individual leaves

Three General Outcomes of Natural Selection

Imagine a population of mice with individuals ranging in fur color from very light to very dark gray. If we graph the number of mice in each color category, we get a bell-shaped curve like the one shown at the top of **Figure 25**. If natural selection favors certain fur-color phenotypes over others, the population of mice will change over the generations. Three general outcomes are possible, depending on which phenotypes are favored. These three modes of natural selection are called directional selection, disruptive selection, and stabilizing selection.

Directional selection shifts the overall makeup of a population by selecting in favor of one extreme phenotype—the darkest mice, for example **(Figure 25a)**. Directional selection is most common when the local environment changes or when organisms migrate to a new environment. An actual example is the shift of insect populations toward a greater frequency of pesticide-resistant individuals.

Disruptive selection can lead to a balance between two or more contrasting phenotypes in a population **(Figure 25b)**. A patchy environment, which favors different phenotypes in different patches, is one situation associated with disruptive selection. The variations seen in the snake population in Figure 14 result from disruptive selection.

Stabilizing selection favors intermediate phenotypes **(Figure 25c)**. Such selection typically occurs in relatively stable environments, where conditions tend to reduce physical variation. This evolutionary conservatism works by selecting against the more extreme phenotypes. For example, stabilizing selection keeps the majority of human birth weights between 3 and 4 kg (approximately 6.5 to 9 pounds). For babies much lighter or heavier than this, infant mortality is greater.

Of the three selection modes, stabilizing selection occurs in most situations, resisting change in well-adapted populations. Evolutionary spurts occur when a population is stressed by a change in the environment or by migration to a new place. When challenged with a new set of environmental problems, a population either adapts through natural selection or dies off in that locale. The fossil record tells us that the population's extinction is the most common result. Those populations that do survive crises may change enough to be designated new species. ☑

Sexual Selection

Darwin was the first to explore the implications of **sexual selection**, a form of natural selection in which individuals with certain traits are more likely than other individuals to obtain mates. The males and females of an animal species obviously have different reproductive organs. But they may also have secondary sexual traits, noticeable differences not directly associated with reproduction or survival. This distinction in appearance, called **sexual dimorphism**, is often manifested in a size difference. Among male vertebrates, sexual dimorphism may also be evident in adornment, such as manes on

☑ **CHECKPOINT**
The thickness of fur in a bear population increases over several generations as the climate in the region becomes colder. This is an example of which type of selection: directional, disruptive, or stabilizing?

Answer: directional

◄ Figure 25 **Three possible outcomes for selection working on fur color in imaginary populations of mice.** The large downward arrows symbolize the pressure of natural selection working against certain phenotypes.

Frequency of individuals

Original population

Phenotypes (fur color)

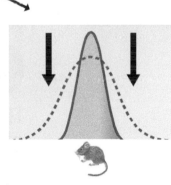

(a) Directional selection shifts the overall makeup of the population by favoring variants at one extreme. In this case, the trend is toward darker color, perhaps because the landscape has been shaded by the growth of trees, making darker mice less noticeable to predators.

(b) Disruptive selection favors variants at opposite extremes over intermediate individuals. Here, the relative frequencies of very light and very dark mice have increased. Perhaps the mice have colonized a patchy habitat where a background of light soil is studded with dark rocks.

(c) Stabilizing selection culls extreme variants from the population, in this case eliminating individuals that are unusually light or dark. The trend is toward reduced phenotypic variation and increased frequency of an intermediate phenotype.

lions, antlers on deer, or colorful plumage on peacocks and other birds (Figure 26a).

In some species, secondary sex structures may be used to compete with members of the same sex (usually males) for mates. Contests may involve physical combat, but are more often ritualized displays (Figure 26b). Such selection is common in species in which the winner acquires a harem of mates—an obvious boost to that male's evolutionary fitness.

> In some species, males engage in nonlethal combat in the hope of mating with females.

In a more common type of sexual selection, individuals of one sex (usually females) are choosy in selecting their mates. Males with the largest or most colorful adornments are often the most attractive to females. The extraordinary feathers of a peacock's tail are an example of this sort of "choose me!" statement. Every time a female chooses a mate based on a certain appearance or behavior, she perpetuates the alleles that caused her to make that choice and allows a male with that particular phenotype to perpetuate his alleles.

What is the advantage to females of being choosy? One hypothesis is that females prefer male traits that are correlated with "good" alleles. In several bird species, research has shown that traits preferred by females, such as bright beaks or long tails, are related to overall male health.

▼ Figure 26 **Sexual dimorphism.**

(a) Sexual dimorphism in a finch species. Among vertebrates, including this pair of green-winged Pytilia (native to Africa), males (right) are usually the showier sex.

(b) Competing for mates. Male Spanish ibex engage in nonlethal combat for the right to mate with females.

Evolution Past, Present, and Future EVOLUTION CONNECTION

The Rising Threat of Antibiotic Resistance

As you probably know, antibiotics are drugs that kill infectious microorganisms. But antibiotics are a relatively recent development in medicine. Before antibiotics, people often died from diseases such as whooping cough, and a minor wound—a razor nick or a scratch from a rose thorn—could result in a fatal infection. A revolution in human health followed the introduction of penicillin, the first widely used antibiotic, in the 1940s. Before long, more antibiotics were developed, and many diseases that had once been fatal could easily be cured. But even amid the enthusiasm for the new wonder drugs, signs of trouble began to appear. Doctors reported cases of bacterial infections that did not respond to antibiotics. By 1952, a researcher had identified the reason: Some bacteria had genetic traits that enabled them to resist the killing power of the drugs. In the same way that pesticides select for resistant insects, antibiotics select for resistant bacteria. A gene that codes for an enzyme that breaks down an antibiotic or a mutation that alters the site where an antibiotic binds can make a bacterium and its offspring resistant to that antibiotic. Again we see both the random and nonrandom aspects of natural selection—the random genetic mutations in bacteria and the nonrandom selective effects as the environment favors the antibiotic-resistant phenotype.

Ironically, our enthusiasm for the curative powers of antibiotics has encouraged the evolution of antibiotic-resistant bacteria. Livestock producers add antibiotics to animal feed, a practice that may select for bacteria resistant to standard antibiotics. Doctors may overprescribe antibiotics—for example, to patients with viral infections, which do not respond to antibiotic treatment. You may also be part of the problem. If you stop taking a prescribed antibiotic as soon as you feel better, instead of taking the full course of medication your doctor has prescribed, you are allowing mutant bacteria that may be killed more slowly by the drug to survive and multiply. Subsequent mutations in such bacteria may lead to full-blown antibiotic resistance.

Natural selection for antibiotic resistance is particularly strong in hospitals, where antibiotic use is extensive. A formidable "superbug" known as MRSA (methicillin-resistant *Staphylococcus aureus*) can cause "flesh-eating disease" and potentially fatal systemic (whole-body) infections. Alarmingly, a growing number of incidents of MRSA infection now begin in community settings, such as athletic facilities, schools, and military barracks (Figure 27).

MRSA is not the only antibiotic-resistant microorganism. According to a report issued by the Centers for Disease Control (CDC), 17 bacterial infections are no longer treatable with standard antibiotics; most of these are considered urgent or serious threats to public health. The most recent "superbug" to emerge is a strain of the bacteria that cause gonorrhea, a sexually transmitted disease. Public health officials fear that as this strain spreads, gonorrhea will become an incurable disease.

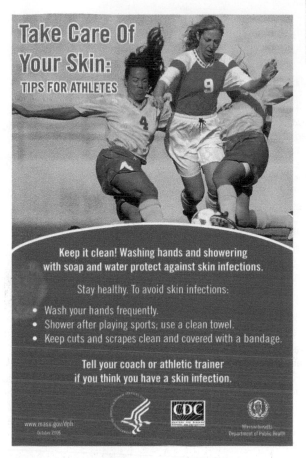

▲ Figure 27 **Cautioning athletes about MRSA.**

Drug resistance has also evolved in disease-causing viruses (for example, HIV and influenza) and parasites (for example, the organism that causes malaria).

Medical and pharmaceutical researchers are racing to develop new antibiotics and other drugs. However, experience suggests that our battle against the evolution of drug-resistant bacteria will continue for the foreseeable future.

Chapter Review

SUMMARY OF KEY CONCEPTS

The Diversity of Life

Naming and Classifying the Diversity of Life

In the Linnaean system of classification, each species is assigned a two-part name. The first part is the genus, and the second part is unique for each species within the genus. In the taxonomic hierarchy, domain > kingdom > phylum > class > order > family > genus > species.

Explaining the Diversity of Life

Present-day biologists accept Darwin's theory of evolution by means of natural selection as the best explanation for the diversity of life. However, when Darwin published his theory in 1859, it was a radical departure from the prevailing views.

Charles Darwin and *The Origin of Species*

Darwin's Journey

During his around-the-world voyage on the *Beagle*, Darwin observed adaptations of organisms that inhabited diverse environments. In particular, Darwin was struck by the geographic distribution of organisms on the Galápagos Islands, off the South American coast. When Darwin considered his observations in light of new evidence for a very old Earth that changed slowly, he arrived at ideas that were at odds with the long-held notion of a young Earth populated by unchanging species.

Evolution: Darwin's Theory

In his book *On the Origin of Species by Means of Natural Selection*, Darwin made two proposals: (1) Existing species descended from ancestral species, and (2) natural selection is the mechanism of evolution.

Evidence of Evolution

Evidence from Fossils

The fossil record shows that organisms have appeared in a historical sequence, and many fossils link ancestral species with those living today. For example, the evolution of whales from ancestral land-dwelling animals is documented by fossils of transitional forms.

Evidence from Homologies

Structural and molecular homologies reveal evolutionary relationships. Closely related species often have similar stages in their embryonic development. All species share a common genetic code, suggesting that all forms of life are related through branching evolution from the earliest organisms.

Evolutionary Trees

An evolutionary tree represents a succession of related species, with the most recent at the tips of the branches. Each branch point represents a common ancestor of all species that radiate from it.

Natural Selection as the Mechanism for Evolution

Darwin proposed natural selection as the mechanism that produces adaptive evolutionary change. In a population that varies, individuals best suited for a particular environment are more likely to survive and reproduce than those that are less suited to that environment.

Natural Selection in Action

Natural selection has been observed in many scientific studies, including in the evolution of pesticide-resistant insects.

Key Points about Natural Selection

Individuals do not evolve. Only heritable traits, not those acquired during an individual's lifetime, can be amplified or diminished by natural selection. Natural selection only works on existing variation—new variation does not arise in response to an environmental change. Natural selection does not produce perfect organisms.

The Evolution of Populations

Sources of Genetic Variation

Mutation and sexual reproduction produce genetic variation. Mutation is the ultimate source of genetic variation. Individual mutations have little short-term effect on a large gene pool, but in the long term, mutation is the source of genetic variation.

Populations as the Units of Evolution

A population, members of the same species living in the same time and place, is the smallest biological unit that can evolve.

Analyzing Gene Pools

A gene pool consists of all the alleles in all the individuals making up a population. The Hardy-Weinberg formula can be used to calculate the frequencies of genotypes in a gene pool from the frequencies of alleles, and vice versa:

| Allele frequencies | $p + q = 1$ |
| Genotype frequencies | $p^2 + 2pq + q^2 = 1$ |

Dominant homozygotes   Heterozygotes   Recessive homozygotes

Population Genetics and Health Science

The Hardy-Weinberg formula can be used to estimate the frequency of a harmful allele, which is useful information for public health programs dealing with genetic diseases.

Microevolution as Change in a Gene Pool

Microevolution is generation-to-generation change in allele frequencies in a population.

Mechanisms That Alter Allele Frequencies in a Population

Genetic Drift

Genetic drift is a change in the gene pool of a small population due to chance. A bottleneck event (a drastic reduction in population size) and the founder effect (occurring in a new population started by a few individuals) are two situations leading to genetic drift.

Gene Flow

A population may gain or lose alleles by gene flow, which is genetic exchange with another population.

Natural Selection: A Closer Look

Of all causes of evolution, only natural selection promotes evolutionary adaptations. Relative fitness is the contribution an individual makes to the gene pool of the next generation relative to the contributions of other individuals. The outcome of natural selection may be directional, disruptive, or stabilizing. Secondary sexual traits (such as sex-specific plumage or behaviors) can promote sexual selection, a type of natural selection in which mating preferences are determined by inherited traits.

Directional selection   **Disruptive selection**   **Stabilizing selection**

MasteringBiology®

For practice quizzes, BioFlix animations, MP3 tutorials, video tutors, and more study tools designed for this text, go to MasteringBiology®

SELF-QUIZ

1. Place these levels of classification in order from least inclusive to most inclusive: class, domain, family, genus, kingdom, order, phylum, species.

2. Which of the following is a true statement about Charles Darwin?
   a. He was the first to discover that living things can change, or evolve.
   b. He based his theory on the inheritance of acquired traits.
   c. He proposed natural selection as the mechanism of evolution.
   d. He was the first to realize that Earth is more than 6,000 years old.

3. How did the insights of Lyell and other geologists influence Darwin's thinking about evolution?

4. In a population with two alleles for a particular genetic locus, B and b, the allele frequency of B is 0.7. If this population is in Hardy-Weinberg equilibrium, what is the frequency of heterozygotes? What is the frequency of homozygous dominants? What is the frequency of homozygous recessives?

5. Define fitness from an evolutionary perspective.

6. Which of the following processes is the ultimate source of the genetic variation that serves as raw material for evolution?
   a. sexual reproduction   c. genetic drift
   b. mutation   d. natural selection

7. As a mechanism of evolution, natural selection can be most closely equated with
   a. random mating.   c. unequal reproductive success.
   b. genetic drift.   d. gene flow.

8. Compare and contrast how the bottleneck effect and the founder effect can lead to genetic drift.

9. In a particular bird species, individuals with average sized wings survive severe storms more successfully than other birds in the same population with longer or shorter wings. Of the three general outcomes of natural selection (directional, disruptive, or stabilizing), this example illustrates _____.

10. Which of the following statements is (are) true about a population in Hardy-Weinberg equilibrium? (More than one may be true.)
    a. The population is quite small.
    b. The population is not evolving.
    c. Gene flow between the population and surrounding populations does not occur.
    d. Natural selection is not occurring.

THE PROCESS OF SCIENCE

11. **Interpreting Data** A population of snails has recently become established in a new region. The snails are preyed on by birds that break the snails open on rocks, eat the soft bodies, and leave the shells. The snails occur in both striped and unstriped forms. In one area, researchers counted both live snails and broken shells. Their data are summarized here:

	Striped Shells	Unstriped Shells
Number of live snails	264	296
Number of broken snail shells	486	377
Total	750	673

Based on these data, which snail form is subject to more predation by birds? Predict how the frequencies of striped and unstriped individuals might change over time.

12. Imagine that the presence or absence of stripes on the snails from the previous question is determined by a single gene locus, with the dominant allele (S) producing striped snails and the recessive allele (s) producing unstriped snails. Combining the data from both the living snails and broken shells, calculate the following: the frequency of the dominant allele, the frequency of the recessive allele, and the number of heterozygotes in the observed groups.

BIOLOGY AND SOCIETY

13. To what extent are people in a technological society exempt from natural selection? Explain your answer.

14. What plants and animals have you seen near your home or school? What evolutionary adaptations suit them to their environment?

Glossary

artificial selection
The selective breeding of domesticated plants and animals to promote the occurrence of desirable traits in the offspring.

binomial
A two-part Latinized name of a species; for example, *Homo sapiens.*

bottleneck effect
Genetic drift resulting from a drastic reduction in population size. Typically, the surviving population is no longer genetically representative of the parent population.

class
In classification, the taxonomic category above order.

directional selection
Natural selection that acts in favor of the individuals at one end of a phenotypic range.

disruptive selection
Natural selection that favors extreme over intermediate phenotypes.

domain
A taxonomic category above the kingdom level. The three domains of life are Archaea, Bacteria, and Eukarya.

evolution
Descent with modification; genetic change in a population or species over generations; the heritable changes that have produced Earth's diversity of organisms.

evolutionary adaptation
Modification resulting from natural selection that suits organisms to their environment.

evolutionary tree
A branching diagram that reflects a hypothesis about evolutionary relationships between groups of organisms.

family
In classification, the taxonomic category above genus.

fossil
A preserved imprint or remains of an organism that lived in the past.

fossil record
The ordered sequence of fossils as they appear in rock layers, marking the passing of geologic time.

founder effect
The genetic drift resulting from the establishment of a new, small population whose gene pool represents only a sample of the genetic variation present in the parent population.

gene flow
The gain or loss of alleles from a population by the movement of individuals or gametes into or out of the population.

gene pool
All the alleles for all the genes in a population at any one time.

genetic drift
A change in the gene pool of a population due to chance.

genus (*jē'-nus*)
(plural, **genera**) In classification, the taxonomic category above species; the first part of a species' binomial; for example, *Homo.*

Hardy-Weinberg equilibrium
The condition describing a nonevolving population (one that is in genetic equilibrium).

homology (*hō-mol'-uh-jē*)
Similarity in characteristics resulting from a shared ancestry.

kingdom
In classification, the broad taxonomic category above phylum.**microevolution**
A change in a population's gene pool over a succession of generations.

order
In classification, the taxonomic category above family.

paleontologist
A scientist who studies fossils.

phylum (*fī'-lum*)
(plural, **phyla**) In classification, the taxonomic category above class. Members of a phylum all have a similar general body plan.

population
A group of interacting individuals belonging to one species and living in the same geographic area at the same time.

relative fitness
The contribution an individual makes to the gene pool of the next generation relative to the contribution of other individuals in the population.

sexual dimorphism
Distinction in appearance based on secondary sexual characteristics, noticeable differences not directly associated with reproduction or survival.

sexual selection
A form of natural selection in which individuals with certain characteristics are more likely than other individuals to obtain mates.

stabilizing selection
Natural selection that favors intermediate variants by acting against extreme phenotypes.

vestigial structure (*ve-sti'-gē-al*)
A structure of marginal, if any, importance to an organism. Vestigial structures are historical remnants of structures that had important functions in ancestors.

Credits

Credits are listed in the order of appearance.

PHOTO CREDITS

ILLUSTRATION AND TEXT CREDITS

Self-Quiz Answers

1. species, genus, family, order, class, phylum, kingdom, domain

2. c

3. Lyell and other geologists presented evidence for the gradual change of geologic features over millions of years. Darwin applied this idea to suggest that species evolve through the slow accumulation of small changes over long periods of time.

4. *Bb*: 0.42; *BB*: 0.49; *bb*: 0.09

5. The fitness of an individual (or of a particular genotype) is measured by the relative number of alleles that it contributes to the gene pool of the next generation compared with the contribution of others. Thus the number of fertile offspring produced determines an individual's fitness.

6. b

7. c

8. Both effects result in populations small enough for significant sampling error in the gene pool for the first few generations. A bottleneck event reduces the size of an existing population in a given location. The founder effect occurs when a new, small population colonizes a new territory.

9. stabilizing selection

10. b, c, d

How Biological Diversity Evolves

How Biological Diversity Evolves

If you drove off the rim of the Grand Canyon, you would pass by 40 rock layers and several hundred million years of geologic history before hitting the ground.

Alleles from two wild grasses could be used to make a better ear of corn.

Piecing together evolutionary histories shows who's related to whom.

Mass Extinctions BIOLOGY AND SOCIETY

The Sixth Mass Extinction

The fossil record reveals that the evolutionary history of life on Earth has been episodic, with long, relatively stable periods punctuated by brief, cataclysmic ones. During these upheavals, new species formed and others died out in great numbers.

Extinctions are inevitable in a changing world, but the fossil record reveals a few instances of great change, times when the majority of life on Earth—between 50% and 90% of living species—suddenly died out, vanishing forever. Scientists have documented five such mass extinctions during the last 540 million years. Today, human activities are modifying the global environment to such an extent that many species are disappearing at an alarming rate. In the past 400 years—a very short time on a geologic scale—more than 1,000 species are known to have become extinct. Scientists estimate that this is 100 to 1,000 times the extinction rate seen in most of the fossil record.

Are we in the midst of a sixth mass extinction? In an extensive analysis published in *Nature* in 2011, researchers compared data from the fossil record of the "big five" mass extinctions with data from the modern era. The good news is that the current loss of biodiversity does not yet qualify as a mass extinction. The bad news is that we're teetering on the brink. The loss of species that are now at critical risk of extinction—like the sea otter pictured here—would push our planet into a period of mass extinction. When the researchers include species that are endangered or threatened (lower

An endangered species. Oil spills, entanglement in commercial fishing nets, and disease are among the causes of declining sea otter populations.

categories of risk) in their calculations, the picture becomes very grim indeed. In contrast to the ancient mass extinctions, which unfolded over hundreds of thousands of years, a human-driven sixth mass extinction could be completed in just a few centuries. And, as with prior mass extinctions, life on Earth may take millions of years to recover.

But the fossil record also shows a creative side to the destruction. Mass extinctions can pave the way for the evolution of many diverse species from a common ancestor, such as the diversification of mammals after the extinction of dinosaurs. Accordingly, we'll begin this chapter by discussing the birth of new species and then examine how biologists trace the evolution of biological diversity. We'll also take a closer look at how scientists classify living organisms.

The Origin of Species

Natural selection, a microevolutionary mechanism, explains the striking ways in which organisms are suited to their environment. But what accounts for the tremendous diversity of life, the millions of species that have existed during Earth's history? This question intrigued Darwin, who referred to it in his diary as "that mystery of mysteries—the first appearance of new beings on this Earth."

When, as a young man, Darwin visited the Galápagos Islands, he realized that he was visiting a place of origins. Though the volcanic islands were geologically young, they were already home to many plants and animals known nowhere else in the world. Among these unique inhabitants were marine iguanas (Figure 1), Galápagos tortoises, and numerous species of small birds called finches, which you will learn more about in this chapter (see Figure 11). Surely, Darwin thought, not all of these species could have been among the original colonists. Some of them must have evolved later on, the myriad descendants of the original colonists, modified by natural selection from those original ancestors.

In the century and a half since the publication of Darwin's *On the Origin of Species by Means of Natural Selection*, new discoveries and technological advances—especially in molecular biology—have given scientists a wealth of new information about the evolution of life on Earth. For example, researchers have explained the genetic patterns underlying the homology of vertebrate limbs. Hundreds of thousands more fossil discoveries have been cataloged, including many of the transitional (intermediate) forms predicted by Darwin. In a fascinating convergence of old and new techniques, researchers have even been able to investigate the genetic material of certain fossils, including our ancient relatives, the Neanderthals. New dating methods have confirmed that Earth is billions of years old, much older than even the most radical geologists of Darwin's time proposed. As you'll learn in this chapter, these dating methods have also enabled researchers to determine the ages of fossils and rocks, providing valuable insight into evolutionary relationships between groups of organisms. In addition, our enhanced understanding of geologic processes, such as the changing positions of continents, explains some of the geographic distributions of organisms and fossils that puzzled Darwin and his contemporaries.

In this chapter, you'll learn how evolution has woven the rich tapestry of life, beginning with **speciation**, the process in which one species splits into two or more species. Other topics include the origin of evolutionary novelty, such as the wings and feathers of birds and the large brains of humans, and the impact of mass extinctions, which clear the way for new adaptive explosions, such as the diversification of mammals following the disappearance of most of the dinosaurs.

▼ Figure 1 **A marine iguana (right), an example of the unique species inhabiting the Galápagos.** Darwin noticed that Galápagos marine iguanas—with a flattened tail that aids in swimming—are similar to, but distinct from, land-dwelling iguanas on the islands and on the South American mainland (left).

What Is a Species?

Species is a Latin word meaning "kind" or "appearance." Indeed, as children we learn to distinguish between the kinds of plants and animals—between dogs and cats, for example, or between roses and dandelions—from differences in their appearance. Although the basic idea of species as distinct life-forms seems intuitive, devising a more formal definition is not so easy.

One way of defining a species (and the main definition used in this text) is the **biological species concept**. It defines a **species** as a group of populations whose members have the potential to interbreed with one another in nature and produce fertile offspring (offspring that can reproduce) **(Figure 2)**. Geography and culture may conspire to keep a Manhattan businesswoman and a Mongolian dairyman apart. But if the two did meet and mate, they could have viable babies who develop into fertile adults because all humans belong to the same species. In contrast, humans and chimpanzees, despite having a shared evolutionary history, are distinct species because they can't successfully interbreed.

We cannot apply the biological species concept to all situations. For example, basing the definition of species on reproductive compatibility excludes organisms that only reproduce asexually (producing offspring from a single parent), such as most prokaryotes. And because fossils are obviously not currently reproducing sexually, they cannot be evaluated by the biological species concept. In response to such challenges, biologists have developed other ways to define species. For example, most of the species named so far have been classified based on measurable physical traits such as number and type of teeth or flower structures. Another approach defines a species as the smallest group of individuals sharing a common ancestor and forming one branch on the tree of life. Yet another approach proposes defining a species solely on the basis of molecular data, a sort of bar code that identifies each species.

Each species concept is useful, depending on the situation and the questions being asked. The biological species concept, however, is particularly useful when focusing on how species originate, that is, when we ask: What prevents a member of one group from successfully interbreeding with a member of another group? You'll learn about the variety of answers to that question next. ☑

☑ **CHECKPOINT**

According to the biological species concept, what defines a species?

Answer: the ability of its members to interbreed with one another and produce fertile offspring in a natural setting

▼ Figure 2 **The biological species concept is based on reproductive compatibility rather than physical similarity.**

Similarity between different species. The eastern meadowlark (left) and the western meadowlark (right) are very similar in appearance, but they are separate species and do not interbreed.

Diversity within one species. Humans, as diverse in appearance as we are, belong to a single species (*Homo sapiens*) and can interbreed.

Reproductive Barriers between Species

Clearly, a fly will not mate with a frog or a fern. But what prevents closely related species from interbreeding? What, for example, maintains the species boundary between the eastern meadowlark and the western meadowlark (shown in Figure 2)? Their geographic ranges overlap in the Great Plains region, and they are so similar that only expert birders can tell them apart. And yet, these two bird species do not interbreed.

A **reproductive barrier** is anything that prevents individuals of closely related species from interbreeding. Let's examine the different kinds of reproductive barriers that isolate the gene pools of species (**Figure 3**). We can classify reproductive barriers as either prezygotic or postzygotic, depending on whether they block interbreeding before or after the formation of zygotes (fertilized eggs).

Prezygotic barriers prevent mating or fertilization between species (**Figure 4**). The barrier may be time-based (temporal isolation). For example, western spotted skunks breed in the fall, but the eastern species breeds in late winter. Temporal isolation keeps the species from mating even where they coexist on the Great Plains. In other cases, species live in the same region but not in the same habitats (habitat isolation). For example, one species of North American garter snake lives mainly in water, while a closely related species lives on land. Traits that enable individuals to recognize potential mates, such as a particular odor, coloration, or courtship ritual, can also function as reproductive barriers (behavioral isolation). In many bird species, for example, courtship

INDIVIDUALS OF DIFFERENT SPECIES

▼ Figure 3 **Reproductive barriers between closely related species.**

Prezygotic Barriers

Temporal isolation: Mating or fertilization occurs at different seasons or times of day.

Habitat isolation: Populations live in different habitats and do not meet.

Behavioral isolation: Little or no sexual attraction exists between populations.

MATING ATTEMPT

Mechanical isolation: Structural differences prevent fertilization.

Gametic isolation: Female and male gametes fail to unite in fertilization.

FERTILIZATION (ZYGOTE FORMS)

Postzygotic Barriers

Reduced hybrid viability: Hybrid zygotes fail to develop or fail to reach sexual maturity.

Reduced hybrid fertility: Hybrids fail to produce functional gametes.

Hybrid breakdown: Hybrids are feeble or sterile.

VIABLE, FERTILE OFFSPRING

No Barriers

▶ Figure 4 **Prezygotic barriers.** Prezygotic barriers prevent mating or fertilization.

PREZYGOTIC BARRIERS

Temporal Isolation

These two closely related species of skunks mate at different times of the year.

Habitat Isolation

These two closely related species of garter snakes do not mate because one lives in the water while the other lives on land.

behavior is so elaborate that individuals are unlikely to mistake a bird of a different species as one of their kind. In still other cases, the egg-producing and sperm-producing structures of different species are anatomically incompatible (mechanical isolation). For example, the two closely related species of snails in Figure 4 cannot join their male and female sex organs because their shells spiral in opposite directions. In still other cases, gametes (eggs and sperm) of different species are incompatible, preventing fertilization (gametic isolation). Gametic isolation is very important when fertilization is external. Male and female sea urchins of many species release eggs and sperm into the sea, but fertilization occurs only if species-specific molecules on the surface of egg and sperm attach to each other.

Postzygotic barriers operate if interspecies mating actually occurs and results in hybrid zygotes **(Figure 5)**. (In this context, "hybrid" means that the egg comes from one species and the sperm from another species.) In some cases, hybrid offspring die before reaching reproductive maturity (reduced hybrid viability). For example, although certain closely related salamander species will hybridize, the offspring fail to develop normally because of genetic incompatibilities between the two species. In other cases of hybridization, offspring may become vigorous adults, but are infertile (reduced hybrid fertility). A mule, for example, is the hybrid offspring of a female horse and a male donkey. Mules are sterile—they cannot successfully breed with each other. Thus, horses and donkeys remain distinct species. In other cases, the first-generation hybrids are viable and fertile, but when these hybrids mate with one another or with either parent species, the offspring are feeble or sterile (hybrid breakdown). For example,

different species of cotton plants can produce fertile hybrids, but the offspring of the hybrids do not survive.

In summary, reproductive barriers form the boundaries around closely related species. In most cases, it is not a single reproductive barrier but some combination of two or more that keeps species isolated. Next, we examine situations that make reproductive isolation and speciation possible. ☑

▼ **Figure 5 Postzygotic barriers.** Postzygotic barriers prevent development of fertile adults.

POSTZYGOTIC BARRIERS		
Reduced Hybrid Viability	**Reduced Hybrid Fertility**	**Hybrid Breakdown**
Some species of salamander can hybridize, but their offspring do not develop fully or, like this one, are frail and will not survive long enough to reproduce.	Horse / Donkey / Mule — The hybrid offspring of a horse and a donkey is a mule, which is sterile.	The rice hybrids at the left and right are fertile, but plants of the next generation (middle) are small and sterile.

Behavioral Isolation	**Mechanical Isolation**	**Gametic Isolation**
Galápagos blue-footed boobies mate only after a specific ritual of high stepping that advertises a mate's bright blue feet.	Because these snails' shells spiral in opposite directions, their genital openings (indicated by arrows) cannot be aligned and mating cannot occur.	Gametes of these red and purple urchins are unable to fuse because proteins on the surface of the eggs and sperm cannot bind to one another.

Evolution Mechanisms of Speciation

A key event in the origin of many species occurs when a population is somehow cut off from other populations of the parent species. With its gene pool isolated, the splinter population can follow its own evolutionary course. Changes in its allele frequencies caused by genetic drift and natural selection will not be diluted by alleles entering from other populations (gene flow). Such reproductive isolation can result from two general scenarios: allopatric ("different country") speciation and sympatric ("same country") speciation. In **allopatric speciation**, the initial block to gene flow is a geographic barrier that physically isolates the splinter population. In contrast, **sympatric speciation** is the origin of a new species without geographic isolation. The splinter population becomes reproductively isolated even though it is in the midst of the parent population.

Allopatric Speciation

Given the vast span of geologic time, we can imagine many scenarios that could fragment a population into two or more isolated populations. A mountain range may emerge and gradually split a population of organisms that can inhabit only lowlands. A land bridge, such as the Isthmus of Panama, may form and separate the marine life on either side. A large lake may subside and form several smaller lakes, with their populations now isolated. Glaciation could force small populations into ice-free areas that would remain isolated for millennia until the glaciers receded.

How formidable must a geographic barrier be to keep allopatric populations apart? The answer depends partly on the ability of the organisms to move about. Birds, mountain lions, and coyotes can cross mountain ranges, rivers, and canyons. Such barriers also do not hinder the windblown pollen of pine trees or the spread of seeds carried by animals capable of crossing the barrier. In contrast, small rodents may find a deep canyon or a wide river an impassable barrier **(Figure 6)**.

Speciation is more common for a small, isolated population because it is more likely than a large population to have its gene pool changed substantially by both genetic drift and natural selection. But for each small, isolated population that becomes a new species, many more simply perish in their new environment. Life on the frontier is harsh, and most pioneer populations become extinct.

Even if a small, isolated population survives, it does not necessarily evolve into a new species. The population may adapt to its local environment and begin to look very different from the ancestral population, but that doesn't necessarily make it a new species. Speciation occurs with the evolution of reproductive barriers between the isolated population and its parent

▼ Figure 6 **Allopatric speciation of antelope squirrels on opposite rims of the Grand Canyon.** Harris's antelope squirrel (*Ammospermophilus harrisii*) is found on the south rim of the Grand Canyon. Just a few miles away on the north rim is the closely related white-tailed antelope squirrel (*Ammospermophilus leucurus*). Birds and other organisms that can disperse easily across the canyon have not diverged into different species on opposite rims.

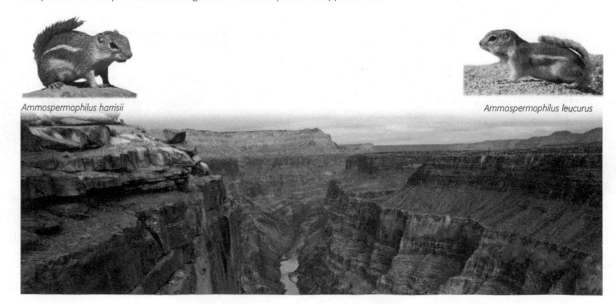

Ammospermophilus harrisii

Ammospermophilus leucurus

► Figure 7 **Possible outcomes after geographic isolation of populations.** In this diagram, the orange and green arrows track populations over time. The mountain symbolizes a period of geographic isolation during which time genetic changes may occur in both populations. After a period of time, the populations are no longer separated by a geographic barrier (right side of diagram) and come back into contact. If the populations can interbreed freely (top diagram), speciation has not occurred. If the populations cannot interbreed (bottom), then speciation has occurred.

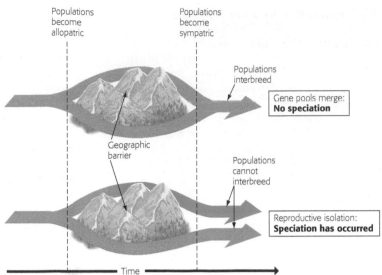

Populations become allopatric

Populations become sympatric

Populations interbreed

Gene pools merge: **No speciation**

Geographic barrier

Populations cannot interbreed

Reproductive isolation: **Speciation has occurred**

Time

population. In other words, if speciation occurs during geographic separation, the new species cannot breed with its ancestral population even if the two populations should come back into contact at some later time (**Figure 7**). ☑

Sympatric Speciation

Speciation doesn't necessarily require vast spans of time, nor is geographic isolation a prerequisite. A species may originate from an accident during cell division that results in an extra set of chromosomes, a condition called **polyploidy**. Examples of polyploid speciation have been found in some animal species, especially fish and amphibians (**Figure 8**). However, it is most common in

plants—an estimated 80% of present-day plant species are descended from ancestors that arose by polyploid speciation (**Figure 9**).

Two distinct forms of polyploid speciation have been observed. In one form, polyploidy arises from a single parent species. For example, a failure of cell division might double the chromosome number from the original diploid number ($2n$) to tetraploid ($4n$). Because the polyploid individual cannot produce fertile hybrids with its parent species, immediate reproductive isolation results.

A second form of polyploid speciation can occur when two different species interbreed and produce hybrid offspring. Most instances of polyploid speciation in plants resulted from such hybridizations. How did these

☑ **CHECKPOINT**

What is necessary for allopatric speciation to occur?

Answer: A population must be split into more than one group by a geographic barrier that interrupts gene flow between the two groups.

▼ Figure 8 **Gray tree frog.** This amphibian is thought to have originated by polyploid speciation.

▼ Figure 9 **Chinese hibiscus.** Many ornamental varieties of this species have been produced through polyploidy, which may make the flowers larger or increase the number of petals.

interspecies hybrids overcome the postzygotic barrier of sterility (see Figure 5)? A mule is sterile because its parents' chromosomes don't match. A horse has 64 chromosomes (32 pairs); a donkey has 62 chromosomes (31 pairs). Therefore, a mule has 63 chromosomes. Recall that gametes are produced by meiosis, a cell division process that involves pairing of homologous chromosomes. Structural differences between the chromosomes of horses and donkeys prevent them from pairing correctly, and the odd number leaves one chromosome without a potential partner. Consequently, mules don't produce viable gametes. Now, let's see why plants don't have the same problem.

In **Figure 10**, species A hybridizes with species B. Like a mule, the resulting hybrid plant has an odd number of chromosomes, and its chromosomes are not homologous. However, the hybrid may be able to reproduce asexually, as many plants can do. If so, there may eventually be an error in cell division that results in polyploidy and thus reproductive isolation from the parent. Biologists have identified several plant species that originated via polyploidy within the past 150 years.

Many of the plant species we grow for food are polyploids, including oats, potatoes, bananas, strawberries, peanuts, apples, sugarcane, and wheat. The wheat used for bread is a hybrid of three different parent species and has six sets of chromosomes, two sets from each parent. Plant geneticists use chemicals to induce errors in cell division and generate new polyploids in the laboratory. By harnessing this evolutionary process, they can produce new hybrid species with desirable qualities.

Biologists have also identified cases in which subpopulations appear to be in the process of sympatric speciation. In some cases, subgroups of a population become adapted for exploiting food sources in different habitats,

CHECKPOINT

What mechanism accounts for most observed instances of sympatric speciation? Why might this be the case?

Answer: Accidents of cell division that result in polyploidy. Polyploidy produces "instant" reproductive isolation.

such as the shallow versus deep habitats of a lake. In another example, a type of sexual selection in which female fish choose mates based on color has contributed to rapid reproductive isolation. Because of its direct effect on reproductive success, sexual selection can interrupt gene flow within a population and may therefore be an important factor in sympatric speciation. But the most frequently observed mechanism of sympatric speciation involves large-scale genetic changes that occur in a single generation. ☑

Island Showcases of Speciation

Volcanic islands, such as the Galápagos and Hawaiian island chains, are initially devoid of life. Over time, colonists arrive via ocean currents or winds. Some of these organisms gain a foothold and establish new populations. In their new environment, these populations may diverge significantly from their distant parent populations. In addition, islands that have physically diverse habitats and that are far enough apart to permit populations to evolve in isolation but close enough to allow occasional dispersals to occur are often the sites of multiple speciation events.

The Galápagos Islands, which were formed by underwater volcanoes from 5 million to 1 million years ago, are one of the world's great showcases of speciation. They are home to numerous plants, snails, reptiles, and birds that are found nowhere else on Earth. For example, the islands have 14 species of closely related finches, which are often called Darwin's finches because he collected them during his around-the-world voyage. These birds share many finch-like traits, but they differ in their feeding habits and their beaks, which are specialized for what they eat. Their various foods include insects, large or small seeds, cactus fruits, and even eggs of other species. The woodpecker finch uses cactus spines or twigs as tools to pry insects from trees. The "vampire" finch supplements its diet of seeds and insects by pecking wounds on the backs of seabirds and drinking their blood. **Figure 11** (facing page) shows some of these birds, with their distinctive beaks adapted for their specific diets. The finches differ in their habitats as well as their beaks—some live in trees and others spend most of their time on the ground.

How might Darwin's finch species have evolved from a small population of ancestral birds that colonized one of the islands? Completely isolated on the island, the founder population may have changed significantly as natural selection adapted it to the new environment, and thus it became a new species. Later, a few individuals of this new species may have migrated to a neighboring island, where, under different conditions, this new founder population was changed enough through

▼ **Figure 10 Sympatric speciation in a plant.** The gametes from two different species result in a sterile hybrid, which may undergo asexual reproduction. Such a hybrid may eventually form a new species by polyploidy.

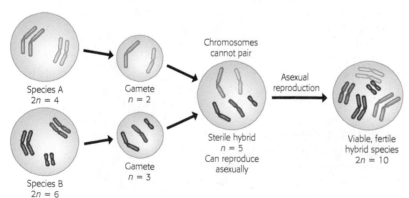

Species A
2n = 4

Gamete
n = 2

Species B
2n = 6

Gamete
n = 3

Chromosomes cannot pair

Sterile hybrid
n = 5
Can reproduce asexually

Asexual reproduction

Viable, fertile hybrid species
2n = 10

Cactus-seed-eater (cactus finch)

Tool-using insect-eater (woodpecker finch)

Blood, seed, and insect-eater (vampire finch)

▲ Figure 11 **Galápagos finches with beaks adapted for specific diets.**

process of speciation is often extremely slow. So you may be surprised to learn that we *can* see speciation occurring. Consider that life has been evolving over hundreds of millions of years and will continue to evolve. The species living today represent a snapshot, a brief instant in this vast span of time. The environment continues to change—sometimes rapidly due to human impact—and natural selection continues to act on affected populations. It is reasonable to assume that some of these populations are changing in ways that could eventually lead to speciation. Studying populations as they diverge gives biologists a window on the process of speciation.

Researchers have documented at least two dozen cases in which populations are currently diverging as they use different food resources or breed in different habitats. Numerous cases involve insects exploiting different food plants. In one well-studied example, a subpopulation of a fly that feeds on hawthorn fruits found a new resource when American colonists planted apple trees. Although the two fly populations are still regarded as subspecies, researchers have identified mechanisms that severely restrict gene flow between them. In other cases, biologists have identified animal populations that are diverging as a result of differences in male courtship behavior.

Although biologists are continually making observations and devising experiments to study evolution in progress, much of the evidence for evolution comes from the fossil record. So what does the fossil record say about the time frame for speciation—the length of time between when a new species forms and when its populations diverge enough to produce another new species? In one survey of 84 groups of plants and animals, the time for speciation ranged from 4,000 to 40 million years. Such long time frames tell us that it has taken vast spans of time for life on Earth to evolve.

As you've seen, speciation may begin with small differences. However, as speciation occurs again and again, these differences accumulate and may eventually lead to new groups that differ greatly from their ancestors, as in the origin of whales from four-legged land animals. The cumulative effects of multiple speciations, as well as extinctions, have shaped the dramatic changes documented in the fossil record. We begin to examine such changes next.

natural selection to become yet another new species. Some of these birds may then have recolonized the first island and coexisted there with the original ancestral species if reproductive barriers kept the species distinct. Multiple rounds of colonization and speciation on the many separate islands of the Galápagos probably followed. Today, each of the Galápagos Islands has several species of finches, with as many as ten on some islands. Reproductive isolation due to species-specific songs helps keep the species separate.

Observing Speciation in Progress

In contrast to microevolutionary change, which may be apparent in a population within a few generations, the

Earth History and Macroevolution

Having examined how new species arise, we are ready to turn our attention to macroevolution. **Macroevolution** is evolutionary change above the species level, for example, the origin of a new group of organisms through a series of speciation events. Macroevolution also includes the impact of mass extinctions on the diversity of life and its subsequent recovery. An understanding of macroevolution begins with a look at the span of geologic time over which life's diversity has evolved.

The Fossil Record

Fossils are evidence of organisms that lived in the past. The strata (layers) of sedimentary rocks provide a record of life on Earth—each rock layer contains a local sample of the organisms that existed at the time the sediment was deposited. Thus, the fossil record, the sequence in which fossils appear in rock strata, is an archive of macroevolution. For example, scan the wall of the Grand Canyon from rim to floor and you look back through hundreds of millions of years (Figure 12). Younger strata formed atop older ones; correspondingly, younger fossils are found in layers closer to the surface, whereas the deepest strata contain the oldest fossils. However, this only gives us the ages of fossils relative to each other. Like peeling off layers of wallpaper in an old house, we can infer the order in which the layers were applied but not the year that each layer was added.

If you drove off the rim of the Grand Canyon, you would pass by 40 rock layers and several hundred million years of geologic history before hitting the ground.

By studying many sites, geologists have established a **geologic time scale** that divides Earth's history into a sequence of geologic periods. The time line presented in Table 1 is separated into four broad divisions: the Precambrian (a general term for the time before about 540 million years ago), followed by the Paleozoic, Mesozoic, and Cenozoic eras. Each of these divisions represents a distinct age in the history of Earth and its life. The boundaries between eras are marked by mass extinctions, when many forms of life disappeared from the fossil record and were replaced by species that diversified from the survivors.

The most common method geologists use to learn the ages of rocks and the fossils they contain is **radiometric dating**, a method based on the decay of radioactive isotopes. For example, a living organism contains both the common isotope carbon-12 and the radioactive isotope carbon-14 in the same ratio as that present in the atmosphere. Once an organism dies, it stops accumulating carbon, and the stable carbon-12 in its tissues does not change. Carbon-14, however, spontaneously decays to another element. Carbon-14 has a half-life of 5,730 years, so half the carbon-14 in a specimen decays in about 5,730 years, half the remaining carbon-14 decays in the next 5,730 years, and so on. Scientists measure the ratio of carbon-14 to carbon-12 in a fossil to calculate its age.

Carbon-14 is useful for dating relatively young fossils—up to about 75,000 years old. There are isotopes with longer half-lives, such as uranium-235 (half-life 71.3 million years) and potassium-40 (half-life 1.3 billion years). However, organisms don't incorporate those elements into their bodies. Therefore, scientists use indirect methods to date older fossils. One commonly used method is to date layers of volcanic rock or ash above and below the sedimentary layer in which fossils are found. By inference, the age of the fossils is between those two dates. Potassium-argon dating is often used for volcanic rock, for example. Isotopes of uranium are useful for other types of ancient rock.

▼ **Figure 12 Strata of sedimentary rock at the Grand Canyon.** The Colorado River has cut through more than a mile of rock, exposing sedimentary strata that are like huge pages from the book of life. Each stratum entombs fossils that represent some of the organisms from that period of Earth's history.

Table 1	The Geologic Time Scale				
Geologic Time	**Period**	**Epoch**	**Age (millions of years ago)**	**Some Important Events in the History of Life**	**Relative Time Span**
Cenozoic era	Quaternary	Recent		Historical time	Cenozoic
			0.01		Mesozoic
		Pleistocene		Ice ages; humans appear	
			1.8		Paleozoic
	Tertiary	Pliocene		Origin of genus *Homo*	
			5		
		Miocene		Continued speciation of mammals and angiosperms	
			23		
		Oligocene		Origins of many primate groups, including apes	
			34		
		Eocene		Angiosperm dominance increases; origins of most living mammalian orders	
			56		
		Paleocene		Major speciation of mammals, birds, and pollinating insects	
			65		
Mesozoic era	Cretaceous			Flowering plants (angiosperms) appear; many groups of organisms, including most dinosaur lineages, become extinct at end of period (Cretaceous extinctions)	
			145		
	Jurassic			Gymnosperms continue as dominant plants; dinosaurs become dominant	
			200		
	Triassic			Cone-bearing plants (gymnosperms) dominate landscape; speciation of dinosaurs, early mammals, and birds	
			251		
Paleozoic era	Permian			Extinction of many marine and terrestrial organisms (Permian extinctions); speciation of reptiles; origins of mammal-like reptiles and most living orders of insects	
			299		
	Carboniferous			Extensive forests of vascular plants; first seed plants; origin of reptiles; amphibians become dominant	Pre-cambrian
			359		
	Devonian			Diversification of bony fishes; first amphibians and insects	
			416		
	Silurian			Early vascular plants dominate land	
			444		
	Ordovician			Marine algae are abundant; colonization of land by diverse fungi, plants, and animals	
			488		
	Cambrian			Origin of most living animal phyla (Cambrian explosion)	
			542		
Precambrian			600	Diverse algae and soft-bodied invertebrate animals appear	
			635	Oldest animal fossils	
			2,100	Oldest eukaryotic fossils	
			2,700	Oxygen begins accumulating in atmosphere	
			3,500	Oldest fossils known (prokaryotes)	
			4,600	Approximate time of origin of Earth	

Plate Tectonics and Biogeography

If photographs of Earth were taken from space every 10,000 years and then spliced together, it would make a remarkable movie. The seemingly "rock solid" continents we live on drift about Earth's surface. According to the theory of **plate tectonics**, the continents and seafloors form a thin outer layer of solid rock, called the crust, which covers a mass of hot, viscous material called the mantle. The crust is not one continuous expanse, however. It is divided into giant, irregularly shaped plates that float atop the mantle (Figure 13). In a process called continental drift, movements in the mantle cause the plates to move. The boundaries of some plates are hotspots of geologic activity. In some cases, we feel an immediate, violent symptom of this activity, as when an earthquake signals that two plates are scraping past or colliding with each other (Figure 14). Although most movement is extremely slow, not much faster than the speed at which fingernails grow, continents have wandered thousands of miles over the long course of earth's history.

By reshaping the physical features of the planet and altering the environments in which organisms live, continental drift has had a tremendous impact on the evolution of life's diversity. Two chapters in the continuing saga of continental drift had an especially strong influence on life. About 250 million years ago, near the end of the Paleozoic era, plate movements brought all the previously separated landmasses together into a supercontinent called Pangaea, which means "all land" (Figure 15, facing page). Imagine some of the possible effects on life. Species that had been evolving in isolation came together and competed. As the landmasses joined, the total amount of shoreline was reduced. There is also evidence that the ocean basins increased in depth, lowering sea level and draining the shallow coastal seas. Then, as now, most

▲ Figure 14 **A tsunami caused by an earthquake off the coast of Japan in March 2011.** Japan sits atop four different plates. Frequent earthquakes occur as the plates move and bump against each other.

marine species inhabited shallow waters, and the formation of Pangaea destroyed a considerable amount of that habitat. It was probably a long, traumatic period for terrestrial life as well. The continental interior, which was drier and had a more erratic climate than the coastal regions, increased in area substantially when the land came together. Changing ocean currents also undoubtedly affected land life as well as sea life. Thus, the formation of Pangaea had a tremendous environmental impact that reshaped biological diversity by causing extinctions and providing new opportunities for diversification of the survivors.

The second dramatic chapter in the history of continental drift began during the mid-Mesozoic era. Pangaea started to break up, causing geographic isolation of colossal proportions. As the landmasses drifted apart, each continent became a separate evolutionary arena as its climates changed and its organisms diverged.

The history of continental mergers and separations explains many patterns of **biogeography**, the study of the past and present distribution of organisms. For example, almost all the animals and plants that live on Madagascar, a large island located off the southern coast of Africa, are unique—they diversified from ancestral populations after Madagascar was isolated from Africa and India. The more than 50 species of lemurs that currently inhabit Madagascar, for instance, evolved from a common ancestor over the past 40 million years.

▼ Figure 13 **Earth's tectonic plates.** The red dots indicate zones where violent geologic activity, such as earthquakes and volcanic eruptions, take place. Arrows indicate direction of continental drift.

Key

• Zones of violent tectonic activity

↑ Direction of movement

Continental drift also separated Australia from other landmasses. Australia and its neighboring islands are home to more than 200 species of marsupials, most of which are found nowhere else in the world (**Figure 16**). Marsupials are mammals such as kangaroos, koalas, and wombats whose young complete their embryonic development in a pouch outside the mother's body. The rest of the world is dominated by eutherian (placental) mammals, whose young complete their development in the mother's uterus. Looking at a current map of the world, you might hypothesize that marsupials evolved only on the island continent of Australia. But marsupials are not unique to Australia. More than a hundred species live in Central and South America. North America is also home to a few, including the Virginia opossum. The distribution of marsupials only makes sense in the context of continental drift—marsupials must have originated when the continents were joined. Fossil evidence suggests that marsupials originated in what is now Asia and later dispersed to the tip of South America while it was still connected to Antarctica. They made their way to Australia before continental drift separated Antarctica from Australia, setting "afloat" a great raft of marsupials. The few early eutherians that lived in Australia became extinct, whereas on other continents, most marsupials became extinct. Isolated on Australia, marsupials evolved and diversified, filling ecological roles analogous to those filled by eutherians on other continents. ☑

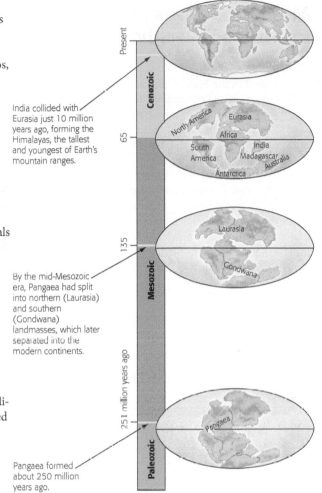

India collided with Eurasia just 10 million years ago, forming the Himalayas, the tallest and youngest of Earth's mountain ranges.

By the mid-Mesozoic era, Pangaea had split into northern (Laurasia) and southern (Gondwana) landmasses, which later separated into the modern continents.

Pangaea formed about 250 million years ago.

◄ **Figure 15 The history of plate tectonics.** The continents continue to drift, though not at a rate that's likely to cause any motion sickness for their passengers.

☑ **CHECKPOINT**

How many continents did Earth have at the time of Pangaea?

Answer: one

▼ **Figure 16 Australian marsupials.** The continent of Australia is home to many unique plants and animals, including diverse marsupials, mammals that have ecological roles filled by eutherians on other continents.

Tasmanian devil, a carnivore

Sugar glider, an omnivore

Koala, an herbivore

Mass Extinctions and Explosive Diversifications of Life

As discussed in the Biology and Society section at the beginning of the chapter, the fossil record reveals that five mass extinctions have occurred over the last 540 million years. In each of these events, 50% or more of Earth's species died out. Of all the mass extinctions, those marking the ends of the Permian and Cretaceous periods have been the most intensively studied.

The Permian mass extinction, at about the time the merging continents formed Pangaea, claimed about 96% of marine species and took a tremendous toll on terrestrial life as well. Equally notable is the mass extinction at the end of the Cretaceous period. For 150 million years prior, dinosaurs dominated Earth's land and air, whereas mammals were few and small, resembling today's rodents. Then, about 65 million years ago, most of the dinosaurs became extinct, leaving behind only the descendants of one lineage, the birds. Remarkably, the massive die-off (which also included half of all other species) occurred in less than 10 million years—a brief period in geologic time.

But there is a flip side to the destruction. Each massive dip in species diversity has been followed by explosive diversification of certain survivors. Extinctions seem to have provided the surviving organisms with new environmental opportunities. For example, mammals existed for at least 75 million years before undergoing an explosive increase in diversity just after the Cretaceous period. Their rise to prominence was undoubtedly associated with the void left by the extinction of the dinosaurs. The world would be a very different place today if many dinosaur lineages had escaped the Cretaceous extinctions or if none of the mammals had survived.

Mass Extinctions THE PROCESS OF SCIENCE

Did a Meteor Kill the Dinosaurs?

For decades, scientists have been debating the cause of the rapid dinosaur die-off that occurred 65 million years ago. Many **observations** provide clues. The fossil record shows that the climate had cooled and that shallow seas were receding from continental lowlands. It also shows that many plant species died out. Perhaps the most telling evidence was discovered by physicist Luis Alvarez and his geologist son Walter Alvarez, both of the University of California, Berkeley. In 1980, they found that rock deposited around 65 million years ago contains a thin layer of clay rich in iridium, an element very rare on Earth but common in meteors and other extraterrestrial material that occasionally falls to Earth. This discovery led the Alvarez team to ask the following **question**: Is the iridium layer the result of fallout from a huge cloud of dust that billowed into the atmosphere when a large meteor or asteroid hit Earth?

The father and son formed the **hypothesis** that the mass extinction 65 million years ago was caused by the impact of an extraterrestrial object. This hypothesis makes a clear **prediction**: A huge impact crater of the right age should be found somewhere on Earth's surface. (This is a good example of using verifiable observations rather than a direct **experiment** to test a hypothesis.) In 1981, two petroleum geologists found the **results** predicted by the Alvarezes' hypothesis: the Chicxulub crater, located near Mexico's Yucatán Peninsula in the Caribbean Sea **(Figure 17)**. This impact site, about 180 km wide (about 112 miles) and dating from the predicted time, was created when a meteor or asteroid about 10 km in diameter (about 6 miles, more than the length of 100 football fields) slammed into Earth, releasing thousands of times more energy than is stored in the world's combined stockpile of nuclear weapons. Such a cloud could have blocked sunlight and disturbed climate severely for months, perhaps killing off many plant species and, later, the animals that depended on those plants for food.

Debate continues about whether this impact alone caused the dinosaurs to die out or whether other factors—such as continental movements or volcanic activity—also contributed. Most scientists agree, however, that the collision that created the Chicxulub crater could indeed have been a major factor in global climatic change and mass extinctions.

▼ **Figure 17 Trauma for planet Earth and its Cretaceous life.**

An artist's representation of the impact of an asteroid or comet.

The impact's immediate effect was most likely a cloud of hot vapor and debris that could have killed many of the plants and animals in North America within hours.

Chicxulub crater

The 65-million-year-old Chicxulub impact crater is located in the Caribbean Sea near the Yucatán Peninsula of Mexico. The horseshoe shape of the crater and the pattern of debris in sedimentary rocks indicate that an asteroid or comet struck at a low angle from the southeast.

Mechanisms of Macroevolution

The fossil record can tell us what the great events in the history of life have been and when they occurred. Continental drift and mass extinctions followed by the diversification of survivors provide a big-picture view of how those changes came about. But now scientists are increasingly able to explain the basic biological mechanisms that underlie the macroevolutionary changes seen in the fossil record.

Large Effects from Small Genetic Changes

Scientists working at the interface of evolutionary biology and developmental biology—the research field abbreviated **evo-devo**—are studying how slight genetic changes can become magnified into major structural differences between species. Homeotic genes, the master control genes, program development by controlling the rate, timing, and spatial pattern of changes in an organism's form as it develops from a zygote into an adult. These genes determine such basic developmental events as where a pair of wings or legs will appear on a fruit fly. A subtle change in the developmental program can have profound effects. Accordingly, changes in the number, nucleotide sequence, and regulation of homeotic genes have led to the huge diversity in body forms.

Changes in rate of developmental events explains changes in the homologous limb bones of vertebrates. Increased growth rates produced the extra-long "finger"

bones in bat wings. Slower growth rates of leg and pelvic bones led to the eventual loss of hind limbs in whales. On the other hand, the loss of limbs in the evolution of snakes from a four-limbed lizard-like ancestor resulted from different spatial patterns of expression of homeotic genes.

Striking evolutionary transformations may also result from a change in the timing of developmental events. **Figure 18** is a photograph of an axolotl, a salamander that illustrates a phenomenon called **paedomorphosis**, the retention in the adult of body structures that were juvenile features in an ancestral species. The axolotl grows to full size and reproduces without losing its external gills, a juvenile feature in most species of salamanders.

Gills

◄ **Figure 18**
Paedomorphosis. The axolotl, a salamander, becomes an adult (shown here) and reproduces while retaining certain tadpole characteristics, including gills.

Paedomorphosis has also been important in human evolution. Humans and chimpanzees are even more alike in body form as fetuses than they are as adults. In the fetuses of both species, the skulls are rounded and the jaws are small, making the face rather flat (Figure 19). As development proceeds, accelerated growth in the jaw produces the elongated skull, sloping forehead, and massive jaws of an adult chimpanzee. In the human lineage, genetic changes that slowed the growth of the jaw relative to other parts of the skull produced an adult whose head proportions still resembled that of a child—and that of a baby chimpanzee. Our large skull and complex brain are among our most distinctive features. The human brain is proportionately larger than the chimpanzee brain because growth of the organ is switched off much later in human development. Compared with the brain of a chimpanzee, our brain continues to grow for several more years, which can be interpreted as the prolonging of a juvenile process.

Next, we see how the process of evolution can produce new, complex structures.

The Evolution of Biological Novelty

The two squirrels in Figure 6 are different species, but they are very similar animals that live very much the same way. How do we account for the dramatic differences between dissimilar groups—squirrels and birds, for example? Let's see how the Darwinian theory of gradual change can explain the evolution of intricate structures such as eyes or of new kinds of structures (novel structures) such as feathers.

Chimpanzee infant

Chimpanzee adult

Chimpanzee fetus

Chimpanzee adult

Human fetus

Human adult
(paedomorphic features)

▲ **Figure 19 Comparison of human and chimpanzee skull development.** Starting with fetal skulls that are very similar (left), the differential growth rates of the bones making up the skulls produce adult heads with very different proportions. The grid lines will help you relate the fetal skulls to the adult skulls.

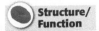 **Structure/ Function** **Adaptation of Old Structures for New Functions**

The feathered flight of birds is a perfect marriage of structure and function. Consider the evolution of feathers, which are clearly essential to avian aeronautics. In a flight feather, separate filaments called barbs emerge from a central shaft that runs from base to tip. Each barb is linked to the next by tiny hooks that act much like the teeth of a zipper, forming a tightly connected sheet of barbs that is strong but flexible. In flight, the shapes and arrangements of various feathers produce lift, smooth airflow, and help with steering and balance. How did such a beautifully intricate structure evolve? Reptilian features apparent in fossils of *Archaeopteryx*, one of the earliest birds, offered clues in Darwin's time (Figure 20), but the definitive answer came in 1996. Birds were not the first feathered animals on Earth—dinosaurs were.

The first feathered dinosaur to be discovered, a 130-million-year-old fossil found in northeastern China, was named *Sinosauropteryx* ("Chinese lizard-wing"). About the size of a turkey, it had short arms and ran on its hind legs, using its long tail for balance. Its

▼ **Figure 20 An extinct bird.** Called *Archaeopteryx* ("ancient wing"), this animal lived near tropical lagoons in central Europe about 150 million years ago. Despite its feathers, *Archaeopteryx* has many features in common with reptiles. *Archaeopteryx* is not considered an ancestor of today's birds. Instead, it probably represents an extinct side branch of the bird lineage.

Claws on forelimbs (like reptile)

Teeth like reptile

Long tail with many vertebrae (like reptile)

Feathers

unimpressive plumage consisted of a downy covering of hairlike feathers. Since the discovery of *Sinosauropteryx*, thousands of fossils of feathered dinosaurs have been found and classified into more than 30 different species. Although none was unequivocally capable of flying, many of these species had elaborate feathers that would be the envy of any modern bird. But the feathers seen in these fossils could not have been used for flight, nor would their reptilian anatomy have been suited to flying. So if feathers evolved before flight, what was their function? Their first utility may have been for insulation. It is possible that longer, winglike forelimbs and feathers, which increased the surface area of these forelimbs, were co-opted for flight after functioning in some other capacity, such as mating displays, thermoregulation, or camouflage (all functions that feathers still serve today). The first flights may have been only short glides to the ground or from branch to branch in tree-dwelling species. Once flight itself became an advantage, natural selection would have gradually remodeled feathers and wings to fit their additional function.

Structures such as feathers that evolve in one context but become co-opted for another function are called exaptations. However, exaptation does not mean that a structure evolves in anticipation of future use. Natural selection cannot predict the future; it can only improve an existing structure in the context of its current use. ☑

From Simple to Complex Structures in Gradual Stages

Most complex structures have evolved in small steps from simpler versions having the same basic function—a process of refinement rather than the sudden appearance of complexity. Consider the amazing camera-like eyes of vertebrates and squids. Although these complex eyes evolved independently, the origin of both can be traced from a simple ancestral patch of photoreceptor cells through a series of incremental modifications that benefited their owners at each stage. Indeed, there appears to have been a single evolutionary origin of light-sensitive cells, and all animals with eyes—vertebrates and invertebrates alike—share the same master genes that regulate eye development.

Figure 21 illustrates the range of complexity in the structure of eyes among present-day molluscs, a large and diverse phylum of animals. Simple patches of pigmented cells enable limpets, single-shelled molluscs that cling to seaside rocks, to distinguish light from dark. When a shadow falls on them, they hold on more tightly—a behavioral adaptation that reduces the risk of being eaten. Other molluscs have eyecups that have no lenses or other means of focusing images but can indicate light direction. In those molluscs that do have complex eyes, the organs probably evolved in small steps of adaptation. You can see examples of such small steps in Figure 21.

▼ **Figure 21 A range of eye complexity among molluscs.** The complex eye of the squid evolved in small steps. Even the simplest eye was useful to its owner.

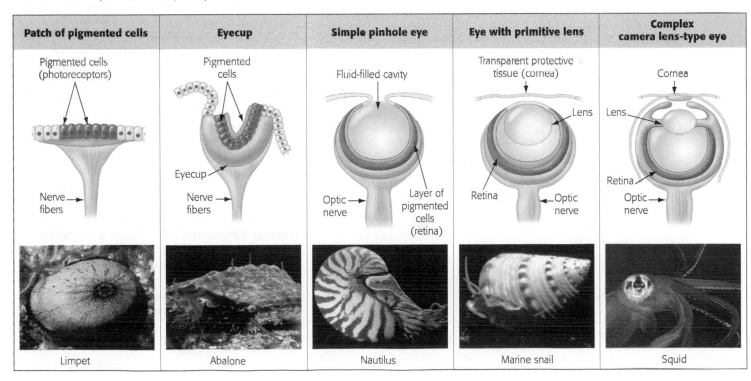

Patch of pigmented cells	Eyecup	Simple pinhole eye	Eye with primitive lens	Complex camera lens-type eye
Pigmented cells (photoreceptors); Nerve fibers	Pigmented cells; Eyecup; Nerve fibers	Fluid-filled cavity; Optic nerve; Layer of pigmented cells (retina)	Transparent protective tissue (cornea); Lens; Retina; Optic nerve	Cornea; Lens; Retina; Optic nerve
Limpet	Abalone	Nautilus	Marine snail	Squid

Classifying the Diversity of Life

The Linnaean system of taxonomy is quite a useful method of organizing life's diversity into groups. Ever since Darwin, however, biologists have had a goal beyond simple organization: to have classification reflect evolutionary relationships. In other words, how an organism is named and classified should reflect its place within the evolutionary tree of life. **Systematics**, which includes taxonomy, is a discipline of biology that focuses on classifying organisms and determining their evolutionary relationships.

Classification and Phylogeny

Biologists use **phylogenetic trees** to depict hypotheses about the evolutionary history, or phylogeny, of species. These branching diagrams reflect the hierarchical classification of groups nested within more inclusive groups. The tree in **Figure 22** shows the classification of some carnivores and their probable evolutionary relationships. Note that each branch point represents the divergence of two lineages from a common ancestor.

Alleles from two wild grasses could be used to make a better ear of corn.

Understanding phylogeny can have practical applications. For example, maize (corn) is an important food crop worldwide; it also provides us with snack favorites such as popcorn, tortilla chips, and corn dog batter. Thousands of years of artificial selection (selective breeding) transformed a scrawny grass with small ears of rock-hard kernels into the maize we know today. In the process, much of the plant's original genetic variation was stripped away. By constructing a phylogeny of maize, researchers have identified two species of wild grasses that may be maize's closest living relatives. The genomes of these plants may harbor alleles that offer disease resistance or other useful traits that could be transferred into cultivated maize by crossbreeding or genetic engineering—insurance against future disease outbreaks or other environmental changes that might threaten corn crops.

Identifying Homologous Characters

Homologous structures in different species may vary in form and function but exhibit fundamental similarities because they evolved from the same structure in a common ancestor. Among the vertebrates, for instance, the whale forelimb is adapted for steering in the water, whereas the bat wing is adapted for flight. Nonetheless, there are many basic similarities in the bones supporting these two structures. Thus, homologous structures are one of the best sources of information for phylogenetic relationships. The greater the number of homologous structures between two species, the more closely the species are related.

There are pitfalls in the search for homology: Not all likeness is inherited from a common ancestor. Species from different evolutionary branches may have certain structures that are superficially similar if natural selection has shaped analogous adaptations. This is called **convergent evolution**. Similarity due to convergence is called **analogy**, not homology. For example, the wings of insects and those of birds are analogous flight equipment: They evolved independently and are built from entirely different structures.

▼ **Figure 22 The relationship of classification and phylogeny for some members of the order Carnivora.** The hierarchical classification is reflected in the finer and finer branching of the phylogenetic tree. Each branch point in the tree represents an ancestor common to species to the right of that branch point.

▲ **Figure 23** **Artist's reconstruction of Neanderthal.** DNA extracted from Neanderthals, extinct members of the human family, has allowed scientists to study their evolutionary relationship with modern humans.

Comparing the embryonic development of two species can often reveal homology that is not apparent in the mature structures. There is another clue to distinguishing homology from analogy: The more complex two similar structures are, the less likely it is they evolved independently. For example, compare the skulls of a human and a chimpanzee. Although each is a fusion of many bones, they match almost perfectly, bone for bone. It is highly improbable that such complex structures matching in so many details could have separate origins. Most likely, the genes required to build these skulls were inherited from a common ancestor.

If homology reflects common ancestry, then comparing the DNA sequences of organisms gets to the heart of their evolutionary relationships. The more recently two species have branched from a common ancestor, the more similar their DNA sequences should be. Scientists have sequenced well over 150 billion bases of DNA from thousands of species. This enormous database has fueled a boom in the study of phylogeny and clarified many evolutionary relationships. In addition, some fossils are preserved in such a way that DNA fragments can be extracted for comparison with living organisms **(Figure 23)**. ☑

Inferring Phylogeny from Homologous Characters

Once homologous characters—characters that reflect an evolutionary relationship—have been identified

for a group of organisms, how are these characters used to construct phylogenies? The most widely used approach is called cladistics. In **cladistics**, organisms are grouped by common ancestry. A **clade** (from the Greek word for "branch") consists of an ancestral species and all its evolutionary descendants—a distinct branch in the tree of life. Thus, identifying clades makes it possible to construct classification schemes that reflect the branching pattern of evolution.

Cladistics is based on the Darwinian concept of "descent with modification from a common ancestor"—species have some characters in common with their ancestors, but they also differ from them. To identify clades, scientists compare an ingroup with an outgroup **(Figure 24)**. The ingroup (for example, the three mammals in Figure 24) is the group of species that is actually being analyzed. The outgroup (in Figure 24, the iguana, representing reptiles) is a species or group of species known to have diverged before the lineage that contains the groups being studied. By comparing members of the ingroup with each other and with the outgroup, we can determine what characters distinguish the ingroup from the outgroup. All the mammals in the ingroup have hair and mammary glands. These characters were present in the ancestral mammal, but not in the outgroup. Next, gestation, the carrying of offspring in the uterus within the female parent, is absent from the duck-billed platypus (which lays eggs with a shell). From this absence we might infer that the duck-billed platypus represents an early branch point in the mammalian clade. Proceeding in this manner, we can construct a phylogenetic tree. Each branch represents the divergence of two groups from a

Piecing together evolutionary histories shows who's related to whom.

☑ **CHECKPOINT**
Our forearms and a bat's wings are derived from the same ancestral prototype; thus, they are _____. In contrast, the wings of a bat and the wings of a bee are derived from totally unrelated structures; thus, they are _____.

Answer: homologous; analogous

▼ **Figure 24** **A simplified example of cladistics.**

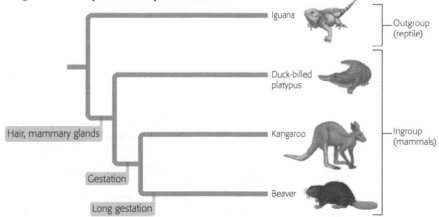

common ancestor, with the emergence of a lineage possessing one or more new features. The sequence of branching represents the order in which they evolved and when groups last shared a common ancestor. In other words, cladistics focuses on the changes that define the branch points in evolution.

The cladistics approach to phylogeny clarifies evolutionary relationships that were not always apparent in other taxonomic classifications. For instance, biologists traditionally placed birds and reptiles in separate classes of vertebrates (class Aves and class Reptilia, respectively). This classification, however, is inconsistent with cladistics. An inventory of homologies indicates that birds and crocodiles make up one clade, and lizards and snakes form another. If we go back as far as the ancestor that crocodiles share with lizards and snakes to make up a clade, then the class Reptilia must also include birds. The tree in **Figure 25** is thus more consistent with cladistics than with traditional classifications. ☑

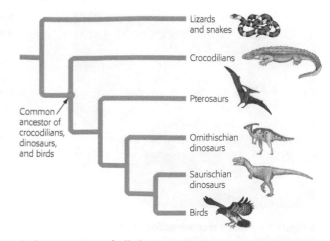

▲ **Figure 25 How cladistics is shaking phylogenetic trees.** Strict application of cladistics sometimes produces phylogenetic trees that conflict with classical taxonomy.

Classification: A Work in Progress

Phylogenetic trees are hypotheses about evolutionary history. Like all hypotheses, they are revised (or in some cases rejected) based on new evidence. Molecular systematics and cladistics are combining to remodel phylogenetic trees and challenge traditional classifications.

Linnaeus divided all known forms of life between the plant and animal kingdoms, and the two-kingdom system prevailed in biology for over 200 years. In the mid-1900s, the two-kingdom system was replaced by a five-kingdom system that placed all prokaryotes in one kingdom and divided the eukaryotes among four other kingdoms.

In the late 20th century, molecular studies and cladistics led to the development of a **three-domain system (Figure 26)**. This current scheme recognizes three basic groups: two domains of prokaryotes—Bacteria and Archaea—and one domain of eukaryotes, called Eukarya. The domains Bacteria and Archaea differ in a number of important structural, biochemical, and functional features.

The domain Eukarya is currently divided into kingdoms, but the exact number of kingdoms is still under debate. Biologists generally agree on

the kingdoms Plantae, Fungi, and Animalia. These kingdoms consist of multicellular eukaryotes that differ in structure, development, and modes of nutrition. Plants make their own food by photosynthesis. Fungi live by decomposing the remains of other

► **Figure 26 The three-domain classification system.** Molecular and cellular evidence supports the phylogenetic hypothesis that two lineages of prokaryotes, the domains Bacteria and Archaea, diverged very early in the history of life. Molecular evidence also suggests that domain Archaea is more closely related to domain Eukarya than to domain Bacteria.

organisms and absorbing small organic molecules. Most animals live by ingesting food and digesting it within their bodies.

The remaining eukaryotes, the protists, include all those eukaryotes that do not fit the definition of plant, fungus, or animal   effectively, a taxonomic grab bag. Most protists are unicellular (amoebas, for example). But the protists also include certain large, multicellular organisms that are believed to be direct descendants of unicellular protists. For example, many biologists classify the seaweeds as protists because they are more closely related to some single-celled algae than they are to true plants.

It is important to understand that classifying Earth's diverse species is a work in progress as we learn more about organisms and their evolution. Charles Darwin envisioned the goals of modern systematics when he wrote in *The Origin of Species*, "Our classifications will come to be, as far as they can be so made, genealogies." ☑

☑ **CHECKPOINT**

What lines of evidence caused biologists to develop the three-domain system of classification?

Answer: molecular studies and cladistics

 Mass Extinctions EVOLUTION CONNECTION

Rise of the Mammals

In this chapter, you've read about mass extinctions and their effects on the evolution of life on Earth. In the fossil record, each mass extinction was followed by a period of evolutionary change. Many new species arose as survivors became adapted to occupy new habitats or fill community roles vacated by extinctions.

For example, fossil evidence indicates that the number of mammal species increased dramatically after the extinction of most of the dinosaurs around 65 million years ago **(Figure 27)**. Although mammals originated 180 million years ago, fossils older than 65 million years indicate that they were mostly small and not very diverse. Early mammals may have been eaten or outcompeted by the larger and more diverse dinosaurs. With the disappearance of most of the dinosaurs, mammals expanded greatly in both diversity and size, filling the ecological roles once occupied by dinosaurs. Had it not been for the dinosaur extinction, mammals may never have expanded their territories and become the predominant land animals. Therefore, we humans may owe our existence to the demise of older species. Through the process of evolution by natural selection, this pattern of death and renewal is repeated throughout the history of life on Earth.

▼ **Figure 27 The increase in mammalian species after the extinction of dinosaurs.** Although mammals originated more than 150 million years ago, they did not begin to widely diverge until after the demise of the dinosaurs.

American black bear

Chapter Review

SUMMARY OF KEY CONCEPTS

The Origin of Species

What Is a Species?

The diversity of life evolved through speciation, the process in which one species splits into two or more species. According to the biological species concept, a species is a group of populations whose members have the potential to interbreed in nature to produce fertile offspring. The biological species concept is just one of several possible ways to define species.

Reproductive Barriers between Species

Evolution: Mechanisms of Speciation

When the gene pool of a population is severed from other gene pools of the parent species, the splinter population can follow its own evolutionary course.

Hybridization leading to polyploids is a common mechanism of sympatric speciation in plants.

Earth History and Macroevolution

Macroevolution refers to evolutionary change above the species level, for example, the origin of evolutionary novelty and new groups of species and the impact of mass extinctions on the diversity of life and its subsequent recovery.

The Fossil Record

Geologists have established a geologic time scale with four broad divisions: Precambrian, Paleozoic, Mesozoic, and Cenozoic. The most common method for determining the ages of fossils is radiometric dating.

Plate Tectonics and Biogeography

Earth's crust is divided into large, irregularly shaped plates that float atop the viscous mantle. About 250 million years ago, plate movements brought all the landmasses together into the supercontinent Pangaea, causing extinctions and providing new opportunities for the survivors to diversify. About 180 million years ago, Pangaea began to break up, causing geographic isolation. Continental drift accounts for patterns of biogeography, such as the diversity of unique marsupials in Australia.

Mass Extinctions and Explosive Diversifications of Life

The fossil record reveals long, relatively stable periods punctuated by mass extinctions followed in turn by explosive diversification of certain survivors. For example, during the Cretaceous extinctions, about 65 million years ago, the world lost an enormous number of species, including most of the dinosaurs. Mammals greatly increased in diversity after the Cretaceous period.

Mechanisms of Macroevolution

Large Effects from Small Genetic Changes

A subtle change in the genes that control a species' development can have profound effects. In paedomorphosis, for example, the adult retains body features that were strictly juvenile in ancestral species.

The Evolution of Biological Novelty

An exaptation is a structure that evolves in one context and gradually becomes adapted for other functions. Most complex structures have evolved incrementally from simpler versions having the same function.

Classifying the Diversity of Life

Systematics, which includes taxonomy, focuses on classifying organisms and determining their evolutionary relationships.

Classification and Phylogeny

The goal of classification is to reflect phylogeny, the evolutionary history of species. Classification is based on the fossil record, homologous structures, and comparisons of DNA sequences. Homology (similarity based on shared ancestry) must be distinguished from analogy (similarity based on convergent evolution). Cladistics uses shared characters to group related organisms into clades—distinctive branches in the tree of life.

Classification: A Work in Progress

Biologists currently classify life into a three-domain system: Bacteria, Archaea, and Eukarya.

MasteringBiology®

For practice quizzes, BioFlix animations, MP3 tutorials, video tutors, and more study tools designed for this text, go to MasteringBiology®

SELF-QUIZ

1. Distinguish between microevolution, speciation, and macroevolution.

2. Bird guides once listed the myrtle warbler and Audubon's warbler as distinct species that lived side by side in parts of their ranges. However, recent books describe them as the eastern and western forms of a single species, the yellow-rumped warbler. Apparently, the two kinds of warblers
   a. live in the same areas.
   b. successfully interbreed.
   c. are almost identical in appearance.
   d. are merging to form a single species.

3. Identify each of the following reproductive barriers as prezygotic or postzygotic.
   a. One lilac species lives on acidic soil, another on basic soil.
   b. Mallard and pintail ducks mate at different times of the year.
   c. Two species of leopard frogs have different mating calls.
   d. Hybrid offspring of two species of jimsonweed always die before reproducing.
   e. Pollen of one kind of pine tree cannot fertilize another kind.

4. Why is a small, isolated population more likely to undergo speciation than a large one?

5. Many species of plants and animals adapted to desert conditions probably did not arise there. Their success in living in deserts could be due to _____, structures that originally had one use but became adapted for different functions.

6. Mass extinctions
   a. cut the number of species to the few survivors left today.
   b. resulted mainly from the separation of the continents.
   c. occurred regularly, about every million years.
   d. were followed by diversification of the survivors.

7. The animals and plants of India are almost completely different from the species in nearby Southeast Asia. Why might this be true?
   a. They have become separated by convergent evolution.
   b. The climates of the two regions are completely different.
   c. India is in the process of separating from the rest of Asia.
   d. India was a separate continent until relatively recently.

8. A paleontologist estimates that when a particular rock formed, it contained 12 mg of the radioactive isotope potassium-40. The rock now contains 3 mg of potassium-40. The half-life of potassium-40 is 1.3 billion years. From this information, you can conclude that the rock is approximately _____ billion years old.

9. Why are biologists careful to distinguish similarities due to homology from similarities due to analogy when constructing phylogenetic trees?

10. In the three-domain system, which two domains contain prokaryotic organisms?

THE PROCESS OF SCIENCE

11. Imagine you are conducting fieldwork and discover two groups of mice living on opposite sides of a river. Assuming that you will not disturb the mice, design a study to determine whether these two groups belong to the same species. If you could capture some of the mice and bring them to the lab, how might that affect your experimental design?

12. **Interpreting Data** The carbon-14/carbon-12 ratio of a fossilized skull is about 6.25% that of the skull of a present-day animal. Using the graph below, what is the approximate age of the fossil?

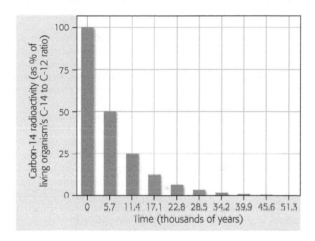

BIOLOGY AND SOCIETY

13. Most biologists are alarmed at the current rate of species extinction. What are some reasons for their concern? Considering that life has endured numerous mass extinctions and has always bounced back, how would this sixth mass extinction be different? What might be some consequences for the surviving species?

14. The red wolf (*Canis rufus*) was once widespread in the southeastern United States but was declared to be extinct in the wild. Biologists bred captive red wolf individuals and reintroduced them into areas of eastern North Carolina, where they are federally protected as endangered species. The current wild population is estimated to be about 100 individuals. However, a new threat to red wolves has arisen: hybridization with coyotes (*Canis latrans*), which have become more numerous in the areas inhabited by red wolves. Although red wolves and coyotes differ in morphology and DNA, they are capable of interbreeding and producing fertile offspring. Social behavior is the main reproductive barrier between the species and is more easily overcome when same-species mates are rare. For this reason, some people think that the endangered status of the red wolf should be withdrawn and resources should not be spent to protect what is not a "pure" species. Do you agree? Why or why not?

Glossary

allopatric speciation
The formation of a new species in populations that are geographically isolated from one another. *See also* sympatric speciation.

analogy
The similarity between two species that is due to convergent evolution rather than to descent from a common ancestor with the same trait.

biogeography
The study of the past and present distribution of organisms.

biological species concept
The definition of a species as a population or group of populations whose members have the potential in nature to interbreed and produce fertile offspring.

clade
An ancestral species and all its descendants—a distinctive branch in the tree of life.

cladistics (*kluh-dis'-tiks*)
The study of evolutionary history; specifically, an approach to systematics in which organisms are grouped by common ancestry.

convergent evolution
The evolution of similar features in different evolutionary lineages, which can result from living in very similar environments.

evo-devo
Evolutionary developmental biology, which studies the evolution of developmental processes in multicellular organisms.

geologic time scale
A time scale established by geologists that reflects a consistent sequence of geologic periods, grouped into four divisions: Precambrian, Paleozoic, Mesozoic, and Cenozoic.

macroevolution
Evolutionary change above the species level. Examples of macroevolutionary change include the origin of a new group of organisms through a series of speciation events and the impact of mass extinctions on the diversity of life and its subsequent recovery.

paedomorphosis (*pē'-duh-mōr'-fuh-sis*)
The retention in the adult of features that were juvenile in ancestral species.

phylogenetic tree (*fī'-lō-juh-net'-ik*)
A branching diagram that represents a hypothesis about evolutionary relationships between organisms.

plate tectonics (*tek-tahn'-iks*)
The theory that the continents are part of great plates of Earth's crust that float on the hot, underlying portion of the mantle. Movements in the mantle cause the continents to move slowly over time.

polyploidy
Having more than two complete sets of chromosomes as a result of an accident of cell division.

postzygotic barrier (*pōst'-zī-got'-ik*)
A reproductive barrier that operates if interspecies mating occurs and forms hybrid zygotes.

prezygotic barrier (*prē'-zī-got'-ik*)
A reproductive barrier that impedes mating between species or hinders fertilization of eggs if members of different species attempt to mate.

radiometric dating
A method for determining the age of fossils and rocks from the ratio of a radioactive isotope to the nonradioactive isotope(s) of the same element in the sample.

speciation (*spē'-sē-ā'-shun*)
An evolutionary process in which one species splits into two or more species.

sympatric speciation
The formation of a new species in populations that live in the same geographic area. *See also* allopatric speciation.

systematics
A discipline of biology that focuses on classifying organisms and determining their evolutionary relationships.

three-domain system
A system of taxonomic classification based on three basic groups: Bacteria, Archaea, and Eukarya.

Credits

Self-Quiz Answers

1. Microevolution is a change in the gene pool of a population, often associated with adaptation. Speciation is an evolutionary process in which one species splits into two or more species. Macroevolution is evolutionary change above the species level, for example, the origin of evolutionary novelty and new taxonomic groups and the impact of mass extinctions on the diversity of life and its subsequent recovery. Macroevolution is marked by major changes in the history of life, and these changes are often noticeable enough to be evident in the fossil record.

2. b

3. prezygotic: a, b, c, e; postzygotic: d

4. because a small gene pool is more likely to be changed substantially by genetic drift and natural selection

5. exaptations

6. d

7. d

8. 2.6

9. Homologies reflected a shared evolutionary history, while analogies do not. Analogies result from convergent evolution.

10. Archaea and Bacteria

The Evolution of Microbial Life

From Chapter 15 of *Campbell Essential Biology with Physiology*, Fifth Edition. Eric J. Simon, Jean L. Dickey, Kelly A. Hogan, Jane B. Reece. Copyright © 2016 by Pearson Education, Inc. All rights reserved.

The Evolution of Microbial Life

Why Microorganisms Matter

If your family took a vacation in which you traveled 1 mile for every million years in the history of life, you'd still be asking, "Are we there yet?" after driving from Miami to Seattle.

According to a ▶ recent study, infection by the parasite *Toxoplasma* makes mice lose their fear of cats.

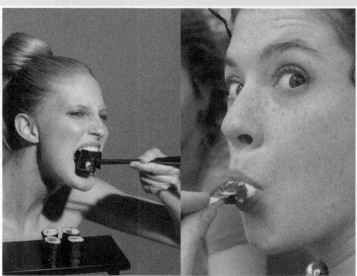

▲ Seaweeds aren't just used for wrapping sushi—they're in your ice cream, too.

▲ You have microorganisms to thank for the clean water you drink every day.

Human Microbiota BIOLOGY AND SOCIETY

Our Invisible Inhabitants

You probably know that your body contains trillions of individual cells, but did you know that they aren't all "you"? In fact, microorganisms residing in and on your body outnumber your own cells by 10 to 1. That means 100 trillion bacteria, archaea, and protists call your body home. Your skin, mouth, and nasal passages and your digestive and urogenital tracts are prime real estate for these microorganisms. Although each individual is so tiny that it would have to be magnified hundreds of times for you to see it, the weight of your microbial residents totals two to five pounds.

We acquire our microbial communities during the first two years of life, and they remain fairly stable thereafter. However, modern life is taking a toll on that stability. We alter the balance of these communities by taking antibiotics, purifying our water, sterilizing our food, attempting to germproof our surroundings, and scrubbing our skin and teeth. Scientists hypothesize that disrupting our microbial communities may increase our susceptibility to infectious diseases, predispose us to certain cancers, and contribute to conditions such as asthma and other allergies, irritable bowel syndrome, Crohn's disease, and autism. Researchers are even investigating whether having the wrong microbial community could make us fat. In addition, scientists are studying

Colorized scanning electron micrograph of bacteria on a human tongue (14,500×).

how our microbial communities have evolved over the course of human history. As you'll discover in the Evolution Connection section at the end of this chapter, for example, dietary changes invited decay-causing bacteria to make themselves at home on our teeth.

Throughout this chapter, you will learn about the benefits and drawbacks of human-microbe interactions. You will also sample a bit of the remarkable diversity of prokaryotes and protists. We begin with the prokaryotes, Earth's first life-form, and the protists, the bridge between unicellular eukaryotes and multicellular plants, fungi, and animals.

Major Episodes in the History of Life

To put our survey of diversity into perspective, let's look at a brief overview of major events in the history of life on Earth. Our planet's history began 4.6 billion years ago, a time span that is difficult to grasp. To visualize this immense scale, imagine taking a road trip across North America in which each mile traveled is the equivalent of passing through 1 million years. Our journey will take us from Kamloops, British Columbia, in Canada, to the finish line of the Boston Marathon in Boston, Massachusetts, on a route that covers 4,600 miles **(Figure 1)**.

Setting out from Kamloops, we head southwest to Seattle, Washington, and then south toward San Francisco,

California. By the time we reach the California border, nearly 750 million years have passed, and the first rocks have formed on Earth's cooling surface.

Our arrival at the Golden Gate Bridge coincides with the appearance of the first cells in the fossil record. After 1,100 million years, life on Earth has begun! Those earliest organisms were all **prokaryotes**, having cells that lack true nuclei. You'll learn more about the origin of these first cells in the next section.

Conditions on the young Earth were very different from conditions today. One difference that was critical to the origin and

► Figure 1 **Some major episodes in the history of life.** On this 4,600-mile metaphorical road trip, each mile equals 1 million years in Earth's history.

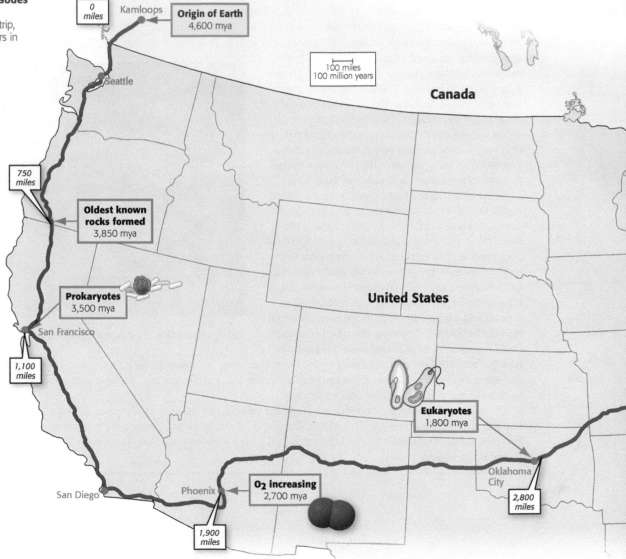

0 miles Kamloops	**Origin of Earth** 4,600 mya
	100 miles 100 million years
	Canada
Seattle	
750 miles	**Oldest known rocks formed** 3,850 mya
	Prokaryotes 3,500 mya
San Francisco	
1,100 miles	**United States**
	Eukaryotes 1,800 mya
San Diego	Oklahoma City
Phoenix	**O₂ increasing** 2,700 mya
1,900 miles	*2,800 miles*

evolution of life was the lack of atmospheric O_2. As we continue driving south on our metaphoric journey, diverse metabolic pathways are evolving among the prokaryotes. However, we won't reach our next milestone for another 800 million years. By that time we have passed through San Diego and turned east across the desert. At Phoenix, Arizona, Earth is 2,700 million years old, and atmospheric O_2 has begun to increase as a result of photosynthesis by autotrophic prokaryotes.

Nine hundred million years later, just past Oklahoma City, we find the first fossils of eukaryotic organisms. **Eukaryotes** are composed of one or more cells that contain nuclei and many other membrane-bound organelles absent in prokaryotic cells. Eukaryotic cells evolved from ancestral host cells that engulfed smaller prokaryotes. The mitochondria of our cells and those of every other eukaryote are descendants of those prokaryotes, as are the chloroplasts of plants and algae.

Prokaryotes had been on Earth for 1.7 billion years before eukaryotes evolved. The appearance of these more complex cells, however, launched a period of tremendous diversification of eukaryotic forms. These new organisms were the protists. Protists are mostly microscopic and unicellular, and as you will learn in this chapter, they are represented today by a great diversity of species.

The next great event in the evolution of life was multicellularity. The oldest fossils that are clearly multicellular are 1.2 billion years old, or about midway between St. Louis, Missouri, and Terre Haute, Indiana, on our road trip. The organisms that left these fossils were tiny and not at all complex.

It isn't until 600 million years later (roughly 600 million years ago) that large, diverse, multicellular organisms appeared in the fossil record. At this point, we have traveled 4,000 miles—4 billion years—and now find ourselves in Erie, near the western edge of Pennsylvania (coincidentally, where one of the authors was born). Less than 15% of our journey remains, and we still have not encountered much diversity. But that's about to change. A great diversification of animals, the so-called Cambrian explosion, marked the beginning of the Paleozoic era, about 542 million years ago. By the end of that period, all the major animal body plans, as well as all the major groups, had evolved.

The colonization of land by plants, fungi, and insects also occurred during the Paleozoic. This evolutionary transition began about 500 million years ago, a time that, in our road trip, corresponds to reaching Buffalo, New York.

By the time we get to Albany, New York, we're in the middle of the Mesozoic era, sometimes called the age of dinosaurs. At the end of the Mesozoic, 65 million years ago, we find ourselves about halfway across the state of Massachusetts. As we draw closer to Boston, more and more familiar organisms begin to dominate the landscape—flowering plants, birds, and mammals, including primates.

Modern humans, *Homo sapiens*, appeared roughly 195,000 years ago. At that point, we are less than two blocks shy of the finish line of our journey from the origin of Earth to the present day. Thus, spans of time that seem lengthy in the context of our own lives are brief moments in the history of life on Earth.

Colonization of land
500 mya

Mid-Mesozoic
180 mya

Homo sapiens
0.195 mya

Boston

Albany

4,600 miles

Buffalo

Large, complex multicellular organisms
600 mya

Erie

4,000 miles

Oldest multicellular fossils
1,200 mya

Terre Haute

St Louis

3,400 miles

If your family took a vacation in which you traveled 1 mile for every million years in the history of life, you'd still be asking, "Are we there yet?" after driving from Miami to Seattle.

The Origin of Life

Looking at the abundant diversity of life around us, it is difficult to imagine that Earth was not always like this. But early in its 4.6-billion-year history, our planet had no oceans, no lakes, very little oxygen, and no life at all. It was bombarded by debris left over from the formation of the solar system—gigantic chunks of rock and ice whose impact with Earth generated heat so fierce that it vaporized all available water. Indeed, for the first several hundred million years of its existence, conditions on the young Earth were so harsh that it's doubtful life could have originated; if it did, it could not have survived.

Although conditions had become considerably calmer, the Earth of 4 billion years ago was still in violent turmoil. Water vapor had condensed into oceans on the planet's cooling surface, but volcanic eruptions belched gases such as carbon dioxide, methane, and ammonia and other nitrogen compounds into its atmosphere (**Figure 2**). Although lack of atmospheric O_2 would be deadly to most of Earth's present-day inhabitants, this environment made the origin of life possible—O_2 is a corrosive agent that tends to disrupt chemical bonds and would have prevented the formation of complex molecules.

Life is an emergent property that arises from the specific arrangement and interactions of its molecular parts. To learn how life originated from nonliving substances, biologists draw on research from the fields of chemistry,

geology, and physics. In the next sections, we'll look at the attributes that must have arisen during the origin of life. Scientists agree on these properties, but which of several plausible scenarios led to them is still the subject of vigorous debate. ☑

A Four-Stage Hypothesis for the Origin of Life

According to one hypothesis for the origin of life, the first organisms were products of chemical evolution in four stages: (1) the synthesis of small organic molecules, such as amino acids and nucleotide monomers; (2) the joining of these small molecules into macromolecules, including proteins and nucleic acids; (3) the packaging of all these molecules into pre-cells, droplets with membranes that maintained an internal chemistry different from the surroundings; and (4) the origin of self-replicating molecules that eventually made inheritance possible. Although we'll never know for sure how life on Earth began, this hypothesis leads to predictions that can be tested in the laboratory. Let's look at some of the observations and experimental evidence for each of these four stages.

Stage 1: Synthesis of Organic Compounds

The chemicals mentioned above that formed Earth's early atmosphere, such as water (H_2O), methane (CH_4), and ammonia (NH_3), are all small, inorganic molecules. In contrast, the structures and functions of life depend on more complex organic molecules, such as sugars, fatty acids, amino acids, and nucleotides, which are composed of the same elements. Could these complex molecules have arisen from the ingredients available?

This stage was the first to be extensively studied in the laboratory. In 1953, Stanley Miller, a graduate student of Nobel laureate Harold Urey, performed a now-classic experiment. He devised an apparatus to simulate conditions thought to prevail on early Earth (**Figure 3**, facing page). A flask of warmed water simulated the primordial sea. An "atmosphere"—in the form of gases added to a reaction chamber—contained hydrogen gas, methane, ammonia, and water vapor. To mimic the prevalent lightning of the early Earth, electrical sparks were discharged into the chamber. A condenser cooled the atmosphere, causing water and any dissolved compounds to "rain" into the miniature "sea."

The results of the Miller-Urey experiments were front-page news. After the apparatus had run for a

☑ **CHECKPOINT**

One reason why the spontaneous generation of life on Earth could not occur today is the abundance of _____ in our modern atmosphere.

Answer: oxygen (O_2)

▼ Figure 2 **An artist's rendition of conditions on early Earth.**

▲ Figure 3 Apparatus used to simulate early-Earth chemistry in Urey and Miller's experiments.

of amino acids, some in large amounts. Recent studies have shown that this meteorite also contains other key organic molecules, including lipids, simple sugars, and nitrogenous bases such as uracil.

Stage 2: Abiotic Synthesis of Polymers

Once small organic molecules were present on Earth, how were they linked together to form polymers such as proteins and nucleic acids without the help of enzymes and other cellular equipment? Researchers have brought about such polymerization in the laboratory by dripping solutions of organic monomers onto hot sand, clay, or rock. The heat vaporizes the water in the solutions and concentrates the monomers on the underlying material. Some of the monomers then spontaneously bond together to form polymers. On the early Earth, raindrops or waves may have splashed dilute solutions of organic monomers onto fresh lava or other hot rocks and then washed polypeptides and other polymers back into the sea. There they could accumulate in great quantities (since no life existed to consume them). ☑

Stage 3: Formation of Pre-Cells

The cell membrane forms a boundary that separates a living cell and its functions from the external environment. A key step in the origin of life would have been the isolation of a collection of organic molecules within a membrane. We'll call these molecular aggregates pre-cells—not really cells, but molecular packages with some of the properties of life. Within a confined space, certain combinations of molecules could be concentrated and interact more efficiently.

Researchers have demonstrated that pre-cells could have formed spontaneously from fatty acids. The presence of a specific type of clay thought to be common on early Earth greatly speeds up the rate of spontaneous pre-cell formation. Unlike the plasma membranes of today's cells, these rudimentary membranes were quite porous, allowing organic monomers such as RNA nucleotides and amino acids to cross freely. However, polymers that formed inside the pre-cells were too large to exit. In addition to physically corralling molecules into a fluid-filled space, these pre-cells may have had certain properties of life. They may have had the ability to use chemical energy and grow. Most intriguingly, pre-cells made in laboratory experiments can divide to produce new pre-cells—a simple form of reproduction.

Stage 4: Origin of Self-Replicating Molecules

Life is defined partly by the process of inheritance, which is based on self-replicating molecules. Today's cells store their genetic information as DNA. They transcribe the information into RNA and then translate

☑ **CHECKPOINT**

What is the name of the chemical reaction whereby monomers are linked together into polymers?

Answer: dehydration reaction

week, an abundance of organic molecules essential for life, including amino acids, the monomers of proteins, had collected in the "sea." Many laboratories have since repeated Miller's experiment using various atmospheric mixtures and have also produced organic compounds. In 2008, one of Miller's former graduate students discovered some samples from an experiment that Miller had designed with a different atmosphere, one that would mimic volcanic conditions. Reanalyzing these samples using modern equipment, he identified additional organic compounds that had been synthesized. Indeed, 22 amino acids had been produced under Miller's simulated volcanic conditions, compared with the 11 produced with the atmosphere in his original 1953 experiment.

Scientists are also testing other hypotheses for the origin of organic molecules on Earth. Some researchers are exploring the hypothesis that life may have begun in submerged volcanoes or deep-sea hydrothermal vents, gaps in Earth's crust where hot water and minerals gush into deep oceans. These environments, among the most extreme environments in which life exists today, could have provided the initial chemical resources for life.

Another intriguing hypothesis proposes that meteorites were the source of Earth's first organic molecules. Fragments of a 4.5-billion-year-old meteorite that fell to Earth in Australia in 1969 contain more than 80 types

RNA messages into specific enzymes and other proteins. This mechanism of information flow probably emerged gradually through a series of small changes to much simpler processes.

What were the first genes like? One hypothesis is that they were short strands of RNA that replicated without the assistance of proteins. In laboratory experiments, short RNA molecules can assemble spontaneously from nucleotide monomers in the absence of enzymes (Figure 4). The result is a population of RNA molecules, each with a random sequence of monomers. Some of the molecules self-replicate, but their success at this reproduction varies. What happens can be described as molecular evolution: The RNA varieties that replicate fastest increase their frequency in the population.

In addition to the experimental evidence, there is another reason the idea of RNA genes in the primordial world is plausible. Cells actually have RNAs that can act as enzymes; they are called ribozymes. Perhaps early ribozymes catalyzed their own replication. That would help with the "chicken and egg" paradox of which came first, enzymes or genes. Maybe the "chicken and egg" came together in the same RNA molecules. The molecular biology of today may have been preceded by an ancient "RNA world."

The pre-cells described above could assemble spontaneously, reproduce, and grow. These abilities, however, would only result in endless copies of the original pre-cell. So how did cells acquire the ability to evolve? We consider this question next. ☑

From Chemical Evolution to Darwinian Evolution

Recall how present-day organisms evolve by natural selection. Genetic variation arises by mutations, errors that change the nucleotide sequence of the DNA. Some variations increase an organism's chance of reproductive success and are thus perpetuated in subsequent generations. In the same way, natural selection would have begun to shape the properties of pre-cells that contained self-replicating RNA. Those that contained genetic information that helped them grow and reproduce more efficiently than others would have increased in number, passing their abilities on to later generations. Mutations would have resulted in additional variation on which natural selection could work, and the most successful of these pre-cells would have continued to evolve. Of course, the gap between such pre-cells and even the simplest of modern cells is enormous. But with millions of years of incremental changes through natural selection, these molecular cooperatives could have become more and more cell-like. At some point during this time, pre-cells passed a fuzzy border to become true cells. The stage was then set for the evolution of diverse life-forms, changes that we see documented in the fossil record.

☑ **CHECKPOINT**

What are ribozymes? Why are they a logical step in the formation of life?

Answer: A ribozyme is an RNA molecule that functions as an enzyme. Ribozymes can perform some of the functions of both DNA and protein.

▼ Figure 4 **Self-replication of RNA "genes."**

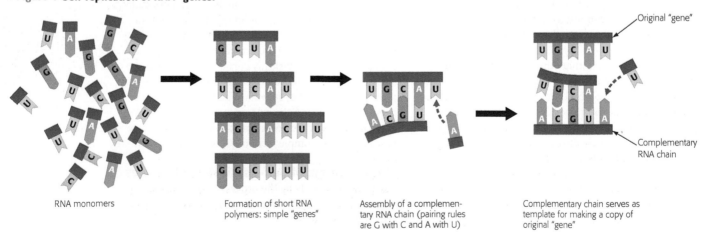

RNA monomers

Formation of short RNA polymers: simple "genes"

Assembly of a complementary RNA chain (pairing rules are G with C and A with U)

Complementary chain serves as template for making a copy of original "gene"

Prokaryotes

The history of prokaryotic life is a success story spanning billions of years. Prokaryotes lived and evolved all alone on Earth for about 2 billion years. They have continued to adapt and flourish on a changing Earth and in turn have helped to modify the planet. In this section, you will learn about prokaryotic structure and function, diversity, relationships, and ecological significance.

They're Everywhere!

Today, prokaryotes are found wherever there is life, including in and on the bodies of multicellular organisms. The collective biological mass (biomass) of prokaryotes is at least ten times that of all eukaryotes. Prokaryotes also thrive in habitats too cold, too hot, too salty, too acidic, or too alkaline for any eukaryote (Figure 5). Scientists are just beginning to investigate the extensive prokaryotic diversity in the oceans. Biologists have even discovered prokaryotes living on the walls of a gold mine 3.3 km (2 miles) below Earth's surface.

Though individual prokaryotes are small organisms (Figure 6), they are giants in their collective impact on Earth and its life. We hear most about the relatively few species that cause illness. Bacterial infections are responsible for about half of all human diseases, including tuberculosis, cholera, many sexually transmitted infections, and certain types of food poisoning. However, prokaryotic life is much more than just a rogues' gallery. The Biology and Society section introduced our **microbiota**, the community of microorganisms that live in and on our bodies. Each of us harbors several hundred different species and genetic strains of prokaryotes, including a few whose positive effects are well studied. For example, some of our intestinal inhabitants supply essential vitamins and enable us to extract nutrition from food molecules that we can't otherwise digest. Many of the bacteria that live on our skin perform helpful housekeeping functions such as decomposing dead skin cells. Prokaryotes also guard the body against disease-causing intruders.

It would be hard to overstate the importance of prokaryotes to the health of the environment. Prokaryotes living in the soil and at the bottom of lakes, rivers, and oceans help to decompose dead organisms and other

◄ **Figure 5 A window to early life?** An instrument on a research submarine samples the water around a hydrothermal vent more than 1.5 km (about a mile) below the ocean's surface. Prokaryotes that live near the vent use the emitted gases as an energy source. This environment, which is very dark, hot, and under high pressure, is among the most extreme in which life is known to exist.

► **Figure 6 Bacteria on the point of a pin.** The orange rods are individual bacteria, each about 5 μm long, on the point of a pin. Besides highlighting their tiny size, this micrograph will help you understand why a pin prick can cause infection.

Colorized SEM 605x

waste materials, returning vital chemical elements such as nitrogen to the environment. If prokaryotes were to disappear, the chemical cycles that sustain life would come to a halt, and all forms of eukaryotic life would also be doomed. In contrast, prokaryotic life would undoubtedly persist in the absence of eukaryotes, as it once did for 2 billion years.

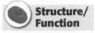 **Structure/Function**

Prokaryotes

Prokaryotes have a cellular organization fundamentally different from that of eukaryotes. Whereas eukaryotic cells have a membrane-enclosed nucleus and numerous other membrane-enclosed organelles, prokaryotic cells lack these structural features. And nearly all species of prokaryotes have cell walls exterior to their plasma membranes. Despite the simplicity of the cell structures, though, prokaryotes display a remarkable range of diversity. In this section, you'll learn about aspects of their form, reproduction, and nutrition that help these organisms survive in their environments.

Prokaryotic Forms

Determining cell shape by microscopic examination is an important step in identifying a prokaryote. The micrographs in **Figure 7** show the three most common shapes. Spherical prokaryotic cells are called **cocci** (singular, *coccus*). Rod-shaped prokaryotes are called **bacilli** (singular, *bacillus*). Spiral-shaped prokaryotes include spirochetes, different species of which cause syphilis and Lyme disease.

Although all prokaryotes are unicellular, the cells of some species usually exist as groups of two or more cells. For example, cocci that occur in clusters are called staphylococci. Other cocci, including the bacterium that causes strep throat, occur in chains; they are called streptococci. Some prokaryotes grow branching chains of cells **(Figure 8a)**. And some species even exhibit a simple division of labor among specialized types of cells **(Figure 8b)**. Among unicellular species, moreover, there are some giants that actually dwarf most eukaryotic cells **(Figure 8c)**.

▼ **Figure 8 A diversity of prokaryotic shapes and sizes.**

(a) Actinomycete. An actinomycete is a mass of branching chains of rod-shaped cells. These bacteria are common in soil, where they secrete antibiotics that inhibit the growth of other bacteria. Various antibiotic drugs, such as streptomycin, are obtained from actinomycetes.

(b) Cyanobacteria. These photosynthetic cyanobacteria exhibit division of labor. The box highlights a cell that converts atmospheric nitrogen to ammonia, which can then be incorporated into amino acids and other organic compounds.

(c) Giant bacterium. The larger white blob in this photo is the marine bacterium *Thiomargarita namibiensis*. This prokaryotic cell is more than 0.5 mm in diameter, about the size of the fruit fly's head below it.

▼ **Figure 7 Three common shapes of prokaryotic cells.**

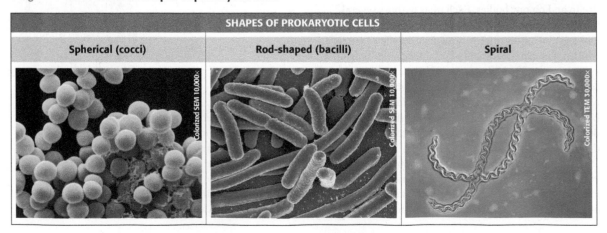

SHAPES OF PROKARYOTIC CELLS

| Spherical (cocci) | Rod-shaped (bacilli) | Spiral |

About half of all prokaryotic species are mobile. Many of those that travel have one or more flagella that propel the cells away from unfavorable places or toward more favorable places, such as nutrient-rich locales.

In many natural environments, prokaryotes attach to surfaces in a highly organized colony called a **biofilm**. A biofilm may consist of one or several species of prokaryotes, and it may include protists and fungi as well. As a biofilm becomes larger and more complex, it develops into a "city" of microbes. Communicating by chemical signals, members of the community engage in division of labor, including defense against invaders, among other activities.

Biofilms can form on almost any type of surface, such as rocks, organic material (including living tissue), metal, and plastic. A biofilm known as dental plaque (Figure 9) can cause tooth decay, a topic you'll learn more about in the Evolution Connection section at the end of this chapter. Biofilms are common among bacteria that cause disease in humans. For instance, ear infections and urinary tract infections are often the result of biofilm-forming bacteria. Biofilms of harmful bacteria can also form on implanted medical devices such as catheters, replacement joints, and pacemakers. The structure of biofilms makes these infections especially difficult to defeat. Antibiotics may not be able to penetrate beyond the outer layer of cells, leaving much of the community intact.

Prokaryotic Reproduction

Many prokaryotes can reproduce at a phenomenal rate if conditions are favorable. The cells copy their DNA almost continuously and divide again and again by the

▼ Figure 9 **Dental plaque, a biofilm that forms on teeth.**

Colorized SEM 6,000x

▼ Figure 10 **Household sponge contaminated with bacteria (red, green, yellow, and blue objects in this colorized micrograph).**

Colorized SEM 8,400x

process of **binary fission**. Dividing by binary fission, a single cell becomes 2 cells, which then become 4, 8, 16, and so on. Some species can produce a new generation in only 20 minutes under optimal conditions. If reproduction continued unchecked at this rate, a single prokaryote could give rise to a colony outweighing Earth in only three days! Also, each time DNA is replicated prior to binary fission, spontaneous mutations occur. As a result, rapid reproduction generates a great deal of genetic variation in a prokaryotic population. If the environment changes, an individual that possesses a beneficial gene can quickly take advantage of the new conditions. For example, exposure to antibiotics may select for antibiotic resistance in a bacterial population.

Fortunately, few prokaryotic populations can sustain exponential growth for long. Environments are usually limiting in resources such as food and space. Prokaryotes also produce metabolic waste products that may eventually pollute the colony's environment. Still, you can understand why kitchen sponges may harbor large numbers of bacteria (Figure 10) and why food can spoil so rapidly. Refrigeration retards food spoilage not because the cold kills bacteria, but because most microorganisms reproduce very slowly at such low temperatures.

Some prokaryotes can survive during very harsh conditions by forming specialized cells called endospores. An **endospore** is a thick-coated, protective cell produced within the prokaryotic cell when the prokaryote is exposed to unfavorable conditions. The endospore can survive all sorts of trauma and extreme temperatures—not even boiling water kills most of these resistant cells. And when the environment becomes more hospitable, the endospore can absorb water and resume growth. To ensure that all cells, including endospores, are killed when laboratory equipment is sterilized, microbiologists use an appliance called an autoclave, a pressure cooker that applies high-pressure steam at a temperature of 121°C (250°F). The food-canning industry uses similar methods to kill endospores of dangerous bacteria such as *Clostridium botulinum*, the cause of the potentially fatal disease botulism. ☑

Prokaryotic Nutrition

You are probably familiar with the methods by which multicellular organisms obtain energy and carbon, the two main resources needed for synthesizing organic compounds. Plants use carbon dioxide and the sun's energy in the process of photosynthesis; animals and fungi obtain both carbon and energy from organic matter. These modes of nutrition are both common among prokaryotes as well (**Figure 11**). But the metabolic capabilities of prokaryotes are far more diverse than those of eukaryotes. Some species harvest energy from inorganic substances such as ammonia (NH_3) and hydrogen sulfide (H_2S). Soil bacteria that obtain energy from inorganic nitrogen compounds are essential to the chemical cycle that makes nitrogen available to plants. Because they don't depend on sunlight for energy, these prokaryotes can thrive in conditions that seem totally inhospitable to life—even between layers of rocks buried hundreds of feet below Earth's surface! Near hydrothermal vents, where scalding water and hot gases surge into the sea more than a mile below the surface, bacteria that use sulfur compounds as a source of energy support diverse animal communities.

The metabolic talents of prokaryotes make them excellent symbiotic partners with animals, plants, and fungi. **Symbiosis** ("living together") is a close association between organisms of two or more species. In some cases of symbiosis, both organisms benefit from the partnership. For example, many of the animals that inhabit hydrothermal vent communities, including the giant tube worm shown in **Figure 12**, harbor sulfur bacteria within their bodies. The animals absorb sulfur compounds from the water. The bacteria use the compounds as an energy source to convert CO_2 from seawater into organic molecules that, in turn, provide food for their hosts. Similarly, photosynthesis by cyanobacteria

☑ CHECKPOINT

1. Using a microscope, how could you distinguish the cocci that cause staph infections from those that cause strep throat?
2. Why do microbiologists autoclave their laboratory instruments and glassware rather than just washing them in very hot water?

Answers: 1. by the arrangement of the cell aggregates: grapelike clusters for staphylococcus and chains for streptococcus 2. to kill bacterial endospores, which can survive boiling water

▼ **Figure 12 Giant tube worm.** These animals, which can grow up to 2 m (over 6 ft) long, depend on symbiotic prokaryotes to supply them with food.

▼ **Figure 11 Two methods of obtaining energy and carbon.**

(a) *Oscillatoria.* This is a species of cyanobacteria, a type of prokaryote that undergoes photosynthesis.

LM 65×

(b) *Salmonella.* These bacteria, which cause a type of food poisoning, obtain energy and carbon from organic matter—in this case, living human cells.

Colorized SEM 21,000×

▲ Figure 13 *Azolla* (water fern, inset) floating in rice paddy. These small plants grow rapidly and cover the water's surface, which helps exclude weeds. Decomposition of the short-lived plants releases nitrogen that fertilizes the rice.

provides food for a fungal partner in the symbiosis that forms some lichens.

In addition to photosynthesis, many cyanobacteria are also capable of nitrogen fixation, the process of converting atmospheric nitrogen (N_2) into a form usable by plants. Symbiosis with cyanobacteria gives plants such as the water fern *Azolla* an advantage in nitrogen-poor environments. This tiny, floating plant has been used to boost rice production for more than a thousand years (Figure 13). Other nitrogen-fixing bacteria live symbiotically in root nodules of plants in the legume family, a large group that includes many economically important species such as beans, soybeans, peas, and peanuts.

The Ecological Impact of Prokaryotes

As a result of their nutritional diversity, prokaryotes perform a variety of ecological services that are essential to our well-being. Let's turn our attention now to the vital role that prokaryotes play in sustaining the biosphere.

Prokaryotes and Chemical Recycling

Not too long ago, the atoms making up the organic molecules in your body were part of inorganic compounds found in soil, air, and water, as they will be again one day. Life depends on the recycling of chemical elements between the biological and physical components of ecosystems. Prokaryotes play essential roles in these chemical cycles. For example, nearly all the nitrogen that plants use to make proteins and nucleic acids comes from prokaryotic metabolism in the soil. In turn, animals get their nitrogen compounds from plants.

Another vital function of prokaryotes, mentioned earlier in the chapter, is the breakdown of organic wastes and dead organisms. Prokaryotes decompose organic matter and, in the process, return elements to the environment in inorganic forms that can be used by other organisms. If it were not for such decomposers, carbon, nitrogen, and other elements essential to life would become locked in the organic molecules of corpses and waste products.

Putting Prokaryotes to Work

People have put the metabolically diverse prokaryotes to work in cleaning up the environment. **Bioremediation** is the use of organisms to remove pollutants from water, air, or soil. One example of bioremediation is the use of prokaryotic decomposers to treat our sewage. Raw sewage is first passed through a series of screens and shredders, and solid matter settles out from the liquid waste. This solid matter, called sludge, is then gradually added to a culture of anaerobic prokaryotes, including both bacteria and archaea. The microbes decompose the organic matter in the sludge, converting it to material that can be used as landfill or fertilizer. The liquid wastes may then be passed through a trickling filter system consisting of a long horizontal bar that slowly rotates, spraying liquid wastes onto a bed of rocks (Figure 14). Aerobic prokaryotes and fungi growing on the rocks remove much of the organic matter from the liquid. The outflow from the rock bed is then sterilized and released back into the environment.

You have microorganisms to thank for the clean water you drink every day.

▼ Figure 14 Putting microbes to work in sewage treatment facilities. This is a diagram of a trickling filter system, which uses bacteria, archaea, and fungi to treat liquid wastes after sludge is removed.

Rotating arm spraying liquid wastes

Rock bed coated with aerobic prokaryotes and fungi

Liquid wastes

Outflow

© Pearson Education, Inc.

Bioremediation has also become an important tool for cleaning up toxic chemicals released into the soil and water by industrial processes. Naturally occurring prokaryotes capable of degrading pollutants such as oil, solvents, and pesticides are often present in contaminated soil, but environmental workers may use methods of speeding up their activity. In **Figure 15**, an airplane is spraying chemical dispersants on oil from the disastrous 2010 Deepwater Horizon spill in the Gulf of Mexico. Like detergents that help clean greasy dishes, these chemicals break oil into smaller droplets that offer more surface area for microbial attack. Prokaryotes are also helping to decontaminate old mining sites where the soil and water are laced with heavy metals and other poisons. We are just beginning to explore the great potential that prokaryotes offer for bioremediation. In the future, genetically engineered microbes may be put to

▲ **Figure 15 Spraying chemical dispersants on an oil spill in the Gulf of Mexico.**

work cleaning up the wide variety of toxic waste products that continue to accumulate in our landscapes and landfills. ☑

☑ **CHECKPOINT**

How do bacteria help restore the atmospheric CO_2 required by plants for photosynthesis?

Answer: By decomposing the organic molecules of dead organisms and organic refuse such as leaf litter, bacteria release carbon from the organic matter in the form of CO_2.

The Two Main Branches of Prokaryotic Evolution: Bacteria and Archaea

By comparing diverse prokaryotes at the molecular level, biologists have identified two major branches of prokaryotic evolution: **bacteria** and **archaea**. Thus, life is organized into three domains—**Bacteria**, **Archaea**, and **Eukarya**. Although bacteria and archaea have prokaryotic cell organization in common, they differ in many structural and physiological characteristics. In this section, we'll focus on the special characteristics of archaea before turning our attention to bacteria.

Archaea are abundant in many habitats, including places where few other organisms can survive. One group of archaea, the extreme thermophiles ("heat lovers"), live in very hot water **(Figure 16)**; some archaea even populate the deep-ocean vents that gush near-boiling water, such as the one shown in Figure 5. Another group is the extreme halophiles ("salt lovers"), archaea that thrive in such environments as Utah's Great Salt Lake, the Dead Sea, and seawater-evaporating ponds used to produce salt.

A third group of archaea are methanogens, which live in anaerobic (oxygen-free) environments and give off methane as a waste product. They are abundant in the mud at the bottom of lakes and swamps. You may have seen methane, also called marsh gas, bubbling up from a swamp. Methanogens flourish in the anaerobic conditions of solid waste landfills, where the large amount of methane they produce is a significant contributor to global warming. Many municipalities collect this methane and use it as a source of energy **(Figure 17)**.

Great numbers of methanogens also inhabit the digestive tracts of animals. In humans, intestinal gas is largely the result of their metabolism. More important, methanogens aid digestion in cattle, deer, and other animals that depend heavily on cellulose for their nutrition. Normally, bloating does not occur in these animals because they regularly expel large volumes of gas produced by the methanogens. (And that may be more than you wanted to know about these gas-producing microbes!)

Archaea are also abundant in more moderate conditions, especially the oceans, where they can be found at all depths. They are a substantial fraction of the prokaryotes in waters 150 m (nearly 500 ft) below the surface and half of the prokaryotes that live below 1,500 m (0.9 mi). Archaea are thus one of the most abundant cell types in Earth's largest habitat.

Bacteria That Cause Disease

Although most bacteria are harmless or even beneficial to us, a tiny minority of species cause a disproportionate amount of misery. Bacteria and other organisms that cause disease are called **pathogens**. We're healthy most of the time because our body's defenses check the growth of pathogen populations. Occasionally, the balance shifts in favor of a pathogen, and we become ill. Even some of

▼ **Figure 16 Heat-loving archaea.** In this photo, you can see yellow and orange colonies of heat-loving prokaryotes growing in the Abyss Pool, West Thumb Geyser, in Yellowstone Park, Wyoming.

▲ Figure 17 **Pipes for collecting gas generated by methanogenic archaea from a landfill.**

◄ Figure 18 **Bacteria that cause meningitis.** *Neisseria meningitidis*, an endotoxin-producing pathogen.

Colorized SEM 18,000x

the bacteria that are normal residents of the human body can make us sick when our defenses have been weakened by poor nutrition or a viral infection.

Most pathogenic bacteria cause disease by producing a poison—either an exotoxin or an endotoxin. **Exotoxins** are proteins that bacterial cells secrete into their environment. For example, *Staphylococcus aureus* (abbreviated *S. aureus*) produces several exotoxins. Although *S. aureus* is commonly found on the skin and in the nasal passages, if it enters the body through a wound, it can cause serious disease. One of its exotoxins causes layers of skin to slough off ("flesh-eating disease"); another can produce a potentially deadly disease called toxic shock syndrome, which has been associated with improper use of tampons. *S. aureus* exotoxins are also a leading cause of food poisoning. If food contaminated with *S. aureus* is not refrigerated, the bacteria reproduce and release exotoxins so potent that ingesting a millionth of a gram causes vomiting and diarrhea. Once the food has been contaminated, even boiling it will not destroy the exotoxins.

Endotoxins are chemical components of the outer membrane of certain bacteria. All endotoxins induce the same general symptoms: fever, aches, and sometimes a dangerous drop in blood pressure (septic shock). Septic shock triggered by an endotoxin of the pathogen that causes bacterial meningitis **(Figure 18)** can kill a healthy person in a matter of days, or even hours. Because the bacteria are easily transmitted among people living in close contact, many colleges require students to be vaccinated against this disease. Other examples of endotoxin-producing bacteria include the species of *Salmonella* that cause food poisoning and typhoid fever.

Sanitation is generally the most effective way to prevent bacterial disease. The installation of water treatment and sewage systems continues to be a public health priority throughout the world. Antibiotics have been discovered that can cure most bacterial diseases.

However, resistance to widely used antibiotics has evolved in many of these pathogens.

In addition to sanitation and antibiotics, a third defense against bacterial disease is education. A case in point is Lyme disease, which is caused by a spirochete bacterium carried by ticks **(Figure 19)**. Disease-carrying ticks live on deer and field mice but also bite humans. Lyme disease usually starts as a red rash shaped like a bull's-eye around a tick bite. Antibiotics can cure the disease if administered within a month of exposure. If untreated, Lyme disease can cause debilitating arthritis, heart disease, and nervous system disorders. Because there is no vaccine, the best defense against Lyme disease is public education about avoiding tick bites and the importance of seeking treatment if a rash develops.

▼ Figure 19 **Lyme disease, a bacterial disease transmitted by ticks.** The bacterium that causes Lyme disease (shown in micrograph at right) is carried from deer to humans by ticks.

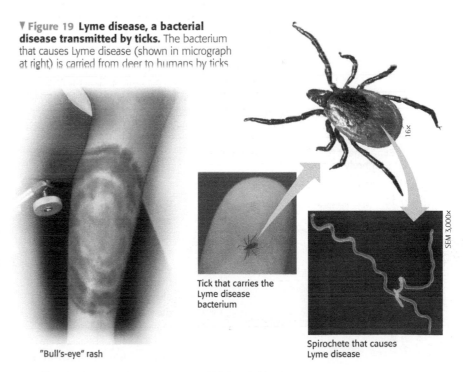

16x

SEM 3,000x

"Bull's-eye" rash

Tick that carries the Lyme disease bacterium

Spirochete that causes Lyme disease

The potential of some pathogens to cause serious harm has led to their use as biological weapons. One of the greatest threats is from endospores of the bacterium that causes anthrax. When anthrax endospores enter the lungs, they germinate, and the bacteria multiply, producing an exotoxin that eventually accumulates to lethal levels in the blood. Although the bacteria can be killed by certain antibiotics, the antibiotics don't eliminate the toxin already in the body. As a result, inhalation anthrax has a very high death rate. In an incident in 2001, five people died when anthrax spores were mailed to members of the news media and the U.S. Senate.

Another bacterium considered to have dangerous potential as a weapon is *Clostridium botulinum*. Unlike other biological agents, the weapon form of *C. botulinum* is the exotoxin it produces, botulinum, rather than the living microbes. Botulinum, the deadliest poison on Earth, blocks transmission of the nerve signals that cause muscle contraction, resulting in paralysis of the muscles required for breathing. Thirty grams of botulinum, a bit more than an ounce, could kill every person in the United States. On the other hand, the minute amount of botulinum in Botox is used for cosmetic purposes. When the toxin is injected under the skin, it relaxes the facial muscles that cause wrinkles. ✓

Human Microbiota THE PROCESS OF SCIENCE

Are Intestinal Microbiota to Blame for Obesity?

As you learned in the Biology and Society section, our bodies are home to trillions of bacteria that cause no harm or are even beneficial to our health. In the past decade, researchers have made enormous strides in characterizing our microbiota and have begun to investigate the specific effects of these residents on our physiological processes. Because our intestinal microbes are known to be involved in some aspects of food processing, researchers speculate that they might be involved in obesity. Let's examine how a team of scientists investigated the impact of microbiota on body composition—the amount of fat versus lean body mass.

Using **observations** from previous studies, the scientists asked the following **question**: Can microbiota from an obese person affect the body composition of another person? Although this is the question that we ultimately want answered, researchers routinely test hypotheses in animal models before using human subjects. Mice that have been raised in germ-free conditions have no microbiota, making them ideal subjects for this type of experiment. Therefore, the scientists formed the **hypothesis** that intestinal microbiota of an obese person would increase the amount of body fat in mice. Their **prediction** was that if the hypothesis was correct, then lean, germ-free mice

that received transplants of microbes from the intestines of obese individuals would show a greater increase of body fat than would germ-free mice that received transplants of microbes from the intestines of lean individuals.

The researchers recruited four pairs of female twins for the **experiment**. In each pair, one twin was obese and the other was lean. Microbiota from the feces of each individual were transplanted into separate groups of germ-free mice (**Figure 20**). The **results**, shown in **Figure 21**, supported the hypothesis. Mice that received microbiota from an obese donor became more obese; mice that received microbiota from a lean donor remained lean.

Is a microbe-based cure for obesity just around the corner? It's not likely. The experiment described here—and many similar experiments—represent an early stage of scientific investigation. A great deal more research is needed to determine whether our microbial residents are responsible for obesity. If that proves to be the case, the next challenge will be figuring out how to safely manipulate the complex ecosystem within our bodies.

▼ Figure 20 **Experiment to investigate the effect of microbiota on body composition.**

◄ Figure 21 **Results of microbiota transplantation experiment.** The graph shows the change in body composition (lean vs. fat mass) of mice that received microbiota from a lean donor (left) or an obese donor (right).
Data from: V. K. Ridaura et al., Gut microbiota from twins discordant for obesity modulate metabolism in mice. *Science* 341 (2013). DOI: 10.1126/science.1241214.

Protists

The fossil record indicates that the first eukaryotes evolved from prokaryotes around 2 billion years ago. **Endosymbiosis**, a relationship in which one organism lives inside the cell or cells of a host organism, played a key role in the evolution of eukaryotic cells. Extensive evidence supports the theory that mitochondria and chloroplasts originated as prokaryotes that established residence inside larger host cells. Hosts and endosymbionts became interdependent and eventually became single organisms with inseparable parts. These primal eukaryotes were not only the predecessors of the great variety of modern protists; they were also ancestral to all other eukaryotes—plants, fungi, and animals.

The term protists is not a taxonomic category. At one time, protists were classified in a fourth eukaryotic kingdom (kingdom Protista). However, recent genetic and structural studies shattered the notion of protists as a unified group—some protists are more closely related to fungi, plants, or animals than they are to each other. Hypotheses about protist phylogeny (and thus, classification) are changing rapidly as new information causes scientists to revise their ideas. Although there is general agreement about some relationships, others are hotly disputed. Thus, **protist** is a bit of a catch-all category that includes all eukaryotes that are not fungi, animals, or plants. Most, but not all, protists are unicellular. Because their cells are eukaryotic, even the simplest protists are much more complex than any prokaryote.

One mark of protist diversity is the variety of ways they obtain their nutrition. Some protists are autotrophs, producing their food by photosynthesis. Photosynthetic protists belong to an informal category called **algae** (singular, *alga*), which also includes cyanobacteria. Protistan algae may be unicellular, colonial, or multicellular, such as the one shown in **Figure 22a**. Other protists are heterotrophs, acquiring their food from other organisms. Some heterotrophic protists eat bacteria or other protists; some are fungus-like and obtain organic molecules by absorption. Still others are parasitic. A **parasite** derives its nutrition from a living host, which is harmed by the interaction. For example, the parasitic trypanosomes shown among human red blood cells in **Figure 22b** cause sleeping sickness, a debilitating disease common in parts of Africa. Yet other protists are mixotrophs, capable of both photosynthesis and heterotrophy. *Euglena* **(Figure 22c)**, a common inhabitant of pond water, can change its mode of nutrition, depending on availability of light and nutrients.

Protist habitats are also diverse. Most protists are aquatic, living in oceans, lakes, and ponds, but they are found almost anywhere there is moisture, including terrestrial habitats such as damp soil and leaf litter. Others are symbionts that reside in the bodies of various host organisms.

Because the classification of protists remains a work in progress, our brief survey of protists is not organized to correspond with any hypothesis about phylogeny. Instead, we'll look at four informal categories of protists: protozoans, slime molds, unicellular and colonial algae, and seaweeds.

▼ **Figure 22 Protist modes of nutrition.**

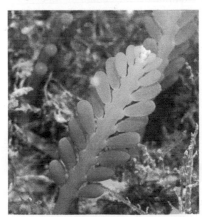

(a) An autotroph: *Caulerpa*, a multicellular alga

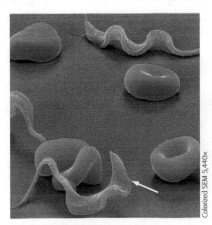

Colorized SEM 5,440x

(b) A heterotroph: parasitic trypanosome (arrow)

LM 700x

(c) A mixotroph: *Euglena*

Protozoans

Protists that live primarily by ingesting food are called **protozoans (Figure 23)**. Protozoans thrive in all types of aquatic environments. Most species eat bacteria or other protozoans, but some can absorb nutrients dissolved in the water. Protozoans that live as parasites in animals, though in the minority, cause some of the world's most harmful diseases.

Flagellates are protozoans that move by means of one or more flagella. Most species are free-living (nonparasitic). However, this group also includes some nasty parasites that make people sick. An example is *Giardia*, a common waterborne parasite that causes severe diarrhea. People most often pick up *Giardia* by drinking water contaminated with feces containing the parasite. For example, a swimmer in a lake or river might accidentally ingest water, or a hiker might drink contaminated water from a seemingly pristine stream. (Boiling the water first will kill *Giardia*.) Another flagellate is *Trichomonas*, a common sexually transmitted parasite. The parasite travels through the reproductive tract by moving its flagella and undulating part of its membrane. In women, these protozoans feed on white blood cells and bacteria living on the cells lining the vagina. *Trichomonas* also infects the cells lining the male reproductive tract, but limited availability of food results in very small population sizes. Consequently, males typically have no symptoms of infection.

Other flagellates live symbiotically in a relationship that benefits both partners. Termites are notoriously destructive to wooden structures, but they lack enzymes to digest the tough, complex cellulose molecules that make up wood. Flagellates that reside in the termite's digestive tract break down the cellulose into simpler molecules, sharing the bounty with their hosts.

Amoebas are characterized by great flexibility in their body shape and the absence of permanent organelles for locomotion. Most species move and feed by means of **pseudopodia** (singular, *pseudopodium*), temporary extensions of the cell. Amoebas can assume virtually any shape as they creep over rocks, sticks, or mud at the bottom of a pond or ocean. One species of parasitic amoeba causes amoebic dysentery, a disease that is responsible for an estimated 100,000 deaths worldwide every year. Other protozoans with pseudopodia include the **forams**, which have shells. Although they are single-celled, the largest forams grow to a diameter of several centimeters. Ninety percent of forams that have been identified are fossils. The fossilized shells, which are a component of sedimentary rock such as limestone, are excellent markers for relating the ages of rocks in different parts of the world.

Apicomplexans are all parasitic, and some cause serious human diseases. They are named for a structure at their apex (tip) that is specialized for penetrating host cells and tissues. This group of protozoans includes *Plasmodium*, the parasite that causes malaria. Another apicomplexan is *Toxoplasma*, which requires a feline host to complete its complex life cycle. Cats that eat wild birds or rodents may be infected and shed the parasite in their feces. People can become infected by handling cat litter of outdoor cats, but they don't become sick because the immune system keeps the parasite in check. However, a woman who is newly infected with *Toxoplasma* during pregnancy can pass the parasite to her unborn child, who may suffer damage to the nervous system as a result.

Ciliates are protozoans named for their hairlike structures called cilia, which provide movement of the protist and sweep food into the protist's "mouth." Nearly all ciliates are free-living (nonparasitic) and include both heterotrophs and mixotrophs. If you have had the opportunity to explore protist diversity in a droplet of pond water, you may have seen the common freshwater ciliate *Paramecium*. ☑

> According to a recent study, infection by the parasite *Toxoplasma* makes mice lose their fear of cats.

☑ CHECKPOINT

According to a recent study, mice infected with *Toxoplasma* lose their fear of cats. How would altering the behavior of mice in this way be a beneficial adaptation for the *Toxoplasma* parasite?

Answer: Fearless mice are more likely to be caught and eaten by a cat, thus transmitting the parasite to a host in which it can complete its life cycle (that is, successfully reproduce).

▼ **Figure 23 A diversity of protozoans.**

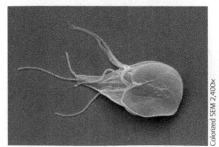

A flagellate: *Giardia*. This flagellated protozoan parasite can colonize and reproduce within the human intestine, causing disease.

Colorized SEM 2,400x

Another flagellate: *Trichomonas*. This common sexually transmitted parasite causes an estimated 5 million new infections each year.

Colorized SEM 3,200x

An amoeba. This amoeba is beginning to wrap pseudopodia around an algal cell in preparation for engulfing it.

Colorized TEM 2,300x

Slime Molds

Slime molds are multicellular protists related to amoebas. Although slime molds were once classified as fungi, DNA analysis showed that they arose from different evolutionary lineages. Like many fungi, slime molds feed on dead plant material. Two distinct types of slime molds have been identified.

In plasmodial slime molds, the feeding body is an amoeboid mass called a plasmodium **(Figure 24)** that extends pseudopodia among the leaf litter and other decaying material on a forest floor. A plasmodium can measure several centimeters across, with its network of fine filaments taking in bacteria and bits of dead organic matter amoeboid-style. Large as it is, though, the plasmodium is actually a single cell with many nuclei. Its mass of cytoplasm is not divided by plasma membranes. When the plasmodium runs out of food, or its environment dries up, the slime mold grows reproductive structures. Stalked bodies that arise from the plasmodium bear tough-coated spores that can survive harsh conditions. If you look closely at a decaying log or the mulch in landscaped areas, you may notice these spore-bearing structures. Like the endospores of anthrax bacteria, slime mold spores can absorb water and grow once favorable conditions return.

In cellular slime molds, the feeding stage consists of solitary amoeboid cells that function independently of each other rather than a plasmodium **(Figure 25)**. But when food is in short supply, the amoeboid cells swarm together to form a slug-like colony that moves and functions as a single unit. After a brief period of mobility, the colony extends a stalk and develops into a multicellular reproductive structure.

Slug-like colony

Amoeboid cells

Reproductive structure

▲ **Figure 24 A plasmodial slime mold.** The weblike form of the slime mold's feeding stage (yellow structure) is an adaptation that enlarges the organism's surface area, increasing its contact with food, water, and oxygen.

▲ **Figure 25 Life stages of a cellular slime mold.**

A foram. A foram cell secretes a shell made of organic material hardened with calcium carbonate. The pseudopodia, seen here as thin rays, extend through small pores in the shell.

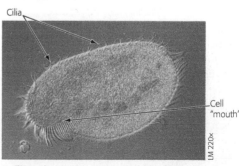

Apical complex

Red blood cell

An apicomplexan. *Plasmodium*, which causes malaria, enters red blood cells of its human host. The parasite feeds on the host cell from within, eventually destroying it.

Cilia

Cell "mouth"

A ciliate. The ciliate *Paramecium* uses its cilia to move through pond water. Cilia lining the oral groove keep a current of water containing food moving toward the cell "mouth."

Unicellular and Colonial Algae

Algae are protists and cyanobacteria whose photosynthesis supports food chains in freshwater and marine ecosystems. Researchers are currently trying to harness their ability to convert light energy to chemical energy for another purpose—to produce biofuels. We'll look at four groups of protistan algae. Three of these groups—dinoflagellates, diatoms, and green algae—are unicellular, and one group is colonial.

Many unicellular algae are components of **phytoplankton**, the photosynthetic organisms, mostly microscopic, that drift near the surfaces of ponds, lakes, and oceans. Dinoflagellates are abundant in the vast aquatic pastures of phytoplankton. Each **dinoflagellate** species has a characteristic shape reinforced by external plates made of cellulose **(Figure 26a)**. The beating of two flagella in perpendicular grooves produces a spinning movement. Dinoflagellate blooms—population explosions—sometimes cause warm coastal waters to turn pinkish orange, a phenomenon known as a red tide. Toxins produced by some red-tide dinoflagellates have caused massive fish kills and are poisonous to humans as well. One group of dinoflagellates resides within the cells of reef-building corals. Without these algal partners, corals could not build and sustain the massive reefs that provide the food, living space, and shelter that support the splendid diversity of the reef community.

Diatoms have glassy cell walls containing silica, the mineral used to make glass **(Figure 26b)**. The cell wall consists of two halves that fit together like the bottom and lid of a shoe box. Diatoms store their food reserves in the form of an oil that provides buoyancy, keeping diatoms floating as plankton near the sunlit surface. The organic remains of diatoms that lived hundreds of millions of years ago are thought to be the main component of oil deposits. But why wait millions of years?

Researchers are currently working on methods of growing diatoms and processing the oil into biodiesel.

Green algae are named for their grass-green chloroplasts. Unicellular green algae flourish in most freshwater lakes and ponds, as well as many home pools and aquariums. The green algal group also includes colonial forms, such as *Volvox*, shown in **Figure 26c**. Each *Volvox* colony is a hollow ball of flagellated cells (the small green dots in the photo) that are very similar to certain unicellular green algae. The balls within the balls in Figure 25c are daughter colonies that will be released when the parent colonies rupture. Of all photosynthetic protists, green algae are the most closely related to plants.

Seaweeds

Defined as large, multicellular marine algae, **seaweeds** grow on rocky shores and just offshore. Their cell walls have slimy and rubbery substances that cushion their bodies against the agitation of the waves. Some seaweeds are as large and complex as many plants. And although the word *seaweed* implies a plantlike appearance, the similarities between these algae and plants are a consequence of convergent evolution. In fact, the closest relatives of seaweeds are certain unicellular algae, which is why many biologists include seaweeds with the protists. Seaweeds are classified into three different groups **(Figure 27)**, based partly on the types of pigments present in their chloroplasts: green algae, red algae, and brown algae (some of which are known as kelp).

Many coastal people, particularly in Asia, harvest seaweeds for food. For example, in Japan and Korea, some seaweed species, including brown algae called kombu, are ingredients in soups. Other seaweeds, such as red algae called nori, are used to wrap sushi. Marine algae are rich

▼ Figure 26 **Unicellular and colonial algae.**

(a) **Dinoflagellate:** Note the wall of protective plates

Colorized SEM 667×

(b) **Diatom:** Note the glassy walls

Colorized SEM 165×

(c) **Volvox:** A colonial green alga

LM 195×

▼ Figure 27 **The three major groups of seaweeds.**

Green algae. This sea lettuce is an edible species that inhabits the intertidal zone, where the land meets the ocean.

Red algae. These seaweeds are most abundant in the warm coastal waters of the tropics.

Brown algae. This group includes the largest seaweeds, known as kelp, which grow as marine "forests."

in iodine and other essential minerals, but much of their organic material consists of unusual polysaccharides that humans cannot digest. They are eaten mostly for their rich tastes and unusual textures. The gel-forming substances in the cell walls of seaweeds are widely used as thickeners for such processed foods as puddings, ice cream, and salad dressing. The seaweed extract called agar provides the gel-forming base for the media microbiologists use to culture bacteria in petri dishes. ☑

Seaweeds aren't just used for wrapping sushi—they're in your ice cream, too.

 Human Microbiota EVOLUTION CONNECTION

The Sweet Life of *Streptococcus mutans*

Did you ever wonder why candy causes cavities? A biofilm-forming species of bacteria called *Streptococcus mutans* is the culprit. *S. mutans* thrives in the anaerobic environment found in the tiny crevices in tooth enamel. Using sucrose (table sugar) to make a sticky polysaccharide, the bacteria glue themselves in place and build up thick deposits of plaque. Unless you make an effort to remove it, the plaque becomes mineralized, turning into a crusty tartar that must be scraped off your teeth by a dental hygienist (**Figure 28**). Within this fortress, *S. mutans* ferments sugars to obtain energy, releasing lactic acid as a by-product. The acid attacks tooth enamel and eventually eats through it. Other bacteria then use the entrance and infect the soft tissue in the interior of the tooth.

Early humans were hunter-gatherers, living on food foraged in the wild. In a major cultural shift, this lifestyle was replaced by agriculture, which provided a diet rich in carbohydrates from grain. A later dietary shift brought processed flour and sugar to the table. Each change in diet altered the environment inhabited by our oral microbiota. Studies of prehistoric human remains have correlated dental disease with these changes in diet.

Recent research links *S. mutans* directly to these increases in tooth decay. In one study, researchers analyzed DNA from tartar on the teeth of prehistoric humans who lived in Europe from 7,500 to 400 years ago. The tartar of hunter-gatherers included many species of bacteria but few known to cause tooth decay. *S. mutans* first appeared as one member of a diverse bacterial community after the agricultural diet had been established. Diversity of the oral microbiota dropped dramatically about 400 years ago, around the time sugar was introduced into the diet, and *S. mutans* became the overwhelmingly dominant species. Thus, we can infer that natural selection in the high-sugar environment favored *S. mutans*.

What adaptations gave *S. mutans* an advantage over other species? Another research team investigated genetic changes that allowed *S. mutans* to thrive in a high-sugar environment. Their results turned up more than a dozen genes that improved the ability of *S. mutans* to metabolize sugars and survive increased acidity. They also discovered chemical weapons produced by *S. mutans* that kill harmless bacteria—their competitors for space in the limited terrain of the human oral cavity.

It appears that *S. mutans* took full advantage of an evolutionary opportunity afforded by the human sweet tooth. Having adapted to new environmental conditions and ousted its competitors, it is now firmly entrenched as the dominant member of the mouth's microbial community.

▲ Figure 28 **Checking the effects of *Streptococcus mutans*.**

Chapter Review

SUMMARY OF KEY CONCEPTS

Major Episodes in the History of Life

Major Episode	Millions of Years Ago
Plants and fungi colonize land	500
Fossils of large, diverse multicellular organisms	600
Oldest fossils of multicellular organisms	1,200
Oldest eukaryotic fossils	1,800
Beginning of atmospheric accumulation of O_2	2,700
Oldest prokaryotic fossils	3,500
Origin of Earth	4,600

The Origin of Life

A Four-Stage Hypothesis for the Origin of Life

One scenario suggests that the first organisms were products of chemical evolution in four stages:

Inorganic compounds → **Abiotic synthesis of organic monomers** | Organic monomers → **Abiotic synthesis of polymers** | Polymer → **Formation of pre-cells** | Membrane-enclosed compartment → **Self-replicating molecules** | Complementary chain

From Chemical Evolution to Darwinian Evolution

Over millions of years, natural selection favored the most efficient pre-cells, which evolved into the first prokaryotic cells.

Prokaryotes

They're Everywhere!

Prokaryotes are found wherever there is life and greatly outnumber eukaryotes. Prokaryotes thrive in habitats where eukaryotes cannot live. A few prokaryotic species cause serious disease, but most are either benign or beneficial to other forms of life.

Structure/Function: Prokaryotes

Prokaryotic cells lack nuclei and other membrane-enclosed organelles. Most have cell walls. Prokaryotes exhibit three common shapes.

Spherical   **Rod-shaped**   **Spiral**

About half of all prokaryotic species are mobile, most of these using flagella to move. Some prokaryotes can survive extended periods of harsh conditions by forming endospores. Many prokaryotes can reproduce by binary fission at high rates if conditions are favorable, but growth is usually restricted by limited resources.

Prokaryotes include species that obtain energy from the sun (like plants) and from organic material (like animals and fungi). Some species derive energy from inorganic substances such as ammonia (NH_3) or hydrogen sulfide (H_2S). Some prokaryotes live in symbiotic associations with animals, plants, or fungi.

The Ecological Impact of Prokaryotes

Prokaryotes help recycle chemical elements between the biological and physical components of ecosystems. People use prokaryotes to remove pollutants from water, air, and soil in the process called bioremediation.

The Two Main Branches of Prokaryotic Evolution: Bacteria and Archaea

The prokaryotic lineage includes domains Bacteria and Archaea. Many archaea are "extremophiles" capable of surviving under conditions (such as high heat or salt concentrations) that would kill other forms of life; other archaea are found in more moderate environments. Some bacteria cause disease, mostly by producing exotoxins or endotoxins. Sanitation, antibiotics, and education are the best defenses against bacterial disease.

Protists

Protists are unicellular eukaryotes and their closest multicellular relatives.

Protozoans

Protozoans, including flagellates, amoebas, apicomplexans, and ciliates, primarily live in aquatic environments and ingest their food.

Slime Molds

Slime molds (including plasmodial slime molds and cellular slime molds) resemble fungi in appearance and lifestyle as decomposers but are not at all closely related.

Unicellular and Colonial Algae

Unicellular algae, including dinoflagellates, diatoms, and unicellular green algae, are photosynthetic protists that support food chains in freshwater and marine ecosystems.

Seaweeds

Seaweeds—which include green, red, and brown algae—are large, multicellular marine algae that grow on and near rocky shores.

MasteringBiology®

For practice quizzes, BioFlix animations, MP3 tutorials, video tutors, and more study tools designed for this text, go to MasteringBiology®

SELF-QUIZ

1. Place these events in the history of life on Earth in the order that they occurred.
   a. accumulation of O_2 in Earth's atmosphere
   b. colonization of land by plants and fungi
   c. diversification of animals (Cambrian explosion)
   d. origin of eukaryotes
   e. origin of humans
   f. origin of multicellular organisms
   g. origin of prokaryotes

2. Place the following steps in the origin of life in the order that they are hypothesized to have occurred.
   a. integration of abiotically produced molecules into membrane-enclosed pre-cells
   b. origin of the first molecules capable of self-replication
   c. abiotic joining of organic monomers into polymers
   d. abiotic synthesis of organic monomers
   e. natural selection among pre-cells

3. DNA replication relies on the enzyme DNA polymerase. Why does this suggest that the earliest genes were made from RNA?

4. Contrast exotoxins with endotoxins.

5. Some species of cyanobacteria form symbiotic relationships with other organisms. What benefit might a protist or fungus receive from a cyanobacterial symbiont? What benefit might a plant receive from a cyanobacterial symbiont?

6. The bacteria that cause tetanus can be killed only by prolonged heating at temperatures considerably above boiling. What does this suggest about tetanus bacteria?

7. How is the process used in sewage treatment similar to the decomposition of leaf litter in a forest?

8. What do all protists have in common?

9. Which of the following protists is *not* a human pathogen?
   a. *Toxoplasma*
   b. *Trichomonas*
   c. *Paramecium*
   d. *Giardia*

10. Which algal group is most closely related to plants?
    a. diatoms
    b. green algae
    c. dinoflagellates
    d. seaweeds

THE PROCESS OF SCIENCE

11. Imagine you are on a team designing a moon base that will be self-contained and self-sustaining. Once supplied with building materials, equipment, and organisms from Earth, the base will be expected to function indefinitely. One of the members of your team has suggested that everything sent to the base be chemically treated or irradiated so that no bacteria of any kind are present. Do you think this is a good idea? Predict some of the consequences of eliminating all bacteria from an environment.

12. **Interpreting Data** Because bacteria divide by binary fission, the population size doubles every generation. Suppose the generation time for bacteria that cause food poisoning (for example, *Staphylococcus aureus* or *Salmonella*) is 30 minutes at room temperature. The number of cells in a population can be calculated using this formula.

    Initial number of cells $\times 2^{(\text{Number of generations})}$ = Population size

    For example, if a dish of potato salad is contaminated with 10 bacteria, the bacterial population after 1 hour (2 generations) is $10 \times 2^2 = 40$. Fill in the table below to show how the bacterial population increases when a dish of potato salad is left on the kitchen counter after dinner instead of being refrigerated overnight.

Time (Hours)	Number of Generations	Number of Bacteria
0	0	10
1	2	40
2	4	
3	6	
4	8	
5	10	
6	12	
8	16	
10	20	
12	24	

Why does the rate of increase change over time? Describe how a graph of the data would look.

BIOLOGY AND SOCIETY

13. State or local public health departments regularly inspect restaurants to ensure that safe food-handling procedures are used. In most states, detailed reports are available online. Locate such a report for a restaurant in your area. Mark the items on the checklist that cover hygiene and food handling, and explain how each item prevents potential contamination by pathogenic prokaryotes. Use the same checklist to inspect your own kitchen and evaluate whether corrective measures are needed.

14. Probiotics, foods and supplements that contain living microorganisms, are thought to cure problems of the digestive tract by restoring the natural balance of its microbial community. Sales of these products total billions of dollars a year. Explore the topic of probiotics and evaluate the scientific evidence for their beneficial effects. A good starting point is the website of the U.S. Food and Drug Administration, the agency that regulates advertising claims of health benefits of dietary supplements (www.fda.gov/Food/DietarySupplements/default.htm).

Glossary

alga (*al'-guh*)
(plural, **algae**) An informal term that describes a great variety of photosynthetic protists, including unicellular, colonial, and multicellular forms. Prokaryotes that are photosynthetic autotrophs are also regarded as algae.

amoeba (*uh-mē'-buh*)
A general term for a protozoan (animal-like protist) characterized by great structural flexibility and the presence of pseudopodia.

apicomplexan (*ap'-ē-kom-pleks'-un*)
A type of parasitic protozoan (animal-like protist). Some apicomplexans cause serious human disease.

Archaea (*ar-kē'-uh*)
One of two prokaryotic domains of life, the other being Bacteria.

archaean (*ar-kē'-uhn*)
(plural, **archaea**) An organism that is a member of the domain Archaea.

bacillus (*buh-sil'-us*)
(plural, **bacilli**) A rod-shaped prokaryotic cell.

Bacteria
One of two prokaryotic domains of life, the other being Archaea.

bacterium
(plural, **bacteria**) An organism that is a member of the domain Bacteria.

binary fission
A means of asexual reproduction in which a parent organism, often a single cell, divides into two individuals of about equal size.

biofilm
A surface-coating cooperative colony of prokaryotes.

bioremediation
The use of living organisms to detoxify and restore polluted and degraded ecosystems.

ciliate (*sil'-ē-it*)
A type of protozoan (animal-like protist) that moves and feeds by means of cilia.

coccus (*kok'-us*)
(plural, **cocci**) A spherical prokaryotic cell.

diatom (*dī'-uh-tom*)
A unicellular photosynthetic alga with a unique glassy cell wall containing silica.

dinoflagellate (*dī'-nō-flaj'-uh-let*)
A unicellular photosynthetic alga with two flagella situated in perpendicular grooves in cellulose plates covering the cell.

endospore
A thick-coated, protective cell produced within a prokaryotic cell exposed to harsh conditions.

endotoxin
A poisonous component of the outer membrane of certain bacteria.

Eukarya (*yū-kār'-yuh*)
The domain of eukaryotes, organisms made up of eukaryotic cells; includes all of the protists, plants, fungi, and animals.

eukaryote (*yū-kār'-ē-ōt*)
An organism characterized by eukaryotic cells.

exotoxin
A poisonous protein secreted by certain bacteria.

flagellate (*flaj'-uh-lit*)
A protozoan (animal-like protist) that moves by means of one or more flagella.

foram
A marine protozoan (animal-like protist) that secretes a shell and extends pseudopodia through pores in its shell.

green alga
One of a group of photosynthetic protists that includes unicellular, colonial, and multicellular species. Green algae are the photosynthetic protists most closely related to plants.

microbiota
The community of microorganisms that live in and on the body of an animal.

parasite
An organism that lives in or on another organism (the host) from which it obtains nourishment; an organism that benefits at the expense of another organism, which is harmed in the process.

pathogen
A disease-causing virus or organism.

phytoplankton
Photosynthetic organisms, mostly microscopic, that drift near the surfaces of ponds, lakes, and oceans.

prokaryote (*prō-kār'-ē-ōt*)
An organism characterized by prokaryotic cells.

protozoan (*prō'-tō-zō'-un*)
A protist that lives primarily by ingesting food; a heterotrophic, animal-like protist.

pseudopodium (*sū'-dō-pō'-dē-um*)
(plural, **pseudopodia**) A temporary extension of an amoeboid cell. Pseudopodia function in moving cells and engulfing food.

seaweed
A large, multicellular marine alga.

slime mold
A multicellular protist related to amoebas.

symbiosis (*sim'-bē-ō'-sis*)
An interaction between organisms of different species in which one species, the symbiont, lives in or on another species, the host.

Credits

Credits are listed in the order of appearance.

PHOTO CREDITS

opening photo bottom right vlabo/Shutterstock; **opening photo bottom left** Harry Vorsteher/Cultura Creative (RF)/Alamy; **opening photo bottom center** Odilon Dimier/PhotoAlto sas/Alamy; **right** Steve Gschmeissner/Science Source; **top left** Steve Gschmeissner/Science Source; **2** Mark Garlick/Science Photo Library/Corbis; **5** George Luther; **6 left to right** Jupiter Images; Dr. Tony Brain and David Parker/Science Photo Library/Science Source; **7 left to right** Scimat/Science Source; Niaid/CDC/Science Source; CNRI/SPL/Science Source; **8a** David M. Phillips/Science Source; **8b** Susan M. Barns; **8c** Heide Schulz/Max-Planck Institut für Marine Mikrobiologie; **9** Science Photo Library - Steve Gschmeissner/Brand X Pictures/Getty Images; **10** Eye of Science/Science Source; **11a** Sinclair Stammers/Science Source; **11b** Dr. Gary Gaugler/Science Source; **12** Image Quest Marine; **13 inset** Arco Images/Huetter, C./Alamy; **13** Nigel Cattlin/Alamy; **15** SIPA USA/SIPA/Newscom; **16** Eric J. Simon; **17 left** Jim West/Alamy; **18 right** SPL/Science Source; **19 left to right** Centers for Disease Control and Prevention (CDC); Scott Camazine/Science Source; Dariusz Majgier/Shutterstock; David M. Phillips/Science Source; **22a** Carol Buchanan/F1online/Age Fotostock; **22b** Oliver Meckes/Science Source; **22c** blickwinkel/Alamy; **23 left to right** Eye of Science/Science Source; David M. Phillips/The Population Council/Science Source; Biophoto Associates/Science Source; **23 left to right** Claude Carre/Science Source; Dr. Masamichi Aikawa; Michael Abbey/Science Source; **24** The Hidden Forest, www.hiddenforest.co.nz; **25 right top to bottom** Courtesy of Matt Springer, Stanford University; Courtesy of Robert Kay, MRC Cambridge; Courtesy of Robert Kay, MRC Cambridge; **26a** Eye of Science/Science Source; **26b** Steve Gschmeissner/Science Source; **26c** Manfred Kage/Science Source; **27 left to right** Marevision/Age Fotostock; Marevision/Age Fotostock; David Hall/Science Source; **28** Lucidio Studio, Inc/Moment/Getty Images.

ILLUSTRATION AND TEXT CREDITS

14: Gut Microbiota from Twins Discordant for Obesity Modulate Metabolism in Mice, Vanessa K. Ridaura et al., *Science* 341 (2013); DOI: 10.1126/science.1241214. 9th Ed., © 2007. Reprinted and electronically reproduced by permission of Pearson education, Inc., Upper Saddle River, New Jersey; **21:** V. K. Ridaura et al., "Gut Microbiota from Twins Discordant for Obesity Modulate Metabolism in Mice," *Science*, 341.

Self-Quiz Answers

1. g, a, d, f, c, b, e
2. d, c, a, b, e
3. DNA polymerase is a protein, which must be transcribed from a gene. But a DNA gene requires DNA polymerase to be replicated. This creates a paradox about which came first—DNA or protein. But RNA can act as both an information storage molecule and an enzyme, suggesting that dual-role RNA may have preceded both DNA and proteins.
4. Exotoxins are poisons secreted by pathogenic bacteria; endotoxins are components of the outer membrane of pathogenic bacteria.
5. food (products of photosynthesis); usable form of nitrogen
6. They can form endospores.
7. Prokaryotes in soil or water decompose the organic matter in leaves and other plant and animal remains, returning the elements to the environment in inorganic form. Prokaryotes in a sewage treatment facility decompose the organic matter in sewage, converting it to an inorganic form.
8. They are eukaryotes that are not plants, animals, or fungi.
9. c
10. b

The Evolution of Plants and Fungi

From Chapter 16 of *Campbell Essential Biology with Physiology*, Fifth Edition. Eric J. Simon, Jean L. Dickey, Kelly A. Hogan, Jane B. Reece. Copyright © 2016 by Pearson Education, Inc. All rights reserved.

The Evolution of Plants and Fungi

Why Plants and Fungi Matter

If you were to hug one of the largest giant sequoia trees, you would need more than a dozen friends to help you reach around its circumference.

If you've ever had mushroom pizza, you've snacked on the fungi's reproductive structure.

Fungi may not always be pretty, but if you find the right one, it could pay your way through college.

The most expensive coffee in the world has passed through the digestive tract of a catlike animal called a civet.

Plant-Fungus Interactions BIOLOGY AND SOCIETY

The Diamond of the Kitchen

To the untrained eye, a truffle (the fungus, not the chocolate) is an unappealing lump that you probably wouldn't eat on a dare. But despite their unappetizing appearance, truffles are treasured by gourmets as "diamonds of the kitchen." They command prices up to hundreds of dollars per ounce for the best specimens. A 3.3-pound white truffle—an unusually large individual of the rarest variety—brought a record $330,000 at auction. What's the attraction? Rather than their taste, truffles are prized for their powerful scent, which has been described as earthy or moldy. A little truffle goes a long way. Chefs only need to add a few shavings from a truffle to infuse a dish with its delectable essence.

Truffles are the subterranean reproductive bodies of certain fungi. Their job is to produce spores, single cells that are capable of growing into a new fungus, just as a seed can grow into a new plant. It is generally advantageous for seeds or spores to start their lives in a new place, away from the ground inhabited by their parents. And that's where the potent truffle smell comes in. Attracted by the heady aroma, certain animals excavate and eat the fungi and later deposit the hardy spores in their feces. Human noses are not sensitive enough to locate the buried treasures, so truffle hunters use pigs or trained dogs to sniff out their quarry.

Thinly sliced black truffles top a pasta dish. Black truffles, which can be cultivated, are much less expensive than the white variety, which are found only in a small region of Italy.

Besides being culinary gems, truffles represent the essential role of fungi as the hidden power behind the throne of the plant kingdom. The roots of most plants are surrounded—in some cases even permeated—by a finely woven web of fungal filaments. Truffles, for example, have such a relationship with certain species of trees, which is why skilled truffle hunters look for their treasures beneath oak and hazelnut trees. This association is an example of symbiosis, an interaction in which one species lives in or on another species. The ultrathin fungal filaments reach into pockets between the soil grains that are too small for roots to enter, absorbing water and inorganic nutrients and passing them to the plant. The plant returns the favor by supplying the fungus with sugars and other organic molecules. This relationship between fungus and root is evident in some of the oldest plant fossils, suggesting that the mutually beneficial symbiosis was crucial to the colonization of land.

Colonizing Land

What exactly is a plant? A **plant** is a multicellular eukaryote that carries out photosynthesis and has a set of adaptations for living on land. Photosynthesis distinguishes plants from the animal and fungal kingdoms, which are also made up of eukaryotic, multicellular organisms. Large algae, including seaweeds, are also eukaryotic, multicellular, and photosynthetic. However, they lack terrestrial adaptations and thus are classified as protists rather than plants. It is true that some, such as water lilies, have returned to the water, but they evolved from terrestrial ancestors (just as several species of aquatic mammals, such as whales, evolved from terrestrial mammals).

Terrestrial Adaptations of Plants

Why does life on land require a special set of adaptations? Consider how algae fare after being washed up on the

beach. Bodies that were upright in the buoyant water go limp on land and soon shrivel in the drying air. In addition, algae are not equipped to obtain the carbon dioxide needed for photosynthesis from the air. Clearly, living on land poses different problems than living in water. In this section, we discuss some of the terrestrial adaptations that distinguished plants from algae and allowed plants to colonize land. As you will see in later sections, it took more than 100 million years to complete the transition. The earliest land plants lacked some of the adaptations that made subsequent groups more successful in the terrestrial environment.

Structure/Function Adaptations of the Plant Body

For algae, carbon dioxide and minerals are available by diffusion from the surrounding water **(Figure 1)**. Resources on land are found in two very different places: Carbon dioxide is mainly available in the air, whereas mineral nutrients and water are found mainly in the soil. Thus, the complex bodies of plants have organs specialized in different ways to function in these two environments. Subterranean organs called **roots** anchor the plant in soil and absorb minerals and water from the soil. Aboveground, **shoots** are organ systems that consist of photosynthetic leaves supported by stems.

Roots typically have many fine branches that thread among the grains of soil, providing a large surface area that maximizes contact with mineral-bearing water in the soil. In addition, as you learned in the Biology and Society section in the beginning of this chapter, most plants have symbiotic fungi associated with their roots. These root-fungus combinations, called **mycorrhizae** ("fungus roots"), enlarge the root's functional surface area **(Figure 2)**. For their part, the fungi absorb water and essential minerals from the soil and provide these materials to the plant. The sugars produced by the plant nourish the fungi. Mycorrhizae are key adaptations that made it possible for plants to live on land.

Shoots also show structural adaptations to the terrestrial environment. Leaves are the main photosynthetic organs of most plants. Exchange of carbon dioxide (CO_2) and oxygen (O_2) between the atmosphere and the photosynthetic interior of a leaf occurs via **stomata** (singular, *stoma*), the microscopic pores found on a leaf's surface. A waxy layer called the **cuticle** coats the leaves and other aerial parts of most plants, helping the plant body retain water.

To transport vital materials between roots and shoots, most plants have **vascular tissue**, a network

▼ Figure 1 **Structural adaptations of algae and plants.**

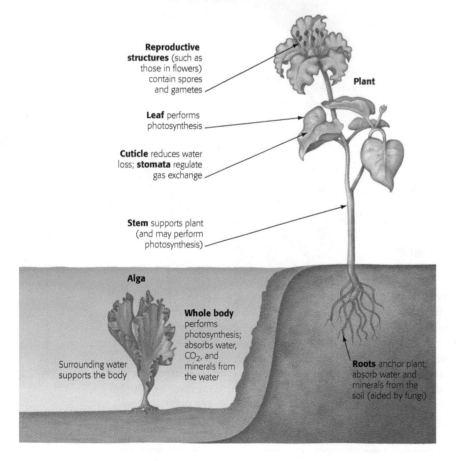

Reproductive structures (such as those in flowers) contain spores and gametes

Plant

Leaf performs photosynthesis

Cuticle reduces water loss; stomata regulate gas exchange

Stem supports plant (and may perform photosynthesis)

Alga

Whole body performs photosynthesis; absorbs water, CO_2, and minerals from the water

Surrounding water supports the body

Roots anchor plant; absorb water and minerals from the soil (aided by fungi)

▼ Figure 2 Mycorrhizae: symbiotic associations of fungi and roots. The finely branched filaments of the fungus (white in the photo) provide an extensive surface area for absorption of water and minerals from the soil.

Roots

Fungus

Root surrounded by fungus

▼ Figure 3 Network of vascular tissue in a leaf. The vascular tissue is visible as yellow veins on the underside of the leaf in the photograph.

Vascular tissue

Oak leaf

of tube-shaped cells that branch throughout the plant **(Figure 3)**. There are two types of vascular tissue. One type is specialized for transporting water and minerals from roots to leaves, and the other distributes sugars from the leaves to the roots and other nonphotosynthetic parts of the plant.

Vascular tissue also solved the problem of structural support on land. The cell walls of many of the cells in vascular tissue are hardened by a chemical called **lignin**. The structural strength of lignified vascular tissue, otherwise known as wood, is amply demonstrated by its use as a building material.

Reproductive Adaptations

Adapting to land also required a new mode of reproduction. For algae, the surrounding water ensures that gametes (sperm and eggs) and developing offspring stay moist. The aquatic environment also provides a means of dispersing the gametes and offspring. Plants, however, must keep their gametes and developing offspring from drying out in the air. Plants produce their gametes in a structure that allows gametes to develop without dehydrating. In addition, the egg remains within tissues of the mother plant and is fertilized there. In plants, but not algae, the zygote (fertilized egg) develops into an embryo while still contained within the female parent, which protects the embryo and keeps it from dehydrating **(Figure 4)**. Further adaptations in some plant groups allow sperm to travel via air and improve the survival of offspring during dispersal. ☑

▼ Figure 4 The protected embryo of a plant. Internal fertilization, with sperm and egg combining within a moist chamber on the female plant, is an adaptation for living on land. The female plant continues to nourish and protect the plant embryo, which develops from the zygote.

LM 55x

Embryo

Maternal tissue

The Origin of Plants from Green Algae

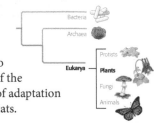

▼ Figure 5 Two species of charophytes, the closest algal relatives of plants.

LM 265x

The algal ancestors of plants carpeted moist fringes of lakes or coastal salt marshes more than 500 million years ago. These shallow-water habitats were subject to occasional drying, and natural selection would have favored algae that could survive periodic droughts. Some species accumulated adaptations that enabled them to live permanently above the water line. A modern-day lineage of green algae, the **charophytes** (Figure 5), may resemble one of these early plant ancestors. Plants and present-day charophytes probably evolved from a common ancestor.

Adaptations making life on dry land possible had accumulated by about 470 million years ago, the age of the oldest known plant fossils. The evolutionary novelties of these first land plants opened the new frontier of a terrestrial habitat. Early plant life would have thrived in the new environment. Bright sunlight was abundant on land, the atmosphere had a wealth of carbon dioxide, and at first there were relatively few pathogens and plant-eating animals. The stage was set for an explosive diversification of plant life.

Plant Diversity

As we survey the diversity of modern plants, remember that the evolutionary past is the key to the present. The history of the plant kingdom is a story of adaptation to diverse terrestrial habitats.

▼ Figure 6 Highlights of plant evolution. This phylogenetic tree highlights the evolution of structures that allowed plants to move onto land; these structures still exist in modern plants. As we survey the diversity of plants, miniature versions of this tree will help you place each plant group in its evolutionary context.

Highlights of Plant Evolution

The fossil record chronicles four major periods of plant evolution, which are also evident in the diversity of modern plants (Figure 6). Each stage is marked by the evolution of structures that opened new opportunities on land.

1 After plants originated from an algal ancestor approximately 470 million years ago, early diversification gave rise to nonvascular plants, including mosses, liverworts, and hornworts. These plants, called **bryophytes**, lack true roots and leaves. Bryophytes also lack lignin, the wall-hardening material that enables other plants to stand tall. Without lignified cell walls, bryophytes have weak upright support. The most familiar bryophytes are **mosses**. A mat of moss actually consists of many plants growing in a tight pack, holding one another up. Structures that protect the gametes and embryos are a terrestrial adaptation that originated in bryophytes.

2 The second period of plant evolution, begun about 425 million years ago, was the diversification of

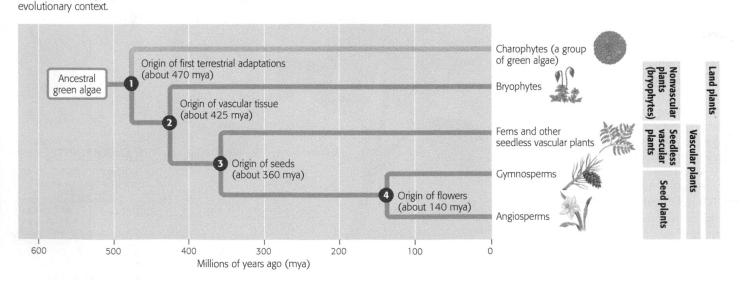

Origin of first terrestrial adaptations (about 470 mya)

Ancestral green algae

1

Origin of vascular tissue (about 425 mya)

2

Origin of seeds (about 360 mya)

3

Origin of flowers (about 140 mya)

4

Charophytes (a group of green algae)

Bryophytes

Ferns and other seedless vascular plants

Gymnosperms

Angiosperms

Nonvascular plants (bryophytes)

Seedless vascular plants

Seed plants

Vascular plants

Land plants

600   500   400   300   200   100   0

Millions of years ago (mya)

plants with vascular tissue. The presence of conducting tissues hardened with lignin allowed vascular plants to grow much taller, rising above the ground to achieve significant height. The earliest vascular plants lacked seeds. Today, this seedless condition is retained by **ferns** and a few other groups of vascular plants.

❸ The third major period of plant evolution began with the origin of the seed about 360 million years ago. Seeds advanced the colonization of land by further protecting plant embryos from drying and other hazards. A **seed** consists of an embryo packaged along with a store of food within a protective covering. The seeds of early seed plants were not enclosed in any specialized chambers. These plants gave rise to the **gymnosperms** ("naked seeds"). Today, the most widespread and diverse

gymnosperms are the **conifers**, consisting mainly of cone-bearing trees, such as pines.

❹ The fourth major episode in the evolutionary history of plants was the emergence of flowering plants, or **angiosperms** ("contained seeds"), at least 140 million years ago. The **flower** is a complex reproductive structure that bears seeds within protective chambers called ovaries. This contrasts with the naked seeds of gymnosperms. The great majority of living plants—some 250,000 species—are angiosperms, including all our fruit and vegetable crops, grains and other grasses, and most trees.

With these highlights as our framework, we are now ready to survey the four major groups of modern plants: bryophytes, ferns, gymnosperms, and angiosperms **(Figure 7)**. ☑

▼ **Figure 7** **The major groups of plants.**

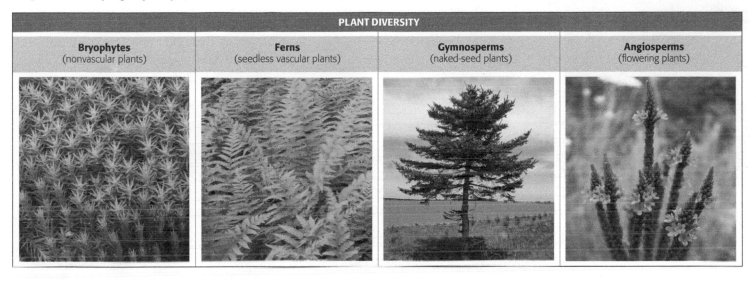

PLANT DIVERSITY			
Bryophytes (nonvascular plants)	**Ferns** (seedless vascular plants)	**Gymnosperms** (naked-seed plants)	**Angiosperms** (flowering plants)

Bryophytes

Mosses, which are bryophytes, may sprawl as low mats over acres of land **(Figure 8)**. Mosses display two of the key terrestrial adaptations that made the move onto land possible: (1) a waxy cuticle that helps prevent dehydration and (2) the retention of developing embryos within the female plant. However, mosses are not totally liberated from their ancestral aquatic habitat. Mosses need water to reproduce because their sperm need to swim to reach eggs located within the female plant. (A film of rainwater or dew is enough moisture for the sperm to travel.) In addition, because most mosses have no vascular

Bryophytes
Ferns
Gymnosperms
Angiosperms

▼ **Figure 8** **A peat moss bog in Scotland.** Mosses are bryophytes, which are nonvascular plants. Sphagnum mosses, collectively called peat moss, carpet at least 3% of Earth's land surface. They are most commonly found in high northern latitudes. The ability of peat moss to absorb and retain water makes it an excellent addition to garden soil.

tissue to carry water from soil to aerial parts of the plant, they need to live in damp places.

If you examine a mat of moss closely, you can see two distinct forms of the plant. The green, spongelike plant that is the more obvious is called the **gametophyte**. Careful examination will reveal the other form of the moss, called a **sporophyte**, growing out of a gametophyte as a stalk with a capsule at its tip (**Figure 9**). The cells of the gametophyte are haploid—they have one set of chromosomes. In contrast, the sporophyte is made up of diploid cells (with two chromosome sets). These two different stages of the plant life cycle are named for the types of reproductive cells they produce. Gametophytes produce gametes (sperm and eggs), while sporophytes produce spores. A **spore** is a haploid cell that can develop into a new individual without fusing with another cell (two gametes must fuse to form a zygote). Spores usually have tough coats that enable them to survive in harsh environments. Seedless plants, including mosses and ferns, disperse their offspring as spores rather than as multicellular seeds.

The gametophyte and sporophyte are alternating generations that take turns producing each other. Gametophytes produce gametes that unite to form zygotes, which develop into new sporophytes. And sporophytes produce spores that give rise to new gametophytes. This type of life cycle, called **alternation of generations**, occurs only in plants and multicellular green algae (**Figure 10**). Among plants, mosses and other bryophytes are unique in having the gametophyte as the larger, more obvious plant. As we continue our survey of plants, we'll see an increasing dominance of the sporophyte as the more highly developed generation. ☑

▼ Figure 9 The two forms of a moss. The feathery plant we generally know as a moss is the gametophyte. The stalk with the capsule at its tip is the sporophyte.

Spore capsule

Sporophytes

Gametophytes

► Figure 10 Alternation of generations. Plants have life cycles very different from ours. Each of us is a diploid individual; the only haploid stages in the human life cycle, as for nearly all animals, are sperm and eggs. By contrast, plants have alternating generations: Diploid (2*n*) individuals (sporophytes) and haploid (*n*) individuals (gametophytes) generate each other in the life cycle.

Spores (*n*)

Mitosis

Gametophyte (*n*)

Mitosis

Gametes: sperm and eggs (*n*)

MEIOSIS

FERTILIZATION

Spore capsule

Sporophyte (2*n*)

Zygote (2*n*)

Mitosis

Key

Haploid (*n*)

Diploid (2*n*)

☑ **CHECKPOINT**

Bryophytes, like all plants, have a life cycle that involves an alternation of generations. What are the two generations called? Which generation dominates in bryophytes?

Answer: gametophyte, sporophyte; gametophyte

Ferns

The evolution of vascular tissue allowed ferns to colonize a greater variety of habitats than mosses. Ferns are by far the most diverse seedless vascular plants, with more than 12,000 known species. However, the sperm of ferns, like those of mosses, have flagella and must swim through a film of water to fertilize eggs. Most ferns inhabit the tropics, although many species are found in temperate forests, such as many woodlands in the United States **(Figure 11)**.

During the Carboniferous period, from about 360 to 300 million years ago, ancient ferns were part of a much greater diversity of seedless plants that formed vast, swampy tropical forests over much of what is now Eurasia and North America **(Figure 12)**. As the plants died, they fell into stagnant wetlands and did not decay completely. Their remains formed thick organic deposits. Later, seawater flooded the swamps, marine sediments covered the organic deposits, and pressure and heat gradually converted them to coal. Coal is black sedimentary rock made up of fossilized plant material. Like coal, oil and natural gas also formed from the remains of long-dead organisms; thus, all three are known as **fossil fuels**. Since the Industrial Revolution, coal has been a crucial source of energy for people. However, burning these fossil fuels releases CO_2 and other gases that contribute to global climate change. ☑

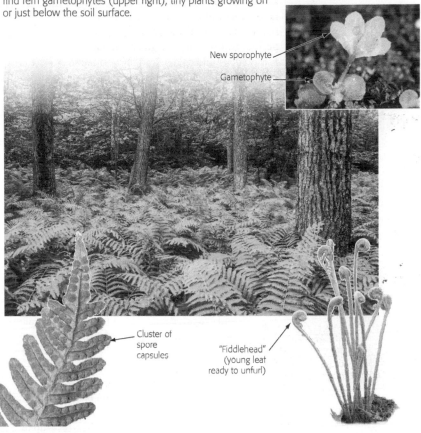

▼ **Figure 11 Ferns (seedless vascular plants).** The ferns in the foreground are growing on the forest floor in Redwood National Park, California. The fern generation familiar to us is the sporophyte generation. You would have to crawl on the forest floor and explore with careful hands and sharp eyes to find fern gametophytes (upper right), tiny plants growing on or just below the soil surface.

New sporophyte

Gametophyte

Cluster of spore capsules

"Fiddlehead" (young leaf ready to unfurl)

◀ **Figure 12 A "coal forest" of the Carboniferous period.** This painting, based on fossil evidence, reconstructs one of the great seedless forests. Most of the large trees belong to ancient groups of seedless vascular plants that are represented by just a few present-day species. The plants near the base of the trees are ferns.

☑ **CHECKPOINT**

Why are ferns able to grow taller than mosses?

Answer: Vascular tissue hardened with lignin allows ferns to stand taller and transport nutrients farther.

Gymnosperms

"Coal forests" dominated the North American and Eurasian landscapes until near the end of the Carboniferous period. At that time, the global climate turned drier and colder, and the vast swamps began to disappear. This climatic change provided an opportunity for seed plants, which can complete their life cycles on dry land and withstand long, harsh winters. Of the earliest seed plants, the most successful were the gymnosperms, and several kinds grew along with the seedless plants in the Carboniferous swamps. Their descendants include the conifers, or cone-bearing plants.

▼ **Figure 13 A coniferous forest in Tetlin National Wildlife Refuge, Alaska.** Coniferous forests are widespread in northern North America and Eurasia; conifers also grow in the Southern Hemisphere, though they are less numerous there.

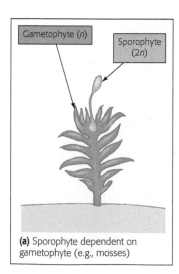

Conifers

Perhaps you have had the fun of hiking or skiing through a forest of conifers, the most common gymnosperms. Pines, firs, spruces, junipers, cedars, and redwoods are all conifers. A broad band of coniferous forests covers much of northern Eurasia and North America and extends southward in mountainous regions (**Figure 13**). Today, about 190 million acres of coniferous forests in the United States are designated national forests.

Conifers are among the tallest, largest, and oldest organisms on Earth. Coastal redwoods, native to the northern California coast, are the world's tallest trees—up to 110 m, the height of a 33-story building. Giant sequoias, relatives of redwoods that grow

in the Sierra Nevada mountains of California, are massive. One, known as the General Sherman tree, is about 84 m (275 feet) high and outweighs the combined weight of a dozen space shuttles. Bristlecone pines, another species of California conifer, are among the oldest organisms alive. A specimen discovered in 2012 is more than 5,000 years old; it was a seedling when people invented writing.

Nearly all conifers are evergreens, meaning they retain leaves throughout the year. Even during winter, they perform a limited amount of photosynthesis on sunny days. And when spring comes, conifers already have fully developed leaves that can take advantage of the sunnier days. The needle-shaped leaves of pines and firs are also adapted to survive dry seasons. A thick cuticle covers the leaf, and the stomata are located in pits, further reducing water loss.

Coniferous forests are highly productive; you probably use products harvested from them every day. For example, conifers provide much of our lumber for building and wood pulp for paper production. What we call wood is actually an accumulation of vascular tissue with lignin, which gives the tree structural support.

If you were to hug one of the largest giant sequoia trees, you would need more than a dozen friends to reach around its circumference.

Evolution Terrestrial Adaptations of Seed Plants

Compared with ferns, most gymnosperms have three additional adaptations that make survival in diverse terrestrial habitats possible: (1) further reduction of the gametophyte, (2) pollen, and (3) seeds.

The first adaptation is an even greater development of the diploid sporophyte compared with the haploid gametophyte generation (**Figure 14**). A pine tree or

► **Figure 14 Three variations on alternation of generations in plants.**

Key
- ▮ Haploid (*n*)
- ▮ Diploid (*2n*)

(a) Sporophyte dependent on gametophyte (e.g., mosses)

(b) Large sporophyte and small, independent gametophyte (e.g., ferns)

(c) Reduced gametophyte dependent on sporophyte (seed plants) other conifer is a sporophyte with tiny gametophytes living in its cones (Figure 15). In contrast to what is seen in bryophytes and ferns, gymnosperm gametophytes are totally dependent on and protected by the tissues of the parent sporophyte.

A second adaptation of seed plants to dry land came with the evolution of pollen. A **pollen grain** is actually the much-reduced male gametophyte; it houses cells that will develop into sperm. In the case of conifers, **pollination**, the delivery of pollen from the male parts of a plant to the female parts of a plant, occurs via wind. This mechanism for sperm transfer contrasts with the swimming sperm of mosses and ferns. In seed plants, the use of tough, airborne pollen that carries sperm to egg is a terrestrial adaptation that led to even greater success and diversity of plants on land.

The third important terrestrial adaptation of seed plants is the seed itself. A seed consists of a plant embryo packaged along with a food supply within a protective coat. Seeds develop from **ovules**, structures that contain the female gametophytes (Figure 16). In conifers, the ovules are located on the scales of

female cones. Once released from the parent plant, the seed can remain dormant for days, months, or even years. Under favorable conditions, the seed can then **germinate**, or sprout: Its embryo emerges through the seed coat as a seedling. Some seeds drop close to their parents, while others are carried far by the wind or animals. ☑

▼ Figure 15 **A pine tree, the sporophyte, bearing two types of cones containing gametophytes.** Each scale of the female cone is actually a modified leaf that bears a structure called an ovule containing a female gametophyte. Male cones release clouds of millions of pollen grains, the male gametophytes. Some of these pollen grains land on female cones on trees of the same species. The sperm can fertilize eggs in the ovules of the female cones. The ovules eventually develop into seeds.

Ovule-producing cones; the scales contain female gametophytes

Pollen-producing cones; they produce male gametophytes

Ponderosa pine

▼ Figure 16 **From ovule to seed.**

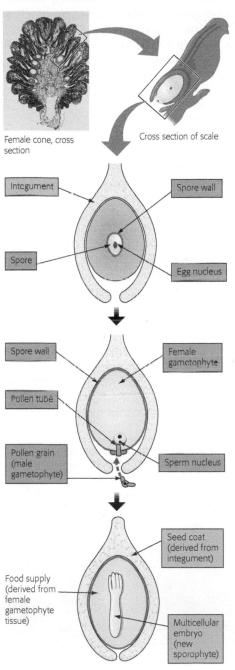

Female cone, cross section

Cross section of scale

Key

Haploid (*n*)

Diploid (2*n*)

(a) Ovule. The sporophyte produces spores within a tissue surrounded by a protective integument, which may be multilayered. The spore develops into a female gametophyte, which produces an egg nucleus.

(b) Fertilized ovule. After pollination, the pollen grain grows a tiny tube that enters the ovule, where it releases a sperm nucleus that fertilizes the egg.

(c) Seed. Fertilization triggers the transformation of ovule to seed. The fertilized egg (zygote) develops into a multicellular embryo; the rest of the gametophyte forms a tissue that stockpiles food; and the integument of the ovule hardens to become the seed coat.

Angiosperms

Angiosperms dominate the modern landscape. About 250,000 angiosperm species have been identified, compared to about 700 species of gymnosperms. Several unique adaptations account for the success of angiosperms. For example, refinements in vascular tissue make water transport even more efficient in angiosperms than in gymnosperms. Of all terrestrial adaptations, however, it is the flower that accounts for the unparalleled success of the angiosperms.

Flowers, Fruits, and the Angiosperm Life Cycle

No organism makes a showier display of its sex life than the angiosperm. From roses to dandelions, flowers are the site of procreation. This showiness helps to attract go-betweens—insects and other animals—that transfer pollen from one flower to another of the same species. Angiosperms that rely on wind pollination, including grasses and many trees, have much smaller, less flamboyant flowers. In those species, the plant's reproductive energy is allocated to making massive amounts of pollen for release into the wind.

A flower is a short stem bearing modified leaves that are attached in concentric circles at its base (**Figure 17**). The outer layer consists of the **sepals**, which are usually green. They enclose the flower before it opens (think of the green "wrapping" on a rosebud). When the sepals are peeled away, the next layer is the **petals**, which are often colorful—these are the showy structures that attract pollinators. Plucking off the petals reveals the **stamens**, the male reproductive structures. Pollen grains develop in the **anther**, a sac at the top of each stamen. At the center of the flower is the **carpel**, the female reproductive structure. It includes the **ovary**, a protective chamber containing one or more ovules, in which eggs develop. The sticky tip of the carpel, called the **stigma**, traps pollen. As you can see in **Figure 18,** the basic structure of a flower can exist in many beautiful variations.

Petal
Stamen
Anther
Filament
Stigma
Style
Ovary
Carpel
Ovule
Sepal

◀ **Figure 17 Structure of a flower.**

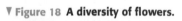
▼ **Figure 18 A diversity of flowers.**

Prickly pear cactus

Bleeding heart

California poppy

Summer snapdragon

▼ **Figure 19 The angiosperm life cycle.**

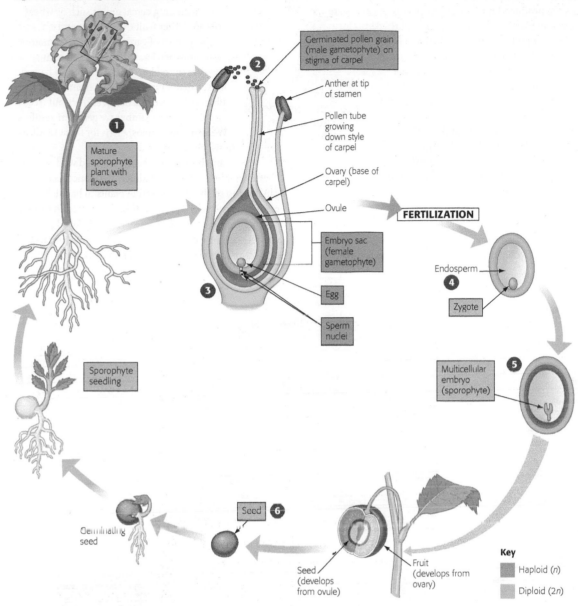

① Mature sporophyte plant with flowers

② Germinated pollen grain (male gametophyte) on stigma of carpel

Anther at tip of stamen

Pollen tube growing down style of carpel

Ovary (base of carpel)

Ovule

③ Embryo sac (female gametophyte)

Egg

Sperm nuclei

FERTILIZATION

④ Endosperm

Zygote

⑤ Multicellular embryo (sporophyte)

⑥ Seed

Seed (develops from ovule)

Fruit (develops from ovary)

Germinating seed

Sporophyte seedling

Key

Haploid (*n*)

Diploid (2*n*)

In angiosperms, as in gymnosperms, the sporophyte generation is dominant and produces the gametophyte generation within its body. **Figure 19** highlights key stages in the angiosperm life cycle. ❶ The flower is part of the sporophyte plant. As in gymnosperms, the pollen grain is the male gametophyte of angiosperms. The female gametophyte is located within an ovule, which in turn resides within a chamber of the ovary. ❷ After a pollen grain lands on the stigma, a pollen tube grows down to the ovule and ❸ releases a sperm nucleus that fertilizes an egg within the embryo sac. ❹ This produces a zygote, which ❺ develops into an embryo. The tissue surrounding the embryo develops into nutrient-rich **endosperm**, which will provide a food supply for the growing plant. ❻ The whole ovule develops into a seed, which can germinate and develop into a new sporophyte to begin the cycle anew. The seed's enclosure within an ovary is what distinguishes angiosperms (from the Greek *angion*, container, and *sperm*, seed) from gymnosperms (from the Greek *gymnos*, naked), which have a naked seed.

A **fruit** is the ripened ovary of a flower. Thus, fruits are produced only by angiosperms. As seeds are developing from ovules, the ovary wall thickens, forming the fruit that encloses the seeds. A pea pod is an example of a fruit with seeds (mature ovules, the peas) encased in the ripened ovary (the pod). Fruits protect and help disperse seeds. As **Figure 20** demonstrates, many angiosperms depend on animals to disperse seeds, often passing them through the digestive tract. Conversely, most land animals, including humans, rely on angiosperms as a food source, directly or indirectly. ☑

> The most expensive coffee in the world has passed through the digestive tract of a catlike animal called a civet.

Angiosperms and Agriculture

Whereas gymnosperms supply most of our lumber and paper, angiosperms supply nearly all of our food—as well as the food eaten by domesticated animals, such as cows and chickens. More than 90% of the plant kingdom is made up of angiosperms, including cereal grains such as wheat and corn, citrus and other fruit trees, coffee and tea, and cotton. Many types of garden produce—tomatoes, squash, strawberries, and oranges, to name just a few—are the edible fruits of plants we have domesticated. Fine hardwoods from flowering plants such as oak, cherry, and walnut trees supplement the lumber we get from conifers. We also grow angiosperms for fiber, medications, perfumes, and decoration.

Early humans probably collected wild seeds and fruits. Agriculture gradually developed as people began sowing seeds and cultivating plants to have a more dependable food source. And as they domesticated certain plants, people began to select those with improved yield and quality. Agriculture can thus be seen as yet another facet of the evolutionary relationship between plants and animals.

☑ CHECKPOINT

What are the four main parts of a flower? Where do pollen grains develop? Where do eggs develop?

Answer: sepals, petals, stamens, carpels; in the anther within the stamen; in the ovary within the carpel

▼ Figure 20 **Fruits and seed dispersal.** Different types of fruits are adapted for different methods of dispersal.

Wind dispersal. Some angiosperms depend on wind for seed dispersal. Here, milkweed pods open to release masses of seeds (brown) carried by silken parachutes (part of the seed coat).

Animal transportation. Some fruits are adapted to hitch free rides on animals. The cockleburs attached to the fur of this dog may be carried miles before opening and releasing seeds.

Animal ingestion. Many angiosperms produce fleshy, edible fruits that are attractive to animals as food. The animal digests the fleshy part of the fruit, but most of the tough seeds pass unharmed through the digestive tract. The seeds are later deposited, along with a fertilizer supply, some distance from where the fruit was eaten. The Asian palm civet shown here is eating coffee berries. The civet's digestive enzymes reportedly give the seeds (coffee beans) an exquisite flavor. Coffee beans "processed" in this way, known as kopi luwak, cost up to $500 per pound.

Plant Diversity as a Nonrenewable Resource

The ever-increasing human population, with its demand for space and natural resources, is extinguishing plant species at an unprecedented rate. The problem is especially critical for forest ecosystems, which are home to as many as 80% of the world's plant and animal species. Deforestation has been an ongoing human activity for centuries. Worldwide, less than 25% of the original forests remain; the figure in the contiguous United States is around 10%. Typically, forests are cut down to harvest timber or to clear land for housing or large-scale agriculture (Figure 21). Much of the forest that remains is tropical, and it is disappearing at an estimated 150,000 km² per year (about 58,000 mi²), which is roughly equal to the area of Illinois. Government policies in Brazil have produced a marked slowdown in Amazonian deforestation. Nevertheless, the global rate of tropical deforestation has increased by 2,101 km² (more than 800 mi²) per year over the past decade.

Why does the loss of tropical forests matter? In addition to forests being centers of biodiversity, millions of people worldwide depend on these forests for their livelihood. There are other practical reasons to be concerned about the loss of plant diversity represented in tropical forests. More than 120 prescription drugs are made from substances derived from plants (Table 1). Pharmaceutical companies were led to most of these species by local peoples who use the plants in preparing their traditional medicines. Today, researchers are seeking to combine their scientific skills with the stores of local knowledge in partnerships that will develop new drugs and also benefit the local economies.

Scientists are working to slow the loss of plant diversity, in part by researching sustainable ways for people to benefit from forests. The goal of such efforts is to encourage management practices that use forests as resources without damaging them. The solutions we propose must be economically realistic; people who live where there are tropical rain forests must be able to make a living. But if the only goal is profit for the short term, then the destruction will continue until the forests are gone. We need to appreciate the rain forests and other ecosystems as living treasures that can regenerate only slowly. Only then will we learn to work with them in ways that preserve their biological diversity for the future.

Throughout our survey of plants in this chapter, we have seen how entangled the botanical world is with other terrestrial life. We switch our attention now to that other group of organisms that moved onto land with plants: the kingdom Fungi. ✓

▼ Figure 21 **Cultivated land bordering a tropical forest in Uganda.** Bwindi Impenetrable National Park (on the right) is renowned for its biodiversity, which includes half the world's remaining mountain gorillas.

Table 1	A Sampling of Medicines Derived from Plants		
Compound	**Source**		**Example of Use**
Atropine	Belladonna plant		Pupil dilator in eye exams
Digitalin	Foxglove		Heart medication
Menthol	Wild mint		Ingredient in cough medicines, decongestants
Morphine	Opium poppy		Pain reliever
Quinine	Quinine tree		Malaria preventive
Paclitaxel (Taxol)	Pacific yew		Ovarian cancer drug
Tubocurarine	Curare tree		Muscle relaxant during surgery
Vinblastine	Periwinkle		Leukemia drug

Source: Adapted from Randy Moore et al., Botany, 2nd ed. Dubuque, IA: Brown, 1998, Table 2.2, p. 37.

Fungi

The word *fungus* often evokes unpleasant images. Fungi rot timbers, spoil food, and afflict people with athlete's foot and worse.

However, ecosystems would collapse without fungi to decompose dead organisms, fallen leaves, feces, and other organic materials. Fungi recycle vital chemical elements back to the environment in forms that other organisms can assimilate. And you have already learned that nearly all plants have mycorrhizae, fungus-root associations that help plants absorb minerals and water from the soil. In addition to these ecological roles, fungi have been used by people in various ways for centuries. We eat fungi (mushrooms and extremely expensive truffles, for instance), culture fungi to produce antibiotics and other drugs, add them to dough to make bread rise, culture them in milk to produce a variety of cheeses, and use them to ferment beer and wine.

Fungi are eukaryotes, and most are multicellular, but many have body structures and modes of reproduction unlike those of any other organism **(Figure 22)**. Molecular studies indicate that fungi and animals arose from a common ancestor around 1.5 billion years ago. The oldest undisputed fossils of fungi, however, are only about 460 million years old, perhaps because the ancestors of terrestrial fungi were microscopic and fossilized poorly. Despite appearances, a mushroom is more closely related to you than it is to any plant!

Biologists who study fungi have described more than 100,000 species, but there may be as many as 1.5 million. Classifying fungi is an ongoing area of research. (One widely accepted phylogenetic tree divides the kingdom Fungi into five groups.) You are probably familiar with several kinds of fungi, including mushrooms, mold, and yeast. In this section, we'll discuss the characteristics common to all fungi and then survey their wide-ranging ecological impact. ☑

> Fungi may not always be pretty, but if you find the right one, it could pay your way through college.

☑ CHECKPOINT

Name three ways that we benefit from fungi in our environment.

Answer: Fungi help recycle nutrients by decomposing dead organisms; mycorrhizae help plants absorb water and nutrients; some fungi serve us as food.

▼ **Figure 22 A gallery of diverse fungi.**

Bracket fungi. These are the reproductive structures of a fungus that absorbs nutrients as it decomposes a fallen tree on a forest floor. The green "leafy" material is lichens, which are described in the Evolution Connection section in this chapter.

A "fairy ring." Some mushroom-producing fungi poke up "fairy rings," which can appear on a lawn overnight. A ring develops at the edge of the main body of the fungus, which consists of an underground mass of tiny filaments (hyphae) within the ring. As the underground fungal mass grows outward from its center, the diameter of the fairy ring produced at its expanding perimeter increases annually.

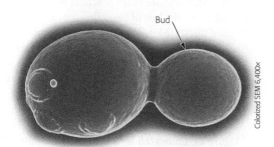

Colorized SEM 6,400x

Bud

Budding yeast. Yeasts are unicellular fungi. This yeast cell is reproducing asexually by a process called budding.

Colorized SEM 2,800x

Mold. Molds grow rapidly on their food sources, which are often our food sources as well. The mold on this orange reproduces asexually by producing chains of microscopic spores (inset) that are dispersed via air currents.

Corn smut. This parasitic fungus plagues corn growers. To gourmets, however, it is a delicacy known as *huitlacoche*.

Structure/ Function ## Characteristics of Fungi

We'll begin our look at the structure and function of fungi with an overview of how fungi obtain nutrients.

Fungal Nutrition

Fungi are heterotrophs that acquire their nutrients by absorption. In this mode of nutrition, small organic molecules are absorbed from the surrounding medium. A fungus digests food outside its body by secreting powerful digestive enzymes into the food. The enzymes decompose complex molecules to simpler compounds that the fungus can absorb. Fungi absorb nutrients from such nonliving organic material as fallen logs, animal corpses, and the wastes of live organisms.

Fungal Structure

The bodies of most fungi are constructed of threadlike filaments called **hyphae** (singular, *hypha*). Fungal hyphae are minute threads of cytoplasm surrounded by a plasma membrane and cell wall. The cell walls of fungi differ from the cellulose walls of plants. Fungal cell walls are usually built mainly of chitin, a strong but flexible polysaccharide that is also found in the external skeletons of insects. Most fungi have multicellular hyphae, which consist of chains of cells separated by cross-walls with pores. In many fungi, cell-to-cell channels allow ribosomes, mitochondria, and even nuclei to flow between cells.

Fungal hyphae branch repeatedly, forming an interwoven network called a **mycelium** (plural, *mycelia*), the feeding structure of the fungus (**Figure 23**). Fungal mycelia usually escape our notice because they are often subterranean, but they can be huge. In fact, scientists have discovered that the mycelium of one humongous fungus in Oregon is 5.5 km—that's 3.4 miles!—in diameter and spreads through 2,200 acres of forest. This fungus is at least 2,600 years old and weighs hundreds of tons, qualifying it as one of Earth's oldest and largest organisms.

A mycelium maximizes contact with its food source by mingling with the organic matter it is decomposing and absorbing. A bucketful of rich organic soil may contain as much as a kilometer of hyphae. A fungal mycelium grows rapidly, adding hyphae as it branches within its food. The great majority of fungi are nonmotile; they cannot run, swim, or fly in search of food. But the mycelium makes up for the lack of mobility by swiftly extending the tips of its hyphae into new territory. ☑

Fungal Reproduction

The mushroom in Figure 23 is actually made up of tightly packed hyphae. Mushrooms arise from an underground mycelium. While the mycelium obtains food from organic material via absorption, the function of the mushroom is reproduction. Unlike a truffle, which relies on animals to disperse its spores, a mushroom pops up above ground to disperse its spores on air currents.

Fungi typically reproduce by releasing haploid spores that are produced either sexually or asexually. The output of spores is mind-boggling. For example, puffballs, which are the reproductive structures of certain fungi, can spew clouds containing trillions of spores. Easily carried by wind or water, spores germinate to produce mycelia if they land in a moist place where there is food. Spores thus function in dispersal and account for the wide geographic distribution of many species of fungi. The airborne spores of fungi have been found more than 160 km (100 miles) above Earth. Closer to home, try leaving a slice of bread out for a week and you will observe the furry mycelia that grow from the invisible spores raining down from the surrounding air.

If you've ever had mushroom pizza, you've snacked on the fungi's reproductive structure.

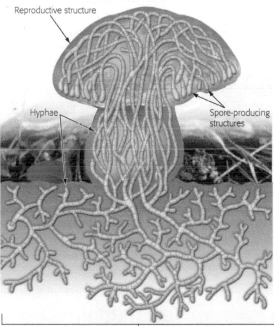

Reproductive structure

Hyphae

Spore-producing structures

Mycelium

◄ **Figure 23 The fungal mycelium.** A mushroom consists of tightly packed hyphae that extend upward from a much more massive mycelium of hyphae growing underground. The photo at the bottom shows a mycelium made up of the cottony threads that decompose organic litter.

☑ **CHECKPOINT**

Describe how the structure of a fungal mycelium reflects its function.

Answer: The extensive network of hyphae puts a large surface area in contact with the food source.

The Ecological Impact of Fungi

Fungi have been major players in terrestrial communities ever since plants and fungi together moved onto land. Let's examine a few examples of how fungi continue to have an enormous ecological impact, including numerous interactions with people.

Fungi as Decomposers

Fungi and bacteria are the principal decomposers that keep ecosystems stocked with the inorganic nutrients essential for plant growth. Without decomposers, carbon, nitrogen, and other elements would accumulate in nonliving organic matter. Plants and the animals they feed would starve because elements taken from the soil would not be returned.

Fungi are well adapted as decomposers of organic refuse. Their invasive hyphae enter the tissues and cells of dead organisms and digest polymers, including the cellulose of plant cell walls. A succession of fungi, in concert with bacteria and, in some environments, invertebrate animals, is responsible for the complete breakdown of organic litter. The air is so loaded with fungal spores that as soon as a leaf falls or an insect dies, it is covered with spores and soon after infiltrated by fungal hyphae.

We may applaud fungi that decompose forest litter or dung, but it's a different story when molds attack our food or our shower curtains. A significant amount of the world's fruit harvest is lost each year to fungal attack. And a wood-digesting fungus does not distinguish between a fallen oak limb and the oak planks of a boat. During the Revolutionary War, the British lost more ships to fungal rot than to enemy attack. What's more, soldiers stationed in the tropics during World War II watched as their tents, clothing, and boots were destroyed by molds.

Parasitic Fungi

Parasitism is a relationship in which two species live in contact and one organism benefits while the other is harmed. Parasitic fungi absorb nutrients from the cells or body fluids of living hosts. Of the 100,000 known species of fungi, about 30% make their living as parasites.

About 500 species of fungi are known to be parasitic in humans and other animals. A baffling disease known as coccidioidomycosis, or valley fever, causes devastating illness in some people; others suffer only mild flu-like symptoms. People contract the disease when they inhale the spores of a fungus that lives in the soil of the southwestern United States. In recent years, researchers have noticed an uptick in reported cases of valley fever, perhaps due to changes in climate patterns or development of once-rural areas inhabited by the fungus. Less serious fungal diseases include vaginal yeast infections and ringworm, so named because it appears as circular red areas on the skin. The ringworm fungus can infect almost any skin surface, where it produces intense itching and sometimes blisters. One species attacks the feet, causing athlete's foot. Another species is responsible for the misery known as jock itch.

The great majority of fungal parasites infect plants. American chestnut and American elm trees, once common in forests, fields, and city streets, were devastated by fungal epidemics in the 20th century (**Figure 24a**). Fungi are also serious agricultural pests, and some of the fungi that attack food crops are toxic to humans. The seed heads of many kinds of grain and grasses, including rye, wheat, and oats, are sometimes infected with fungal growths called ergots (**Figure 24b**). Consumption of flour made from ergot-infested grain can cause hallucinations, temporary insanity, and death. In fact, lysergic acid, the raw material from which the hallucinogenic drug LSD is made, has been isolated from ergots. This fact may help explain a centuries-old mystery, as we'll see next.

(a) An American elm tree killed by Dutch elm disease fungus

Ergots

(b) Ergots on rye

◀ **Figure 24 Parasitic fungi that cause plant disease.** (a) The parasitic fungus that causes Dutch elm disease evolved with European species of elm trees, and it is relatively harmless to them. But it has been deadly to American elms since it was accidentally introduced in 1926. (b) Ergots, parasitic fungi, are the dark structures on these rye seed heads.

Plant-Fungus Interactions THE PROCESS OF SCIENCE

Did a Fungus Lead to the Salem Witch Hunt?

In January 1692, eight young girls in the town of Salem, Massachusetts, began to act bizarrely. The girls suffered from incomprehensible speech, odd skin sensations, convulsions, and hallucinations. The worried community blamed the girls' symptoms on witchcraft and began to accuse one another. By the time the hysteria ended that autumn, more than 150 villagers had been accused of witchcraft, and 20 of them had been hanged as a result. Finding the cause behind the "Salem witch hunt" has long intrigued historians.

In 1976, a University of California psychology graduate student offered a new explanation. She began with the **observation** that the symptoms reported by the girls were consistent with ergot poisoning (**Figure 25**). This led her to **question** whether an ergot outbreak could have been behind the witch hunt. The researcher tested her **hypothesis** by examining the historical records, making the **prediction** that facts consistent with ergot poisoning would be uncovered.

Her **results** were suggestive, though not conclusive. Agricultural records confirm that rye—the principal host for ergot—grew abundantly around Salem at that time and that the growing season of 1691 had been particularly warm and wet, conditions under which ergot thrives. This suggests that the rye crop consumed during the winter of 1691–1692 could easily have been contaminated. The summer of 1692, when the accusations began to die down, was dry, consistent with an ergot die-off. Most important, the reported symptoms appear consistent with those of ergot poisoning. These clues suggest (but do not prove) that the girls, and perhaps others in Salem, were in the grips of ergot-induced illness. Some historians dispute this idea, and other hypotheses have been proposed. Conclusive evidence may never be found, but this story reinforces the unifying thread of this chapter—the importance of the interaction of plants and fungi—and illustrates how the scientific method can be applied in a wide variety of academic disciplines.

▼ **Figure 25 Ergot and the Salem witch hunt.** Ergot poisoning may have been the catalyst for the Salem witch hunt of 1692.

Commercial Uses of Fungi

It would not be fair to fungi to end our discussion with an account of diseases. In addition to their positive global impact as decomposers, fungi also have a number of practical uses for people.

Most of us have eaten mushrooms, although we may not have realized that we were ingesting the reproductive extensions of subterranean fungi. Your grocery store probably stocks Portobello, shiitake, and oyster mushrooms along with common button mushrooms. If you like to cook with mushrooms, you can buy a mushroom "garden"—mycelium embedded in a rich food source—that makes it easy to grow your own. Some enthusiasts gather edible fungi from fields and forests (**Figure 26**), but only experts should dare to eat wild fungi. Some poisonous species resemble edible ones, and there are no simple rules to help the novice distinguish one from the other.

Other fungi are used in food production. The distinctive flavors of certain kinds of cheeses, including Roquefort and blue cheese, come from the fungi used to ripen them. And people have used yeasts (unicellular fungi) for thousands of years to produce alcoholic beverages and cause bread to rise.

▼ **Figure 26 Fungi eaten by people.**

Chicken of the woods. This fleshy shelf fungus is said to taste like chicken.

Chanterelle mushrooms. Gourmet mushrooms are highly prized by chefs for their earthy flavors and interesting textures.

Giant puffball. These humongous fungi can grow to more than 2 feet in diameter. They are only edible when immature, before the spores form. Beware: Deadly fungi often resemble small puffballs.

Fungi are medically valuable as well. Some fungi produce antibiotics that are used to treat bacterial diseases. In fact, the first antibiotic discovered was penicillin, made by the common mold *Penicillium* (**Figure 27**). Researchers are also investigating fungal products that show potential as anticancer drugs.

As sources of medicines and food, as decomposers, and as partners with plants in mycorrhizae, fungi play vital roles in life on Earth. ☑

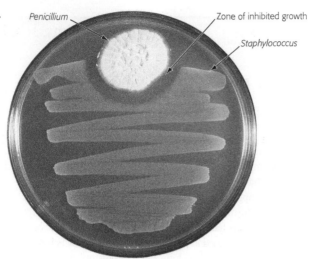

Penicillium

Zone of inhibited growth

Staphylococcus

▶ **Figure 27 Fungal production of an antibiotic.** Penicillin is made by the common mold *Penicillium*. In this petri dish, the clear area between the mold and the growing *Staphylococcus* bacteria is where the antibiotic produced by the *Penicillium* inhibits the growth of the bacteria.

Plant-Fungus Interactions EVOLUTION CONNECTION

A Mutually Beneficial Symbiosis

Discussing fungi in the same chapter as plants may seem to indicate that these two kingdoms are close relatives, but as we've discussed, fungi are more closely related to animals than to plants. However, the success of plants on land and the great diversity of fungi are interconnected; neither could have populated the land without the other.

Evolution is not just about the origin and adaptation of individual species. Relationships between species are also an evolutionary product. For example, prokaryotes and protists partner with a variety of organisms in mutually beneficial symbioses. Bacteria living in the roots of certain plants provide nitrogen compounds to their host and receive food in exchange. We even have our own symbiotic bacteria that help keep our skin healthy and produce certain vitamins in our intestines. Particularly relevant to this chapter is the symbiotic association of fungi and plant roots—mycorrhizae—that made life's move onto land possible.

Lichens, symbiotic associations of unicellular algae or photosynthetic bacteria held in a mass of fungal hyphae, are striking examples of how intimate these relationships can be. At a distance, it is easy to mistake lichens for mosses or other simple plants growing on rocks, rotting logs, or trees (**Figure 28**). The partners are so closely entwined that they appear to be a single organism. The fungus receives food from its photosynthetic partner. The fungal mycelium, in turn, provides a suitable habitat for the algae, helping the algae absorb and retain water and minerals. The merger is so complete that lichens are actually named as species, as though they were individual organisms.

After protists and plants, fungi is the third group of eukaryotes that we have surveyed so far. Strong evidence suggests that they evolved from protist ancestors that also gave rise to the fourth and most diverse group of eukaryotes: the animals.

▼ **Figure 28 Lichens: symbiotic associations of fungi and algae.** Lichens generally grow very slowly, sometimes less than a millimeter per year. Some lichens are thousands of years old, rivaling the oldest plants as Earth's elders. The close relationship between the fungal and algal partners is evident in the microscopic blowup of a lichen.

Algal cell

Fungal hyphae

Colorized SEM 1,000×

Chapter Review

SUMMARY OF KEY CONCEPTS

Colonizing Land

Terrestrial Adaptations of Plants

Plants are multicellular photosynthetic eukaryotes with adaptations for living on land.

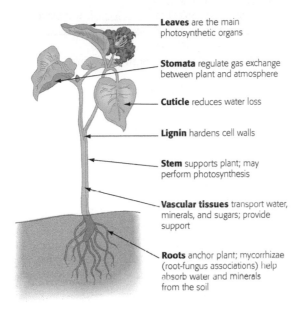

Leaves are the main photosynthetic organs

Stomata regulate gas exchange between plant and atmosphere

Cuticle reduces water loss

Lignin hardens cell walls

Stem supports plant; may perform photosynthesis

Vascular tissues transport water, minerals, and sugars; provide support

Roots anchor plant; mycorrhizae (root-fungus associations) help absorb water and minerals from the soil

The Origin of Plants from Green Algae

Plants evolved from a group of multicellular green algae called charophytes.

Plant Diversity

Highlights of Plant Evolution

Four periods of plant evolution are marked by terrestrial adaptations in major plant groups.

| **Bryophytes** have structures that protect gametes and embryos. | **Ferns** have vascular tissue that conducts water and nutrients. | **Gymnosperms** have seeds that protect embryos from dessication. | **Angiosperms** have ovaries that protect ovules and disperse seeds. |

Bryophytes

 The most familiar bryophytes are mosses. Mosses display two key terrestrial adaptations: a waxy cuticle that prevents dehydration and the retention of developing embryos within the female plant's body. Mosses are most common in moist environments because their sperm must swim to the eggs and because they lack lignin in their cell walls and thus cannot stand tall. Bryophytes are unique among plants in having the gametophyte as the dominant generation in the life cycle.

Ferns

 Ferns are seedless plants that have vascular tissues but still use flagellated sperm to fertilize eggs. During the Carboniferous period, giant ferns were among the plants that decayed to thick deposits of organic matter, which were gradually converted to coal.

Gymnosperms

 A drier and colder global climate near the end of the Carboniferous period favored the evolution of the first seed plants. The most successful were the gymnosperms, represented by conifers. Needle-shaped leaves with thick cuticles and sunken stomata are adaptations to dry conditions. Conifers and most other gymnosperms have three additional terrestrial adaptations: (1) further reduction of the haploid gametophyte and greater development of the diploid sporophyte; (2) sperm-bearing pollen, which doesn't require water for transport; and (3) seeds, which consist of a plant embryo packaged along with a food supply inside a protective coat.

Angiosperms

Angiosperms supply nearly all our food and much of our fiber for textiles. The evolution of the flower and more efficient water transport help account for the success of the angiosperms. The dominant stage is a sporophyte with gametophytes in its flowers. The female gametophyte is located within an ovule, which in turn resides within a chamber of the ovary. Fertilization of an egg in the female gametophyte produces a zygote, which develops into an embryo. The whole ovule develops into a seed. The seed's enclosure within an ovary is what distinguishes angiosperms from gymnosperms, which have naked seeds. A fruit is the ripened ovary of a flower. Fruits protect and help disperse seeds. Angiosperms are a major food source for animals, while animals aid plants in pollination and seed dispersal. Agriculture constitutes a unique kind of evolutionary relationship among plants, people, and other animals.

Plant Diversity as a Nonrenewable Resource

Deforestation to meet the demand of human activities for space and natural resources is causing the extinction of plant species at an unprecedented rate. The problem is especially critical for tropical forests.

Fungi

Characteristics of Fungi

Fungi are unicellular or multicellular eukaryotes; they are heterotrophs that digest their food externally and absorb the nutrients from the environment. They are more closely related to animals than to plants. A fungus usually consists of a mass of threadlike hyphae, forming a mycelium. The cell walls of fungi are mainly composed of chitin. Although most fungi are nonmotile, a mycelium can grow very quickly, extending the tips of its hyphae into new territory. Mushrooms are reproductive structures that extend from the underground mycelium. Fungi reproduce and disperse by releasing spores that are produced either sexually or asexually.

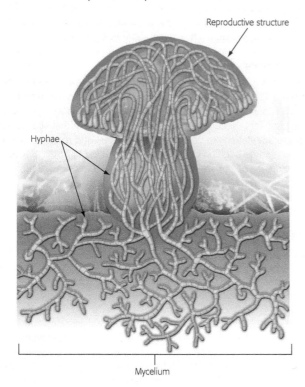

Reproductive structure

Hyphae

Mycelium

The Ecological Impact of Fungi

Fungi and bacteria are the principal decomposers of ecosystems. Many molds destroy fruit, wood, and human-made materials. About 500 species of fungi are known to be parasites of people and other animals. Fungi are also commercially important as food and in baking, beer and wine production, and the manufacture of antibiotics.

MasteringBiology®

For practice quizzes, BioFlix animations, MP3 tutorials, video tutors, and more study tools designed for this text, go to MasteringBiology®

SELF-QUIZ

1. Which of the following structures is common to all four major plant groups? vascular tissue, flowers, seeds, cuticle, pollen

2. Angiosperms are distinguished from all other plants because only angiosperms have reproductive structures called _____.

3. Complete the following analogies:
   a. Gametophyte is to haploid as _____ is to diploid.
   b. _____ are to conifers as flowers are to _____.
   c. Ovule is to seed as ovary is to _____.

4. Under a microscope, a piece of a mushroom would look most like
   a. jelly.
   b. a tangle of string.
   c. grains of sand.
   d. a sponge.

5. During the Carboniferous period, the dominant plants, which later formed the great coal beds, were mainly
   a. mosses and other bryophytes.
   b. ferns and other seedless vascular plants.
   c. charophytes and other green algae.
   d. conifers and other gymnosperms.

6. You discover a new species of plant. Under the microscope, you find that it produces flagellated sperm. A genetic analysis shows that its dominant generation has diploid cells. What kind of plant do you have?

7. How does the evergreen nature of pines and other conifers adapt the plants for living where the growing season is very short?

8. Which of the following terms includes all others in the list? angiosperm, fern, vascular plant, gymnosperm, seed plant

9. Plant diversity is greatest in
   a. tropical forests.
   b. the temperate forests of Europe.
   c. deserts.
   d. the oceans.

10. What is a fruit?

11. Lichens are symbionts of photosynthetic _____ with _____.

12. Contrast the heterotrophic nutrition of a fungus with your own heterotrophic nutrition.

THE PROCESS OF SCIENCE

13. In April 1986, an accident at a nuclear power plant in Chernobyl, Ukraine, scattered radioactive fallout for hundreds of miles. In assessing the biological effects of the radiation, researchers found mosses to be especially valuable as organisms for monitoring the damage. Radiation damages organisms by causing mutations. Explain why it is faster to observe the genetic effects of radiation on mosses than on other types of

plants. Imagine that you are conducting tests shortly after a nuclear accident. Using potted moss plants as your experimental organisms, design an experiment to test the hypothesis that the frequency of mutations decreases with the organism's distance from the source of radiation.

14. **Interpreting Data** Airborne pollen of wind-pollinated plants such as pines, oaks, weeds, and grasses causes seasonal allergy symptoms in many people. As global warming lengthens the growing season for plants, scientists predict longer periods of misery for allergy sufferers. However, global warming does not affect all regions equally. The table below shows the length of the average season in nine locations for ragweed pollen, an allergen that affects millions of people. Calculate the change in length of the pollen season from 1995 to 2009 for each location and graph this information against latitude. Is there a latitudinal trend in the length of ragweed season? You may want to record the data on a map to help you visualize the geographic locations at which samples were taken.

Average Length of Ragweed Pollen Season in Nine Locations (averages obtained from at least 15 years of data)				
Location	Latitude (°N)	Length of Pollen Season in 1995 (days)	Length of Pollen Season in 2009 (days)	Change in Length of Pollen Season (days)
Oklahoma City, OK	35.47	88	89	
Rogers, AR	36.33	64	69	
Papillion, WI	41.15	69	80	
Madison, WI	43.00	64	76	
La Crosse, WI	43.80	58	71	
Minneapolis, MN	45.00	62	78	
Fargo, ND	46.88	36	52	
Winnipeg, MB, Canada	50.07	57	82	
Saskatoon, SK, Canada	52.07	44	71	

Data from: L. Ziska et al., Recent warming by latitude associated with increased length of ragweed pollen season in central North America. *Proceedings of the National Academy of Sciences* 108: 4248–4251 (2011).

BIOLOGY AND SOCIETY

15. Why are tropical forests being destroyed so rapidly? What kinds of social, technological, and economic factors are responsible? Most forests in more industrialized Northern Hemisphere countries have already been cut. Do the more industrialized nations have a right to pressure the less industrialized nations in the Southern Hemisphere to slow or stop the destruction of their forests? Defend your answer. What kinds of benefits, incentives, or programs might slow the destruction of tropical forests?

16. As you learned in this chapter, many prescription drugs are derived from natural plant products. Numerous other plant substances, including caffeine and nicotine, have effects in the human body, as well. There is also a wide array of plant products, in the form of pills, powders, or teas, marketed as herbal medicines. Some people prefer taking these "natural" products to pharmaceuticals. Others use herbal supplements to boost energy, promote weight loss, strengthen the immune system, relieve stress, and more. The U.S. Federal Drug Administration, which approves pharmaceuticals, is also responsible for regulating herbal remedies. What does the label "FDA-approved" on an herbal remedy mean? How does that compare to FDA approval of a drug? The FDA website http://www.fda.gov/ForConsumers/default.htm is a good place to start your research. (Note that the FDA classifies herbal remedies as dietary supplements.)

Glossary

absorption
The uptake of small nutrient molecules by an organism's own body. In animals, absorption is the third main stage of food processing, following digestion; in fungi, it is acquisition of nutrients from the surrounding medium.

alternation of generations
A life cycle in which there is both a multicellular diploid form, the sporophyte, and a multicellular haploid form, the gametophyte; a characteristic of plants and multicellular green algae.

angiosperm (*an'-jē-ō-sperm*)
A flowering plant, which forms seeds inside a protective chamber called an ovary.

anther
A sac in which pollen grains develop, located at the tip of a flower's stamen.

bryophyte (*brī'-uh-fīt*)
A type of plant that lacks xylem and phloem; a nonvascular plant. Bryophytes include mosses and their close relatives.

carpel (*kar'-pul*)
The egg-producing part of a flower, consisting of a stalk with an ovary at the base and a stigma, which traps pollen, at the tip.

charophyte (*kār'-uh-fīt'*)
A member of the green algal group that shares features with land plants. Charophytes are considered the closest relatives of land plants; modern charophytes and modern plants likely evolved from a common ancestor.

conifer (*kon'-uh-fer*)
A gymnosperm, or naked-seed plant, most of which produce cones.

cuticle (*kyū'-tuh-kul*)
(1) In animals, a tough, nonliving outer layer of the skin. (2) In plants, a waxy coating on the surface of stems and leaves that helps retain water.

endosperm
In flowering plants, a nutrient-rich mass formed by the union of a sperm cell with the diploid central cell of the embryo sac during double fertilization; provides nourishment to the developing embryo in the seed.

fern
Any of a group of seedless vascular plants.

flower
In an angiosperm, a short shoot with four sets of modified leaves, bearing structures that function in sexual reproduction.

fossil fuel
An energy deposit formed from the fossilized remains of long-dead plants and animals.

fruit
A ripened, thickened ovary of a flower, which protects dormant seeds and aids in their dispersal.

fungus
(plural, **fungi**) A heterotrophic eukaryote that digests its food externally and absorbs the resulting small nutrient molecules. Most fungi consist of a netlike mass of filaments called hyphae. Molds, mushrooms, and yeasts are examples of fungi.**gametophyte** (*guh-mē'-tō-fīt*)
The multicellular haploid form in the life cycle of organisms undergoing alternation of generations; results from a union of spores and mitotically produces haploid gametes that unite and grow into the sporophyte generation.

germinate
To initiate growth, as in a plant seed or a plant or fungal spore.

gymnosperm (*jim'-nō-sperm*)
A naked-seed plant. Its seed is said to be naked because it is not enclosed in an ovary.**hypha** (*hī'-fuh*)
(plural, **hyphae**) One of many

filaments making up the body of a fungus.

lichen (*lī'-ken*)
A symbiotic association between a fungus and an alga or between a fungus and a cyanobacterium.

lignin (*lig'-nin*)
A chemical that hardens the cell walls of plants. Lignin makes up most of what we call wood.

moss
Any of a group of seedless nonvascular plants.

mycelium (*mī-sē'-lē-um*)
(plural, **mycelia**) The densely branched network of hyphae in a fungus.

mycorrhiza (*mī'-kō-rī'-zuh*)
(plural, **mycorrhizae**) A mutually beneficial symbiotic association of a plant root and fungus.

ovary
(1) In animals, the female gonad, which produces egg cells and reproductive hormones. (2) In flowering plants, the base of a carpel in which the egg-containing ovules develop.

ovule (*ō'-vyūl*)
In a seed plant, a reproductive structure that contains the female gametophyte and the developing egg. An ovule develops into a seed.**petal**
A modified leaf of a flowering plant. Petals are the often colorful parts of a flower that advertise it to insects and other pollinators.

plant
A multicellular eukaryote that carries out photosynthesis and has a set of structural and reproductive terrestrial adaptations, including a multicellular, dependent embryo.

pollen grain
In a seed plant, the male gametophyte that develops within the anther of a stamen. It houses cells that will develop into sperm.

pollination
In seed plants, the delivery, by wind or animals, of pollen from the male (pollen-producing) parts of a plant to the stigma of a carpel on the female part of a plant.

seed
A plant embryo packaged with a food supply within a protective covering.

sepal (*sē'-pul*)
A modified leaf of a flowering plant. A whorl of sepals encloses and protects the flower bud before it opens.

shoot
The aerial organ of a plant, consisting of stem and leaves. Leaves are the main photosynthetic structures of most plants.

spore
(1) In plants and algae, a haploid cell that can develop into a multicellular haploid individual, the gametophyte, without fusing with another cell. (2) In fungi, a haploid cell that germinates to produce a mycelium.

sporophyte (*spōr'-uh-fīt*)
The multicellular diploid form in the life cycle of organisms undergoing alternation of generations; results from a union of gametes and meiotically produces haploid spores that grow into the gametophyte generation.

stamen (*stā'-men*)
A pollen-producing part of a flower, consisting of a stalk (filament) and an anther.

stigma (*stig'-muh*)
(plural, **stigmata**) The sticky tip of a flower's carpel that traps pollen.

vascular tissue
Plant tissue consisting of cells joined into tubes that transport water and nutrients throughout the plant body. Xylem and phloem make up vascular tissue.

Credits

Credits are listed in the order of appearance.

PHOTO CREDITS

ILLUSTRATION AND TEXT CREDITS

Self-Quiz Answers

1. cuticle
2. flowers
3. a. sporophyte b. cones; angiosperms c. fruit
4. b
5. b
6. a fern
7. Because the plants do not lose their leaves during autumn and winter, the leaves are already fully developed for photosynthesis when the short growing season begins in spring.
8. vascular plant
9. a
10. a ripened ovary of a flower that protects and aids in the dispersal of seeds contained in the fruit
11. algae or cyanobacteria; fungi
12. A fungus digests its food externally by secreting digestive juices into the food and then absorbing the small nutrients that result from digestion. In contrast, humans and most other animals ingest relatively large pieces of food and digest the food within their bodies.

The Evolution of Animals

From Chapter 17 of *Campbell Essential Biology with Physiology*, Fifth Edition. Eric J. Simon, Jean L. Dickey, Kelly A. Hogan, Jane B. Reece. Copyright © 2016 by Pearson Education, Inc. All rights reserved.

The Evolution of Animals

Why Animal Diversity Matters

▲ If you want to find nightcrawlers for fishing bait, look in a field of dairy cows.

◀ According to recent DNA analysis, many of us have a bit of Neanderthal in our genes.

▼ Evolutionary biologists have discovered the answer to the riddle "Which came first, the chicken or the egg?"

▲ If all the arthropods on Earth were divided equally among the human population, we would each get about 140 million.

Human Evolution BIOLOGY AND SOCIETY

The Discovery of the Hobbit People

In 2003, Australian anthropologists digging on the Indonesian island of Flores stumbled upon bones of some highly unusual people, including the nearly complete skeleton of an adult female. Next to a modern woman, this fully grown individual would stand about waist-high. Features of her skull, such as the shape and thickness of the bones, were human-like, but its size was proportional to her tiny body, and her brain was the size of a chimpanzee's. Surprisingly, the bones were accompanied by tools for hunting and butchering animals, along with evidence of cooking fires. Most startling of all, the remains dated to roughly 18,000 years ago, a time when scientists had thought that *Homo sapiens* was the only surviving human species. Since the initial discovery, researchers have unearthed the bones of a dozen or so more of these miniature humans.

The discoverers attributed their astonishing find to a previously unknown species, which they named *Homo floresiensis* and nicknamed "hobbits." They speculated that a band of ancestral humans arrived on Flores millions of years ago from Africa and, within the isolated environment of the island, evolved into the diminutive *Homo floresiensis*. There is precedent for animal evolution of this type: Biologists have discovered island-bound dwarf populations of deer, elephants, and hippos. One hypothesis is that a lack of predators favors the evolution of smaller, more energy-efficient forms. Controversy erupted as soon as the research team announced their findings. Skeptical scientists suggested that the bones were from *Homo sapiens* with diseases that cause skeletal malformations. As you'll find out in the Process of Science section, the more scientists learn about the "hobbit" people, the more puzzling their findings become.

A skull from one of Indonesia's "hobbit people." Scientists are debating whether the skull is from an ancient human-like species.

Homo sapiens and *Homo floresiensis* are just two of the 1.3 million species of animals that have been named and described by biologists. This amazing diversity arose through hundreds of millions of years of evolution as natural selection shaped animal adaptations to Earth's many environments. In this chapter, we'll look at the 9 most abundant and widespread of the roughly 35 phyla (major groups) in the kingdom Animalia. We'll give special attention to the major milestones in animal evolution and conclude by reconnecting with the fascinating subject of human evolution.

The Origins of Animal Diversity

Animal life began in Precambrian seas with the evolution of multicellular creatures that ate other organisms. We are among their descendants.

What Is an Animal?

Animals are eukaryotic, multicellular, heterotrophic organisms that obtain nutrients by eating. This mode of nutrition contrasts animals with plants and other organisms that construct organic molecules through photosynthesis. It also contrasts with fungi, which obtain nutrients by absorption after digesting the food outside their bodies. Most animals digest food within their bodies after ingesting other organisms, dead or alive, whole or by the piece (**Figure 1**).

Animal cells lack the cell walls that provide strong support in the bodies of plants and fungi. And most animals have muscle cells for movement and nerve cells that control the muscles. The most complex animals can use their muscular and nervous systems for many functions other than eating. Some species even use massive networks of nerve cells called brains to think.

Most animals are diploid and reproduce sexually; eggs and sperm are the only haploid cells. The life cycle of a sea star (**Figure 2**) includes basic stages found in most animal life cycles. ① Male and female adult animals make haploid gametes by meiosis, and ② an egg and a sperm fuse, producing a zygote. ③ The zygote divides by mitosis, forming ④ an early embryonic stage called a **blastula**, which is usually a hollow ball of cells. ⑤ In most animals, one side of the blastula folds inward, forming a stage called a **gastrula**. ⑥ The gastrula develops into a saclike embryo with inner, outer, and middle cell layers and an opening at one end. After the gastrula stage, many animals develop directly into adults. Others, such as the sea star, develop into a **larva** ⑦, an immature individual that looks different from the adult animal. (A tadpole, for another example, is a larval frog.) ⑧ The larva undergoes a major change of body form, called **metamorphosis**, in becoming an adult capable of reproducing sexually. ☑

☑ CHECKPOINT

What mode of nutrition distinguishes animals from fungi, both of which are heterotrophs?

Answer: ingestion (eating)

▼ **Figure 2 The life cycle of a sea star as an example of animal development.**

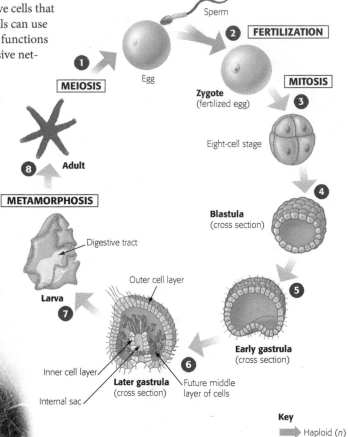

Sperm

Egg

① MEIOSIS

② FERTILIZATION

Zygote (fertilized egg)

MITOSIS ③

Eight-cell stage

④

Blastula (cross section)

⑤

Early gastrula (cross section)

⑥

Outer cell layer

Inner cell layer

Internal sac

Later gastrula (cross section)

Future middle layer of cells

Larva ⑦

Digestive tract

METAMORPHOSIS

⑧ Adult

Key
➡ Haploid (*n*)
➡ Diploid (2*n*)

▼ **Figure 1 Nutrition by ingestion, the animal way of life.** Few animals ingest a piece of food as large as the gazelle being eaten by this rock python. The snake will spend two weeks or more digesting its meal.

Early Animals and the Cambrian Explosion

Scientists hypothesize that animals evolved from a colonial flagellated protist (Figure 3). Although molecular data point to a much earlier origin, the oldest animal fossils that have been found are 550–575 million years old. Animal evolution must have already been under way for some time prior to that—the fossils reveal a variety of shapes, and sizes range from 1 cm to 1 m in length (Figure 4).

Animal diversification appears to have accelerated rapidly from 535 to 525 million years ago, during the Cambrian period. Because so many animal body plans and new phyla appear in the fossils from such an evolutionarily short time span, biologists call this episode the Cambrian explosion. The most celebrated source of Cambrian fossils is located in the mountains of British Columbia, Canada. The Burgess Shale, as it is known, provided a cornucopia of perfectly preserved animal fossils. In contrast to the Precambrian animals, many Cambrian animals had hard parts such as shells, and many are clearly related to existing animal groups. For example, scientists have classified more than a third of the species found in the Burgess Shale as arthropods, the group that includes present-day crabs, shrimps, and insects (Figure 5). Other fossils are more difficult to place. Some are downright weird, like the spiky creature near the center of the drawing, known as *Hallucigenia*, and *Opabinia*, the five-eyed predator grasping a worm with the long, flexible appendage that protrudes in front of its mouth.

What ignited the Cambrian explosion? Scientists have proposed several hypotheses, including increasingly complex predator-prey relationships and an increase in atmospheric oxygen. But whatever the cause of the rapid diversification, it is likely that the set of "master control" genes—the genetic framework for complex bodies—was already in place. Much of the diversity in body form among the animal phyla is associated with variations in where and when these genes are expressed within developing embryos.

In the last half billion years, animal evolution has to a large degree merely generated variations of the animal forms that originated in the Cambrian seas. Continuing research will help test hypotheses about the Cambrian explosion. But even as the explosion becomes less mysterious, it will seem no less wondrous. ☑

◄ Figure 3
Hypothetical common ancestor of animals. As you'll learn shortly, the individual cells of this colonial flagellated protist resemble the feeding cells of sponges.

Individual protists

Stalk

► Figure 4 **Fossils of Precambrian animals.** All of the oldest animal fossils are impressions of soft-bodied animals. Most of them do not appear to be related to any living group of animals.

Sea pen, possibly related to present-day colonial Cnidarians

Impression of upper surface of *Tribrachidium heraldicum*, which had a hemispheric shape and three-part symmetry unlike any living animal (up to 5 cm across)

▼ Figure 5 **A Cambrian seascape.** This drawing is based on fossils from the Burgess Shale. The flat-bodied animals are extinct arthropods called trilobites. A photo of a fossil trilobite is shown at the right.

Evolution Animal Phylogeny

Historically, biologists have categorized animals by "body plan"—general features of body structure. Distinctions between body plans were used to construct phylogenetic trees showing the evolutionary relationships among animal groups. More recently, a wealth of genetic data has allowed evolutionary biologists to modify and refine groups. **Figure 6** represents a revised set of hypotheses about the evolutionary relationships among nine major animal phyla based on both structural and genetic similarities.

▼ Figure 7 **Body symmetry.**

Radial symmetry. Parts radiate from the center, so any slice through the central axis divides into mirror-images.

Bilateral symmetry. Only one slice can divide left and right sides into mirror-image halves.

(handwritten notes on figure: "single opening, funds as mouth and anus"; "no body, simplest cavity animal, host to sepn"; "impact, decompose")

▶ **Figure 6 An overview of animal phylogeny.** Only 9 of the more than 30 animal phyla (the exact number is not agreed upon) are included in the tree and in the text. The branching takes into account the body plan, embryonic development, and genetic relationships of the organisms.

Tree labels: Ancestral protist — No true tissues — Sponges; Radial symmetry — Cnidarians; Tissues; Molluscs; Flatworms; Annelids; Roundworms; Arthropods; Bilateral symmetry; Echinoderms; Chordates

that first encounters food, danger, and other stimuli when traveling. In most bilateral animals, a nerve center in the form of a brain is at the head end, near a concentration of sense organs such as eyes. Thus, bilateral symmetry is an adaptation that aids movement, such as crawling, burrowing, or swimming. Indeed, many radial animals are stationary, whereas most bilateral animals are mobile.

Among bilateral animals, analysis of embryonic development sets the echinoderms and chordates apart from the evolutionary branch that includes molluscs, flatworms, annelids, roundworms, and arthropods. Molluscs, flatworms, and annelids have genetic similarities that are not shared by roundworms and arthropods.

The evolution of body cavities also helped lead to more complex animals. A **body cavity** (**Figure 8**, facing page) is a fluid-filled space separating the digestive tract from the outer body wall. The cavity enables the internal organs to grow and move independently of the outer body wall, and the fluid cushions them from injury. In soft-bodied animals such as earthworms, the fluid is under pressure and functions as a hydrostatic skeleton. Of the phyla shown in Figure 6, only sponges, cnidarians, and flatworms lack a body cavity.

With the overview of animal evolution in Figure 6 as our guide, we're ready to take a closer look at the nine most numerous animal phyla. ☑

☑ CHECKPOINT

1. In the phylogeny shown in Figure 6, chordates (the phylum that includes humans) are most closely related to which other animal phylum?
2. A round pizza displays _____ symmetry, whereas a slice of pizza displays _____ symmetry.

Answers: **1.** echinoderms **2.** radial; bilateral

A major branch point in animal evolution distinguishes sponges from all other animals based on structural complexity. Unlike more complex animals, sponges lack true tissues, groups of similar cells that perform a function (such as nervous tissue). A second major evolutionary split is based on body symmetry: radial versus bilateral (**Figure 7**). Like the flowerpot, the sea anemone has **radial symmetry**, identical all around a central axis. The shovel has **bilateral symmetry**, which means there's only one way to split it into two equal halves—right down the midline. A bilateral animal, such as the lobster in Figure 7, has a definite "head end"

▼ **Figure 8 Body plans of bilateral animals.** The various organ systems of these animals develop from the three tissue layers that form in the embryo.

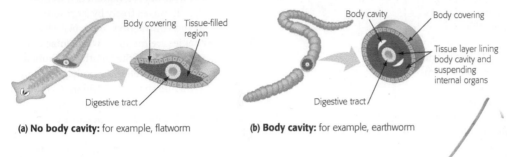

(a) No body cavity: for example, flatworm

(b) Body cavity: for example, earthworm

Major Invertebrate Phyla

Living on land as we do, our sense of animal diversity is biased in favor of vertebrates, animals with a backbone, such as amphibians, reptiles, and mammals. However, vertebrates make up less than 5% of all animal species. If we were to sample the animals in an aquatic habitat, such as a pond, tide pool, or coral reef, or if we were to consider the millions of insects that share our terrestrial world, we would find ourselves in the realm of **invertebrates**, animals without backbones. We give special attention to the vertebrates simply because we humans are among the backboned ones. However, by exploring the other 95% of the animal kingdom—the invertebrates—we'll discover an astonishing diversity of beautiful creatures that too often escape our notice.

is drawn through the pores into a central cavity and then flows out of the sponge through a larger opening **(Figure 9)**. Flagella on specialized cells called choanocytes sweep water through the sponge's porous body. Tiny nets encircling the flagella trap bacteria and other food particles, which the choanocytes then engulf. Specialized cells called amoebocytes pick up food from the choanocytes, digest it, and carry the nutrients to other cells. Amoebocytes also manufacture the fibers that make up a sponge's skeleton. In some sponges, these fibers are sharp and spur-like, like the ones shown in Figure 9. Other sponges have softer, more flexible skeletons; these pliable, honeycombed skeletons are often used as natural sponges in the bath or to wash cars. ☑

Sponges

Sponges (phylum Porifera) are stationary animals that appear so immobile that you might mistake them for plants. The simplest of all animals, sponges probably evolved very early from colonial protists. They have no nerves or muscles, but their individual cells can sense and react to changes in the environment. The cell layers of sponges are loose associations that are not considered true tissues. Sponges range in height from 1 cm (about half an inch) to 2 m (over 6 ft). Although some live in fresh water, the majority of the 5,500 or so species of sponges are marine.

Sponges are examples of suspension feeders, animals that collect food particles from water passed through some type of food-trapping equipment. The body of a sponge resembles a sac perforated with holes. Water

Sponges
Cnidarians
Molluscs
Flatworms
Annelids
Roundworms
Arthropods
Echinoderms
Chordates

☑ **CHECKPOINT**

In what fundamental way does the structure of a sponge differ from that of all other animals?

Answer: A sponge has no true tissues.

▼ **Figure 9 Anatomy of a sponge.** To obtain enough food to grow by 3 ounces, a sponge must filter roughly 275 gallons of water through its body, enough to fill 3.5 typical-size bathtubs.

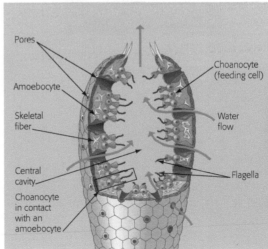

Pores
Amoebocyte
Skeletal fiber
Central cavity
Choanocyte in contact with an amoebocyte
Choanocyte (feeding cell)
Water flow
Flagella

Cnidarians

Cnidarians (phylum Cnidaria) are characterized by the presence of body tissues—as are all the remaining animals we will discuss—as well as by radial symmetry and tentacles with stinging cells. Cnidarians include sea anemones, hydras, corals, and jellies (sometimes called jellyfish, though they are not fish). Most of the 10,000 cnidarian species are marine.

The basic body plan of a cnidarian is a sac with a central digestive compartment, the **gastrovascular cavity**. A single opening to this cavity functions as both mouth and anus. This basic body plan has two variations: the stationary **polyp** and the floating **medusa** **(Figure 10)**. Polyps adhere to larger objects and extend their tentacles, waiting for prey. Examples of the polyp body plan are corals, sea anemones, and hydras. A medusa (plural, *medusae*) is a flattened, mouth-down version of the polyp. It moves freely by a combination of passive drifting and contractions of its bell-shaped body. The largest jellies are medusae with tentacles 60–70 m long (more than half the length of a football field) dangling from an umbrella-like body up to 2 m in diameter. There are some species of cnidarians that live only as polyps, others only as medusae, and still others that pass through both a medusa stage and a polyp stage in their life cycle.

Cnidarians are carnivores that use tentacles arranged in a ring around the mouth to capture prey and push the food into the gastrovascular cavity, where digestion begins. The undigested remains are eliminated through the mouth/anus. The tentacles are armed with batteries of cnidocytes ("stinging cells") that function in defense and in the capture of prey **(Figure 11)**. The phylum Cnidaria is named for these stinging cells. ☑

▼ **Figure 10 Polyp and medusa forms of cnidarians.** Note that cnidarians have two tissue layers, distinguished in the diagrams by blue and yellow. The gastrovascular cavity has only one opening, which functions as both mouth and anus.

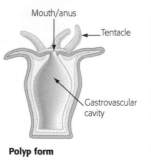

Mouth/anus
Tentacle
Gastrovascular cavity

Polyp form

Coral

Sea anemone

Hydra

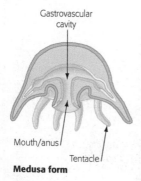

Gastrovascular cavity
Mouth/anus
Tentacle

Medusa form

Jelly

▼ **Figure 11 Cnidocyte action.** When a trigger on a tentacle is stimulated by touch, a fine thread shoots out from a capsule. Some cnidocyte threads entangle prey, while others puncture the prey and inject a poison.

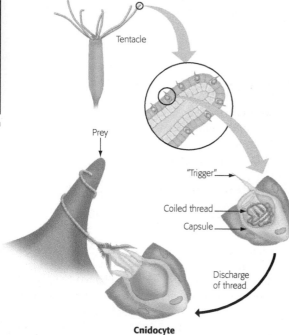

Tentacle
Prey
"Trigger"
Coiled thread
Capsule
Discharge of thread
Cnidocyte

Molluscs

Snails and slugs, oysters and clams, and octopuses and squids are all **molluscs** (phylum Mollusca). Molluscs are soft-bodied animals, but most are protected by a hard shell. Many molluscs feed by extending a file-like organ called a **radula** to scrape up food. For example, the radula of some aquatic snails slides back and forth like a backhoe, scraping and scooping algae off rocks. You can observe a radula in action by watching a snail graze on the glass wall of an aquarium. In cone snails, a group of predatory marine molluscs, the radula is modified to inject venom into prey. The sting of some cone snails is painful, or even fatal, to people.

There are 100,000 known species of molluscs, with most being marine animals. All molluscs have a similar body plan (**Figure 12**). The body has three main parts: a muscular foot, usually used for movement; a visceral mass containing most of the internal organs; and a fold of tissue called the mantle. The **mantle** drapes over the visceral mass and secretes the shell if one is present. The three major groups of molluscs are gastropods, bivalves, and cephalopods (**Figure 13**).

Most **gastropods**, including snails, are protected by a single spiraled shell into which the animal can retreat when threatened. Slugs and sea slugs lack shells. Many gastropods have a distinct head with eyes at the tips of tentacles (think of a garden snail). Marine, freshwater, and terrestrial gastropods make up about three-quarters of the living mollusc species.

The **bivalves**, including clams, oysters, mussels, and scallops, have shells divided into two halves hinged together. None of the bivalves have a radula. There are both marine and freshwater species, with most being sedentary, using their muscular foot for digging and anchoring in sand or mud.

Cephalopods are all marine animals and generally differ from gastropods and sedentary bivalves in that their bodies are fast and agile. A few have large, heavy shells, but in most the shell is small and internal (as in squids) or missing (as in octopuses). Cephalopods have large brains and sophisticated sense organs, which contribute to their success as mobile predators. They use beak-like jaws and a radula to crush or rip prey apart. The mouth is at the base of the foot, which is drawn out into several long tentacles for catching and holding prey. The colossal squid, discovered in the ocean depths near Antarctica, is the largest living invertebrate. Scientists estimate that this massive cephalopod grows to an average length of 13 m—as long as a school bus. ☑

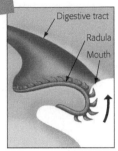

◄ **Figure 12 The general body plan of a mollusc.** Note the small body cavity (brown) and the complete digestive tract, with both mouth and anus (pink).

☑ **CHECKPOINT**

Classify these molluscs: A garden snail is an example of a _____; a clam is an example of a _____; a squid is an example of a _____.

Answer: gastropod; bivalve; cephalopod

▼ **Figure 13 Mollusc diversity.**

MAJOR GROUPS OF MOLLUSCS		
Gastropods	**Bivalves** (hinged shell)	**Cephalopods** (large brain and tentacles)
Snail (spiraled shell) **Sea slug** (no shell)	**Scallop.** This scallop has many eyes (small round structures) peering out between the two halves of the hinged shell.	**Octopus.** Octopuses live on the seafloor, where they search for crabs and other food. They have no shell. The brain of an octopus is larger and more complex, proportionate to body size, than that of any other invertebrate. **Nautilus.** The shell of the nautilus is a coiled series of chambers. The animal inhabits only the outermost chamber; the others contain gas and fluid that enable the nautilus to regulate its buoyancy.

Flatworms

Flatworms (phylum Platyhelminthes) are the simplest animals with bilateral symmetry. True to their name, these worms are ribbonlike and range from about 1 mm to about 20 m (about 65 ft) in length. Most flatworms have a gastrovascular cavity with a single opening. There are about 20,000 species of flatworms living in marine, freshwater, and damp terrestrial habitats (Figure 14).

The gastrovascular cavity of free-living flatworms called planarians is highly branched, providing an extensive surface area for the absorption of nutrients. When the animal feeds, a muscular tube projects through the mouth and sucks food in. Planarians live on the undersurfaces of rocks in freshwater ponds and streams.

Parasitic flatworms include blood flukes called schistosomes, which are a major health problem in the tropics. These worms have suckers that attach to the inside of the blood vessels near the human host's intestines. Infection by these flatworms causes a long-lasting disease called schistosomiasis, with such symptoms as severe abdominal pain, anemia, and dysentery. Although schistosomes are not found in the United States, more than 200 million people around the world are infected by these parasites each year.

Tapeworms parasitize many vertebrates, including people. Most tapeworms have a very long, ribbonlike body with repeated parts. There is no mouth and no gastrovascular cavity. The head of a tapeworm is equipped with suckers and hooks that lock the worm to the intestinal lining of the host. Bathed in partially digested food in the intestines of its host, the tapeworm simply absorbs nutrients across its body surface. Behind the head is a long ribbon of units that are little more than sacs of sex organs. At the back of the worm, mature units containing thousands of eggs break off and leave the host's body with the feces. People can become infected with tapeworms by eating undercooked beef, pork, or fish containing tapeworm larvae. The larvae are microscopic, but the adults can reach lengths of 2 m (6.5 ft) in the intestine. Such large tapeworms can cause intestinal blockage and rob enough nutrients from the host to cause nutritional deficiencies. Fortunately, an orally administered drug can kill the adult worms. ☑

☑ CHECKPOINT

Flatworms are the simplest animals to display a body plan that is _____.

Answer: *bilaterally symmetric*

▼ **Figure 14 Flatworm diversity.**

Digestive tract (gastrovascular cavity)

Nerve cords

Mouth

Eyespots (detect light)

Nervous tissue clusters (simple brain)

Planarian

Bilateral symmetry

Suckers

Male Female

Blood flukes

Reproductive unit with skin removed

Head

Hooks

Suckers

Tapeworm

Annelids

Annelids (phylum Annelida) are worms that have **body segmentation**, which is the subdivision of the body along its length into a series of repeated parts called segments. In annelids, the segments look like a set of fused rings. There are about 16,500 annelid species, ranging in length from less than 1 mm to the giant Australian earthworm, which can grow up to 3 m (nearly 10 ft) long. Annelids live in damp soil, the sea, and most freshwater habitats. There are three main groups: earthworms, polychaetes, and leeches (**Figure 15**).

Annelids exhibit two characteristics shared by all other bilateral animals except flatworms. One is a **complete digestive tract**, which is a digestive tube with two openings: a mouth and an anus. A complete digestive tract can process food and absorb nutrients as a meal moves in one direction from one specialized digestive organ to the next. In people, for example, the mouth, stomach, and intestines act as digestive organs. A second characteristic is a body cavity (see Figure 8b).

Earthworms, like all annelids, are segmented both externally and internally (**Figure 16**). The body cavity is partitioned by walls (only two segment walls are fully shown here). Many of the internal structures, such as the nervous system (yellow in the figure) and organs that dispose of fluid wastes (green) are repeated in each segment. Segmental blood vessels include one main heart and five pairs of accessory hearts. The digestive tract, however, is not segmented; it passes through the segment walls from the mouth to the anus.

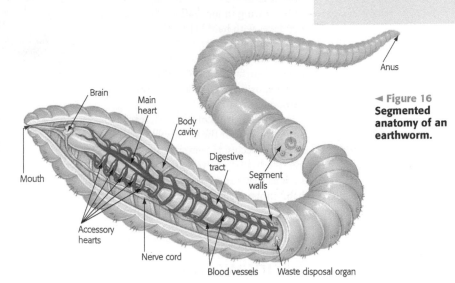

Sponges
Cnidarians
Molluscs
Flatworms
Annelids
Roundworms
Arthropods
Echinoderms
Chordates

◄ **Figure 16**
Segmented anatomy of an earthworm.

Brain
Main heart
Body cavity
Anus
Mouth
Digestive tract
Segment walls
Accessory hearts
Nerve cord
Blood vessels
Waste disposal organ

Earthworms eat their way through the soil, extracting nutrients from organic matter as the soil passes through the digestive tract. Undigested material is eliminated as castings through the anus. Farmers and gardeners value earthworms because the animals aerate the soil and increase the amount of mineral nutrients available to plants. Because crops provide the earthworms' food, land use and farming practices have a huge effect on earthworm populations. In one study, for example, corn fields that were plowed yearly averaged 39,000 earthworms per acre, while populations in unplowed dairy pastures numbered at least 1,333,000 million per acre.

If you want to find nightcrawlers for fishing bait, look in a field of dairy cows.

▼ **Figure 15 Annelid diversity.**

MAJOR GROUPS OF ANNELIDS		
Earthworms	**Polychaetes**	**Leeches**
This giant Australian earthworm is bigger than many snakes. Perhaps you've slipped on slimy worms, but imagine actually tripping over one!	Polychaetes have segmental appendages that function in movement and as gills. This species is called a Christmas tree worm. The feathery, spiral structures are a pair of gills from a single worm.	The parasitic fish leech has a sucker on each end of its body. It attaches one sucker to a rock or plant. It then extends its body to wave freely in the water, using the other sucker to latch on to a passing host.

In contrast to earthworms, most **polychaetes** are marine, mainly crawling on or burrowing in the seafloor. Segmental appendages with hard bristles help the worm wriggle about in search of small invertebrates to eat. The appendages also increase the animal's surface area for taking up oxygen and disposing of metabolic wastes, including carbon dioxide.

The third group of annelids, **leeches**, are notorious for the bloodsucking habits of some species. However, most species are free-living carnivores that eat small invertebrates such as snails and insects. A few terrestrial species inhabit moist vegetation in the tropics, but the majority of leeches live in fresh water. A European freshwater

Medicinal leech

species called *Hirudo medicinalis* is used for the treatment of circulatory complications. Most commonly, leeches are applied after reconstructive microsurgery in which limbs or digits are reattached. Because arteries (which transport blood into a reattached area) are easier to reconnect than veins (which transport blood out), blood can pool in the reattached area and stagnate, starving the healing tissue of oxygen. Medicinal leeches have razor-like jaws with hundreds of tiny teeth that cut through the skin. They secrete saliva containing an anesthetic and an anticoagulant into the wound. The anesthetic makes the bite virtually painless, and the anticoagulant prevents clotting as the leech drains excess blood from the wound. ☑

Roundworms

Roundworms (also called **nematodes**, members of the phylum Nematoda) get their common name from their cylindrical body, which is usually tapered at both ends **(Figure 17)**. Roundworms are among the most numerous and widespread of all animals. About 25,000 species of roundworms are known, and perhaps ten times that number actually exist. Roundworms range in length from about 1 mm to 1 m. They

Sponges
Cnidarians
Molluscs
Flatworms
Annelids
Roundworms
Arthropods
Echinoderms
Chordates

are found in most aquatic habitats, in wet soil, and as parasites in the body fluids and tissues of plants and animals.

Free-living roundworms are important decomposers. They live virtually everywhere there is decaying organic matter, and their numbers are huge. Ninety thousand nematodes have been found in a single rotting apple. Recently, researchers even found nematodes living 2 miles underground, where they survive by grazing on microbes. Other species of nematodes thrive as parasites in plants and animals. Some are major agricultural pests that attack the roots of plants. At least 50 parasitic roundworm species infect people; they include pinworms, hookworms, and the parasite that causes trichinosis. ☑

▼ **Figure 17 Roundworm diversity.**

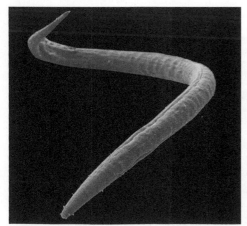

(a) A free-living roundworm. This species has the classic roundworm shape: cylindrical with tapered ends. The ridges indicate muscles that run the length of the body.

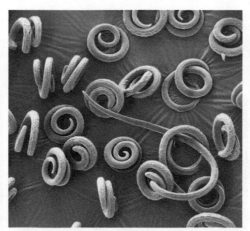

(b) Parasitic roundworms in pork. The potentially fatal disease trichinosis is caused by eating undercooked pork infected with *Trichinella* roundworms. The worms (shown here in pork tissue) burrow into a person's intestine and then invade muscle tissue.

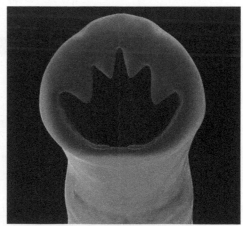

(c) Head of hookworm. Hookworms sink their hooks into the wall of the host's small intestine and feed on blood. Although the worms are small (less than 1 cm), a severe infestation can cause serious anemia.

Arthropods

Arthropods (phylum Arthropoda) are named for their jointed appendages. Crustaceans (such as crabs and lobsters), arachnids (such as spiders and scorpions), and insects (such as grasshoppers and moths) are examples of arthropods **(Figure 18)**. Zoologists estimate that the total arthropod population numbers about a billion billion (10^{18}) individuals. Researchers have identified more than a million arthropod species, mostly insects. In fact, two out of every three species of life that have been scientifically described are arthropods. And arthropods are represented in nearly all habitats of the biosphere. In species diversity, distribution, and sheer numbers, arthropods must be regarded as the most successful animal phylum.

Sponges
Cnidarians
Molluscs
Flatworms
Annelids
Roundworms
Arthropods
Echinoderms
Chordates

If all the arthropods on Earth were divided equally among the human population, we would each get about 140 million.

◀ **Figure 18 Arthropod diversity.**

MAJOR GROUPS OF ARTHROPODS

Arachnids

Crustaceans

Millipedes and Centipedes

Insects

General Characteristics of Arthropods

Arthropods are segmented animals. In contrast with the repeating similar segments of annelids, however, arthropod segments and their appendages have become specialized for a great variety of functions. This evolutionary flexibility contributed to the great diversification of arthropods. Specialization of segments (or of fused groups of segments) provides for an efficient division of labor among body regions. For example, the appendages of different segments may be adapted for walking, feeding, sensory reception, swimming, or defense **(Figure 19)**.

The body of an arthropod is completely covered by an **exoskeleton**, an external skeleton. This coat is constructed from layers of protein and a tough polysaccharide called chitin. The exoskeleton can be a thick, hard armor over some parts of the body (such as the head), yet be paper-thin and flexible in other locations (such as the joints). The exoskeleton protects the animal and provides points of attachment for the muscles that move the appendages. There are, of course, advantages to wearing hard parts on the outside. Our own skeleton is interior to most of our soft tissues, an arrangement that doesn't provide much protection from injury. But our skeleton does offer the advantage of being able to grow along with the rest of our body. In contrast, a growing arthropod must occasionally shed its old exoskeleton and secrete a larger one. This process, called molting, leaves the animal temporarily vulnerable to predators and other dangers. The next five pages explore the major groups of arthropods. ☑

◀ **Figure 19 Anatomy of a lobster, a crustacean.** The whole body, including the appendages, is covered by an exoskeleton. The body is segmented, but this characteristic is obvious only in the abdomen.

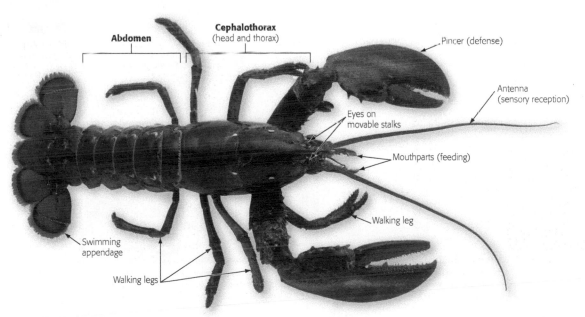

Abdomen

Cephalothorax (head and thorax)

Pincer (defense)

Antenna (sensory reception)

Eyes on movable stalks

Mouthparts (feeding)

Walking leg

Swimming appendage

Walking legs

Arachnids

Arachnids include scorpions, spiders, ticks, and mites (Figure 20). Most arachnids live on land. Members of this arthropod group usually have four pairs of walking legs and a specialized pair of feeding appendages. In spiders, these feeding appendages are fang-like and equipped with poison glands. As a spider uses these appendages to immobilize and dismantle its prey, it spills digestive juices onto the torn tissues and sucks up its liquid meal.

▼ **Figure 20 Arachnid characteristics and diversity.**

Pair of feeding appendages

Leg (four pairs)

Pair of silk-spinning appendages

Scorpion. Scorpions have a pair of large pincers that function in defense and food capture. The tip of the tail bears a poisonous stinger. Scorpions sting people only when prodded or stepped on.

Dust mite. This microscopic house dust mite is a ubiquitous scavenger in our homes. Dust mites are harmless except to people who are allergic to the mites' feces.

Spider. Like most spiders, including the tarantula in the large photo above, this black widow spins a web of liquid silk, which solidifies as it comes out of specialized glands. A black widow's venom can kill small prey but is rarely fatal to humans.

Wood tick. Wood ticks and other species carry bacteria that cause Rocky Mountain spotted fever. Lyme disease is carried by several different species of ticks.

Crustaceans

Crustaceans, which are nearly all aquatic, include delectable species of crabs, lobsters, crayfish, and shrimps (Figure 21). Barnacles, which anchor themselves to rocks, boat hulls, and even whales, are also crustaceans. One group of crustaceans, the isopods, is represented on land by pill bugs. All of these animals exhibit the arthropod characteristic of multiple pairs of specialized appendages.

▼ **Figure 21 Crustacean characteristics and diversity.**

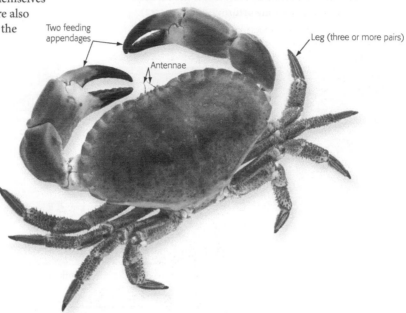

Two feeding appendages

Antennae

Leg (three or more pairs)

Crab. Ghost crabs are common along shorelines throughout the world. They scurry along the surf's edge and then quickly bury themselves in sand.

Shrimp. Naturally found in Pacific waters from Africa to Asia, giant prawns are widely cultivated as food.

Pill bug. Commonly found in moist locations with decaying leaves, such as under logs, pill bugs get their name from their tendency to roll up into a tight ball when they sense danger.

Crayfish. The red swamp crayfish, cultivated worldwide for food, is native to the southeastern United States. When released outside its native range, it competes aggressively with other species, endangering the local ecosystem.

Barnacles. Barnacles are stationary crustaceans with exoskeletons hardened into shells by calcium carbonate (lime). The jointed appendages projecting from the shell capture small plankton.

Millipedes and Centipedes

Millipedes and **centipedes** are terrestrial arthropods that have similar segments over most of the body. Although they superficially resemble annelids, their jointed legs reveal they are arthropods **(Figure 22)**.

Millipedes eat decaying plant matter. They have two pairs of short legs per body segment. Centipedes are carnivores, with a pair of poison claws used in defense and to paralyze prey, such as cockroaches and flies. Each of a centipede's body segments bears a single pair of legs.

► **Figure 22 Millipedes and centipedes.**

Two pairs of legs per segment

Millipede. Like most millipedes, this one has an elongated body with two pairs of legs per trunk segment.

One pair of legs per segment

Centipede. Centipedes can be found in dirt and leaf litter. Their venomous claws can harm cockroaches and spiders but not people.

Insect Anatomy

Like the grasshopper in **Figure 23**, most **insects** have a three-part body: head, thorax, and abdomen. The head usually bears a pair of sensory antennae and a pair of eyes. The mouthparts of insects are adapted for particular kinds of eating—for example, for biting and chewing plant material in grasshoppers, for lapping up fluids in houseflies, and for piercing skin and sucking blood in mosquitoes. Most adult insects have three pairs of legs and one or two pairs of wings, all extending from the thorax.

Flight is obviously one key to the great success of insects. An animal that can fly can escape many predators, more readily find food and mates, and disperse to new habitats much faster than an animal that must crawl on the ground. Because their wings are extensions of the exoskeleton and not true appendages, insects can fly without sacrificing legs. By contrast, the flying vertebrates—birds and bats—have one of their two pairs of legs modified for wings, which explains why these vertebrates are generally not very swift on the ground.

▼ **Figure 23 Anatomy of a grasshopper.**

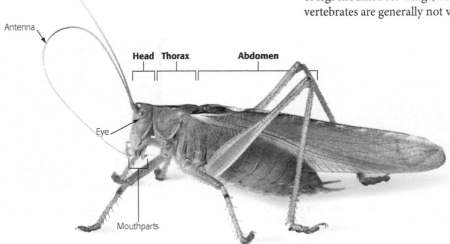

Antenna

Head Thorax Abdomen

Eye

Mouthparts

Insect Diversity

In species diversity, insects outnumber all other forms of life combined (**Figure 24**). They live in almost every terrestrial habitat and in fresh water, and flying insects fill the air. Insects are rare in the seas, where crustaceans are the dominant arthropods. The oldest insect fossils date back to about 400 million years ago. Later, the evolution of flight sparked an explosion in insect variety.

▼ Figure 24 **Insect diversity.**

Rhinoceros beetle. Only males have a "horn," which is used for fighting other males and for digging.

Robber fly. This predatory insect injects prey with enzymes that liquefy the tissues, and then suck in the resulting fluid.

Candy-striped leafhopper. Leafhoppers are tiny insects—about the width of the nail on your little finger—that can jump 40 times their body length.

Greater arid-land katydid. Often called the red-eyed devil, this scary-looking predator displays its wings and spiny legs when threatened.

Praying mantis. There are more then 2,000 species of praying mantises throughout the world.

Weevil. Light reflected from varying thicknesses of chitin produces the brilliant colors of this weevil.

Buckeye butterfly. The eyespots on the wings of this butterfly may startle predators.

Blue dasher dragonfly. The huge multifaceted eyes of dragonflies wrap around the head for nearly 360° vision. Each of the four wings works independently, giving dragonflies excellent maneuverability as they pursue prey.

Many insects undergo metamorphosis in their development. In the case of grasshoppers and some other insect groups, the young resemble adults but are smaller and have different body proportions. The animal goes through a series of molts, each time looking more like an adult, until it reaches full size. In other cases, insects have distinctive larval stages specialized for eating and growing that are known by such names as maggots (fly larvae), grubs (beetle larvae), or caterpillars (larvae of moths and butterflies). The larval stage looks entirely different from the adult stage, which is specialized for dispersal and reproduction. Metamorphosis from the larva to the adult occurs during a pupal stage (**Figure 25**).

Forensic entomologists (forensic scientists who study insects) use their knowledge of insect life cycles to help solve criminal cases. For example, blowfly maggots feed on decaying flesh. Female blowflies, which can smell a dead body from up to a mile away, typically arrive and lay their eggs in a fresh corpse within minutes. By knowing the length of each stage in the life cycle of a blowfly, an entomologist can determine how much time has passed since death occurred.

Animals so numerous, diverse, and widespread as insects are bound to affect the lives of all other terrestrial organisms, including people, in many ways. On the one hand, we depend on bees, flies, and other insects to pollinate our crops and orchards. On the other hand, insects are carriers of the microbes that cause many human diseases, such as malaria and West Nile disease. Insects also compete with people for food by eating our field crops. In an effort to minimize their losses, farmers in the United States spend billions of dollars each year on pesticides, spraying crops with massive doses of insecticide poisons. But try as they might, not even humans have significantly challenged the preeminence of insects and their arthropod kin. Rather, the evolution of pesticide resistance has caused humans to change their pest-control methods. ☑

▼ Figure 25 **Metamorphosis of a monarch butterfly.**

The **larva (caterpillar)** spends its time eating and growing, molting as it grows.

After several molts, the larva becomes a **pupa** encased in a cocoon.

Within the pupa, the larval organs break down and adult organs develop from cells that were dormant in the larva.

Finally, the **adult** emerges from the cocoon.

The butterfly flies off and reproduces, nourished mainly by calories stored when it was a caterpillar.

Echinoderms

The **echinoderms** (phylum Echinodermata) are named for their spiny surfaces (*echin* is Greek for "spiny"). Among the echinoderms are sea stars, sea urchins, sea cucumbers, and sand dollars **(Figure 26)**.

Echinoderms include about 7,000 species, all of them marine. Most move slowly, if at all. Echinoderms lack body segments, and most have radial symmetry as adults. Both the external and the internal parts of a sea star, for instance, radiate from the center like the spokes of a wheel. In contrast to the adult, the larval stage of echinoderms is bilaterally symmetrical. This supports other evidence that echinoderms are not closely related to other radial animals, such as cnidarians, that never show bilateral symmetry. Most echinoderms have an **endoskeleton** (interior skeleton) constructed from hard plates just beneath the skin. Bumps and spines of this endoskeleton account for the animal's rough or prickly surface. Unique to echinoderms is the **water vascular system**, a network of water-filled canals that circulate water throughout the echinoderm's body, facilitating gas exchange (the entry of O_2 and the removal of CO_2) and waste disposal. The water vascular system also branches into extensions called tube feet. A sea star or sea urchin pulls itself slowly over the seafloor using its suction-cup-like tube feet. Sea stars also use their tube feet to grip prey during feeding.

Looking at sea stars and other adult echinoderms, you may think they have little in common with humans and other vertebrates. But as shown by the phylogenetic tree at the left, echinoderms share an evolutionary branch with chordates, the phylum that includes vertebrates. Analysis of embryonic development can differentiate the echinoderms and chordates from the evolutionary branch that includes molluscs, flatworms, annelids, roundworms, and arthropods. With this context in mind, we're now ready to make the transition in our discussion from invertebrates to vertebrates. ☑

▼ **Figure 26 Echinoderm diversity.**

Sea star. When a sea star encounters an oyster or clam, it grips the mollusc's shell with its tube feet (see inset) and positions its mouth next to the narrow opening between the two halves of the prey's shell. The sea star then pushes its stomach out through its mouth and the crack in the mollusc's shell.

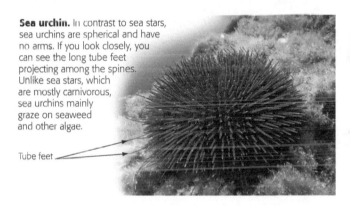

Sea urchin. In contrast to sea stars, sea urchins are spherical and have no arms. If you look closely, you can see the long tube feet projecting among the spines. Unlike sea stars, which are mostly carnivorous, sea urchins mainly graze on seaweed and other algae.

Tube feet

Sea cucumber. On casual inspection, this sea cucumber does not look much like other echinoderms. However, a closer look would reveal many echinoderm traits, including five rows of tube feet.

Sand dollar. Live sand dollars have a skin of short, movable spines covering a rigid skeleton. A set of five pores (arranged in a star pattern) allows seawater to be drawn into the sand dollar's body.

Vertebrate Evolution and Diversity

Most of us are curious about our family ancestry. Biologists are also interested in the larger question of tracing human ancestry within the animal kingdom. In this section, we trace the evolution of the vertebrates, the group that includes humans and their closest relatives. All vertebrates have endoskeletons, a characteristic shared with most echinoderms. However, vertebrate endoskeletons are unique in having a skull and a backbone, a series of bones called vertebrae (singular, *vertebra*), for which the group is named (Figure 27). Our first step in tracing the vertebrate lineage is to determine where vertebrates fit in the animal kingdom.

▼ **Figure 27 A vertebrate endoskeleton.** This snake skeleton, like those of all vertebrates, has a skull and a backbone consisting of vertebrae.

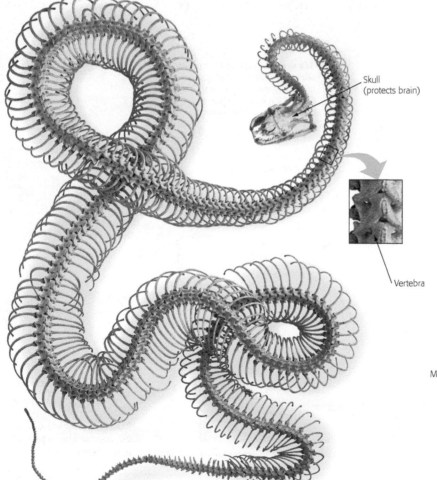

Skull
(protects brain)

Vertebra

Characteristics of Chordates

The last phylum in our survey of the animal kingdom is the phylum Chordata. **Chordates** share four key features that appear in the embryo and sometimes in the adult (Figure 28). These four chordate characteristics are (1) a **dorsal, hollow nerve cord**, (2) a **notochord**, which is a flexible, longitudinal rod located between the digestive tract and the nerve cord, (3) **pharyngeal slits**, which are grooves in the pharynx, the region of the digestive tube just behind the mouth, and (4) a **post-anal tail**, which is a tail to the rear of the anus. Though these chordate characteristics are often difficult to recognize in the adult animal, they are always present in chordate embryos. For example, the notochord, for which our phylum is named, persists in adult humans only in the form of the cartilage disks that function as cushions between the vertebrae. Back injuries described as "ruptured disks" or "slipped disks" refer to these notochord remnants.

Body segmentation is another chordate characteristic. Chordate segmentation is apparent in the backbone of vertebrates (see Figure 27) and is also evident in the segmental muscles of all chordates (see the chevron-shaped—<<<<—muscles in the lancelet in Figure 29). Segmental musculature is not so obvious in adult humans unless one is motivated to sculpt "washboard abs."

Two groups of chordates, **tunicates** and **lancelets** (Figure 29), are invertebrates. All other chordates are

▼ **Figure 28 Chordate characteristics.**

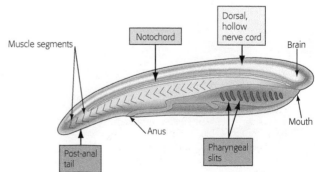

Sponges
Cnidarians
Molluscs
Flatworms
Annelids
Roundworms
Arthropods
Echinoderms
Chordates

Muscle segments
Notochord
Dorsal, hollow nerve cord
Brain
Anus
Mouth
Post-anal tail
Pharyngeal slits

vertebrates, which retain the basic chordate characteristics but have additional features that are unique—including, of course, the backbone. **Figure 30** is an overview of chordate and vertebrate evolution that will provide a context for our survey. ☑

▼ **Figure 29 Invertebrate chordates.**

Lancelet. This marine invertebrate owes its name to its bladelike shape. Only a few centimeters long, lancelets wiggle backward into the gravel, leaving their mouth exposed, and filter tiny food particles from the seawater.

Tunicates. The tunicate, or sea squirt, is a stationary animal that filters food from the water. These pastel sea squirts get their nickname from their coloration and the fact that they can quickly expel water to startle intruders.

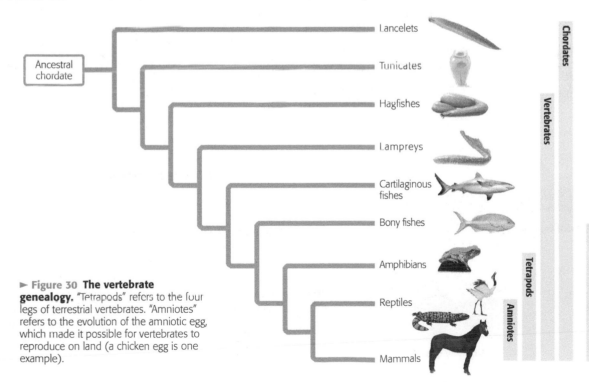

► **Figure 30 The vertebrate genealogy.** "Tetrapods" refers to the four legs of terrestrial vertebrates. "Amniotes" refers to the evolution of the amniotic egg, which made it possible for vertebrates to reproduce on land (a chicken egg is one example).

☑ **CHECKPOINT**

During our early embryonic development, what four features do we share with invertebrate chordates such as lancelets?

Answer: (1) dorsal, hollow nerve cord, (2) notochord, (3) pharyngeal slits, (4) post-anal tail

Fishes

The first vertebrates were aquatic and probably evolved during the early Cambrian period about 542 million years ago. In contrast with most living vertebrates, they lacked jaws, hinged bone structures that work the mouth.

Two types of jawless fishes survive today: hagfishes and lampreys. Present-day hagfishes scavenge dead or dying animals on the cold, dark seafloor (**Figure 31a**). When threatened, a hagfish exudes an enormous amount of slime from special glands on the sides of its body. Recently, some hagfishes have become endangered because their skin is used to make "eel-skin" belts, purses, and boots. Most species of lampreys are parasites that use their jawless mouths as suckers to attach to the sides of large fish (**Figure 31b**). The rasping tongue then penetrates the skin, allowing the lamprey to feed on its victim's blood and tissues.

We know from the fossil record that the first jawed vertebrates were fishes that evolved about 440 million years ago. They had two pairs of fins, making them agile swimmers. Some early fishes were active predators up to 10 m (33 ft) in length that could chase prey and bite off chunks of flesh. Even today, most fishes are carnivores.

Cartilaginous fishes, such as sharks and rays, have a flexible skeleton made of cartilage (**Figure 31c**). Most sharks are adept predators because they are fast swimmers with streamlined bodies, acute senses, and powerful jaws. A shark does not have keen eyesight, but its sense of smell is very sharp. In addition, special electrosensors on the head can detect minute electrical fields produced by muscle contractions in nearby animals. Sharks also have a **lateral line system**, a row of sensory organs running along each side of the body. Sensitive to changes in water pressure, the lateral line system enables a shark to detect minor vibrations caused by animals swimming in its neighborhood. There are about 1,000 living species of cartilaginous fishes, nearly all of them marine.

The skeletons of **bony fishes** are reinforced by calcium (**Figure 31d**). Bony fishes have a lateral line system, a keen sense of smell, and excellent eyesight. On each side of the head, a protective flap called the **operculum** (plural, *opercula*) covers a chamber housing the gills, feathery external organs that extract oxygen from water. Movement of the operculum allows the fish to breathe without swimming. By contrast, sharks lack opercula and must swim to pass water over their gills. The need to move water over the gills is why a shark must keep moving to stay alive. Also unlike sharks, bony fishes have a **swim bladder**, a gas-filled sac that enables the fish to control its buoyancy. Thus, many bony fishes can conserve energy by remaining almost motionless, in contrast to sharks, which sink if they stop swimming.

Most bony fishes, including familiar species such as tuna, trout, and goldfish, are **ray-finned fishes**. Their fins are webs of skin supported by thin, flexible skeletal rays, the feature for which the group was named. There are approximately 27,000 species of ray-finned fishes, the greatest number of species of any vertebrate group.

A second evolutionary branch includes the **lobe-finned fishes**. In contrast to the ray-finned fishes, their fins are muscular and are supported by stout bones that are homologous to amphibian limb bones. Early lobe-fins lived in coastal wetlands and may have used their fins to "walk" underwater. Today, three lineages of lobe-fins survive. The coelacanth is a deep-sea dweller once thought to be extinct. The lungfishes are represented by several Southern Hemisphere species that inhabit stagnant waters and gulp air into lungs connected to the pharynx. The third lineage of lobe-fins adapted to life on land and gave rise to amphibians, the first terrestrial vertebrates. ☑

Lancelets
Tunicates
Hagfishes
Lampreys
Cartilaginous fishes
Bony fishes
Amphibians
Reptiles
Mammals

✓ CHECKPOINT

A shark has a _____ skeleton, whereas a tuna has a _____ skeleton.

Answer: cartilaginous; bony

▼ **Figure 31 Fish diversity.**

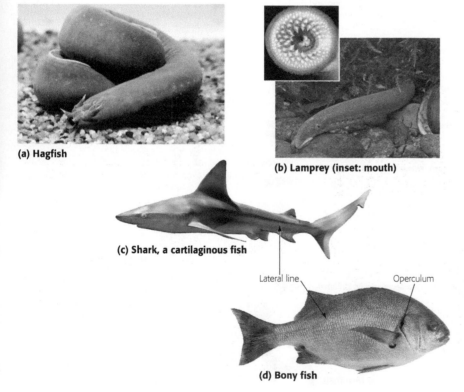

(a) Hagfish

(b) Lamprey (inset: mouth)

(c) Shark, a cartilaginous fish

Lateral line

Operculum

(d) Bony fish

Amphibians

In Greek, the word *amphi-bios* means "living a double life." Most **amphibians** exhibit a mixture of aquatic and terrestrial adaptations. Most species are tied to water because their eggs, lacking shells, dry out quickly in the air. A frog may spend much of its time on land, but it lays its eggs in water **(Figure 32a)**. An egg develops into a larva called a tadpole, a legless, aquatic algae-eater with gills, a lateral line system resembling that of fishes, and a long-finned tail. The tadpole undergoes a radical metamorphosis when changing into

a frog **(Figure 32b)**. When a young frog crawls onto shore and begins life as a terrestrial insect-eater, it has four legs, air-breathing lungs instead of gills, external eardrums, and no lateral line system. But even as adults, amphibians are most abundant in damp habitats, such as swamps and rain forests. This is partly because amphibians depend on their moist skin to supplement lung function in exchanging gases with the environment. Thus, even those frogs that are adapted to relatively dry habitats spend much of their time in humid burrows or under piles of moist leaves. The amphibians of today, including frogs and salamanders, account for about 12% of all living vertebrates, or about 6,000 species **(Figure 32c)**.

Amphibians were the first vertebrates to colonize land. They descended from fishes that had lungs and fins with muscles and skeletal supports strong enough to enable some movement, however clumsy, on land **(Figure 33)**. The fossil record chronicles the evolution of four-limbed amphibians from fishlike ancestors. Terrestrial vertebrates—amphibians, reptiles, and mammals—are collectively called **tetrapods**, which means "four feet." ☑

▼ Figure 32 **Amphibian diversity.**

(a) Frog eggs

(b) Tadpole and adult tree frog (right)

Malayan horned frog   Texas barred tiger salamander
(c) **Frogs and salamanders: the two major groups of amphibians**

▼ Figure 33 **The origin of tetrapods.**

Lobe-finned fish. Fossils of some lobe-finned fishes have skeletal supports extending into their fins.

Early amphibian. Fossils of early amphibians have limb skeletons that probably functioned in helping them move on land.

Reptiles

Reptiles (including birds) and mammals are **amniotes**. The evolution of amniotes from an amphibian ancestor included many adaptations for living on land. The adaptation that gives the group its name is the **amniotic egg**, a fluid-filled egg with a waterproof shell that encloses the developing embryo (**Figure 34**). The amniotic egg functions as a self-contained "pond" that enables amniotes to complete their life cycle on land.

The **reptiles** include snakes, lizards, turtles, crocodiles, alligators, and birds, along with a number of extinct groups, including most of the dinosaurs. The European grass snake in Figure 34 displays two reptilian adaptations to living on land: scaled waterproof skin, preventing dehydration in dry air, and amniotic eggs with shells, providing a watery, nutritious internal environment where the embryo can develop. These adaptations allowed reptiles to break their ancestral ties to aquatic habitats. Reptiles cannot breathe through their dry skin and so obtain most of their oxygen through their lungs.

Evolutionary biologists have discovered the answer to the riddle "Which came first, the chicken or the egg?"

Lancelets
Tunicates
Hagfishes
Lampreys
Cartilaginous fishes
Bony fishes
Amphibians
Reptiles
Mammals

☑ CHECKPOINT

What is an amniotic egg?

Answer: a shelled egg surrounding fluid that contains an embryo

Nonbird Reptiles

Nonbird reptiles are sometimes referred to as "cold-blooded" animals because they do not use their metabolism extensively to control body temperature. Reptiles do regulate body temperature, but largely through behavioral adaptations. For example, many lizards regulate their internal temperature by basking in the sun when the air is cool and seeking shade when the air is too warm. Because lizards and other nonbird reptiles absorb external heat rather than generating much of their own, they are said to be **ectotherms**, a term more accurate than "cold-blooded." By heating directly with solar energy rather than through the metabolic breakdown of food, a nonbird reptile can survive on less than 10% of the calories required by a mammal of equivalent size.

As successful as reptiles are today, they were far more widespread, numerous, and diverse during the Mesozoic era, which is sometimes known as the "age of reptiles." Reptiles diversified extensively during that era, producing a dynasty that lasted until about 65 million years ago. Dinosaurs, the most diverse reptile group, included the largest animals ever to inhabit land. Some were gentle giants that lumbered about while browsing vegetation. Others were voracious carnivores that chased their larger prey on two legs.

The age of reptiles began to fade about 70 million years ago. Around that time, the global climate became cooler and more variable. This was a period of mass extinctions that claimed all the dinosaurs by about 65 million years ago, except for one lineage. That lone surviving lineage is represented today by the reptilian group we know as birds. ☑

▶ **Figure 34 Reptile diversity.**

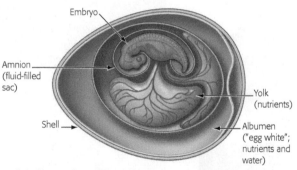

Embryo

Amnion (fluid-filled sac)

Yolk (nutrients)

Shell

Albumen ("egg white"; nutrients and water)

Amniotic egg. The embryo and its life-support system are enclosed in a waterproof shell.

Snake. The shells of nonbird reptile eggs are leathery and flexible. This European grass snake is nonvenomous. When threatened, it may hiss and strike. If the bluff fails, it goes limp, pretending to be dead.

Lizard. The Gila monster, a desert-dweller of the Southwest, is the only venomous lizard native to the United States. Although large (up to 2 feet long), it moves too slowly to pose any danger to people.

Birds

You may have noticed that the reptilian egg resembles the more familiar chicken egg. Birds have scaly skin on their legs and feet; even feathers—their signature feature—are modified scales. Genetic and fossil evidence shows that **birds** are indeed reptiles, having evolved from a lineage of small, two-legged dinosaurs called theropods. Today, birds look quite different from reptiles because of their distinctive flight equipment—almost all of the 10,000 living bird species are airborne. The few flightless species, including the ostrich and the penguin, evolved from flying ancestors.

Almost every element of bird anatomy is adapted in some way that enhances flight. The bones have a honeycombed structure that makes them strong but light. (The wings of airplanes have the same basic construction.) For example, a huge seagoing species called the frigate bird has a wingspan of more than 2 m (6.6 ft), but its whole skeleton weighs only about 113 g (a mere 4 ounces, about as much as an iPhone). Another adaptation that reduces the weight of birds is the absence of some internal organs found in other vertebrates. Female birds, for instance, have only one ovary instead of a pair. Also, today's birds are toothless, an adaptation that trims the weight of the head, preventing uncontrolled nosedives. Birds do not chew food in the mouth but grind it in the gizzard, a muscular chamber of the digestive tract near the stomach.

Flying requires a great expenditure of energy and an active metabolism. Unlike other reptiles, birds are **endotherms**, meaning they use their own metabolic heat to maintain a warm, constant body temperature.

A bird's most obvious flight equipment is its wings. Bird wings are airfoils that illustrate the same principles of aerodynamics as the wings of an airplane **(Figure 35)**. A bird's flight motors are its powerful breast muscles, which are anchored to a keel-like breastbone. It is mainly these flight muscles that we call "white meat" on chicken and turkey breasts. Some birds, such as eagles and hawks, have wings adapted for soaring on air currents and flap their wings only occasionally. Other birds, including hummingbirds, excel at maneuvering but must flap continuously to stay aloft. Feathers are made of the same protein that forms the scales of reptiles. Feathers may have functioned first as insulation, helping birds retain body heat, or for courtship displays. Only later were they adapted as flight gear. ✔

▶ Figure 35 **The aerodynamics of a bald eagle in flight.** Both birds and airplanes owe their "lift" to changes in air pressure caused by the shape of their wings.

Lower air pressure

Higher air pressure

Airfoil

Crocodile. Found throughout central and southern Africa, the Nile crocodile can grow up to 20 feet long and weigh nearly 2,000 pounds.

Birds. These red-crowned cranes, native to China, are performing an elaborate courtship dance.

Dinosaur. This *Herrerasaurus* skeleton is from a carnivorous theropod discovered in Argentina.

Mammals

There are two major lineages of amniotes: one that led to the reptiles and one that produced the mammals. The first **mammals** arose about 200 million years ago and were probably small, nocturnal insect-eaters. Mammals became much more diverse after the downfall of the dinosaurs. Most mammals are terrestrial. These include nearly 1,000 species of winged mammals, the bats. And the roughly 80 species of dolphins, porpoises, and whales are totally aquatic. The blue whale—an endangered mammal that grows to lengths of nearly 30 m (about as long as a basketball court)—is the largest animal that has ever lived. Mammals have two unique characteristics: mammary glands (which produce milk, a nutrient-rich substance to feed the young) and hair. The main function of hair is to insulate the body and help maintain a warm, constant internal temperature; like birds, mammals are endotherms.

The major groups of mammals are monotremes, marsupials, and eutherians **(Figure 36)**. The duck-billed platypus and the echidna, or spiny anteater, are the only existing species of **monotremes**, egg-laying mammals. The platypus lives along rivers in eastern Australia and on the nearby island of Tasmania. The female usually lays two eggs and incubates them in a leaf nest. After

hatching, the young nurse by licking up milk secreted by rudimentary mammary glands onto the mother's fur.

Most mammals are born rather than hatched. During pregnancy in marsupials and eutherians, the embryos are nurtured inside the mother by an organ called the **placenta**. Consisting of both embryonic and maternal tissues, the placenta joins the embryo to the mother within the uterus. The embryo receives oxygen and nutrients from maternal blood that flows close to the embryonic blood system in the placenta.

Marsupials, the so-called pouched mammals, include kangaroos, koalas, and opossums. These mammals have a brief pregnancy and give birth to embryonic offspring. After birth, the tiny offspring make their way to an external pouch on the mother's abdomen, where they attach to mammary glands. Nearly all marsupials live in Australia, New Zealand, and North and South America. Australian marsupials have diversified extensively, filling terrestrial habitats that on the other continents are occupied by eutherian mammals.

Eutherians are also called **placental mammals** because their placentas provide a more intimate and longer-lasting association between the mother and her developing young than do marsupial placentas. Eutherians make up almost 95% of the 5,300 species of living mammals. Dogs, cats, cows, rodents, rabbits, bats, and whales are all examples of eutherian mammals. One of the eutherian groups is the primates, which include monkeys, apes, and humans. ☑

Lancelets
Tunicates
Hagfishes
Lampreys
Cartilaginous fishes
Bony fishes
Amphibians
Reptiles

Mammals

▼ **Figure 36 Mammalian diversity.**

MAJOR GROUPS OF MAMMALS		
Monotremes (hatched from eggs)	**Marsupials** (embryonic at birth)	**Eutherians** (fully developed at birth)
Monotremes, such as this duck-billed platypus, are the only mammals that lay eggs. Like other mammals, platypus mothers nourish their young with milk.	The young of marsupials are born very early in their development. The newborn kangaroo will finish its growth while nursing from a nipple in its mother's pouch.	In eutherians (placental mammals), young develop within the uterus of the mother. There they are nurtured by the flow of blood through the dense network of vessels in the placenta. This newborn foal is coated by remnants of the placenta.

Handwritten notes:

- only short durable pregnancy phase
- eggs can be hidden away from prey
- very dependent on mother

- easier to get birth
- better equipped when prey is opposing on mother and child
- more vulnerable to infection, because microbia hasn't fully developed yet

- more vulnerable, very hard on body
- juvenile can survive without mother
- more labour intense, higher chance of mother dying

The Human Ancestry

We have now traced animal phylogeny to the **primates**, the mammalian group that includes us—*Homo sapiens*—and our closest kin. To understand what that means, we must follow our ancestry back to the trees, where some of our most treasured traits originated.

The Evolution of Primates

Primate evolution provides a context for understanding human origins. The fossil record supports the hypothesis that primates evolved from insect-eating mammals during the late Cretaceous period, about 65 million years ago. Those early primates were small, arboreal (tree-dwelling) mammals. Thus, primates were first distinguished by characteristics that were shaped, through natural selection, by the demands of living in the trees. For example, primates have limber shoulder joints, which make it possible to swing from branch to branch. The agile hands of primates can hang on to branches and manipulate food. Nails have replaced claws in many primate species, and the fingertips are very sensitive. The eyes of primates are close together on the front of the face. The overlapping fields of vision of the two eyes enhance depth perception, an obvious advantage when swinging in trees. Excellent eye-hand coordination is also important for arboreal maneuvering. Parental care is essential for young animals in the trees. Mammals devote more energy to caring for their young than most other vertebrates, and primates are among the most attentive parents of all mammals. Most primates have single births and nurture their offspring for a long time. Although humans never lived in trees, we retain in modified form many traits that originated there.

Taxonomists divide the primates into three main groups **(Figure 37)**. The first includes lemurs, lorises, and bush babies. These primates live in Madagascar, southern Asia, and Africa. Tarsiers, small nocturnal tree-dwellers found only in Southeast Asia, form the second group of primates. The third group of primates, **anthropoids**, includes monkeys and apes. All monkeys in the New World (the Americas) are arboreal and are distinguished by prehensile (grasping) tails that function as an extra appendage for swinging. If you see a monkey in a zoo swinging by its tail, you know it's from the New World. Although some Old World (African and Asian) monkeys are also arboreal, their tails are not prehensile. And many Old World monkeys, including baboons, macaques, and mandrills, are mainly ground-dwellers.

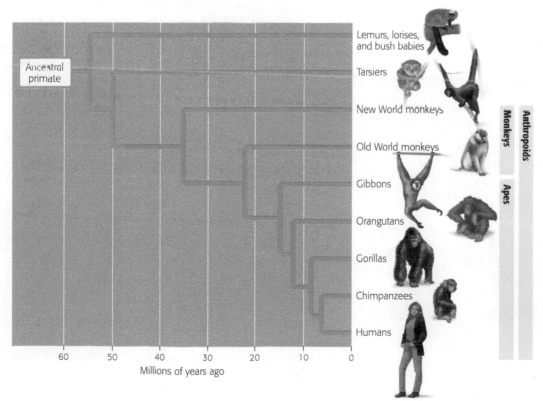

◄ **Figure 37** **Primate phylogeny.**

Ancestral primate

Lemurs, lorises, and bush babies

Tarsiers

New World monkeys

Old World monkeys

Gibbons

Orangutans

Gorillas

Chimpanzees

Humans

Monkeys

Apes

Anthropoids

60 50 40 30 20 10 0

Millions of years ago

271

Anthropoids also have a fully opposable thumb; that is, they can touch the tips of all four fingers with their thumb.

Our closest anthropoid relatives are the nonhuman apes: gibbons, orangutans, gorillas, and chimpanzees. They live only in tropical regions of the Old World. Except for some gibbons, apes are larger than monkeys, with relatively long arms, short legs, and no tail.

Although all apes are capable of living in trees, only gibbons and orangutans are primarily arboreal. Gorillas and chimpanzees are highly social. Apes have larger brains proportionate to body size than monkeys, and their behavior is more adaptable. And, of course, the apes include humans. **Figure 38** shows examples of primates.

▼ **Figure 38 Primate diversity.**

Red ruffed lemur   **Tarsier**

Black spider monkey
(New World monkey)

Patas monkey (Old World monkey)

Gibbon (ape)

Orangutan (ape)

Gorilla (ape)

Chimpanzee (ape)

Human

The Emergence of Humankind

Humanity is one very young twig on the tree of life. In the continuum of life spanning 3.5 billion years, the fossil record and molecular systematics indicate that humans and chimpanzees have shared a common African ancestry for all but the last 6–7 million years (see Figure 37). Put another way, if we compressed the history of life to a year, the human branch has existed for only 18 hours.

Some Common Misconceptions

Certain misconceptions about human evolution persist in the minds of many, long after these myths have been debunked by the fossil evidence. One of these myths is expressed in the question "If chimpanzees were our ancestors, then why do they still exist?" In fact, scientists do not think that humans evolved from chimpanzees. Rather, as illustrated in Figure 37, the lineages that led to present-day humans and chimpanzees diverged from a common ancestor several million years ago. Each branch then evolved separately. As an analogy, consider a large family reunion attended by the descendants of a man who was born in 1830. Although the attendees share this common ancestor who lived several generations ago, they may be only distantly related to each other, as sixth or seventh cousins. Similarly, chimpanzees are not our parent species, but more like our very distant phylogenetic cousins, related through a common ancestor that lived hundreds of thousands of generations in the past.

Another myth envisions human evolution as a ladder with a series of steps leading directly from an ancestral anthropoid to *Homo sapiens*. This is often illustrated as a parade of fossil **hominins** (members of the human family) becoming progressively more modern as they march across the page. In fact, as **Figure 39** shows, there were times in hominin history when several human species coexisted. Scientists have identified about 20 species of fossil hominins, demonstrating that human phylogeny is more like a multibranched bush than a ladder, with our species being the tip of the only twig that still lives.

Although evidence from hundreds of thousands of hominin fossils debunks these and other myths about human evolution, many fascinating questions about our ancestry remain. The discovery of each new hominin fossil brings scientists a little closer to solving the puzzle of how we became human. In the following pages, you'll learn about some of the important clues that have been discovered so far.

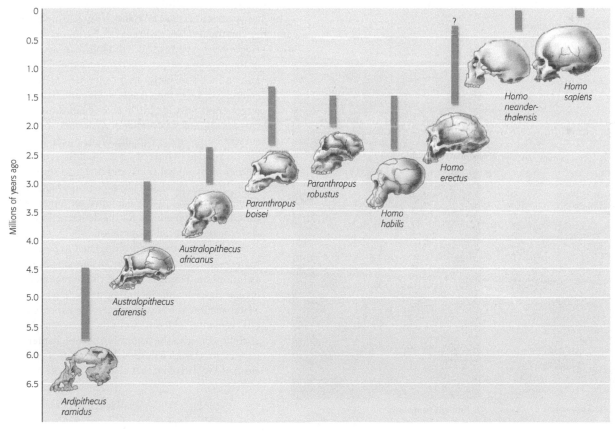

◄ **Figure 39 A time line of human evolution.** The orange bars indicate the time span during which each species lived. Notice that there have been times when two or more hominin species coexisted. The skulls are all drawn to the same scale so you can compare brain sizes.

Australopithecus and the Antiquity of Bipedalism

Present-day humans and chimpanzees clearly differ in two major physical features: Humans are bipedal (walk upright) and have much larger brains. When did these features emerge? In the early 1900s, scientists hypothesized that increased brain size was the initial change that separated hominins from other apes. That hypothesis was overturned when a team of researchers in Ethiopia **(Figure 40a)** unearthed a stunning 3.24-million-year-old female hominin that had a small brain and walked on two legs. Officially named *Australopithecus afarensis*, but nicknamed Lucy by her discoverers, the individual was only about 3 feet tall and with a head about the size of a softball. Corroborating evidence of early bipedalism was found soon after—the footprints of two upright-walking hominins preserved in a 3.6-million-year-old layer of volcanic ash **(Figure 40b)**. Since these initial discoveries, many more *Australopithecus afarensis* fossils have been found, including most of the skeleton of a 3-year-old member of the species. Other species of *Australopithecus* have also been discovered. The first analysis of the most recent addition to the genus, *Australopithecus sediba*, was published in 2010.

☑ CHECKPOINT

Which hominin species was the first to walk upright? Which was the first to spread beyond Africa?

Answer: Australopithecus afarensis; Homo erectus

▼ Figure 40 **The antiquity of upright posture.**

(a) Afar region of Ethiopia, where Lucy was discovered

(b) Ancient footprints

Scientists are now certain that bipedalism is a very old trait. Another lineage known as "robust" australopiths—including *Paranthropus boisei* and *Paranthropus robustus* in Figure 39—were also small-brained bipeds. So was *Ardipithecus ramidus*, the oldest hominin shown in Figure 39.

Homo habilis and the Evolution of Inventive Minds

Enlargement of the human brain is first evident in fossils from East Africa dating to about 2.4 million years ago. Thus, the fundamental human trait of an enlarged brain evolved a few million years after bipedalism.

Anthropologists have found skulls with brain capacities intermediate in size between those of the latest *Australopithecus* species and those of *Homo sapiens*. Simple handmade stone tools are sometimes found with the larger-brained fossils, which have been dubbed *Homo habilis* ("handy man"). After walking upright for about 2 million years, humans were finally beginning to use their manual dexterity and big brains to invent tools that enhanced their hunting, gathering, and scavenging on the African savanna.

Homo erectus and the Global Dispersal of Humanity

The first species to extend humanity's range from Africa to other continents was *Homo erectus*. Skeletons of *Homo erectus* dating to 1.8 million years ago found in the Republic of Georgia represent the oldest known fossils of hominins outside Africa. *Homo erectus* was taller than *Homo habilis* and had a larger brain capacity. Intelligence enabled this species to continue succeeding in Africa and also to survive in the colder climates of the north. *Homo erectus* resided in huts or caves, built fires, made clothes from animal skins, and designed stone tools. In anatomical and physiological adaptations, *Homo erectus* was poorly equipped for life outside the tropics, but made up for the deficiencies with cleverness and social cooperation.

Eventually, *Homo erectus* migrated to populate many regions of Asia and Europe, moving as far as Indonesia. This species gave rise to regionally diverse descendants, including, as you'll learn in a later section, the Neanderthals. Could the "hobbits" (*Homo floresiensis*) from the Biology and Society section at the beginning of this chapter have evolved from a long-isolated group of *Homo erectus*? We'll explore that question next. ☑

Human Evolution THE PROCESS OF SCIENCE

Who Were the Hobbit People?

How do scientists test hypotheses about events that occurred in the distant past? One approach involves using fossils, the historical record of life on Earth. If you have watched TV shows like *Bones*, in which forensic scientists use skeletal remains to solve crimes, you know that even a small piece of a skeleton can provide a wealth of information to an expert. Researchers have applied this method of hypothesis testing to the scientific debate over the "hobbit" people.

The first **observations** made by the researchers who discovered hominin fossils on the island of Flores revealed that the new fossils did not belong to any known species. This led researchers to ask the **question**, Where does this hominin fit in our evolutionary history? The scientists formed the **hypothesis** that the hobbits evolved from an isolated population of *Homo erectus*, the ancient hominin whose far-flung travels predated those of *Homo sapiens*. They made the **prediction** that key traits of the new species, such as its skull characteristics and body proportions, would resemble those of a miniature *Homo erectus* individual. Rather than a controlled **experiment**, the investigation consisted of making detailed measurements and other observations of the new fossils and comparing them with data from *Homo erectus* fossils. The initial **results** supported their hypothesis.

As you have learned, however, preliminary conclusions are often overturned by new evidence. In the past several years, further analyses have been carried out, and additional specimens have been examined. Many scientists now think that the evidence supports an alternative hypothesis: *Homo floresiensis* is most closely related to *Homo habilis*,

a smaller and more ancient species than *Homo erectus*. Other researchers continue to test the hypothesis that the hobbits are not a species at all but a *Homo sapiens* population with a disorder that caused bone malformations.

How can scientists determine which hypothesis is correct? By accumulating further evidence. While some researchers continue to excavate the site where *Homo floresiensis* was discovered **(Figure 41)**, others are widening the search to additional locations. The most helpful information would come from finding a second skull or unearthing bones or teeth from which DNA could be extracted and analyzed. Meanwhile, the mystery of the hobbit people continues.

▼ **Figure 41 Searching for hobbits.** Researchers continue to excavate Liang Bua Cave, on the Indonesian island of Flores, where *Homo floresiensis* was discovered.

Homo neanderthalensis

Homo floresiensis is not the only mystery on our family tree. The first discovery of fossilized remains in the Neander Valley in Germany 150 years ago, *Homo neanderthalensis*—commonly called Neanderthals—stimulated the public's imagination. This intriguing species had a large brain and hunted big game with tools made from stone and wood. Neanderthals were living in Europe as far back as 350,000 years ago and spread to the Near East, central Asia, and southern Siberia. By 28,000 years ago, the species was extinct. Who were the Neanderthals?

Analysis of DNA extracted from Neanderthal fossils proved that humans are not the descendants of Neanderthals, as was once thought. Rather, humans and Neanderthals shared a common ancestor, and their lineages diverged about 400,000 years ago. You may

be surprised to learn that sequencing of Neanderthal genomes suggests that interbreeding between Neanderthals and some populations of *Homo sapiens* left a genetic legacy in our species. Roughly 2% of the genomes of most present-day humans came from Neanderthals. Africans are the exception—their DNA carries no detectable trace of Neanderthal ancestry. Scientists also learned that at least some Neanderthals had pale skin and red hair. In the most recent analysis of a Neanderthal genome, published in 2014, researchers identified specific genes and gene regulation sequences that distinguish modern humans from Neanderthals. Clues such as these will help scientists understand the genetic differences that were important in the evolution of *Homo sapiens*.

According to recent DNA analysis, many of us have a bit of Neanderthal in our genes.

The Origin and Dispersal of *Homo sapiens*

Evidence from fossils and DNA studies is coming together to support a compelling hypothesis about how our own species, *Homo sapiens*, emerged and spread around the world. The oldest known fossils of *Homo sapiens* were discovered in Ethiopia and date from 160,000 to 195,000 years ago. These early humans lacked the heavy browridges of *Homo erectus* and *Homo neanderthalensis* and were more slender, suggesting that they belong to a distinct lineage. The Ethiopian fossils support molecular evidence about the origin of humans: DNA studies strongly suggest that all living humans can trace their ancestry back to a single African *Homo sapiens* lineage that began 160,000 to 200,000 years ago.

The oldest fossils of *Homo sapiens* outside Africa are from the Middle East and date back about 115,000 years.

Evidence suggests that our species emerged from Africa in one or more waves, spreading first into Asia and then to Europe, Southeast Asia, Australia, and finally to the New World (North and South America) **(Figure 42)**. The date of the first arrival of humans in the New World is uncertain, although the generally accepted evidence suggests a minimum of 15,000 years ago.

Certain uniquely human traits have allowed for the development of human societies. The primate brain continues to grow after birth, and the period of growth is longer for a human than for any other primate. The extended period of human development also lengthens the time parents care for their offspring, which contributes to the child's ability to benefit from the experiences of earlier generations. This is the basis of human culture—social transmission of accumulated knowledge, customs, beliefs, and art over generations **(Figure 43)**. The major means of this transmission is language, spoken and written. Humans have evolved culturally as well as biologically.

Nothing has had a greater impact on life on Earth than *Homo sapiens*. The global consequences of human evolution have been enormous. Cultural evolution made modern *Homo sapiens* a new force in the history of life—a species that could defy its physical limitations. We do not have to wait to adapt to an environment through natural selection; we simply change the environment to meet our needs.

We are the most numerous and widespread of all large animals, and wherever we go, we bring environmental change faster than many species can adapt. ☑

▼ Figure 42 **The spread of *Homo sapiens* (dates given as years before present, BP)**

☑ CHECKPOINT

1. Humans first evolved on which continent?
2. When would a *Homo sapiens* individual have had an opportunity to meet a Neanderthal?

Answers: 1. Africa 2. between the time Homo sapiens reached the regions inhabited by Neanderthals (no sooner than 115,000 years ago) and the time when the Neanderthals died out (28,000 years ago)

◄ Figure 43 **Art history goes back a long way.** Beautiful ancient art, such as this 30,000-year-old painting from Lascaux Cave in France, is just one example of our cultural roots in early societies.

Human Evolution EVOLUTION CONNECTION

Are We Still Evolving?

Imagine that you could take a time machine 100,000 years into the past and bring back a *Homo sapiens* man. If you dressed him in jeans and a T-shirt and took him for a stroll around campus, chances are that no one would look twice. Did we stop evolving after becoming *Homo sapiens*? In some ways, yes. The human body has not changed much in the past 100,000 years. And by the time *Homo sapiens* began to travel out of Africa, all of the complex characteristics that define our humanity, including our big-brained intelligence and our capacity for language and symbolic thought, had already evolved.

But as humans wandered far from their site of origin and settled in diverse environments, populations encountered different selective forces. Some traits of people today reflect evolutionary responses of ancient ancestors to their physical and cultural environment. For example, the high frequency of sickle hemoglobin in certain populations is an adaptation that protects against the deadly disease malaria. In other malarial regions, a group of inherited blood disorders called thalassemia serve the same adaptive function.

Diet has had a significant effect on human evolution, too. For example, the ability to digest lactose as adults evolved in populations that kept dairy herds. Reliance by early farmers on starchy crops such as rice or tubers also left a genetic trace: extra copies of the gene that encodes the starch-digesting enzyme amylase.

One of the most striking differences among people is skin color (Figure 44). The loss of skin pigmentation in humans who migrated north from Africa is thought to be an adaptation to low levels of ultraviolet (UV) radiation in northern latitudes. Dark pigment blocks the UV radiation necessary for synthesizing vitamin D—essential for proper bone development—in the skin. Recent research has turned up numerous other examples of adaptations that enabled us to colonize Earth's varied environments. For instance, Tibetans live at altitudes up to 14,000 feet (2.6 miles), where the air has 40% less oxygen than at sea level. Researchers have identified genes that have undergone evolutionary changes in response to this challenging environment (Figure 45). High-altitude adaptations have also been discovered in populations that inhabit the Andes Mountains in South America. Despite evolutionary tweaks such as these, however, we remain a single species.

▼ Figure 45 **Tibetans, a population adapted to living at high altitude.**

▼ Figure 44 **People with different adaptations to UV radiation.**

Chapter Review

SUMMARY OF KEY CONCEPTS

The Origins of Animal Diversity

What Is an Animal?

Animals are eukaryotic, multicellular, heterotrophic organisms that obtain nutrients by ingestion. Most animals reproduce sexually and develop from a zygote to a blastula and then to a gastrula. After the gastrula stage, some develop directly into adults, whereas others pass through a larval stage.

Early Animals and the Cambrian Explosion

Animals probably evolved from a colonial flagellated protist. Precambrian animals were soft-bodied. Animals with hard parts appeared during the Cambrian period. Between 535 and 525 million years ago, animal diversity increased rapidly.

Evolution: Animal Phylogeny

Major branches of animal evolution are defined by two key evolutionary differences: the presence or absence of tissues and radial versus bilateral body symmetry. A tissue-lined body cavity evolved in a number of later branches.

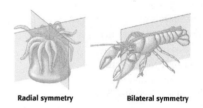

Radial symmetry   Bilateral symmetry

Major Invertebrate Phyla

This tree shows the eight major invertebrate phyla, as well as chordates, which include a few invertebrates.

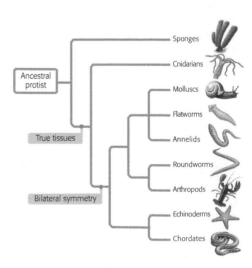

Sponges

Sponges (phylum Porifera) are stationary animals with porous bodies but no true tissues. Specialized cells draw water through pores in the sides of the body and trap food particles.

Cnidarians

Cnidarians (phylum Cnidaria) have radial symmetry, a gastrovascular cavity with a single opening, and tentacles with stinging cnidocytes. The body is either a stationary polyp or a floating medusa.

Molluscs

Molluscs (phylum Mollusca) are soft-bodied animals often protected by a hard shell. The body has three main parts: a muscular foot, a visceral mass, and a fold of tissue called the mantle.

MOLLUSCS		
Gastropods	Bivalves	Cephalopods

Flatworms

Flatworms (phylum Platyhelminthes) are the simplest bilateral animals. They may be free-living (such as planarians) or parasitic (such as tapeworms).

Annelids

Annelids (phylum Annelida) are segmented worms with complete digestive tracts. They may be free-living or parasitic.

Roundworms

Roundworms, also called nematodes (phylum Nematoda), are unsegmented and cylindrical with tapered ends. They may be free-living or parasitic.

Arthropods

Arthropods (phylum Arthropoda) are segmented animals with an exoskeleton and specialized, jointed appendages.

ARTHROPODS			
Arachnids	Crustaceans	Millipedes and Centipedes	Insects

Echinoderms

Echinoderms (phylum Echinodermata) are stationary or slow-moving marine animals that lack body segments and possess a unique water vascular system. Bilaterally symmetric larvae usually change to radially symmetric adults. Echinoderms have a bumpy endoskeleton.

Vertebrate Evolution and Diversity

Characteristics of Chordates

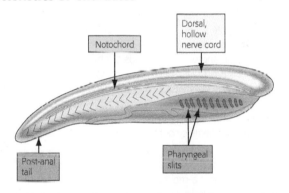

Tunicates and lancelets are invertebrate chordates. The vast majority of chordates are vertebrates, possessing a skull and backbone.

Fishes

Hagfishes and lampreys are jawless vertebrates. Cartilaginous fishes, such as sharks, are mostly predators with powerful jaws and a flexible skeleton made of cartilage. Bony fishes have a stiff skeleton reinforced by calcium. Bony fishes are further classified into ray-finned fishes and lobe-finned fishes (including lungfishes).

Amphibians

Amphibians are tetrapod vertebrates that usually deposit their eggs (lacking shells) in water. Aquatic larvae typically undergo a radical metamorphosis into the adult stage. Their moist skin requires that amphibians spend much of their adult life in humid environments.

Reptiles

Reptiles are amniotes, vertebrates that develop in a fluid-filled egg enclosed by a shell. Reptiles include terrestrial ectotherms with lungs and waterproof skin covered by scales. Scales and amniotic eggs enhanced reproduction on land. Birds are endothermic reptiles with wings, feathers, and other adaptations for flight.

Mammals

Mammals are endothermic vertebrates with mammary glands and hair. There are three major groups of mammals: Monotremes lay eggs; marsupials use a placenta but give birth to tiny embryonic offspring that usually complete development while attached to nipples inside the mother's pouch; and eutherians, or placental mammals, use their placenta in a longer-lasting association between the mother and her developing young.

The Human Ancestry

The Evolution of Primates

The first primates were small, arboreal mammals that evolved from insect-eating mammals about 65 million years ago. Anthropoids consist of New World monkeys (with prehensile tails), Old World monkeys (without prehensile tails), apes, and humans.

The Emergence of Humankind

Chimpanzees and humans evolved from a common ancestor about 6–7 million years ago. Species of the genus *Australopithecus*, which lived at least 4 million years ago, walked upright and had a small brain. Enlargement of the human brain in *Homo habilis* came later, about 2.4 million years ago. *Homo erectus* was the first species to extend humanity's range from its birthplace in Africa to other continents. *Homo erectus* gave rise to regionally diverse descendants, including the Neanderthals (*Homo neanderthalensis*). Current data indicate a relatively recent dispersal of modern Africans that gave rise to today's human diversity.

MasteringBiology®

For practice quizzes, BioFlix animations, MP3 tutorials, video tutors, and more study tools designed for this text, go to MasteringBiology®

SELF-QUIZ

1. Bilateral symmetry in the animal kingdom is best correlated with
   a. an ability to sense equally in all directions.
   b. the presence of a skeleton.
   c. motility and active predation and escape.
   d. development of a body cavity.

2. Identify which of the following categories includes all others in the list: arthropod, arachnid, insect, butterfly, crustacean, millipede.

3. The oldest group of tetrapods is the _____.

4. Reptiles are much more extensively adapted to life on land than amphibians because reptiles
   a. have a complete digestive tract.
   b. lay eggs that are enclosed in shells.
   c. are endothermic.
   d. go through a larval stage.

5. What is the name of the phylum to which humans belong? For what anatomical structure is the phylum named? Where in your body is a derivative of this anatomical structure found?

6. Fossils suggest that the first major trait distinguishing human primates from other primates was _____.

7. Which of the following types of animals is not included in the human ancestry? (*Hint*: See Figure 30.)
   a. a bird
   b. a bony fish
   c. an amphibian
   d. a primate

8. Put the following list of species in order, from the oldest to the most recent: *Homo erectus*, *Australopithecus* species, *Homo habilis*, *Homo sapiens*.

9. Match each of the following animals to its phylum:
   a. human
   b. leech
   c. sea star
   d. lobster
   e. sea anemone

   1. Echinodermata
   2. Arthropoda
   3. Cnidaria
   4. Chordata
   5. Annelida

THE PROCESS OF SCIENCE

10. Imagine that you are a marine biologist. As part of your exploration, you dredge up an unknown animal from the seafloor. Describe some of the characteristics you should look at to determine the phylum to which the creature should be assigned.

11. Vegan and vegetarian diets are increasingly popular. While vegans consume no animals or animal products, many vegetarians are less strict. Talk to acquaintances who describe themselves as vegetarians, or who follow a meat-free diet, and determine which taxonomic groups they avoid eating (see Figures 6 and 30). Try to generalize about their diet. What do they consider "meat"? For example, do they avoid eating vertebrates but eat some invertebrates? Do they avoid only birds and mammals? What about fish? Do they eat dairy products or eggs?

12. What adaptations inherited from our primate ancestors enable humans to make and use tools?

13. **Interpreting Data** Average brain size, relative to body mass, gives a rough indication of the intelligence of a species. Graph the data below for hominins. Which species is most similar to *Homo floresiensis*? Does this information support the hypothesis that *Homo floresiensis* is a dwarf form of *Homo erectus* or an alternative explanation?

Hominin Species	Mean Brain Volume (cm³)	Mean Body Mass (kg)
Australopithecus afarensis	440	37
Homo erectus	940	58
Homo floresiensis	420	32
Homo habilis	610	34
Homo neanderthalensis	1480	65
Homo sapiens	1330	64
Paranthropus boisei	490	41

BIOLOGY AND SOCIETY

14. This chapter presents a scientific understanding of human origins. Science is one approach to understanding the natural world. Reread the Biology and Society section and underline words or phrases that reflect a scientific approach to the study of *Homo floresiensis*. You are probably also familiar with at least one way of understanding human origins that is outside the scope of science. How does that approach to understanding life differ from a scientific one? What might be the potential value of studying human evolution in a scientific context?

15. Coral reefs harbor a greater diversity of animals than any other environment in the sea. Australia's Great Barrier Reef has been protected as a marine reserve and is a mecca for scientists and nature enthusiasts. Elsewhere, such as in Indonesia and the Philippines, coral reefs are in danger. Many reefs have been depleted of fish, and runoff from the shore has covered coral with sediment. Nearly all the changes in the reefs can be traced back to human activities. What kinds of activities do you think might be contributing to the decline of the reefs? What are some reasons to be concerned about this decline? Do you think the situation is likely to improve or worsen in the future? Why? What might the local people do to halt the decline? Should the more industrialized countries help? Why or why not?

16. The human body has not changed much in the last 100,000 years, but human culture has changed a great deal. As a result of our culture, we change the environment at a rate far greater than the rate at which many species, including our own, can evolve. What evidence of rapid environmental change do you see around you? What aspects of human culture are responsible for these changes? Do you see any evidence of a decrease in the rate of human-caused environmental changes?

Glossary

amniote
Member of a clade of tetrapods that has an amniotic egg containing specialized membranes that protect the embryo. Amniotes include mammals and reptiles (including birds).

amniotic egg (*am'-nē-ot'-ik*)
A shelled egg in which an embryo develops within a fluid-filled amniotic sac and is nourished by yolk. Produced by reptiles (including birds) and egg-laying mammals, it enables them to complete their life cycles on dry land.

amphibian
Member of a class of vertebrate animals that includes frogs and salamanders.

animal
A eukaryotic, multicellular, heterotrophic organism that obtains nutrients by ingestion.

annelid (*an'-uh-lid*)
A segmented worm. Annelids include earthworms, polychaetes, and leeches.

anthropoid (*an'-thruh-poyd*)
Member of a primate group made up of the apes (gibbons, orangutans, gorillas, chimpanzees, and bonobos), monkeys, and humans.

arachnid
Member of a major arthropod group that includes spiders, scorpions, ticks, and mites.

arthropod (*ar'-thruh-pod*)
Member of the most diverse phylum in the animal kingdom; includes the horseshoe crab, arachnids (for example, spiders, ticks, scorpions, and mites), crustaceans (for example, crayfish, lobsters, crabs, and barnacles), millipedes, centipedes, and insects. Arthropods are characterized by a chitinous exoskeleton, molting, jointed appendages, and a body formed of distinct groups of segments.

bilateral symmetry
An arrangement of body parts such that an organism can be divided equally by a single cut passing longitudinally through it. A

bilaterally symmetric organism has mirror-image right and left sides.

bivalve
Member of a group of molluscs that includes clams, mussels, scallops, and oysters.

blastula (*blas'-tyū-luh*)
An embryonic stage that marks the end of cleavage during animal development; a hollow ball of cells in many species.

body cavity
A fluid-filled space separating the digestive tract from the outer body wall.

body segmentation
Subdivision of an animal's body into a series of repeated parts called segments.

bony fish
A fish that has a stiff skeleton reinforced by calcium salts.

cartilaginous fish (*kar-ti-laj'-uh-nus*)
A fish that has a flexible skeleton made of cartilage.

centipede
A carnivorous terrestrial arthropod that has one pair of long legs for each of its numerous body segments, with the front pair modified as poisonous claws.

cephalopod
Member of a group of molluscs that includes squids and octopuses.

chordate (*kōr'-dāt*)
An animal that at some point during its development has a dorsal, hollow nerve cord, a notochord, pharyngeal slits, and a post-anal tail. Chordates include lancelets, tunicates, and vertebrates.

cnidarian (*nī-dār'-ē-an*)
An animal characterized by cnidocytes, radial symmetry, a gastrovascular cavity, and a polyp or medusa body form. Cnidarians include hydras, jellies, sea anemones, and corals.

complete digestive tract
A digestive tube with two openings, a mouth and an anus.

crustacean
Member of a major arthropod group

that includes lobsters, crayfish, crabs, shrimps, and barnacles.

dorsal, hollow nerve cord
One of the four hallmarks of chordates; the chordate brain and spinal cord.

earthworm
A type of annelid, or segmented worm, that extracts nutrients from soil.

echinoderm (*ih-kī'-nuh-derm*)
Member of a group of slow-moving or stationary marine animals characterized by a rough or spiny skin, a water vascular system, typically an endoskeleton, and radial symmetry in adults. Echinoderms include sea stars, sea urchins, and sand dollars.

ectotherm (*ek'-tō-therm*)
An animal that warms itself mainly by absorbing heat from its surroundings.

endoskeleton
A hard interior skeleton located within the soft tissues of an animal; found in all vertebrates and a few invertebrates (such as echinoderms).

endotherm
An animal that derives most of its body heat from its own metabolism.

eutherian (*yū-thēr'-ē-un*)
See placental mammal.

exoskeleton
A hard, external skeleton that protects an animal and provides points of attachment for muscles.

flatworm
A bilateral animal with a thin, flat body form, a gastrovascular cavity with a single opening, and no body cavity. Flatworms include planarians, flukes, and tapeworms.

gastropod
Member of the largest group of molluscs, including snails and slugs.

gastrovascular cavity
A digestive compartment with a single opening that serves as both the entrance for food and the exit for undigested wastes; may also function in circulation, body support, and gas exchange. Jellies and hydras

are examples of animals with a gastrovascular cavity.

gastrula (*gas'-trū-luh*)
An embryonic stage in animal development. Most animals have a gastrula made up of three layers of cells: ectoderm, endoderm, and mesoderm.

hominin (*hah'-mi-nin*)
Any anthropoid on the human branch of the evolutionary tree, more closely related to humans than to chimpanzees.

insect
An arthropod that usually has three body segments (head, thorax, and abdomen), three pairs of legs, and one or two pairs of wings.

invertebrate
An animal that does not have a backbone.

lancelet
One of a group of bladelike invertebrate chordates.

larva
An immature individual that looks different from the adult animal.

lateral line system
A row of sensory organs along each side of a fish's body. Sensitive to changes in water pressure, it enables a fish to detect minor vibrations in the water.

leech
A type of annelid, or segmented worm, that typically lives in fresh water.

lobe-finned fish
A bony fish with strong, muscular fins supported by bones. *See also* ray-finned fish.

mammal
Member of a class of endothermic amniotes that possesses mammary glands and hair.

mantle
In molluscs, the outgrowth of the body surface that drapes over the animal. The mantle produces the shell and forms the mantle cavity.

marsupial (*mar-sū'-pē-ul*)
A pouched mammal, such as a kangaroo, opossum, or koala. Marsupials give birth to embryonic

offspring that complete development while housed in a pouch and attached to nipples on the mother's abdomen.

medusa (*med-ū'-suh*)
(plural, **medusae**) One of two types of cnidarian body forms; a floating, umbrella-like body form; also called a jelly.

metamorphosis (*met'-uh-mōr'-fuh-sis*)
The transformation of a larva into an adult.

millipede
A terrestrial arthropod that has two pairs of short legs for each of its numerous body segments and that eats decaying plant matter.

mollusc (*mol'-lusk*)
A soft-bodied animal characterized by a muscular foot, mantle, mantle cavity, and radula. Molluscs include gastropods (snails and slugs), bivalves (clams, oysters, and scallops), and cephalopods (squids and octopuses).

monotreme (*mon'-uh-trēm*)
An egg-laying mammal, such as the duck-billed platypus.

nematode (*nēm'-uh-tōd*)
See roundworm.

notochord (*nō'-tuh-kord*)
A flexible, cartilage-like, longitudinal rod located between the digestive tract and nerve cord in chordate animals, present only in embryos in many species.

operculum (*ō-per'-kyū-lum*)
(plural, **opercula**) A protective flap on each side of a bony fish's head that covers a chamber housing the gills.

pharyngeal slit (*fuh-rin'-jē-ul*)
A gill structure in the pharynx, found in chordate embryos and some adult chordates.

placenta (*pluh-sen'-tuh*)
In most mammals, the organ that provides nutrients and oxygen to the embryo and helps dispose of its metabolic wastes. The placenta is formed from embryonic tissue and the mother's endometrial blood vessels.

placental mammal (*pluh-sen'-tul*)
Mammal whose young complete their embryonic development in the uterus, nourished via the mother's blood vessels in the placenta; also called a eutherian.

polychaete (*pahl'-ē-kēt*)
A type of annelid, or segmented worm, that typically lives on the seafloor.

polyp (*pol'-ip*)
One of two types of cnidarian body forms; a stationary (sedentary), columnar, hydra-like body.

primate
Member of the mammalian group that includes lorises, bush babies, lemurs, tarsiers, monkeys, apes, and humans.

radial symmetry
An arrangement of the body parts of an organism like pieces of a pie around an imaginary central axis. Any slice passing longitudinally through a radially symmetric organism's central axis divides the organism into mirror-image halves.

radula (*rad'-yū-luh*)
A file-like organ found in many molluscs, typically used to scrape up or shred food.

ray-finned fish
A bony fish in which fins are webs of skin supported by thin, flexible skeletal rays. All but one living species of bony fishes are ray-fins. *See also* lobe-finned fish.

reptile
Member of the clade of amniotes that includes snakes, lizards, turtles, crocodiles, alligators, birds, and a number of extinct groups (including most of the dinosaurs).

roundworm
An animal characterized by a cylindrical, wormlike body form and a complete digestive tract; also called a nematode.

sponge
An aquatic stationary animal characterized by a highly porous body, choanocytes (specialized cells used for suspension feeding), and no true tissues.

swim bladder
A gas-filled internal sac that helps bony fishes maintain buoyancy.

tetrapod
A vertebrate with four limbs. Tetrapods include mammals, amphibians, and reptiles (including birds).

tunicate
One of a group of stationary invertebrate chordates.**vertebrate** (*ver'-tuh-brāt*)
A chordate animal with a backbone. Vertebrates include lampreys, cartilaginous fishes, bony fishes, amphibians, reptiles (including birds), and mammals.

water vascular system
In echinoderms, a radially arranged system of water-filled canals that branch into extensions called tube feet. The system provides movement and circulates water, facilitating gas exchange and waste disposal.

Credits

Credits are listed in the order of appearance.

PHOTO CREDITS

opening photo top left Image Source/Getty Images; **opening photo bottom right** David Gomez/E+/ Getty Images; **opening photo right** Vishnevskiy Vasily/Shutterstock; **opening photo bottom center** Nunosilvaphotography/Shutterstock; **opening photo bottom left** S. Plailly/E. Daynes/Science Source; **right** Tim Wiencis/Splash News/Newscom; **top left** Tim Wiencis/ Splash News/Newscom; **1** Gunter Ziesler/Photolibrary/ Getty Images; **4 left to right** Sinclair Stammers/Science Source; Sinclair Stammers/Science Source; **5 left to right** Publiphoto/Science Source; LorraineHudgins/Shutterstock; **9** Image Quest Marine; **10 top left to right** Sue Daly/ Nature Picture Library; Michael Klenetsky/Shutterstock; Lebendkulturen.de/Shutterstock; **10 bottom** Pavlo Vakhrushev/Fotolia; **13 left to right** Georgette Douwman/ Nature Picture Library; Image Quest Marine; Christophe Courteau/Natural Picture Library; Marevision/Age Fotostock; Reinhard Dirscherl/Alamy; **14 bottom** Geoff Brightling/Gary Stabb - modelmaker/Dorling Kindersley; **14 center right** CMB/Age Fotostock; **14 bottom right** Eye of Science/Science Source; **15 left to right** Daphne Keller; Ralph Keller/Photoshot Holdings Ltd.; F1online digitale Bildagentur GmbH/Alamy; Wolfgang Poelzer/ Wa/Age Fotostock; **17a** Steve Gschmeissner/Science Source; **17b** Eye of Science/Science Source; **17c** Sebastian Kaulitzki/Shutterstock; **18 top to bottom** Mark Kostich/ Getty Images; Maximilian Weinzierl/Alamy; Jean Dickey; **19** Dave King/Dorling Kindersley; **20 top left to right** Herbert Hopfensperger/Age Fotostock; Dave King/Dorling Kindersley; Andrew Syred/Science Source; **20 bottom left to right** Mark Kostich/Getty Images; Larry West/Science Source; **21 bottom right** Nancy Sefton/Science Source; **21 top** Dave King/Dorling Kindersley; **21 center left to right** Maximilian Weinzierl/Alamy; Tom McHugh/Science Source; Nature's Images/Science Source; **22 left to right** Jean Dickey; Tom McHugh/Science Source; **23** Radius Images/ Alamy; **24 counterclockwise from top left** NH/ Shutterstock; Doug Lemke/Shutterstock; lkpro/Shutterstock; Jean Dickey; Jean Dickey; Cordier Huguet/Age Fotostock; Jean Dickey; **24 center** Stuart Wilson/Science Source; **25 left to right** Thomas Kitchin & Victoria Hurst/Design Pics Inc./Alamy; Thomas Kitchin & Victoria Hurst/ Design Pics Inc./Alamy; Thomas Kitchin & Victoria Hurst/ Design Pics Inc./Alamy; Thomas Kitchin & Victoria Hurst/ Design Pics Inc./Alamy; Thomas Kitchin & Victoria Hurst/ Design Pics Inc./Alamy; **25 bottom** Keith Dannemiller/ Alamy; **26 top left** Image Quest Marine; **26 inset** Andrew J. Martinez/Science Source; **26 top right** Jose B. Ruiz/ Nature Picture Library; **26 bottom left to right** tbkmedia. de/Alamy; Image Quest Marine; Image Quest Marine; **27** Colin Keates/Courtesy of the Natural History Museum/ Dorling Kindersley; **29 left** Heather Angel/Natural Visions/ Alamy; **29 right** Image Quest Marine; **31a** Tom McHugh/ Science Source; **31b** F Hecker/Blickwinkel/Age Fotostock; **31b inset** A Hartl/Blickwinkel/Age Fotostock; **31c** George Grall/National Geographic/Getty Images; **31d** Christian Vinces/Shutterstock; **32a** LeChatMachine/Fotolia; **32b left** Gary Meszaros/Science Source; **32b right** Bill Brooks/ Alamy; **32c left** Tom McHugh/Science Source; **32c right** Jack Goldfarb/Age Fotostock; **34 left to right** Encyclopaedia Britannica/Alamy; Sylvain Cordier/Getty Images; **34 left to right** Jerry Young/Dorling Kindersley; Dlillc/Corbis; Miguel Periera/Courtesy of the Instituto Fundacion Miguel Lillo, Argentina/Dorling Kindersley; **35** Adam Jones/ Getty Images; **36 left to right** Jean-Philippe Varin/Science Source; Rebecca Jackrel/Age Fotostock; Barry Lewis/Alamy; **38 clockwise from top left** Creativ Studio Heinem/Age Fotostock; Siegfried Grassegger/Age Fotostock; P. Wegner/ Age Fotostock; Arco Images Gmbh/Tuns/Alamy; Juan Carlos Munoz/Age Fotostock; Anup Shah/Nature Picture Library; Ingo Arndt/Nature Picture Library; Lexan/Fotolia; John Kelly/Getty Images; **40b** John Reader/SPL/Science Source; **41** Achmad Ibrahim/AP Images; **43** Hemis.fr/ Superstock; **44** Kablonk/Superstock; **45** Stefan Espenhahn/ Image Broker/Age Fotostock.

ILLUSTRATION AND TEXT CREDITS

39: Drawn from photos of fossils: *A. ramidus* adapted from www.age-of-the-sage.org/evolution/ardi_fossilized_skeleton. html. *H. neanderthalensis* adapted from *The Human Evolution Coloring Book. P. boisei* drawn from a photo by David Bill.

Self-Quiz Answers

1. c
2. arthropod
3. amphibians
4. b
5. chordata; notochord; cartilage disks between your vertebrae
6. bipedalism
7. a
8. *Australopithecus* species, *Homo habilis, Homo erectus, Homo sapiens*
9. a4, b5, c1, d2, e3

An Introduction to Ecology and the Biosphere

From Chapter 18 of *Campbell Essential Biology with Physiology*, Fifth Edition. Eric J. Simon, Jean L. Dickey, Kelly A. Hogan, Jane B. Reece. Copyright © 2016 by Pearson Education, Inc. All rights reserved.

An Introduction to Ecology and the Biosphere

Why Ecology Matters

Airborne pollutants from car exhaust can combine with water and return to Earth as acid precipitation far away—evidence that the water cycle operates on a global scale.

◄ Your "goose bumps" are caused by the same muscles that fluff up geese on a cold day.

Some forms of life on Earth would survive if the sun stopped shining—but we would not be among them. ►

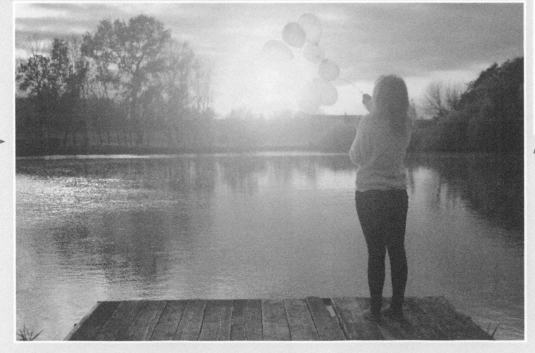

▲ Your home may be infested with "vampire" devices that consume electricity even while you sleep.

Global Climate Change BIOLOGY AND SOCIETY

Penguins, Polar Bears, and People in Peril

Ninety-seven percent of climate scientists agree: The global climate is changing. The change is driven by a rapid rise in temperatures—on average, 0.8°C (about 1.4°F) over the past century, mostly over the last 30 years. The current rate of warming is *ten times* faster than the average rate during the warm-up that followed the last ice age. What do we know about climate change now, and what can we expect for the future?

The northernmost regions of the Northern Hemisphere and the Antarctic Peninsula have heated up the most. In parts of Alaska, for example, winter temperatures have risen by 5–6°F. The permanent Arctic sea ice is shrinking; each summer brings thinner ice and more open water. Polar bears, which stalk their prey on ice and need to store up body fat for the warmer months when there is no ice, are showing signs of starvation as their winter hunting grounds melt away. At the other end of the planet, diminishing sea ice near the Antarctic Peninsula limits the access of Adélie penguins to their food supply, and spring blizzards of unprecedented frequency and severity are taking a heavy toll on their eggs and chicks. But these charismatic animals are just the canaries in the coal mine whose distress alerts us to our own danger. We

An Adélie penguin. Climate change is bad news for some populations of Adélie penguins.

are already feeling the effects of climate change in more frequent and larger wildfires, deadly heat waves, and altered precipitation patterns that bring drought to some regions and torrential downpours to others.

What does climate change mean for the future of life on Earth? Any predictions that scientists make now about future impacts of global climate change are based on incomplete information. Much remains to be discovered about species diversity and about the complex interactions of organisms (living things) with each other and with their environments. There is overwhelming evidence that human enterprises are responsible for the changes that are occurring. How we respond to this crisis will determine whether circumstances improve or worsen. And the process begins with understanding the basic concepts of ecology, which we start to explore in this chapter.

An Overview of Ecology

In your study of biology so far, you have learned about the diversity of life on Earth and about the molecular and cellular structures and processes that make life tick. **Ecology**, the scientific study of the interactions between organisms and their environments, offers a different perspective on life—biology from the skin out, so to speak.

Humans have always had an interest in other organisms and their environments. As hunters and gatherers, prehistoric people had to learn where and when game and edible plants could be found in greatest abundance. Naturalists, from Aristotle to Darwin and beyond, made the process of observing and describing organisms in their natural habitats an end in itself rather than simply a means of survival. We can still gain valuable insight from this discovery-based approach of watching nature and recording its structure and processes **(Figure 1)**. As you might expect, hypothesis-driven science performed in natural environments is fundamental to ecology. But ecologists also test hypotheses using laboratory experiments, where conditions can be simplified and controlled. And some ecologists take a theoretical approach, devising mathematical and computer models, which enable them to simulate large-scale experiments that are impossible to conduct in the field.

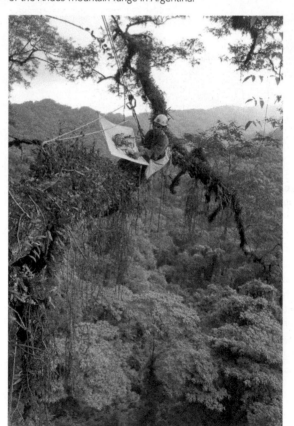

▼ Figure 1 **Discovery science in a rain forest canopy.** A biologist collects insects in a rain forest on the eastern slope of the Andes mountain range in Argentina.

Ecology and Environmentalism

Technological innovations have enabled people to colonize just about every environment on Earth. Even so, our survival depends on Earth's resources, which have been profoundly altered by human activities **(Figure 2)**. Global climate change is just one of the many environmental issues that have stirred public concern in recent decades. Some of our industrial and agricultural practices have contaminated the air, soil, and water. Our relentless quest for land and other resources has endangered a lengthy list of plant and animal species and has even driven some to extinction.

The science of ecology can provide the understanding needed to solve environmental problems. But these problems cannot be solved by ecologists alone, because they require making decisions based on values and ethics. On a personal level, each of us makes daily choices that affect our ecological impact. And legislators and corporations, motivated by environmentally aware voters and consumers, must address questions that have wider implications: How should the use of land and water be regulated? Should we try to save all species or just certain ones? What alternatives to environmentally destructive practices can be developed? How can we balance environmental impacts with economic needs?

▼ Figure 2 **Human impact on the environment.** A man paddles a canoe through a trash-clogged waterway in Manila, capital of the Philippines.

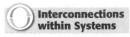

Interconnections within Systems

A Hierarchy of Interactions

Many different factors can potentially affect an organism's interaction with its environment. **Biotic factors**—all of the organisms in the area—make up the living component of the environment. Other organisms may compete with an individual for food and other resources, prey upon it, or change its physical and chemical environment. **Abiotic factors** make up the environment's nonliving component and include chemical and physical factors, such as temperature, light, water, minerals, and air. An organism's **habitat**, the specific environment it lives in, includes the biotic and abiotic factors of its surroundings.

When we study the interactions between organisms and their environments, it is convenient to divide ecology into four increasingly comprehensive levels: organismal ecology, population ecology, community ecology, and ecosystem ecology.

An **organism** is an individual living thing. **Organismal ecology** is concerned with the evolutionary adaptations that enable organisms to meet the challenges posed by their abiotic environments. The distribution of organisms is limited by the abiotic conditions they can tolerate. For example, amphibians such as the salamander in Figure 3a cannot live in cold climates because they gain most of their body warmth by absorbing heat from their surroundings. Temperature and precipitation shifts due to global climate change have already affected the distributions of some salamander species, and many more will feel the impact in the coming decades.

The next level of organization in ecology is the **population**, a group of individuals of the same species living in a particular geographic area. **Population ecology** concentrates mainly on factors that affect population density and growth (Figure 3b). Biologists who study endangered species are especially interested in this level of ecology.

A **community** consists of all the organisms that inhabit a particular area; it is an assemblage of populations of different species. Questions in **community ecology** focus on how interactions between species, such as predation and competition, affect community structure and organization (Figure 3c).

An **ecosystem** includes all the abiotic factors in addition to the community of species in a certain area. For example, a savanna ecosystem includes not only the organisms, such as diverse plants and animals, but also the soil, water sources, sunlight, and other abiotic factors of the environment. In **ecosystem ecology**, questions concern energy flow and the cycling of chemicals among the various biotic and abiotic factors (Figure 3d).

▼ Figure 3 **Examples of questions at different levels of ecology.**

(a) Organismal ecology. What range of temperatures can a red salamander tolerate?

(b) Population ecology. What factors affect the survival of emperor penguin chicks?

(c) Community ecology. How do predators such as this beech marten affect the diversity of rodents in a community?

(d) Ecosystem ecology. What processes recycle vital chemical elements such as nitrogen within a savanna ecosystem in Africa?

The **biosphere** is the global ecosystem—the sum of all the planet's ecosystems, or all of life and where it lives. The most complex level in ecology, the biosphere includes the atmosphere to an altitude of several kilometers, the land down to water-bearing rocks about 1,500 m (almost a mile) deep, lakes and streams, caves, and the oceans to a depth of several kilometers. But despite its grand scale, organisms within the biosphere are linked; events in one part may have far-reaching effects. ✓

✓ CHECKPOINT

What does the ecosystem level of classification have in common with the community level of classification? What does the ecosystem level include that the community level does not?

Answer: all the biotic factors of the area; the abiotic factors of the area

Living in Earth's Diverse Environments

Whether you have seen the world by traveling or through television and movies, you have probably noticed that there are striking regional patterns in the distribution of life. For example, some terrestrial areas, such as the tropical forests of South America and Africa, are home to plentiful plant life, whereas other areas, such as deserts, are relatively barren. Coral reefs are alive with vibrantly colored organisms; other parts of the ocean appear empty by comparison.

The distribution of life varies on a local scale, too. In the aerial view of a New Zealand wilderness in **Figure 4**, we can see a mixture of forest, a large lake, a meandering river, and mountains. Within these different environments, variation occurs on an even smaller scale. For example, we would find that the lake has several different habitats, and each habitat has a characteristic community of organisms.

▼ **Figure 4** **Local variation of the environment in a New Zealand wilderness.**

Abiotic Factors of the Biosphere

Patterns in the distribution of life mainly reflect differences in the abiotic factors of the environment. Let's look at several major abiotic factors that influence where organisms live.

Energy Source

All organisms require a usable source of energy to live. Solar energy from sunlight, captured by chlorophyll during the process of photosynthesis, powers most ecosystems. In the image shown in **Figure 5**, colors are keyed to the relative abundance of chlorophyll. Green areas on land indicate high densities of plant life. Orange areas on land, including the Sahara region of Africa and much of the western United States, are much less productive. Green regions of the ocean contain an abundance of algae and photosynthetic bacteria compared to darker regions.

Lack of sunlight is seldom the most important factor limiting plant growth for terrestrial ecosystems, although shading by trees does create intense competition for light among plants growing on forest floors. In many aquatic environments, however, light cannot penetrate beyond certain depths. As a result, most photosynthesis in a body of water occurs near the surface. Surprisingly, life also thrives in environments that are completely dark. A mile or more below the

Some forms of life on Earth would survive if the sun stopped shining—but we would not be among them.

ocean's surface lies the remarkable world of hydrothermal vents, sites near the adjoining edges of giant plates of Earth's crust where molten rock and hot gases surge upward from Earth's interior. Towering chimneys, some as tall as a nine-story building, emit scalding water and hot gases (**Figure 6**).

These ecosystems are powered by bacteria that derive energy from the oxidation of inorganic chemicals such as hydrogen sulfide. Bacteria with similar metabolic talents support communities of cave-dwelling organisms.

▼ **Figure 5** **Distribution of life in the biosphere.** In this image of Earth, colors are keyed to the relative abundance of chlorophyll, which correlates with the regional densities of photosynthetic organisms.

▼ **Figure 6** **A deep-sea hydrothermal vent.** "Black smokers" west of Vancouver Island spew plumes of hot gases from Earth's interior. Giant tube worms (inset), annelids that may grow to 2 m long, are members of the vent community.

Temperature

Temperature is an important abiotic factor because of its effect on metabolism. Few organisms can maintain a sufficiently active metabolism at temperatures close to 0°C (32°F), and temperatures above 45°C (113°F) destroy the enzymes of most organisms. Most organisms function best within a specific range of environmental temperatures. For example, the American pika (Figure 7) has a high body temperature well suited to the chilly climate of its mountain habitat. On warm days, however, pikas must take refuge in crevices where pockets of cold air prevent fatal overheating. In winter, pikas depend on a blanket of snow to insulate their shelters from the perilous cold.

▲ Figure 7 **An American pika.** This diminutive relative of rabbits lives at high elevations in the western United States and Canada.

Water

Water is essential to all life. Aquatic organisms are surrounded by water, but they face problems of water balance if their own solute concentration does not match that of their surroundings. For terrestrial organisms, the primary threat is drying out in the air. Many land animals have watertight coverings that reduce water loss, such as reptilian scales (Figure 8a). Most plants have waxy coatings on their leaves and other aerial parts (Figure 8b). Wax from carnauba palm leaves is valued for the glossy, waterproof coat it imparts to polishing products for cars, surfboards, furniture, and shoes. Carnauba wax is an ingredient of many other products as well, including cosmetics such as lipstick and mascara.

Inorganic Nutrients

The distribution and abundance of photosynthetic organisms, including plants, algae, and photosynthetic bacteria, depend on the availability of inorganic nutrients such as compounds of nitrogen and phosphorus. Plants obtain these nutrients from the soil. Soil structure, pH, and nutrient content often play major roles in determining the distribution of plants. In many aquatic ecosystems, low levels of nitrogen and phosphorus limit the growth of algae and photosynthetic bacteria.

Other Aquatic Factors

Several abiotic factors are important in aquatic, but not terrestrial, ecosystems. While terrestrial organisms have a plentiful supply of oxygen from the air, aquatic organisms must depend on oxygen dissolved in water. This is a critical factor for many species of fish. Cold, fast-moving water has a higher oxygen content than warm

or stagnant water. Salinity (saltiness), currents, and tides also play a role in many aquatic ecosystems.

Other Terrestrial Factors

Some abiotic factors affect terrestrial, but not aquatic, ecosystems. For example, wind is often an important factor on land. Wind increases an organism's rate of water loss by evaporation. The resulting increase in evaporative cooling can be advantageous on a hot summer day, but it can cause dangerous wind chill in the winter. In some ecosystems, frequent occurrences of natural disturbances such as storms or fire play a role in the distribution of organisms. ☑

☑ CHECKPOINT

Why is solar energy such an important factor for most ecosystems?

Answer: Solar energy captured by the process of photosynthesis provides most of the organic fuel and building material for the organisms in those ecosystems.

▼ Figure 8 **Watertight coverings.**

(a) Scales on a Carolina anole lizard.

(b) Beaded water droplets showing the water repellency of the leaf's waxy coating.

The Evolutionary Adaptations of Organisms

The ability of organisms to live in Earth's diverse environments demonstrates the close relationship between the fields of ecology and evolutionary biology. Charles Darwin was an ecologist, although he predated the word *ecology*. It was the geographic distribution of organisms and their exquisite adaptations to specific environments that provided Darwin with evidence for evolution. Evolutionary adaptation via natural selection results from the interactions of organisms with their environments, which brings us back to our definition of ecology. Thus, events that occur in the short term, during the course of an individual's lifetime, may translate into effects over the longer scale of evolutionary time. For example, because the availability of water affects a plant's growth and ultimately its reproductive success, precipitation has an impact on the gene pool of a plant population. After a period of lower-than-average rainfall, drought-resistant individuals may be more prevalent in a plant population. Organisms also evolve in response to biotic interactions, such as predation and competition. ☑

☑ CHECKPOINT

How are the fields of ecology and evolution linked?

Answer: The process of evolutionary adaptation via natural selection results from the interactions of organisms with their environments (ecology).

Adjusting to Environmental Variability

The abiotic factors in a habitat may vary from year to year, seasonally, or over the course of a day. An individual's abilities to adjust to environmental changes that occur during its lifetime are themselves adaptations refined by natural selection. For instance, if you see a bird on a cold day, it may look unusually fluffy (Figure 9). Small muscles in the skin raise the bird's feathers, a physiological response that traps insulating pockets of air. Some species of birds adjust to seasonal cold by growing heavier feathers. And some bird species respond to the onset of cold weather by migrating to warmer regions—a behavioral response. Note that these responses occur during the lifetime of an individual, so they are not examples of evolution, which is change in a population over time.

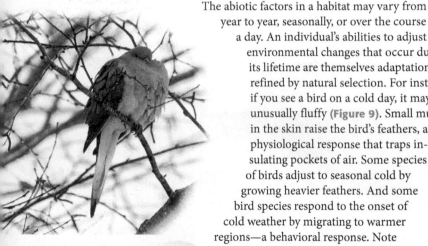

▼ Figure 9 A mourning dove demonstrating its physiological response to cold weather.

Your "goose bumps" are caused by the same muscles that fluff up geese on a cold day.

Physiological Responses

Like birds, mammals can adjust to a cold day by contracting skin muscles—in this case attached to hairs—to create a temporary layer of insulation. (Our own muscles do this, too, but we just get "goose bumps" instead of a furry insulation.) The blood vessels in the skin also constrict, which slows the loss of body heat. In both cases, the adjustment occurs in just seconds.

A gradual, though still reversible, physiological adjustment that occurs in response to an environmental change is called **acclimation**. For example, suppose you moved from Boston, which is essentially at sea level, to the mile-high city of Denver, where there is less oxygen. One physiological response to your new environment would be a gradual increase in the number of your red blood cells, which transport O_2 from your lungs to other parts of your body. Acclimation can take days or weeks. This is why high-altitude climbers, such as those attempting to scale Mount Everest, need extended stays at a high-elevation base camp before proceeding to the summit.

The ability to acclimate is generally related to the range of environmental conditions a species naturally experiences. Species that live in very warm climates, for example, usually cannot acclimate to extreme cold. Among vertebrates, birds and mammals can generally tolerate the greatest temperature extremes because, as endotherms, they use their metabolism to regulate internal temperature. In contrast, ectothermic reptiles can tolerate only a more limited range of temperatures (Figure 10).

▼ Figure 10 **The number of lizard species in different regions of the contiguous United States.** Notice that there are fewer and fewer lizard species in more northern regions. This reflects lizards' ectothermic physiology, which depends on environmental heat for keeping the body warm enough for the animal to be active.

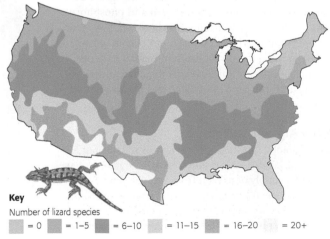

Key
Number of lizard species
■ = 0   ■ = 1–5   ■ = 6–10   ■ = 11–15   ■ = 16–20   ■ = 20+

Anatomical Responses

Many organisms respond to environmental challenge with some type of change in body shape or structure. When the change is reversible, the response is an example of acclimation. Many mammals, for example, grow a heavier coat of fur before the winter cold sets in and shed it when summer comes. In some animals, fur or feather color changes seasonally as well, camouflaging the animal against winter snow and summer vegetation (**Figure 11**).

Other anatomical changes are irreversible over the lifetime of an individual. Environmental variation can affect growth and development so much that there may be remarkable differences in body shape within a population. You can see an example in **Figure 12**, which shows the "flagging" that wind causes in certain trees. In general, plants are more anatomically changeable than animals. Rooted and unable to move to a better location, plants rely entirely on their anatomical and physiological responses to survive environmental fluctuations.

▲ **Figure 11** **The arctic fox in winter and summer coats.**

▼ **Figure 12** **Wind as an abiotic factor that shapes trees.**
The mechanical disturbance of the prevailing wind hinders limb growth on the windward side of this fir tree near the timberline in the Rocky Mountains, while limbs on the other side grow normally. This anatomical response is an evolutionary adaptation that reduces the number of limbs that are broken during strong winds.

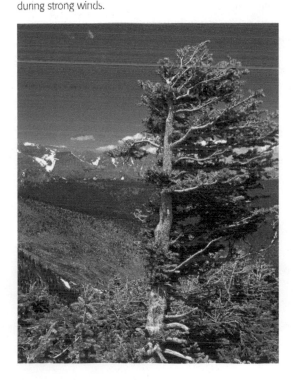

Behavioral Responses

In contrast to plants, most animals can respond to an unfavorable change in the environment by moving to a new location. Such movement may be fairly localized. For example, many desert ectotherms, including reptiles, maintain a reasonably constant body temperature by shuttling between sun and shade. Some animals are capable of migrating great distances in response to such environmental cues as the changing seasons. Many migratory birds overwinter in Central and South America, returning to northern latitudes to breed during summer. And we humans, with our large brains and available technology, have an especially rich range of behavioral responses available to us (**Figure 13**). ☑

 CHECKPOINT

What is acclimation?

Answer: a gradual, reversible change in anatomy or physiology in response to an environmental change

▼ **Figure 13** **Behavioral responses have expanded the geographic range of humans.** Dressing for the weather is a thermoregulatory behavior unique to people.

Biomes

The abiotic factors you learned about in the previous section are largely responsible for the distribution of life on Earth. Using various combinations of these factors, ecologists have categorized Earth's environments into biomes. A **biome** is a major terrestrial or aquatic life zone, characterized by vegetation type in terrestrial biomes and the physical environment in aquatic biomes. In this section, we'll briefly survey the aquatic biomes, followed by the terrestrial biomes.

Aquatic biomes, which occupy roughly 75% of Earth's surface, are determined by their salinity and other physical factors. Freshwater biomes (lakes, streams and rivers, and wetlands) typically have salt concentrations of less than 1%. The salt concentrations of marine biomes (oceans, intertidal zones, and coral reefs) are generally around 3%.

Freshwater Biomes

Freshwater biomes cover less than 1% of Earth, and they contain a mere 0.01% of its water. But they harbor a disproportionate share of biodiversity—an estimated 6% of all described species. Moreover, we depend on freshwater biomes for drinking water, crop irrigation, sanitation, and industry.

Freshwater biomes fall into two broad groups: standing water, which includes lakes and ponds, and flowing water, such as rivers and streams. The difference in water movement results in profound differences in ecosystem structure.

Lakes and Ponds

Standing bodies of water range from small ponds only a few square meters in area to large lakes, such as North America's Great Lakes, that are thousands of square kilometers **(Figure 14)**.

In lakes and large ponds, communities of plants, algae, and animals are distributed according to the depth of the water and the distance from shore **(Figure 15)**. Shallow water near shore and the upper layer of water away from shore make up the **photic zone**, so named because light is available for photosynthesis. Microscopic algae and cyanobacteria grow in the photic zone, joined by rooted plants and floating plants such as water lilies in the photic area near shore. If a lake or pond is deep enough or murky enough, it has an **aphotic zone**, where light levels are too low to support photosynthesis.

The **benthic realm** is at the bottom of all aquatic biomes. Made up of sand and organic and inorganic sediments, the benthic realm is occupied by communities of organisms that may include algae, aquatic plants, worms, insect larvae, molluscs, and microorganisms. Dead material that "rains" down from the productive surface waters of the photic zone is a major source of food for animals of the benthic realm.

The mineral nutrients nitrogen and phosphorus typically regulate the growth of **phytoplankton**, the collective name for microscopic algae and cyanobacteria that drift near the surfaces of aquatic biomes. Many lakes and ponds are affected by large inputs of nitrogen and phosphorus from sewage and runoff from fertilized lawns and farms. These nutrients often produce heavy growth of algae, which reduces light penetration. When the algae die and decompose, a pond or lake can suffer serious oxygen depletion, killing fish that are adapted to high-oxygen conditions. ☑

◀ Figure 14 **A satellite view of the Great Lakes.**

▼ Figure 15 **Zones in a lake.**

▲ Figure 16 **A stream in the Appalachian Mountains.**

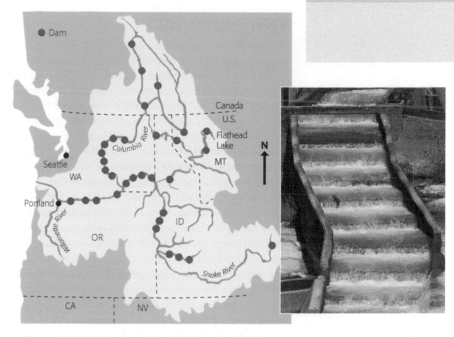

▲ Figure 17 **Damming the Columbia River basin.** This map shows only the largest of the 250 dams that have altered freshwater ecosystems throughout the Pacific Northwest. These great concrete obstacles make it difficult for salmon to swim upriver to their breeding streams, though many dams now have "fish ladders" that provide detours (inset).

Rivers and Streams

Rivers and streams, which are bodies of flowing water, generally support communities of organisms quite different from those of lakes and ponds **(Figure 16)**. A river or stream changes greatly between its source (perhaps a spring or snowmelt in the mountains) and the point at which it empties into a lake or the ocean. Near a source, the water is usually cold, low in nutrients, and clear. The channel is often narrow, with a swift current that does not allow much silt to accumulate on the bottom. The current also inhibits the growth of phytoplankton; most of the organisms found here are supported by the photosynthesis of algae attached to rocks or by organic material (such as leaves) carried into the stream from the surrounding land. The most abundant benthic animals are usually insects that eat algae, leaves, or one another. Trout are often the predominant fishes, locating their food, including insects, mainly by sight in the clear water.

Downstream, a river or stream typically widens and slows. There the water is usually warmer and may be murkier because of sediments and phytoplankton suspended in it. Worms and insects that burrow into mud are often abundant, as are waterfowl, frogs, and catfish and other fishes that find food more by scent and taste than by sight.

People have altered rivers by constructing dams to control flooding, to provide reservoirs of drinking water, or to generate hydroelectric power. In many cases, dams have completely changed the downstream ecosystems, altering the rate and volume of water flow and affecting fish and invertebrate populations **(Figure 17)**. Many streams and rivers have also been affected by pollution from human activities.

Wetlands

A **wetland** is a transitional biome between an aquatic ecosystem and a terrestrial one. Freshwater wetlands include swamps, bogs, and marshes **(Figure 18)**. Covered with water either permanently or periodically, wetlands support the growth of aquatic plants and are rich in species diversity. Migrating waterfowl and many other birds depend on wetland "pit stops" for food and shelter during their journeys. In addition, wetlands provide water storage areas that reduce flooding. Wetlands also improve water quality by trapping pollutants such as metals and organic compounds in their sediments.

► Figure 18 **A wetland near Kent, Ohio.**

Marine Biomes

Gazing out over a vast ocean, you might think that it is the most uniform environment on Earth. But marine habitats can be as different as night and day. The deepest ocean, where hydrothermal vents are located, is perpetually dark. In contrast, the vivid coral reefs nearer the surface are utterly dependent on sunlight. Habitats near shore are different from those in mid-ocean, and the sea-floor hosts different communities than the open waters.

As in freshwater biomes, the seafloor is known as the benthic realm **(Figure 19)**. The **pelagic realm** of the oceans includes all open water. In shallow areas, such as the continental shelves (the submerged parts of continents), the photic zone includes both pelagic and benthic regions. In these sunlit areas, photosynthesis by phytoplankton and multicellular algae provides energy for a diverse community of animals. Sponges, burrowing worms, clams, sea anemones, crabs, and echinoderms inhabit the benthic realm. **Zooplankton** (free-floating animals, including many microscopic ones), fishes, marine mammals, and many other types of animals are abundant in the pelagic photic zone.

The **coral reef** biome occurs in the photic zone of warm tropical waters in scattered locations around the globe **(Figure 20)**. A coral reef is built up slowly by successive generations of coral animals—a diverse group of cnidarians that secrete a hard external skeleton—and by multicellular algae encrusted with limestone. Unicellular algae live within the coral's cells, providing the coral with food. The physical structure and productivity of coral reefs support a huge variety of invertebrates and fishes.

The photic zone extends down a maximum of 200 m (about 656 feet) in the ocean. Although there is not enough light for photosynthesis between 200 and 1,000 m (down a little more than half a mile), some light does reach these depths of the aphotic zone. This dimly lit world, sometimes called the twilight zone, is dominated by a fascinating variety of small fishes and crustaceans. Food sinking from the photic zone provides some sustenance for these animals. In addition, many of them migrate to the surface at night to feed. Some fishes in the twilight zone have enlarged eyes, enabling them to see in the very dim light, and light-emitting organs that attract mates and prey.

Below 1,000 m—a depth greater than the height of two Empire State Buildings—the ocean is completely and permanently dark. Adaptation to this environment has produced many bizarre-looking creatures. Most of the benthic organisms here are deposit feeders, animals that consume dead organic material in the sediments on the seafloor. Crustaceans, polychaete worms, sea anemones, and echinoderms such as sea cucumbers, sea stars,

▼ **Figure 19 Ocean life.** (Zone depths and organisms not drawn to scale.)

▲ Figure 20 **A coral reef in the Red Sea off the coast of Egypt.**

▼ Figure 21 **Organisms clinging to the rocks of an intertidal zone on the Pacific coast of Washington State.**

and sea urchins are common. Food is scarce, however. The density of animals is low except at hydrothermal vents, the prokaryote-powered ecosystems mentioned earlier (see Figure 6).

The marine environment also includes distinctive biomes, such as the intertidal zone and estuaries, where the ocean interfaces with land or with fresh water. In the **intertidal zone**, where the ocean meets land, the shore is pounded by waves during high tide and exposed to the sun and drying winds during low tide. The rocky intertidal zone is home to many sedentary organisms, such as algae, barnacles, and mussels, which attach to rocks and are thus prevented from being washed away (Figure 21). On sandy beaches, suspension-feeding worms, clams, and predatory crustaceans bury themselves in the ground.

Figure 22 shows an **estuary**, a transition area between a river and the ocean. The saltiness of estuaries ranges from nearly that of fresh water to that of the ocean. With their waters enriched by nutrients from rivers, estuaries, like freshwater wetlands, are among the most productive areas on Earth. Oysters, crabs, and many fishes live or reproduce in estuaries. Estuaries are also crucial nesting and feeding areas for waterfowl. Mudflats and salt marshes are extensive coastal wetlands that often border estuaries.

For centuries, people viewed the ocean as a limitless resource, harvesting its bounty with increasingly effective and indiscriminate technologies and using it as a dumping ground for wastes. The negative effects of these practices are now becoming clear. Populations of commercial fish species are declining. Small bits of plastic debris float beneath the surface of vast swaths of the Pacific Ocean, concentrated by converging currents in a region dubbed the "Great Pacific Garbage Patch."

Many marine habitats are polluted by nutrients or toxic chemicals; it will be years before the full extent of damage from the massive Deepwater Horizon oil spill in the Gulf of Mexico in 2010 is known. Because of their proximity to land, estuaries are especially vulnerable. Many have been completely replaced by development on landfill; other threats include pollution and alteration of freshwater inflow. Coral reefs are imperiled by ocean acidification and rising sea surface temperatures due to global warming.

Meanwhile, our knowledge of marine biomes is woefully incomplete. A massive international census of marine life, completed in 2010, announced the discovery of more than 6,000 new species. ☑

☑ CHECKPOINT

What are phytoplankton? Why are they essential to other oceanic life?

Answer: Phytoplankton are photosynthetic algae and bacteria. They are food for animals in the photic zone; those animals in turn may become food for animals in the aphotic zone.

▼ Figure 22 **Waterfowl in an estuary on the southeast coast of England.**

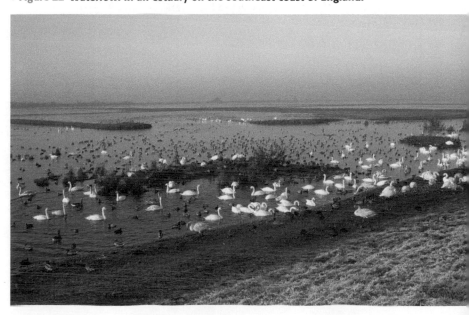

How Climate Affects Terrestrial Biome Distribution

Terrestrial biomes are determined primarily by climate, especially temperature and rainfall. Before we survey these biomes, let's look at the broad patterns of global climate that help explain their locations.

Earth's global climate patterns are largely the result of the input of solar energy, which warms the atmosphere, land, and water, and of the planet's movement in space. Because of Earth's curvature, the intensity of sunlight varies according to latitude (Figure 23). The equator receives the greatest intensity of solar radiation and thus has the highest temperatures, which in turn evaporate water from Earth's surface. As this warm, moist air rises, it cools, diminishing its ability to hold moisture. The water vapor condenses into clouds and rain falls (Figure 24). This process largely explains why rain forests are concentrated in the **tropics**—the region from the Tropic of Cancer to the Tropic of Capricorn.

After losing moisture over equatorial zones, dry high-altitude air masses spread away from the equator until they cool and descend at latitudes of about 30° north and south. Many of the world's great deserts—the Sahara in North Africa and the Arabian on the Arabian Peninsula, for example—are centered at these latitudes because of the dry air they receive.

Latitudes between the tropics and the Arctic Circle and the Antarctic Circle are called **temperate zones**. Generally, these regions have milder climates than the tropics or the polar regions. Notice in Figure 24 that some of the descending, dry air moves into the latitudes above 30°. At first these air masses pick up moisture, but they tend to drop it as they cool at higher latitudes. This is why the north and south temperate zones tend to be relatively wet. Coniferous forests dominate the landscape at the wet but cool latitudes around 60° north.

Proximity to large bodies of water and the presence of landforms such as mountain ranges also affect climate. Oceans and large lakes moderate climate by absorbing heat when the air is warm and releasing heat to cold air. Mountains affect climate in two major ways. First, air temperature drops as elevation increases. As a result, driving up a tall mountain offers a quick tour of several biomes. Figure 25 shows the scenery you might encounter on a journey from the scorching lowlands of the Sonoran Desert to a cool coniferous forest at an elevation of 11,000 feet above sea level.

▼ **Figure 23** **Uneven heating of Earth.**

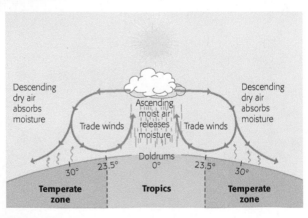

▼ **Figure 24** **How uneven heating of Earth produces various climates.**

▶ **Figure 25** **The effect of altitude on vegetation.** The zones shown are typical of the Sonoran Desert region in southwestern North America.

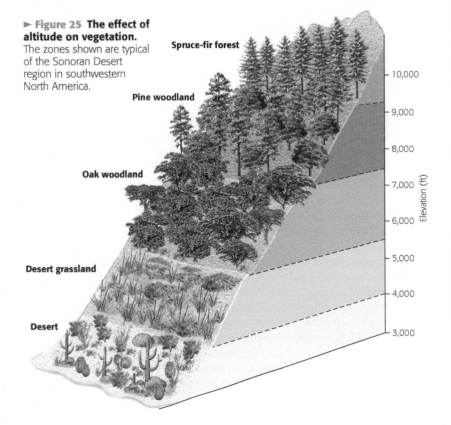

Second, mountains can block the flow of moist air from a coast, causing radically different climates on opposite sides of a mountain range. In the example shown in **Figure 26**, moist air moves in off the Pacific Ocean and encounters the Coast Range in California. Air flows upward, cools at higher altitudes, and drops a large amount of rainfall. The world's tallest trees, the coastal redwoods, thrive here. Precipitation increases again farther inland as the air moves up and over higher mountains (the Sierra Nevada). By the time it reaches the eastern side of the Sierra, the air contains little moisture; as this dry air descends, it absorbs moisture. As a result, there is little precipitation on the eastern side of the mountains. This effect, called a rain shadow, is responsible for the desert that covers much of central Nevada. ☑

▼ **Figure 26** **How mountains affect rainfall.**

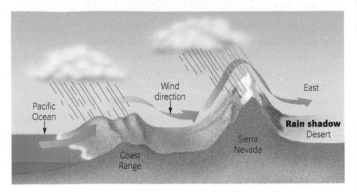

☑ **CHECKPOINT**

Why is there so much rainfall in the tropics?

Answer: Air at the equator rises as it is warmed by direct sunlight. As the air rises, it cools. This causes cloud formation and rainfall because cool air holds less moisture than warm air.

Terrestrial Biomes

Terrestrial ecosystems are grouped into biomes primarily on the basis of their vegetation type **(Figure 27)**. By providing food, shelter, and nesting sites for animals, as well as much of the organic material for the decomposers that recycle mineral nutrients, plants build the foundation for the communities of organisms typical of each biome. The geographic distribution of plants, and thus of biomes, largely depends on climate, with temperature and rainfall often the key factors determining the kind of biome that exists in a particular region. If the climate in two geographically separate areas is similar, the same type of biome may occur in both. Coniferous forests, for instance, extend in a broad band across North America, Europe, and Asia.

Each biome is characterized by a type of biological community rather than an assemblage of particular species. For example, the groups of species living in the deserts of southwestern North America and in the Sahara Desert of Africa are different, but both groups are adapted to desert conditions. Organisms in widely

► **Figure 27** **A map of the major terrestrial biomes.** Although this map has sharp boundaries, biomes actually grade into one another. We'll use smaller versions of this map, highlighted by color coding, during our closer look at the terrestrial biomes in the next several pages.

Key
- Tropical forest
- Savanna
- Desert
- Chaparral
- Temperate grassland
- Temperate broadleaf forest
- Northern coniferous forest
- Tundra
- High mountains (coniferous forest and alpine tundra)
- Polar ice

separated biomes may look alike because of convergent evolution, the appearance of similar traits in independently evolved species living in similar environments.

Local variation within each biome gives the vegetation a patchy, rather than a uniform, appearance. For example, in northern coniferous forests, snowfall may break branches and small trees, causing openings where broadleaf trees such as aspen and birch can grow. Local storms and fires also create openings in many biomes.

The graph in **Figure 28** shows the range of precipitation and temperature that characterize terrestrial biomes. The *x*-axis shows the range of annual average precipitation, and the *y*-axis displays the range of annual average temperature. By studying the plots on this graph, we can compare these abiotic factors in different biomes. For example, although the range of precipitation in temperate broadleaf forests is similar to that of northern coniferous forests, the lower range of temperatures in northern coniferous forests reveals a significant difference in the abiotic environments of these two biomes. Grasslands are typically drier than forests, and deserts are drier still.

Today, concern about global warming is generating intense interest in the effect of climate on vegetation patterns. Using powerful new tools such as satellite imagery, scientists are documenting shifts in latitude of biome borders, decreases in snow and ice coverage, and changes in the length of the growing season. At the same time, many natural biomes have been fragmented and altered by human activity. We'll discuss both of these issues after we survey the major terrestrial biomes, beginning near the equator and generally approaching the poles.

Tropical Forest

Tropical forests occur in equatorial areas where the temperature is warm and days are 11–12 hours long year-round. The type of vegetation is determined primarily by rainfall. Tropical rain forests, like the one shown in **Figure 29**, receive 200–400 cm (6.6 to 13 *feet*!) of rain per year.

The layered structure of tropical rain forests provides many different habitats. Treetops form a closed canopy over one or two layers of smaller trees and a shrub understory. Few plants grow in the deep shade of the forest floor. Many trees are covered by woody vines growing toward the light. Other plants, such as orchids, gain access to sunlight by growing on the branches or trunks of tall trees. Scattered trees reach full sunlight by towering above the canopy. Many of the animals also dwell in trees, where food is abundant. Monkeys, birds, insects, snakes, bats, and frogs find food and shelter many meters above the ground.

Rainfall is less plentiful in other tropical forests. Tropical dry forests predominate in lowland areas that have a prolonged dry season or scarce rainfall at any time. The plants found there are a mixture of thorny shrubs and trees and succulents. In regions with distinct wet and dry seasons, tropical deciduous trees are common. ☑

☑ CHECKPOINT

Why are climbing plants common in tropical rain forests?

Answer: Climbing is a plant adaptation for reaching sunlight in a closed canopy, where little sunlight reaches the forest floor.

▼ Figure 29 **Tropical rain forest in Borneo.**

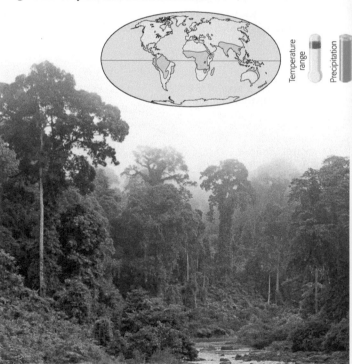

▼ Figure 28 **A climate graph for some major biomes in North America.**

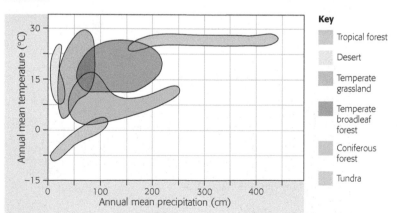

Key

Tropical forest

Desert

Temperate grassland

Temperate broadleaf forest

Coniferous forest

Tundra

Savanna

Savannas, such as the one shown in **Figure 30**, are dominated by grasses and scattered trees. The temperature is warm year-round. Rainfall averages 30–50 cm (roughly 12–20 inches) per year, with dramatic seasonal variation.

Fire, caused by lightning or human activity, is an important abiotic factor in the savanna. The grasses survive burning because the growing points of their shoots are below ground. Other plants have seeds that sprout rapidly after a fire. Poor soil and lack of moisture, along with fire and grazing animals, prevent the establishment of most trees. The luxuriant growth of grasses and small broadleaf plants during the rainy season provides a rich food source for plant-eating animals.

Many of the world's large grazing mammals and their predators inhabit savannas. African savannas are home to zebras and many species of antelope, as well as to lions and cheetahs. Several species of kangaroo are the dominant grazers of Australian savannas. Oddly, though, the large grazers are not the dominant plant-eaters in savannas. That distinction belongs to insects, especially ants and termites. Other animals include burrowers such as mice, moles, gophers, and ground squirrels.

Desert

Deserts are the driest of all biomes, characterized by low and unpredictable rainfall—less than 30 cm (about 12 inches) per year. Some deserts are very hot, with daytime soil surface temperatures above 60°C (140°F) and large daily temperature fluctuations. Other deserts, such as those west of the Rocky Mountains and the Gobi Desert, spanning northern China and southern Mongolia, are relatively cold. Air temperatures in cold deserts may fall below −30°C (−22°F).

Desert vegetation typically includes water-storing plants, such as cacti, and deeply rooted shrubs. Various snakes, lizards, and seed-eating rodents are common inhabitants. Arthropods such as scorpions and insects also thrive in the desert. Evolutionary adaptations of desert plants and animals include a remarkable array of mechanisms that conserve water. For example, the "pleated" stem of saguaro cacti **(Figure 31)** enables the plants to expand when they absorb water during wet periods. Some desert mice *never* drink, deriving all their water from the metabolic breakdown of the seeds they eat. Protective adaptations that deter feeding by mammals and insects, such as spines on cacti and poisons in the leaves of shrubs, are common in desert plants. ☑

☑ CHECKPOINT

1. How does the savanna climate vary seasonally?
2. What abiotic factor characterizes deserts?

Answers: 1. Temperature stays about the same year-round, but rainfall varies dramatically. 2. Rainfall is low and unpredictable.

▼ Figure 30 **Savanna in the Serengeti Plain in Tanzania.**

▼ Figure 31 **Sonoran Desert.**

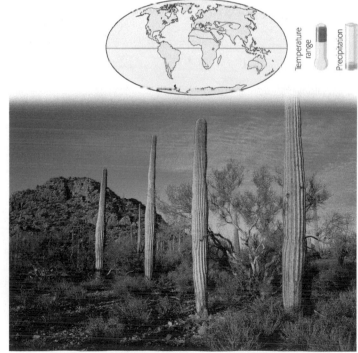

Chaparral

The climate that supports **chaparral** vegetation results mainly from cool ocean currents circulating offshore, producing mild, rainy winters. Summers are hot and dry. This biome is limited to small coastal areas, some in California (**Figure 32**). The largest region of chaparral surrounds the Mediterranean Sea; in fact, Mediterranean is another name for this biome. Dense, spiny, evergreen shrubs dominate chaparral. Annual plants are also common during the wet winter and spring months. Animals characteristic of the chaparral are deer, fruit-eating birds, seed-eating rodents, and lizards and snakes.

Chaparral vegetation is adapted to periodic fires caused by lightning. Many plants contain flammable chemicals and burn fiercely, especially where dead brush has accumulated. After a fire, shrubs use food reserves stored in the surviving roots to support rapid shoot regeneration. Some chaparral plants produce seeds that will germinate only after a hot fire. The ashes of burned vegetation fertilize the soil with mineral nutrients, promoting regrowth of the plant community. Houses do not fare as well. The firestorms that race through the densely populated canyons of Southern California can be devastating to the human inhabitants.

Temperate Grassland

Temperate grasslands have some of the characteristics of tropical savannas, but they are mostly treeless, except along rivers or streams, and are found in regions of relatively cold winter temperatures. Rainfall, averaging between 25 and 75 cm per year (approximately 10–30 inches), with frequent severe droughts, is too low to support forest growth. Periodic fires and grazing by large mammals also prevent invasion by woody plants. These grazers include the bison and pronghorn in North America, the wild horses and sheep of the Asian steppes, and kangaroos in Australia. As in the savanna, however, the dominant plant-eaters are invertebrates, especially grasshoppers and soil-dwelling nematodes.

Without trees, many birds nest on the ground. Many small mammals, such as rabbits, voles, ground squirrels, prairie dogs, and pocket gophers, dig burrows to escape predators. Temperate grasslands like the one shown in **Figure 33** once covered much of central North America.

Because grassland soil is both deep and rich in nutrients, these habitats provide fertile land for agriculture. Most grassland in the United States has been converted to cropland or pasture, and very little natural prairie exists today. ☑

☑ CHECKPOINT

1. What is one way that homeowners in chaparral areas can protect their neighborhoods from fire?
2. How do people now use most of the North American land that was once temperate grassland?

Answers: 1. by keeping the area clear of dead brush, which is flammable 2. for farming

▼ **Figure 32 Chaparral in California.**

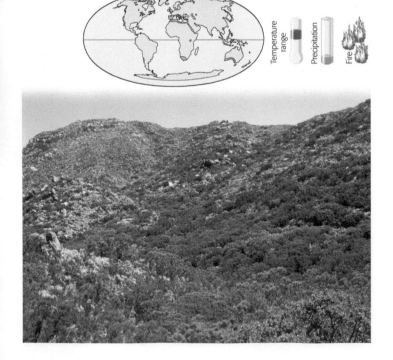

▼ **Figure 33 Temperate grassland in Saskatchewan, Canada.**

Temperate Broadleaf Forest

Temperate broadleaf forests occur throughout mid-latitudes where there is sufficient moisture to support the growth of large trees. Annual precipitation is relatively high at 75–150 cm (30–60 inches) and typically distributed evenly around the year. Temperature varies seasonally over a wide range, with hot summers and cold winters. In the Northern Hemisphere, dense stands of deciduous trees are trademarks of temperate forests, such as the one pictured in **Figure 34**. Deciduous trees drop their leaves before winter, when temperatures are too low for effective photosynthesis and water lost by evaporation is not easily replaced from frozen soil.

Numerous invertebrates live in the soil and the thick layer of leaf litter that accumulates on the forest floor. Some vertebrates, such as mice, shrews, and ground squirrels, burrow for shelter and food, while others, including many species of birds, live in the trees. Predators include bobcats, foxes, black bears, and mountain lions. Many mammals that inhabit these forests enter a dormant winter state called hibernation, and some bird species migrate to warmer climates.

Virtually all the original temperate broadleaf forests in North America were cut for timber or cleared for agriculture or development. These forests tend to recover after disturbance, however, and today we see deciduous trees growing in undeveloped areas over much of their former range.

Coniferous Forest

Cone-bearing evergreen trees such as pine, spruce, fir, and hemlock dominate **coniferous forests** in the Northern Hemisphere. (Other kinds of conifers grow in parts of South America, Africa, and Australia.) The northern coniferous forest, or **taiga** **(Figure 35)**, is the largest terrestrial biome on Earth, stretching in a broad band across North America and Asia south of the Arctic Circle. Taiga is also found at cool, high elevations in more temperate latitudes—for example, in much of the mountainous region of western North America. The taiga is characterized by long, snowy winters and short, wet summers that are sometimes warm. The slow decomposition of conifer needles in the thin, acidic soil makes few nutrients available for plant growth. The conical shape of many conifers prevents too much snow from accumulating on their branches and breaking them. Animals of the taiga include moose, elk, hares, bears, wolves, grouse, and migratory birds. The Asian taiga is home to the dwindling number of Siberian tigers that remain in the wild.

The **temperate rain forests** of coastal North America (from Alaska to Oregon) are also coniferous forests. Warm, moist air from the Pacific Ocean supports this unique biome, which, like most coniferous forests, is dominated by a few tree species, typically hemlock, Douglas fir, and redwood. These forests are heavily logged, and the old-growth stands of trees are rapidly disappearing. ✔

✔ **CHECKPOINT**

1. How does the loss of leaves function as an adaptation of deciduous trees to cold winters?
2. What type of trees are characteristic of the taiga?

Answers: 1. by reducing loss of water from the trees when that water cannot be replaced because of frozen soil. 2. conifers such as pine, spruce, fir, and hemlock

▼ **Figure 34**
Temperate broadleaf forest in Vermont in autumn.

▼ **Figure 35**
Northern coniferous forest in Finland, with the sky lit by the northern lights.

Tundra

Tundra covers expansive areas of the Arctic between the taiga and polar ice. **Permafrost** (permanently frozen subsoil), bitterly cold temperatures, and high winds are responsible for the absence of trees and other tall plants in the arctic tundra shown in **Figure 36**. The arctic tundra receives very little annual precipitation. However, water cannot penetrate the underlying permafrost, so melted snow and ice accumulate in pools on the shallow topsoil during the short summer.

Tundra vegetation includes small shrubs, grasses, mosses, and lichens. When summer arrives, flowering plants grow quickly and bloom in a rapid burst. Caribou, musk oxen, wolves, and small rodents called lemmings are among the mammals found in the arctic tundra. Many migratory birds use the tundra as a summer breeding ground. During the brief but productive warm season, the marshy ground supports the aquatic larvae of insects, providing food for migratory waterfowl, and clouds of mosquitoes often fill the tundra air.

On very high mountaintops at all latitudes, including the tropics, high winds and cold temperatures create plant communities called alpine tundra. Although these communities are similar to arctic tundra, there is no permafrost beneath alpine tundra.

Polar Ice

Polar ice covers the land at high latitudes north of the arctic tundra in the Northern Hemisphere and in Antarctica in the Southern Hemisphere **(Figure 37)**. The temperature in these regions is extremely cold year-round, and precipitation is very low. Only a small portion of these landmasses is free of ice or snow, even during the summer. Nevertheless, small plants, such as mosses and lichens, eke out a living, and invertebrates such as nematodes, mites, and wingless insects called springtails inhabit the frigid soil. Nearby sea ice provides feeding platforms for large animals such as polar bears (in the Northern Hemisphere), penguins (in the Southern Hemisphere), and seals. Seals, penguins, and other marine birds visit the land to rest and breed. The polar marine biome provides the food that sustains these birds and mammals. In the Antarctic, penguins feed at sea, eating a variety of fish, squids, and small shrimplike crustaceans known as krill. Antarctic krill, an important food source for many species of fish, seals, squids, seabirds, and filter-feeding whales as well as penguins, depend on sea ice for breeding and as a refuge from predators. As the amount and duration of sea ice decline as a consequence of global climate change, krill habitat is shrinking. ✓

✓ CHECKPOINT

1. Global warming is melting permafrost in some areas of the arctic tundra. What biome would you expect to replace tundra in these regions?
2. How does the vegetation found in polar ice regions compare with tundra vegetation?

Answers: 1. taiga 2. Neither biome is hospitable to plants because of the cold temperatures. However, tundra supports the growth of small shrubs, while polar ice vegetation is limited to mosses and lichens.

▼ Figure 36 **Arctic tundra in Yukon Territory, Canada.**

▼ Figure 37 **Polar ice in Antarctica.**

Interconnections within Systems
The Water Cycle

Biomes are not self-contained units. Rather, all parts of the biosphere are linked by the global water cycle, illustrated in **Figure 38**, and by nutrient cycles. Consequently, events in one biome may reverberate throughout the biosphere.

As you learned earlier in this chapter, water and air move in global patterns driven by solar energy. Precipitation and evaporation continuously move water between the land, oceans, and the atmosphere. Water also evaporates from plants, which pull it from the soil in a process called transpiration.

Over the oceans, evaporation exceeds precipitation. The result is a net movement of water vapor to clouds that are carried by winds from the oceans across the land. On land, precipitation exceeds evaporation and transpiration. The excess precipitation may stay on the surface, or it may trickle through the soil to become groundwater. Both surface water and groundwater eventually flow back to the sea, completing the water cycle.

Just as the water draining from your shower carries dead skin cells from your body along with the day's grime, the water washing over and through the ground carries traces of the land and its history. For example, water

flowing from land to the sea carries with it silt (fine soil particles) and chemicals such as fertilizers and pesticides.

Erosion from coastal development has caused silt to muddy the waters of some coral reefs, dimming the light available to the photosynthetic algae that power the reef community. Chemicals in surface water may travel hundreds of miles by stream and river to the ocean, where currents then carry them even farther from their point of origin. For instance, traces of pesticides and chemicals from industrial wastes have been found in marine mammals in the Arctic and in deep-sea octopuses and squids. Airborne pollutants such as nitrogen oxides and sulfur oxides, which combine with water to form acid precipitation, are distributed by the water cycle, too.

Human activity also affects the global water cycle itself in a number of important ways. One of the main sources of atmospheric water is transpiration from the dense vegetation making up tropical rain forests. The destruction of these forests changes the amount of water vapor in the air. Pumping large amounts of groundwater to the surface for irrigation increases the rate of evaporation over land and may deplete groundwater supplies. In addition, global warming affects the water cycle in complex ways that will have far-reaching effects on precipitation patterns. We'll consider some of these environmental impacts in the following sections. ☑

Airborne pollutants from car exhaust can combine with water and return to Earth as acid precipitation far away—evidence that the water cycle operates on a global scale.

☑ CHECKPOINT

What is the main way that living organisms contribute to the water cycle?

Answer: Plants move water from the ground to the air via transpiration.

▼ Figure 38 **The global water cycle.**

Solar heat

Water vapor over the sea

Net movement of water vapor by wind

Water vapor over the land

Precipitation over the sea

Evaporation from the sea

Evaporation and transpiration

Precipitation over the land

Oceans

Flow of water from land to sea

Surface water and groundwater

Human Impact on Biomes

For hundreds of years, people have been using increasingly effective technologies to capture or produce food, to extract resources from the environment, and to build cities. It is now clear that the environmental costs of these enterprises are staggering. In this section, you'll see some examples of how human activities are affecting forest and freshwater resources. Ecological knowledge has an important role in achieving **sustainability**, the goal of developing, managing, and conserving Earth's resources in ways that meet the needs of people today without compromising the ability of future generations to meet their needs.

Forests

The map in Figure 27 shows the terrestrial biomes that would be expected to flourish under the prevailing climatic conditions. However, about three-quarters of Earth's land surface has been altered by thousands of years of human occupation. Most of the land that we've appropriated is used for agriculture; another hefty chunk is covered by the asphalt and concrete of development. Changes in vegetation are especially dramatic in regions like tropical forests that escaped large-scale human intervention until recently. Satellite photos of a small area in Brazil show how thoroughly a landscape can be altered in a short amount of time (Figure 39).

Every year, more and more forested land is cleared for agriculture. You might think that this land is needed to feed new mouths as the human population continues to grow, but that's not entirely the case. Unsustainable agricultural practices have degraded much of the world's cropland so severely that it is unusable. Researchers estimate that replacing worn-out farmland accounts for up to 80% of the deforestation occurring today. Tropical forests, such as the one in **Figure 40**, are also being cleared to grow palm oil for products such as cosmetics and a long list of packaged foods, including cookies, crackers, potato chips, chocolate products, and soups. Other forests are being lost to logging, mining, and air pollution, problems that are hitting coniferous forests especially hard. (As we mentioned in the previous section, most temperate broadleaf forests were replaced by human enterprises long ago.) Land that hasn't been directly converted to food production and living space also bears the imprint of our presence. Roads penetrate regions that are otherwise unaltered, bringing pollution to the wilderness, providing avenues for new diseases to emerge, and slicing vast tracts of biome into segments that are too small to support a full array of species.

Land uses that provide resources such as food, fuel, and shelter are clearly beneficial to us. But natural ecosystems also provide services that support the human population—purification of air and water, nutrient cycling, and recreation, to name just a few.

▼ **Figure 39** **Satellite photos of the Rondonia area of the Brazilian rain forest.**

1975. In 1975, the forest in this remote region was virtually intact.

2001. Same area in 2001, after a paved highway through the region brought loggers and farmers. The "fishbone" pattern marks the new network of roads carved through the forest.

▼ **Figure 40** **Tropical forest in Indonesia that was clear-cut for a palm oil plantation.**

Fresh Water

The impact of human activities on freshwater ecosystems may pose an even greater threat to life on Earth—including ourselves—than the damage to terrestrial ecosystems. Freshwater ecosystems are being polluted by large amounts of nitrogen and phosphorus compounds that run off from heavily fertilized farms or from livestock feedlots. A wide variety of other pollutants, such as industrial wastes, also contaminate freshwater habitats, drinking water, and groundwater. Some regions of the world face dire shortages of water as a result of the overuse of groundwater for irrigation, extended droughts (partially caused by global climate change), or poor water management practices.

Las Vegas, the population center of Clark County, Nevada, is one example of a city whose water resources are increasingly stressed by drought and overuse. **Figure 41a** is a satellite photo of Las Vegas in 1973, when the population of Clark County was 319,400. **Figure 41b** shows the same area 40 years later, when the population had swelled to more than 2 million. In contrast to the disappearance of greenery in the photos of Brazilian rain forest, the mark of human activities in Figure 41b is the notable expansion of greenery—the result of watering lawns and golf courses. Las Vegas is situated in a high valley in the Mojave Desert. Where does it get the water to turn barren desert into green fields?

Las Vegas taps underground aquifers for some water, but its main water supply is Lake Mead. Lake Mead is an enormous reservoir formed by the Hoover Dam on the Colorado River, which in turn receives almost all of its water from snowmelt in the Rocky Mountains. With decreased annual snowfall, attributable largely to global warming, the flow of the Colorado has greatly diminished. The water level in Lake Mead has dropped drastically **(Figure 42)**, and parched cities and farms farther downstream are pleading for more water.

To ensure an adequate water supply for the future, Las Vegas is looking for new sources of water. Among other options, Las Vegas is eyeing the abundant supply of groundwater in the northern end of the valley where it lies. Although sparsely populated, that area is home to many ranchers whose livelihoods depend on the groundwater. It is also home to numerous endangered species. Not surprisingly, environmentalists and residents of the north valley are resisting efforts to pipe its groundwater to Las Vegas.

Nevada is just one of many places where the hard realities of climate change are beginning to affect daily life. Battles over water resources are shaping up throughout the arid West and Southwest of the United States, where changing precipitation patterns due to global warming are projected to continue the drought for many years to come. In other regions of the world, including China, India, and North Africa, the increasing demands of economic, agricultural, and population growth are straining water resources that are already scarce.

While policymakers are dealing with current crises and planning how to manage resources in the future, researchers are seeking methods of sustainable agriculture and water use. Basic ecological research is an essential component of ensuring that sufficient food and water will be available for people now—and for the generations to come. Next, we take a closer look at a major threat to sustainability: global climate change. ☑

▼ **Figure 42 Low water level in Lake Mead.** The white "bathtub ring" is caused by mineral deposits on rocks that were once submerged.

▼ **Figure 41 Satellite photos of Las Vegas, Nevada.**

(a) May 1973

(b) October, 2013

☑ **CHECKPOINT**

Why is decreased snowfall in the Rocky Mountains a concern for people who live in Las Vegas?

Answer: Snowmelt from the Rockies flows into the Colorado River, which supplies water for Las Vegas residents.

Global Climate Change

Rising concentrations of carbon dioxide (CO_2) and certain other gases in the atmosphere are changing global climate patterns. This was the overarching conclusion of the assessment report released by the Intergovernmental Panel on Climate Change (IPCC) in 2014. Thousands of scientists and policymakers from more than 100 countries participated in producing the report, which is based on data published in thousands of scientific papers. Thus, there is no debate among scientists about whether climate change is occurring. In this section, you'll learn why it is occurring, how it is affecting the biosphere, and what you can do about it.

The Greenhouse Effect and Global Warming

Why is Earth's atmosphere becoming warmer? A useful analogy is a greenhouse, which is used to grow plants when the weather outside is too cold. Its transparent glass or plastic walls allow solar radiation to pass through, but they also trap some of the heat that accumulates inside the building. On a smaller scale, consider how hot it gets in a closed car on a sunny day. Similarly, certain gases in Earth's atmosphere are transparent to solar radiation but absorb or reflect heat. Some of these so-called **greenhouse gases** are natural, including CO_2, water vapor, and methane. Others, such as chlorofluorocarbons (CFCs, found in some aerosol sprays and refrigerants), are synthetic. As **Figure 43** shows, greenhouse gases act as a blanket that traps heat in the atmosphere. This heating effect, often called the **greenhouse effect**, is highly beneficial. Without it, the average air temperature on Earth would be a frigid −18°C (−2.4°F), far too cold for most life as we know it. However, increasing the insulation that the blanket provides is making Earth overly warm.

The signature effect of rapidly increasing greenhouse gases is the steady increase in the average global temperature, which has risen 0.8°C (1.4°F) over the last 100 years, with 75% of that increase occurring over the last three decades. Further increases of 2–4.5°C are likely by the end of this century, according to the 2014 IPPC report. Ocean temperatures are also rising, in deeper layers as well as at the surface. But the temperature increases are not distributed evenly around the globe. The largest increases are in the northernmost regions of the Northern Hemisphere and parts of Antarctica (**Figure 44**). ☑

▼ Figure 43 **The greenhouse effect.** The atmosphere traps heat in the same way that glass keeps heat inside a greenhouse.

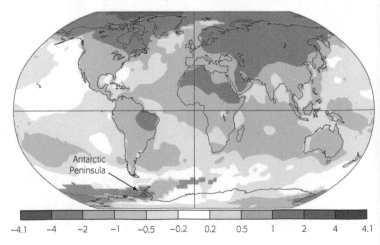

▼ Figure 44 **Differences in average temperatures during 2004–2013 compared with long-term averages during 1951–1980, in °C.** The largest temperature increases are shown in red. Gray indicates regions for which no data are available.

The Accumulation of Greenhouse Gases

After many years of data collection and debate, the vast majority of scientists are confident that human activities have caused the rising concentrations of greenhouse gases. Major sources of emissions include agriculture, landfills, and the burning of wood and fossil fuels (oil, coal, and natural gas).

Let's take a closer look at CO_2, the dominant greenhouse gas. For 650,000 years, the atmospheric concentration of CO_2 did not exceed 300 parts per million (ppm); the concentration before the Industrial Revolution was 280 ppm. In 2013, the average atmospheric CO_2 was 396 ppm, and continuing to rise (Figure 45). The levels of other greenhouse gases have increased dramatically, too. Remember that CO_2 is removed from the atmosphere by the process of photosynthesis and stored in organic molecules such as carbohydrates. These molecules are eventually broken down by cellular respiration, releasing CO_2. Overall, uptake of CO_2 by photosynthesis roughly equals the release of CO_2 by cellular respiration (Figure 46). However, extensive deforestation has significantly decreased the incorporation of CO_2 into organic material. At the same time, CO_2 is flooding into the atmosphere from the burning of fossil fuels and wood,

a process that releases CO_2 from organic material much more rapidly than cellular respiration.

CO_2 is also exchanged between the atmosphere and the surface waters of the oceans. For decades, the oceans have acted as massive sponges, soaking up considerably more CO_2 than they have released. But now, the excess CO_2 has made the oceans more acidic, a change that could have a profound effect on marine communities. As ocean acidification worsens, many species of plankton and marine animals such as corals and molluscs will be unable to build their shells or exoskeletons. Their demise will remove critical links from marine food webs and ultimately damage marine ecosystems around the world. ☑

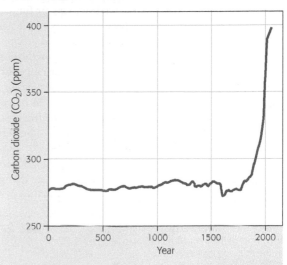

▼ Figure 45 **Atmospheric concentration of CO_2.** Notice that the concentration was relatively stable until the Industrial Revolution, which began in the late 1700s.

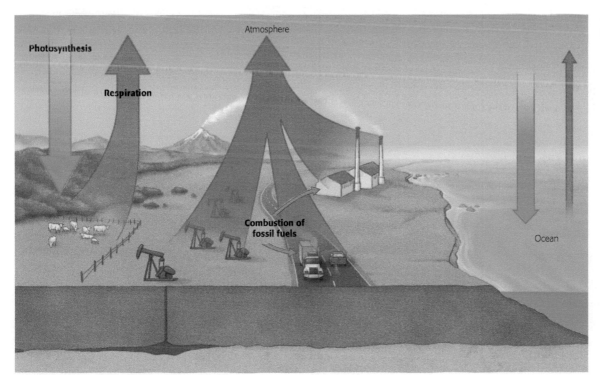

◄ Figure 46 **How CO_2 enters and leaves the atmosphere.**

Global Climate Change THE PROCESS OF SCIENCE

How Does Climate Change Affect Species Distribution?

As you've learned in this chapter, abiotic factors of the environment are fundamental determinants of where organisms live. It stands to reason that changes in temperature and precipitation patterns will have a significant effect on the distribution of life. With rising temperatures, the ranges of many species have already shifted toward the poles or to higher elevations. For example, shifts in the ranges of many bird species have been reported; the Inuit peoples living north of the Arctic Circle have sighted robins in the region for the first time.

Let's examine how a team of ecologists investigated the impact of climate change on European butterflies. Using the **observation** that the average temperature in Europe has risen 0.8°C (about 1.4°F) and that butterflies are sensitive to temperature change, the researchers asked the **question**: Have the ranges of butterflies changed in response to the temperature changes? This question led to the **hypothesis** that butterfly range boundaries are shifting in line with the warming trend. The researchers **predicted** that butterfly species will be establishing new populations to the north of their former ranges, and populations at the southern edges of their ranges will become extinct. The **experiment** involved analyzing historical data on the ranges of 35 species of butterflies in Europe. The **results** showed that more than 60% of the species have pushed their northern range boundaries poleward over the last century, some by as much as 150 miles. The southern boundaries have simultaneously contracted for some species, but not for others. **Figure 47** shows the range shift for the species *Argynnis paphia*.

While some organisms have the dispersal ability and the room for northward population shifts, species that live on mountaintops or in polar regions have nowhere to go. For example, researchers in Costa Rica have reported the disappearance of 20 species of frogs and toads as warmer Pacific Ocean temperatures reduce the dry-season mists in their mountain habitats. And as we mentioned in the Biology and Society section, animals at both poles are also at risk.

► **Figure 47 Northward shift of *Argynnis paphia*.** On the map, orange represents the butterfly's range in 1970; its 1997 range is shown in light green.

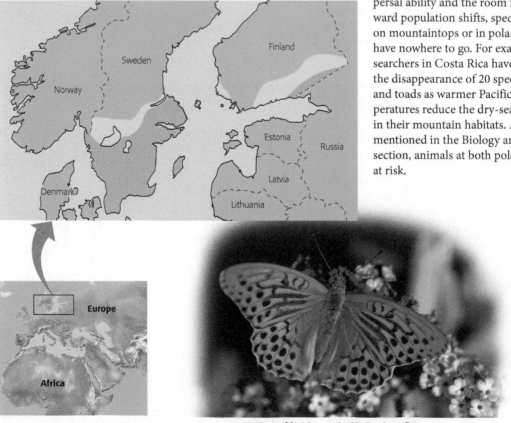

Argynnis paphia (silver-washed fritillary butterfly)

Effects of Climate Change on Ecosystems

The sentiment expressed by the poet John Donne that "no man is an island" is equally true for every other species in nature: Every species needs others to survive. Climate change is knocking some of these interactions out of sync. In temperate and polar climates, life cycle events of many plants and animals are triggered by warming temperatures. Across the Northern Hemisphere, the warm temperatures of spring are arriving earlier. Satellite images show earlier greening of the landscape, and flowering occurs sooner. A variety of species, including birds and frogs, have begun their breeding seasons earlier. But for other species, the environmental cue that spring has arrived is day length, which is not affected by climate change. Consequently, the winter white fur of snowshoe hares may be conspicuous against a greening landscape, or plants may bloom before pollinators have emerged.

The combined effects of climate change on forest ecosystems in western North America have spawned catastrophic wildfire seasons **(Figure 48)**. In these regions, spring snowmelt in the mountains releases water into streams that sustain forest moisture levels over the summer dry season. With the earlier arrival of spring, snowmelt begins earlier and dwindles away before the dry season ends. As a result, the fire season is lasting longer. Meanwhile, bark beetles, which bore into conifers to lay their eggs, have benefited from global warming. Healthy trees can fight off the pests, but drought-stressed trees are too weak to resist **(Figure 49)**. As a bonus for the beetles, the warmer weather allows them to reproduce twice a year rather than once. In turn, vast numbers of dead trees add fuel

to a fire. Wildfires burn longer, and the number of acres burned has increased dramatically.

The map of terrestrial biomes (see Figure 27), which is primarily determined by temperature and rainfall, is also changing. Melting permafrost is shifting the boundary of the tundra northward as shrubs and conifers are able to stretch their ranges into the previously frozen ground. Prolonged droughts are extending the boundaries of deserts. Scientists also predict that great expanses of the Amazonian rain forest will gradually become savanna as increased temperatures dry out the soil.

Global climate change has significant consequences for people, too, as changing temperature and precipitation patterns affect food production, the availability of fresh water, and the structural integrity of buildings and roads. All projections point to an even greater impact in the future. Unlike other species, however, humans can take action to reduce greenhouse gas emissions and maybe even reverse the warming trend. ☑

☑ CHECKPOINT

How have bark beetles benefited from global warming?

Answer: Drought-stressed trees are less resistant to the beetles; with a longer warm season, beetles can reproduce twice in a year rather than once.

▼ **Figure 49 Pines in Colorado infested by bark beetles.** Red or light-colored foliage indicates dead or dying trees. Green trees are still healthy.

▼ **Figure 48 A wildfire in Yosemite National Park, California, August 2013.**

Looking to Our Future

From 1990 to 2013, emissions of greenhouse gases increased 61%, and they continue to rise. At this rate, further climate change is inevitable. However, with effort, ingenuity, and international cooperation, we may be able to begin reducing emissions.

Given the vast scope and complexity of the problem, you might think that your own actions would have little impact on greenhouse gas emissions. But it was the collective activities of individuals that caused—and are still causing—emissions to rise. The amount of greenhouse gas emitted as a result of the actions of a single individual is that person's **carbon footprint** (from the fact that the most important greenhouse gas is CO_2). A carbon footprint can be estimated using a set of rough calculations; several different calculators are available online.

Home energy use is one major contributor to the carbon footprint. It's easy to reduce your energy consumption by turning off the lights, TV, and other electrical appliances when they aren't in use. Unplug "vampire" devices—electronics such as cell phone chargers, videogame consoles, and other computer, video, and audio equipment that draw electricity even when they aren't being used. You can also switch to energy-efficient lightbulbs.

Transportation is another significant part of the carbon footprint. If you have a car, keep it well maintained, consolidate trips, share rides with friends, and use alternative means of transportation whenever possible.

Manufactured goods are a third category in the carbon footprint. Every item you purchase generated its own carbon footprint in the process of going from raw materials to store shelves. You can reduce your carbon emissions by not buying unnecessary goods and by recycling—or better yet, reusing—items instead of putting them in the trash **(Figure 50)**. Landfills are the largest human-related source of methane, a greenhouse gas more potent than CO_2. The methane is released by prokaryotes that decompose (break down) landfill waste.

Changes in your eating habits can also shrink your carbon footprint. Like landfills, the digestive system of cattle depends on methane-producing bacteria. The methane released by cattle and by the bacteria that decompose their manure accounts for about 20% of methane emissions in the United States. Thus, replacing beef and dairy products in your diet with fish, chicken, eggs, and vegetables reduces your carbon footprint. In addition, eating locally grown fresh foods may lower the greenhouse gas emissions that result from food processing and transportation **(Figure 51)**. Many websites offer additional suggestions for reducing your carbon footprint. ☑

Your home may be infested with "vampire" devices that consume electricity even while you sleep.

☑ **CHECKPOINT**

What is a personal carbon footprint?

Answer: the amount of greenhouse gas that a person is responsible for emitting

▼ Figure 50 **Turning trash into treasure.** If you have things that you no longer need, don't trash them when you move out of your dorm or apartment. Environmentally conscious students at the University of North Carolina collect and sell discarded items, donating the proceeds to charity.

▼ Figure 51 **Eating locally grown foods may reduce your carbon footprint—and they taste good, too!**

Global Climate Change EVOLUTION CONNECTION

Climate Change as an Agent of Natural Selection

Environmental change has always been a part of life; in fact, it is a key ingredient of evolutionary change. Will evolutionary adaptation counteract the negative effects of climate change on organisms? Researchers have documented microevolutionary shifts in a few populations, including red squirrels, a few bird species, and a tiny mosquito (Figure 52a). It appears that some populations, especially those with high genetic variability and short life spans, may avoid extinction by means of evolutionary adaptation. However, evolutionary adaptation is unlikely to save long-lived species, such as polar bears and penguins, that are experiencing rapid habitat loss (Figure 52b). The rate of climate change is incredibly fast compared with major climate shifts in evolutionary history. If climate change continues on its present course, thousands of species—the IPCC estimates as many as 30% of all plants and animals—will face extinction by midcentury.

▼ Figure 52 **Which species will survive climate change?**

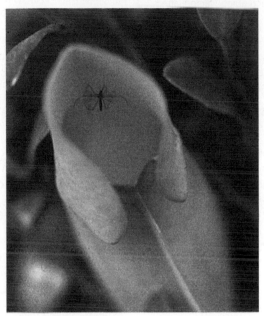

(a) Pitcher plant mosquito. The pitcher plant mosquito, pictured inside the carnivorous plant for which it is named, may be able to evolve quickly enough.

(b) Polar bear. Polar bears, which depend on sea ice for feeding, are not likely to make it.

Chapter Review

■ SUMMARY OF KEY CONCEPTS

An Overview of Ecology

Ecology is the scientific study of interactions between organisms and their environments. The environment includes abiotic (nonliving) and biotic (living) components. Ecologists use observation, experiments, and computer models to test hypothetical explanations of these interactions.

Ecology and Environmentalism

Human activities have had an impact on all parts of the biosphere. Ecology provides the basis for understanding and addressing these environmental problems.

A Hierarchy of Interactions

Ecologists study interactions at four increasingly complex levels.

Organismal ecology (individual)

Population ecology (group of individuals)

Community ecology (all organisms in a particular area)

Ecosystem ecology (all organisms and abiotic factors)

Living in Earth's Diverse Environments

The biosphere is an environmental patchwork in which abiotic factors affect the distribution and abundance of organisms.

Abiotic Factors of the Biosphere

Abiotic factors include the availability of sunlight, water, nutrients, and temperature. In aquatic habitats, dissolved oxygen, salinity, current, and tides are also important. Additional factors in terrestrial environments include wind and fire.

The Evolutionary Adaptations of Organisms

Adaptation via natural selection results from the interactions of organisms with their environments.

Adjusting to Environmental Variability

Organisms also have adaptations that enable them to cope with environmental variability, including physiological, behavioral, and anatomical responses to changing conditions.

Biomes

A biome is a major terrestrial or aquatic life zone.

Freshwater Biomes

Freshwater biomes include lakes, ponds, rivers, streams, and wetlands. Lakes vary, depending on depth, with regard to light penetration (photic and aphotic zones), temperature, nutrients, oxygen levels, and community structure. Rivers change greatly from their source to the point at which they empty into a lake or ocean. The bottom of an aquatic biome is its benthic realm.

Marine Biomes

Marine life is distributed into distinct realms (benthic and pelagic) and zones (photic, aphotic, and intertidal) according to the depth of the water, degree of light penetration, distance from shore, and open water versus deep-sea bottom. Marine biomes include the pelagic realm and the benthic realm of the oceans, coral reefs, intertidal zones, and estuaries. Coral reefs, which occur in warm tropical waters above the continental shelf, have an abundance of biological diversity. An ecosystem found near hydrothermal vents in the deep ocean is powered by chemical energy from Earth's interior instead of sunlight. Estuaries, located where a freshwater river or stream merges with the ocean, are some of the most biologically productive environments on Earth.

How Climate Affects Terrestrial Biome Distribution

The geographic distribution of terrestrial biomes is based mainly on regional variations in climate. Climate is largely determined by the uneven distribution of solar energy on Earth. Proximity to large bodies of water and the presence of landforms such as mountains also affect climate.

Terrestrial Biomes

Most terrestrial biomes are named for their climate and predominant vegetation. The major terrestrial biomes include tropical forest, savanna, desert, chaparral, temperate grassland, temperate broadleaf forest, coniferous forest, tundra, and polar ice. If the climate in two geographically separate areas is similar, the same type of biome may occur in both.

Interconnections within Systems: The Water Cycle

The global water cycle links aquatic and terrestrial biomes. Human activities are disrupting the water cycle.

Human Impact on Biomes

Land use by humans has altered vast tracts of forest and degraded the services provided by natural ecosystems. Unsustainable agricultural practices have depleted cropland fertility. Human activities have polluted freshwater ecosystems, which are vital for life. Agriculture, population growth, drought, and declining snowfall are all factors in the rapid depletion of freshwater resources in some regions.

Global Climate Change

The Greenhouse Effect and Global Warming

So-called greenhouse gases, including CO_2 and methane, increase the amount of heat retained in Earth's atmosphere. The accumulation of these gases has caused increases in the average global temperature.

The Accumulation of Greenhouse Gases

Human activities, especially the burning of fossil fuels, are responsible for the rise in greenhouse gases over the past century. Release of CO_2 has exceeded the amount that can be absorbed by natural processes.

Effects of Climate Change on Ecosystems

Climate change is disrupting interactions between species. Devastating wildfires are among the effects of climate change in certain ecosystems. Climate change is also shifting biome boundaries.

Looking to Our Future

Each person has a carbon footprint—that person's responsibility for a portion of global greenhouse gas emissions. We can take action to reduce our carbon footprints.

MasteringBiology®

For practice quizzes, BioFlix animations, MP3 tutorials, video tutors, and more study tools designed for this text, go to MasteringBiology®

SELF-QUIZ

1. Place these levels of ecological study in order from the least to the most comprehensive: community ecology, ecosystem ecology, organismal ecology, population ecology.
2. Name several abiotic factors that might affect the community of organisms living inside a home fish tank.
3. The formation of goose bumps on your skin in cold weather is an example of a (an) _____ response, while seasonal migration is an example of a (an) _____ response.

4. Which of the following sea creatures might be described as a pelagic animal of the aphotic zone?

   a. a coral reef fish

   b. a giant clam near a deep-sea hydrothermal vent

   c. an intertidal snail

   d. a deep-sea squid

5. Identify the following biomes on the graph below: tundra, coniferous forest, desert, grassland, temperate broadleaf forest, and tropical rain forest.

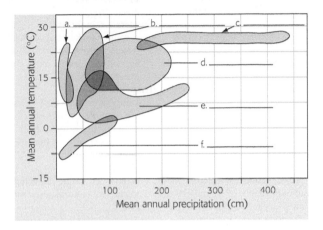

6. We are on a coastal hillside on a hot, dry summer day among ever-green shrubs that are adapted to fire. We are most likely standing in a _____ biome.

7. What three abiotic factors account for the rarity of trees in arctic tundra?

8. What human activity is responsible for the greatest amount of deforestation?

9. What is the greenhouse effect? How is the greenhouse effect related to global warming?

10. The recent increase in atmospheric CO_2 concentration is mainly a result of an increase in

   a. plant growth.

   b. the absorption of heat radiating from Earth.

   c. the burning of fossil fuels and wood.

   d. cellular respiration by the increasing human population.

11. What populations of organisms are most likely to survive climate change via evolutionary adaptation?

THE PROCESS OF SCIENCE

12. Design a laboratory experiment to measure the effect of water tempera-ture on the population growth of a certain phytoplankton species from a pond.

13. **Interpreting Data** This graph shows average monthly temperature and precipitation for a city in the Northern Hemisphere. Based on the biome descriptions given in this chapter, in which biome is this city lo-cated? Explain your answer.

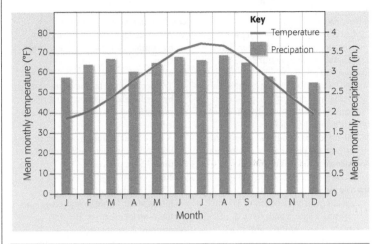

BIOLOGY AND SOCIETY

14. Some people are not convinced that human-induced global climate change is a real phenomenon. Using your knowledge of the scientific process and the information from this chapter, develop arguments you could use to explain the scientific basis for saying that global climate change is truly occurring and that people are responsible for it.

15. Research your country's per capita (per person) carbon emissions. Calculate your own carbon footprint and compare it with the average for your country. Make a list of actions you are willing to take to reduce your personal carbon footprint. What actions could you take to persuade others to reduce their carbon footprints?

16. In the summer of 2007, unprecedented drought conditions brought the city of Atlanta, Georgia, within weeks of running out of water. Most of Atlanta's water comes from Lake Lanier, a reservoir that the Army Corps of Engineers created by damming the Chattahoochee River. With Lake Lanier drying up from lack of rainfall, Georgia petitioned the Corps, which manages the dam, to reduce the amount of water released downstream. The Corps refused, citing its obligation under the Endangered Species Act to protect the habitats of a species of sturgeon (a fish) and two species of mussel (a mollusc). Objections were also raised by Alabama and Florida, where hundreds of towns, recreational facilities, and power plants depend on the water released downstream. Some people thought that Atlanta authorities had brought the water shortage on themselves by allowing developers to build without considering whether adequate water was available. Florida also argued that reduction of freshwater inflows would harm its oyster fisheries. How would you prioritize the competing claims on the water from Lake Lanier? Who should allocate scarce water resources? How can cities and states plan more wisely for future shortages?

Glossary

abiotic factor (ā'-bī-ot'-ik)
A nonliving component of an ecosystem, such as air, water, light, minerals, or temperature.

acclimation (ak'-li-mā'-shun)
Physiological adjustment that occurs gradually, though still reversibly, in response to an environmental change.

aphotic zone (ā-fō'-tik)
The region of an aquatic ecosystem beneath the photic zone, where light levels are too low for photosynthesis to take place.

benthic realm
A seafloor or the bottom of a freshwater lake, pond, river, or stream. The benthic realm is occupied by communities of organisms known as benthos.

biome (bī'-ōm)
A major terrestrial or aquatic life zone, characterized by vegetation type in terrestrial biomes and the physical environment in aquatic biomes.

biotic factor (bī-ot'-ik)
A living component of a biological community; any organism that is part of an individual's environment.

carbon footprint
The amount of greenhouse gas emitted as a result of the actions of a person, nation, or other entity.

chaparral (shap-uh-ral')
A terrestrial biome limited to coastal regions where cold ocean currents circulate offshore, creating mild, rainy winters and long, hot, dry summers; also known as the Mediterranean biome. Chaparral vegetation is adapted to fire.

community
All the organisms inhabiting and potentially interacting in a particular area; an assemblage of populations of different species.

community ecology
The study of how interactions between species affect community structure and organization.

coniferous forest (kō-nif'-rus)
A terrestrial biome characterized by conifers, cone-bearing evergreen trees.

coral reef
Tropical marine biome characterized by hard skeletal structures secreted primarily by the resident cnidarians.

desert
A terrestrial biome characterized by low and unpredictable rainfall (less than 30 cm per year).

ecology
The scientific study of the interactions between organisms and their environments.

ecosystem (ē'-kō-sis-tem)
All the organisms in a given area, along with the nonliving (abiotic) factors with which they interact; a biological community and its physical environment.

ecosystem ecology
The study of energy flow and the cycling of chemicals among the various biotic and abiotic factors in an ecosystem.

estuary (es'-chuh-wār-ē)
The area where a freshwater stream or river merges with seawater.

greenhouse effect
The warming of the atmosphere caused by CO_2, CH_4, and other gases that absorb heat radiation and slow its escape from Earth's surface.

greenhouse gas
Any of the gases in the atmosphere that absorb heat radiation, including CO_2, methane, water vapor, and synthetic chlorofluorocarbons.

habitat
A place where an organism lives; a specific environment in which an organism lives.

intertidal zone (in'-ter-tīd'-ul)
A shallow zone where the waters of an estuary or ocean meet land.

organism
An individual living thing, such as a

bacterium, fungus, protist, plant, or animal.

organismal ecology
The study of the evolutionary adaptations that enable individual organisms to meet the challenges posed by their abiotic environments.

pelagic realm (puh-laj'-ik)
The open-water region of an ocean.

permafrost
Continuously frozen subsoil found in the arctic tundra.

photic zone (fō'-tik)
Shallow water near the shore or the upper layer of water away from the shore; region of an aquatic ecosystem where sufficient light is available for photosynthesis.

polar ice
A terrestrial biome that includes regions of extremely cold temperature and low precipitation located at high latitudes north of the arctic tundra and in Antarctica.

population ecology
The study of how members of a population interact with their environment, focusing on factors that influence population density and growth.

savanna
A terrestrial biome dominated by grasses and scattered trees. The temperature is warm year-round. Frequent fires and seasonal drought are significant abiotic factors.

taiga (tī'-guh)
The northern coniferous forest, characterized by long, snowy winters and short, wet summers. Taiga extends across North America and Eurasia, to the southern border of the arctic tundra; it is also found just below alpine tundra on mountainsides in temperate zones.

temperate broadleaf forest
A terrestrial biome located throughout midlatitude regions where there is sufficient moisture to support the growth of large, broadleaf deciduous trees.

temperate grassland
A terrestrial biome located in the temperate zone and characterized by low rainfall and nonwoody vegetation. Tree growth is hindered by occasional fires and periodic severe drought.

temperate rain forest
A coniferous forest of coastal North America (from Alaska to Oregon) supported by warm, moist air from the Pacific Ocean.

temperate zones
Latitudes between the tropics and the Arctic Circle in the north and the Antarctic Circle in the south; regions with milder climates than the tropics or polar regions.

tropical forest
A terrestrial biome characterized by warm temperatures year-round.

tropics
The region between the Tropic of Cancer and the Tropic of Capricorn; latitudes between 23.5° north and south.

tundra
A terrestrial biome characterized by bitterly cold temperatures. Plant life is limited to dwarf woody shrubs, grasses, mosses, and lichens. Arctic tundra has permanently frozen subsoil (permafrost); alpine tundra, found at high elevations, lacks permafrost.

wetland
An ecosystem intermediate between an aquatic ecosystem and a terrestrial ecosystem. Wetland soil is saturated with water permanently or periodically.

zooplankton
In aquatic environments, free-floating animals, including many microscopic ones.

Credits

Credits are listed in the order of appearance.

PHOTO CREDITS

opening photo bottom Balazs Kovacs Images/Shutterstock; **opening photo top right** Erni/Shutterstock; **opening photo top left** Olegusk/Shutterstock; **opening photo right** Vince Clements/Shutterstock; **right** Jean-Paul Ferrero/Mary Evans Picture Library Ltd/Age Fotostock; **top left** Jean-Paul Ferrero/Mary Evans Picture Library Ltd/Age Fotostock; **1** Philippe Psaila/Science Source; **2** Jay Directo/AFP/Getty Images/Newscom; **3a** Barry Mansell/Nature Picture Library; **3b** Sue Flood/Alamy; **3c** Juniors Bildarchiv/Age Fotostock; **3d** Jeremy Woodhouse/Getty Images; **4** David Wall/Alamy; **5** NASA Earth Observing System; **6 right inset** Image Quest Marine; **6** Verena Tunnicliffe/AFP/Newscom; **7** Wayne Lynch/All Canada Photos/Getty Images; **8a** Jean Dickey; **8b** Age Fotostock/Superstock; **9** Jean Dickey; **11 left to right** Outdoorsman/Shutterstock; Tier und Naturfotografie/J & C Sohns/Age Fotostock; **12** Ed Reschke/Photolibrary/Getty Images; **13** Robert Stainforth/Alamy; **14** WorldSat International/Science Source; **16** Ishbukar Yalilfatar/Shutterstock; **17** Kevin Schafer/Alamy; **18** Jean Dickey; **20** Digital Vision/Photodisc/Getty Images; **21** Ron Watts/All Canada Photos/Getty Images; **22** George McCarthy/Nature Picture Library; **29** Age Fotostock/Superstock; **30** Eric J. Simon; **31** Age Fotostock/Juan Carlos Munoz/Age Fotostock; **32** The California/Chaparral Institute; **33** Mark Coffey/All Canada Photos/Superstock; **34** Joe Sohm/Visions of America, LLC/Alamy; **35** Jorma Luhta/Nature Picture Library; **36** Paul Nicklen/National Geographic/Getty Images; **37** Gordon Wiltsie/National Geographic/Getty Images; **39 top to bottom** UNEP/GRID-Arenda; UNEP/GRID-Arendal; **40** Crack Palinggi/Reuters; **41a** UNEP/GRID-Arenda; **41b** USGS; **42** Jim West/Alamy; **43** Kamira/Shutterstock; **47** Chris Martin Bahr/Science Source; **48** Design Pics/Kip Evans/Newscom; **49** Drake Fleege/Alamy; **50** University of North Carolina; **51** Chris Cheadle/All Canada Photos/Getty Images; **52a** William E. Bradshaw; **52b** Christopher Wood/Shutterstock.

ILLUSTRATION AND TEXT CREDITS

25: J. H. Withgott and S. R. Brennan, *Environment: The Science Behind the Stories*, 3rd Ed., © 2008. Reprinted and electronically reproduced by permission of Pearson Education, Inc., Upper Saddle River, New Jersey; **44:** NASA.gov website GISS Surface Temperature Analysis (global map generator), http://data.giss.nasa.gov/gistemp/maps/ (settings for generating this specific map are shown below the map); **45:** Based on *Climate Change 2013: The Physical Science Basis.* Working Group I Contribution to the Fourth Assessment Report of the Intergovernmental Panel on Climate Change; Based on data from http://www.ncdc.noaa.gov/land-based-station-data/climate-normals/1981-2010-normals-data.

Self-Quiz Answers

1. organismal ecology, population ecology, community ecology, ecosystem ecology
2. light, water temperature, chemicals added
3. physiological; behavioral
4. d
5. a. desert; b. grassland; c. tropical rain forest; d. temperate broadleaf forest; e. coniferous forest; f. tundra
6. chaparral
7. permafrost, very cold winters, and high winds
8. agriculture
9. Carbon dioxide and other gases in the atmosphere absorb heat energy radiating from Earth and reflect it back toward Earth. This is called the greenhouse effect. As the carbon dioxide concentration in the atmosphere increases, more heat is retained, causing global warming.
10. c
11. populations of organisms that have high genetic variability and short life spans

Population Ecology

From Chapter 19 of *Campbell Essential Biology with Physiology*, Fifth Edition. Eric J. Simon, Jean L. Dickey, Kelly A. Hogan, Jane B. Reece. Copyright © 2016 by Pearson Education, Inc. All rights reserved.

Population Ecology

The saying "There are plenty of fish in the sea" could become meaningless if overharvesting continues.

The average American generates about 40 pounds of trash per week, almost three times as much as the average Colombian.

Counting one person per second, it would take more than 225 years to count all the people alive today.

If environmental resources were unlimited, a single pair of elephants would give rise to a population of 19 million in 750 years.

Biological Invasions BIOLOGY AND SOCIETY

Invasion of the Lionfish

Lionfish, with their graceful, flowing fins, bold stripes, and eye-catching array of spines, are striking members of tropical reef communities. They are also favorites of saltwater aquarium enthusiasts—especially the red lionfish, a native to the coral reefs of the South Pacific and Indian Oceans. There are a few drawbacks to owning a red lionfish, however. The spines are venomous and can inflict an intensely painful sting. Lionfish are merciless predators, so any tankmates must be chosen with care. And they are large. A 2-inch juvenile can rapidly become an 18-inch adult that requires, at minimum, a 120-gallon tank. Apparently, some aquarium owners who regretted their purchase released their lionfish into the wild.

Freed from the competitors and predators of their native reefs as well as their tanks, red lionfish have multiplied exponentially. Within a few years of the first sightings off the southeastern coast of Florida, lionfish populations had spread up the East Coast. They have since invaded islands and coastlines throughout the Atlantic and Caribbean regions and are now swarming into the Gulf of Mexico. The speed of the onslaught has stunned scientists, who are just beginning to document its devastating effects on native ecosystems. Lionfish consume prodigious numbers of fish, including species that are key to maintaining the legendary diversity of reef communities and juveniles of economically important fishes such as grouper and snapper. Some biologists think our best hope of stopping the lionfish invasion is for *us* to consume *them*. The National Oceanic and Atmospheric Administration (NOAA) has launched an "Eat Lionfish" campaign to encourage human predation on the tasty fish.

The red lionfish, a beautiful but deadly invader, is a threat to coral reef communities. This lionfish was photographed off the coast of North Carolina, halfway around the world from its native habitat.

For as long as people have traveled the globe, they have carried—intentionally or accidentally—thousands of species to new habitats. Many of these non-native species have established populations that spread far and wide, leaving environmental havoc in their wake. We humans, too, have multiplied and spread far from our point of origin, radically changing our environment in the process. As you explore population ecology in this chapter, you'll also learn about trends in human population growth and other applications of this area of ecological research.

An Overview of Population Ecology

Ecologists usually define a **population** as a group of individuals of a single species that occupy the same general area at the same time. These individuals rely on the same resources, are influenced by the same environmental factors, and are likely to interact and breed with one another. For example, the red lionfish that live in the vicinity of a specific reef are a population.

Population ecology is concerned with changes in population size and the factors that regulate populations over time. A population ecologist might describe a population in terms of its size (number of individuals), age structure (proportion of individuals of different ages), or density (number of individuals per unit area or volume). Population ecologists also study population dynamics, the interactions between biotic and abiotic factors that cause variation in population size. One important aspect of population dynamics—and a major topic for this chapter—is population growth.

Population ecology plays a key role in applied research. For example, it provides critical information for conservation and restoration projects (Figure 1). Population ecology is used to develop sustainable fisheries and to manage wildlife populations. Studying the population ecology of pests provides insight into controlling how they spread.

Population ecologists also study human population growth, one of the most critical environmental issues of our time.

Let's consider what a snapshot of a population might look like. The first question is, Which individuals are included in this population? A population's geographic boundaries may be natural, as with lionfish inhabiting a particular coral reef. But ecologists often define a population's boundaries in more arbitrary ways that fit their research questions. For example, an ecologist studying the contribution of asexual reproduction to the population growth of sea anemones might define a population as all the anemones of one species in a particular tide pool. Another researcher studying the effects of hunting on deer might define a population as all the deer within a particular state. Yet another researcher, attempting to understand the spread of HIV/AIDS, might study the HIV infection rate of the human population in one nation or throughout the world.

▼ Figure 1 **Ecologists getting up close and personal with members of the populations they study.**

(b) A researcher collects data on a puffin for a project to restore nesting colonies of the small seabird in the Gulf of Maine.

(a) After sedating a black bear in La Mauricie National Park, Quebec, Canada, a biologist attaches a radio collar to track its movements.

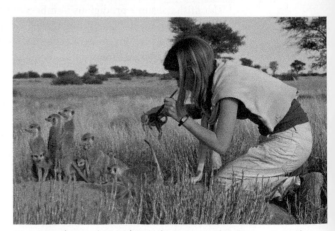

(c) A researcher marks meerkats in the Kuruman River Reserve in Northern Cape, South Africa.

Population Density

Our snapshot of a population would include **population density**, the number of individuals of a species per unit area or volume of the habitat: the number of largemouth bass per cubic kilometer (km^3) of a lake, for example, or the number of oak trees per square kilometer (km^2) in a forest, or the number of nematodes per cubic meter (m^3) in the forest's soil. In rare cases, an ecologist can actually count all the individuals within the boundaries of the population. For example, we could count the total number of oak trees (say, 200) in a forest covering 50 km^2 (about 19 square miles). The population density would be the total number of trees divided by the area, or 4 trees per square kilometer (4/km^2).

In most cases, however, it is impractical or impossible to count all individuals in a population. Instead, ecologists use a variety of sampling techniques to estimate population density. For example, they might estimate the density of alligators in the Florida Everglades based on a count of individuals in a few sample plots of 1 km^2 each. Generally speaking, the larger the number and size of sample plots, the more accurate the estimates. Population densities may also be estimated by indicators such as number of bird nests or rodent burrows **(Figure 2)** rather than by actual counts of organisms.

Keep in mind that population density is not a constant number. It changes when individuals are born or die and when new individuals enter the population (immigration) or leave it (emigration).

Population Age Structure

The **age structure** of a population—the distribution of individuals in different age-groups—reveals information that is not apparent from population density. For instance, age structure can provide insight into the history of a population's survival or reproductive success and how it relates to environmental factors. **Figure 3** shows the age structure of males in a population of cactus finches on the Galápagos Islands in 1987. Four-year-old birds, born in 1983, made up almost half the population, while there were not any 2- or 3-year-olds. Why was there such dramatic variation? For their food, cactus finches depend on plants, which in turn depend on rainfall. The 1983 baby boom resulted from unusually wet weather that produced abundant plant growth and food for the finches. Severe droughts in 1984 and 1985 limited the food supply, preventing reproduction and causing many deaths. As we'll see later in this chapter, age structure is also a useful tool for predicting future changes in a population. ☑

▼ **Figure 2 An indirect census of a prairie dog population.** We could get a rough estimate of the number of prairie dogs in this colony in Saskatchewan, Canada, by counting the number of burrows constructed by the rodents and then multiplying by the number of animals that use a typical burrow.

▼ **Figure 3 Age structure for the males in a population of large cactus finches (inset) on one of the Galápagos Islands in 1987.**

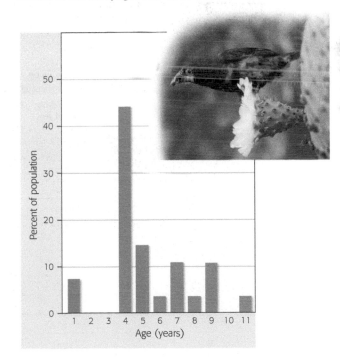

Life Tables and Survivorship Curves

Life tables track survivorship, the chance of an individual in a given population surviving to various ages. The life insurance industry uses life tables to predict how long, on average, a person of a given age will live. Starting with a population of 100,000 people, **Table 1** shows the number of people who are expected to be alive at the beginning of each age interval, based on death rates in 2008. For example, 93,999 out of 100,000 people are expected to live to age 50. Their chance of surviving to age 60, shown in the last column of the same row, is 0.94; 94% of 50-year-olds will reach the age of 60. The chance of 80-year-olds surviving to age 90, however, is only 0.402. Population ecologists have adopted this technique and constructed life tables to help them understand the structure and dynamics of various plant and animal species. By identifying the most vulnerable stage of the life cycle, life table data may also help conservationists develop effective measures to protect species whose populations are declining.

Ecologists represent life table data graphically in a **survivorship curve**, a plot of the number of individuals still alive at each age in the maximum life span (**Figure 4**). By using a percentage scale instead of actual ages on the *x*-axis, we can compare species with widely varying life spans, such as humans and squirrels, on the same graph. The curve for the human population (red) shows that most people survive to the older age intervals. Ecologists refer to the shape of this curve as

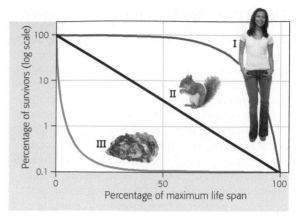

▲ Figure 4 **Three idealized types of survivorship curves.**

Type I survivorship. Species that exhibit a Type I curve—humans and many other large mammals—usually produce few offspring but give them good care, increasing the likelihood that they will survive to maturity.

In contrast, a Type III curve (blue) indicates low survivorship for the very young, followed by a period when survivorship is high for those few individuals who live to a certain age. Species with this type of survivorship curve usually produce very large numbers of offspring but provide little or no care for them. Some species of fish, for example, produce millions of eggs at a time, but most of these offspring die as larvae from predation or other causes. Many invertebrates, including oysters, also have Type III survivorship curves.

A Type II curve (black) is intermediate, with survivorship constant over the life span. That is, individuals are no more vulnerable at one stage of the life cycle than another. This type of survivorship has been observed in some invertebrates, lizards, and rodents. ☑

Evolution Life History Traits as Adaptations

A population's pattern of survivorship is an important feature of its **life history**, the set of traits that affect an organism's schedule of reproduction and survival. Some key life history traits are the age at first reproduction, the frequency of reproduction, the number of offspring, and the amount of parental care given. As you might expect from the different types of survivorship curves, life history traits vary among organisms. Let's take a closer look at how natural selection shapes these traits.

As you may recall, reproductive success is key to evolutionary success. Accordingly,

Table 1	Life Table for the U.S. Population in 2008		
	Number Living at Start of Age Interval	**Number Dying During Interval**	**Chance of Surviving Interval**
Age Interval	(*N*)	(*D*)	$1-(D/N)$
0–10	100,000	833	0.992
10–20	99,167	363	0.996
20–30	98,804	941	0.990
30–40	97,863	1,224	0.987
40–50	96,639	2,640	0.973
50–60	93,999	5,643	0.940
60–70	88,356	11,203	0.873
70–80	77,153	21,591	0.720
80–90	55,562	33,215	0.402
90+	22,347	22,347	0.000

you may wonder why all organisms don't simply produce a large number of offspring. One reason is that reproduction is expensive in terms of time, energy, and nutrients—resources that are available in limited amounts. An organism that gives birth to a large number of offspring will not be able to provide a great deal of parental care. Consequently, the combination of life history traits represents trade-offs that balance the demands of reproduction and survival. In other words, life history traits, like anatomical features, are shaped by evolutionary adaptation.

Because selective pressures vary, life histories are very diverse. Nevertheless, ecologists have observed some patterns that are useful for understanding how natural selection influences life history characteristics.

One life history pattern is typified by small-bodied, short-lived species (for example, insects and small rodents) that develop and reach sexual maturity rapidly, have a large number of offspring, and offer little or no parental care. In plants, "parental care" is measured by the amount of nutritional material stocked in each seed. Many small, non-woody plants (dandelions, for example) produce thousands of tiny seeds. Such organisms have an **opportunistic life history**, one that enables the plant or animal to take immediate advantage of favorable conditions. In general, populations with this life history pattern exhibit a Type III survivorship curve.

In contrast, some organisms have an **equilibrial life history**, a pattern of developing and reaching sexual maturity slowly and producing a few well-cared-for offspring. Organisms that have an equilibrial life history are typically larger-bodied, longer-lived species (for example, bears and elephants). Populations with this life history pattern exhibit a Type I survivorship curve. Plants with comparable life history traits include certain trees. For example, coconut palms produce relatively few seeds, but those seeds are well stocked with nutrient-rich material. **Table 2** compares key traits of opportunistic and equilibrial life history patterns.

What accounts for the differences in life history patterns? Some ecologists hypothesize that the potential survival rate of the offspring and the likelihood that the adult will live to reproduce again are the critical factors. In a harsh, unpredictable environment, an adult may have just one good shot at reproduction, so it may be an advantage to invest in quantity rather than quality. On the other hand, in an environment where favorable conditions are more dependable, an adult is more likely to survive to reproduce again. Seeds are more likely to fall on fertile ground, and newly emerged animals are more likely to survive to adulthood. In that case, it may be more advantageous for the adult to invest its energy in producing a few well-cared-for offspring at a time.

Of course, there is much more diversity in life history patterns than the two extremes described here. Nevertheless, the contrasting patterns are useful for understanding the interactions between life history traits and our next topic, population growth. ✓

Dandelions have an opportunistic life history.

Elephants have an equilibrial life history.

Table 2	Some Life History Characteristics of Opportunistic and Equilibrial Populations	
Characteristic	**Opportunistic Populations (such as many wildflowers)**	**Equilibrial Populations (such as many large mammals)**
Climate	Relatively unpredictable	Relatively predictable
Maturation time	Short	Long
Life span	Short	Long
Death rate	Often high	Usually low
Number of offspring per reproductive episode	Many	Few
Number of reproductions per lifetime	Usually one	Often several
Timing of first reproduction	Early in life	Later in life
Size of offspring or eggs	Small	Large
Parental care	Little or none	Often extensive

Population Growth Models

Population size fluctuates as new individuals are born or move into an area and others die or move out of it. Some populations—for example, trees in a mature forest—are relatively constant over time. Other populations change rapidly, even explosively. Consider a single bacterium that divides every 20 minutes. There would be two bacteria after 20 minutes, four after 40 minutes, eight after 60 minutes, and so on. In just 12 hours, the population would approach 70 billion cells. If reproduction continued at this rate for a day and a half—a mere 36 hours—there would be enough bacteria to form a layer a foot deep over the entire Earth! Population ecologists use idealized models to investigate how the size of a particular population may change over time under different conditions. We'll describe two basic mathematical models that illustrate fundamental concepts of population growth.

If environmental resources were unlimited, a single pair of elephants would give rise to a population of 19 million in 750 years.

The Exponential Population Growth Model: The Ideal of an Unlimited Environment

The first model, known as exponential growth, works like compound interest on a savings account: The principal (population size) grows faster with each interest payment (the individuals added to the population). **Exponential population growth** describes the expansion of a population in an ideal, unlimited environment. In this model, the population size of each new generation is calculated by multiplying the current population size by a constant factor that represents the birth rate minus the death rate. Let's look at how such a population grows. In **Figure 5**, we begin with a population of 20 rabbits, indicated on the *y*-axis. Each month, there are more rabbit births than deaths; as a result, the population size increases each month.

Notice in Figure 5 that each increase is larger than the previous one. In other words, the larger the population, the faster it grows. The increasing speed of population growth produces a J-shaped curve that is typical of exponential growth. The slope of the curve shows how rapidly the population is growing. At the outset, when the population is small, the curve is almost flat: Over the first 4 months, the population increases by a total of only 37 individuals, an average of 9.25 births per month. By the end of 7 months, the growth rate has increased to an average of 15 births per month. The largest increase is seen in the period from 10 to 12 months, when an average of 85 rabbits are born each month.

Exponential population growth is common in certain situations. For example, a disturbance such as a fire, flood, hurricane, drought, or cold snap may suddenly reduce the size of a population. Organisms that have opportunistic life history patterns can rapidly take advantage of the lack of competition and quickly recolonize the habitat by exponential population growth. Human activity can also be a major cause of disturbance, and plants and animals with opportunistic life history traits commonly occupy road cuts, freshly cleared fields and woodlots, and poorly maintained lawns. However, no natural environment can sustain exponential growth indefinitely. ☑

▼ **Figure 5 Exponential growth of a rabbit population.**

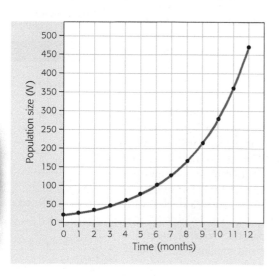

☑ CHECKPOINT

Why does the exponential model of population growth produce a curve shaped like a J?

Answer: Population growth accelerates as population size increases.

The Logistic Population Growth Model: The Reality of a Limited Environment

Most natural environments do not have an unlimited supply of the resources needed to sustain population growth. Environmental factors that restrict population growth are called **limiting factors**. Limiting factors ultimately control the number of individuals that can occupy a habitat. Ecologists define **carrying capacity** as the maximum population size that a particular environment can sustain. In **logistic population growth**, the growth rate decreases as the population size approaches carrying capacity. When the population is at carrying capacity, the growth rate is zero.

You can see the effect of limiting factors in the graph in **Figure 6**, which shows the growth of a population of fur seals on St. Paul Island, off the coast of Alaska. (For simplicity, only the mated bulls were counted. Each has a harem of females, as shown in the photograph.) Before 1925, the seal population on the island remained low—between 1,000 and 4,500 mated bulls—because of uncontrolled hunting. After hunting was controlled, the population increased rapidly until about 1935, when it began to level off and started fluctuating around a population size of about 10,000 bull seals—the carrying capacity for St. Paul Island. In this instance, the main limiting factor was the amount of space suitable for breeding territories.

The carrying capacity for a population varies, depending on the species and the resources available in the habitat. For example, carrying capacity might be considerably less than 10,000 for a fur seal population on a smaller island with fewer breeding sites. Even in one location, it is not a fixed number. Organisms interact with other organisms in their communities, including predators, pathogens, and food sources, and these interactions may affect carrying capacity. Changes in abiotic factors may also increase or decrease carrying capacity. In any case, the concept of carrying capacity expresses an essential fact of nature: Resources are finite.

Ecologists hypothesize that selection for organisms exhibiting equilibrial life history patterns occurs in environments where the population size is at or near carrying capacity. Because competition for resources is keen under these circumstances, organisms gain an advantage by allocating energy to their own survival and to the survival of their descendants.

Figure 7 compares logistic growth (blue) with exponential growth (red). As you can see, the logistic curve is J-shaped at first, but gradually levels off to resemble an S shape as carrying capacity is reached. Both the logistic model and the exponential model of population growth are theoretical ideals. No natural population fits either one perfectly. However, these models are useful starting points for studying population growth. Ecologists use them to predict how populations will grow in certain environments and as a basis for constructing more complex models. ✓

▼ Figure 6 **Logistic growth of a seal population.**

✓ **CHECKPOINT**

What happens when a population reaches its carrying capacity?

Answer: Enough resources are available to sustain that population size, but the population does not continue to increase.

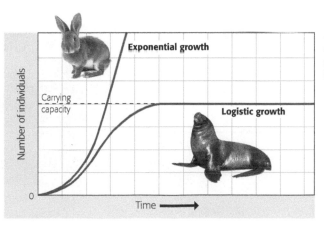

◄ Figure 7
Comparison of exponential and logistic growth.

Regulation of Population Growth

Now let's take a closer look at how population growth is regulated in nature. What stops a population from continuing to increase after reaching carrying capacity?

Density-Dependent Factors

Several **density-dependent factors**—limiting factors whose intensity is related to population density—can limit growth in natural populations. The most obvious is **intraspecific competition**, the competition between individuals of the same species for the same limited resources. As a limited food supply is divided among more and more

individuals, birth rates may decline as individuals have less energy available for reproduction. Density-dependent factors may also depress a population's growth by increasing the death rate. For example, in a population of song sparrows, both factors reduced the number of offspring that survived and left the nest **(Figure 8a)**. As the number of competitors for food increased, female song sparrows laid fewer eggs. In addition, the death rate of eggs and nestlings increased with increasing population density.

Plants that grow close together may experience an increased death rate as intraspecific competition for resources increases. And those that do survive will produce fewer flowers, fruits, and seeds than uncrowded individuals. After seeds sprout, gardeners often pull out some of the seedlings to allow sufficient resources for the remaining plants. Intraspecific competition is also the reason that plants purchased from a nursery come with instructions to space the plants a certain distance apart.

A limited resource may be something other than food or nutrients. Like a game of musical chairs, the number of safe hiding places may limit a prey population by exposing some individuals to a greater risk of predation. For example, young kelp perch hide from predators in "forests" of the large seaweed known as kelp. In the experiment shown in **Figure 8b**, the proportion of perch eaten by a predator increased with increasing perch density. In many animals that defend a territory, the availability of space may limit reproduction. For instance, the number of nesting sites on rocky islands may limit the population size of oceanic birds such as gannets, which maintain breeding territories **(Figure 9)**.

In addition to competition for resources, other factors may cause density-dependent deaths in a population. For example, the death rate may climb as a result of increased disease transmission under crowded conditions or the accumulation of toxic waste products.

▼ Figure 8 **Density-dependent regulation of population growth.**

Data from P. Arcese et al., Stability, Regulation, and the Determination of Abundance in an Insular Song Sparrow Population. *Ecology* 73: 805–882 (1992).

(a) Declining reproductive success of song sparrows (inset) with increasing population density.

Data from T. W. Anderson, Predator Responses, Prey Refuges, and Density-Dependent Death of a Marine Fish, *Ecology* 82: 245–257 (2001).

(b) Increasing death rate of kelp perch (inset) with increasing population density.

▼ Figure 9 **Space as a limiting resource in a population of gannets.**

Density-Independent Factors

In many natural populations, abiotic factors such as weather may limit or reduce population size well before other limiting factors become important. A population-limiting factor whose intensity is unrelated to population density is called a **density-independent factor**. If we look at the growth curve of such a population, we see something like exponential growth followed by a rapid decline rather than a leveling off. **Figure 10** shows this effect for a population of aphids, insects that feed on the sugary sap of plants. These and many other insects undergo virtually exponential growth in the spring and then rapidly die off when the weather turns hot and dry in the summer. A few individuals may remain, allowing population growth to resume if favorable conditions return. In some populations of insects—many mosquitoes and grasshoppers, for instance—the adults die off entirely, leaving behind eggs that will initiate population growth the following year. In addition to seasonal changes in the weather, environmental disturbances, such as fire, floods, and storms, can affect a population's size regardless of its density.

Over the long term, most populations are probably regulated by a complex interaction of density-dependent and density-independent factors. Although some populations remain fairly stable in size and are presumably close to a carrying capacity that is determined by biotic factors such as competition or predation, most populations for which we have long-term data do fluctuate.

Population Cycles

Some populations of insects, birds, and mammals undergo dramatic fluctuations in density with remarkable regularity. "Booms" characterized by rapid exponential growth are followed by "busts," during which the population falls back to a minimal level. Lemmings, small rodents that live in the tundra, are a striking example. In lemming populations, boom-and-bust growth cycles occur every three to four years. Some researchers hypothesize that natural changes in the lemmings' food supply may be the underlying cause. Another hypothesis is that stress from crowding during the "boom" triggers hormonal changes that may cause the "bust" by reducing birth rates.

Figure 11 illustrates another example—the cycles of the snowshoe hare and the lynx. The lynx is one of the main predators of the snowshoe hare in the far northern forests of Canada and Alaska. About every ten years, both hare and lynx populations show a rapid increase followed by a sharp decline. What causes these boom-and-bust cycles? Since ups and downs in the two populations seem to almost match each other on the graph, does this mean that changes in one directly affect the other? For the hare cycles, there are three main hypotheses. First, cycles may be caused by winter food shortages that result from overgrazing. Second, cycles may be due to predator-prey interactions. Many predators other than lynx, such as coyotes, foxes, and great-horned owls, eat hares, and together these predators might overexploit their prey. Third, cycles may be affected by a combination of food resource limitation and excessive predation. Recent field studies support the hypothesis that the ten-year cycles of the snowshoe hare are largely driven by excessive predation, but are also influenced by fluctuations in the hare's food supplies. Long-term studies are the key to unraveling the complex causes of such population cycles. ✔

▼ Figure 10 **Weather change as a density-independent factor limiting growth of an aphid population.**

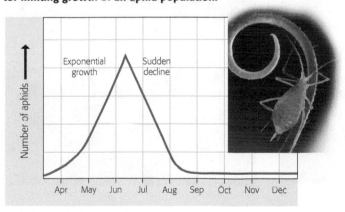

▼ Figure 11 **Population cycles of the snowshoe hare and the lynx.**

Applications of Population Ecology

To a great extent, we humans have converted Earth's natural ecosystems to ecosystems that produce goods and services for our own benefit. In some cases, we try to increase populations of organisms that we wish to harvest and decrease populations of organisms that we consider pests. Other efforts are aimed at saving populations that are perilously close to extinction. Principles of population ecology help guide us toward these various resource management goals.

☑ **CHECKPOINT**

What is a key factor in the recovery of red-cockaded woodpecker populations?

Answer: removal of understory vegetation by controlled burns

Conservation of Endangered Species

The U.S. Endangered Species Act defines an **endangered species** as one that is "in danger of extinction throughout all or a significant portion of its range." **Threatened species** are defined as those that are likely to become endangered in the foreseeable future. Endangered and threatened species are characterized by population sizes that are highly reduced or steadily declining. The challenge for conservationists is to determine the circumstances that threaten a species with extinction and try to remedy the situation.

The red-cockaded woodpecker was one of the first species to be listed as endangered (**Figure 12**). The bird requires longleaf pine forests, where it drills its nest holes in mature, living pine trees. Originally found throughout the southeastern United States, the woodpeckers declined in number as suitable habitats were lost to logging and agriculture. Moreover, we have altered the composition of many of the remaining forests by suppressing the fires that are a natural occurrence in these ecosystems. Research revealed that breeding birds tend to abandon nests when vegetation among the pines is thick and higher than about 4.5 m (15 feet). Apparently, the birds require a clear flight path between their home trees and the neighboring feeding grounds. Armed with an understanding of the factors that regulate population growth of this species, wildlife managers protected critical habitat and began a maintenance program that included controlled fires to reduce forest undergrowth. As a result of such measures, populations of red-cockaded woodpeckers are beginning to recover. ☑

Sustainable Resource Management

A goal of wildlife managers, fishery biologists, and foresters is to gather the largest possible harvest while sustaining the productivity of the resource for future harvests. This means maintaining a high population growth rate to replenish the population. According to the logistic growth model, the fastest growth rate occurs when the population size is at roughly half the carrying capacity of the habitat. Theoretically, a resource manager should achieve the best results by harvesting the population down to this level. However, the logistic model assumes that growth rate and carrying capacity

▼ Figure 12 **The habitat of the red-cockaded woodpecker.**

A red-cockaded woodpecker perches at the entrance to its nest in a longleaf pine tree.

High, dense undergrowth impedes the woodpeckers' access to feeding grounds.

Low undergrowth offers birds a clear flight path between nest sites and feeding grounds.

are stable over time. Calculations based on these assumptions, which are not realistic for some populations, may lead to unsustainably high harvest levels that ultimately deplete the resource. In addition, human economic and political pressures often outweigh ecological concerns, and scientific information is frequently insufficient.

Fish, the only wild animals still hunted on a large scale, are particularly vulnerable to overharvesting. For example, in the northern Atlantic cod fishery, estimates of cod stocks were too high, and the practice of discarding young cod (not of legal size) at sea caused a higher death rate than was predicted. The fishery collapsed in 1992 and has not recovered (**Figure 13**).

Until the 1970s, marine fisheries concentrated on species such as cod that inhabit the continental shelves. As these resources dwindled, attention turned to deeper waters, most commonly the continental slopes below 600 m. In many of these new locations, however, catches are initially high but then quickly fall off as stocks are depleted. Deeper waters are colder, and food is relatively scarce. Fishes that are adapted to this environment, such as Chilean sea bass and orange roughy, typically grow more slowly, take longer to reach maturity, and

The saying "There are plenty of fish in the sea" could become meaningless if overharvesting continues.

have a lower reproductive rate than continental shelf species. Sustainable catch rates can't be estimated without knowing these essential life history traits for the target species. In addition, knowledge of population ecology alone is not sufficient; sustainable fisheries also require knowledge of community and ecosystem characteristics. ☑

☑ CHECKPOINT
Why do managers try to maintain populations of fish and game species at about half their carrying capacity?

Answer: to prevent overharvesting yet maintain lower population levels so that growth rate is high

▼ Figure 13 **The collapse of the northern cod fishery off Newfoundland.** As of 2013, the fishery had not recovered.

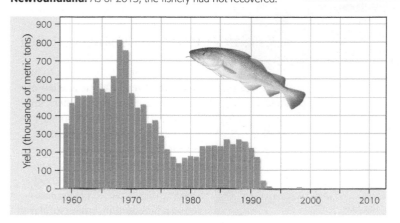

Invasive Species

Like the lionfish featured in the Biology and Society section, organisms that are introduced into non-native habitats can have a devastating effect on the ecosystem. An **invasive species** is a non-native species that has spread far beyond its original point of introduction and causes environmental or economic damage by colonizing and dominating suitable habitats. In the United States alone, there are hundreds of invasive species, including plants, mammals, birds, fishes, arthropods, and molluscs. Worldwide, there are thousands more. Regardless of where you live, an invasive plant or animal is probably living nearby. Invasive species are a leading cause of local extinctions. And the economic costs of invasive species are enormous—an estimated $137 billion a year in the United States.

Not every organism that is introduced to a new habitat is successful, and not every species that survives in its new habitat becomes invasive. There is no single explanation for why any non-native species turns into a damaging pest, but invasive species typically exhibit an opportunistic life history pattern. A female lionfish, for

example, is sexually mature at a year old and can produce 2 million eggs per year.

The life history traits of cheatgrass (*Bromus tectorum*, **Figure 14**), an invasive plant of the arid western United States, have enabled its spectacular success. Its seeds were accidentally carried into the United States with grain from Asia and then spread by livestock. Cheatgrass covers millions of acres of rangeland that was formerly dominated by native grasses and sagebrush, and it claims an additional area the size of Rhode Island every year. Cheatgrass seeds sprout during fall rains, and the roots continue to grow underground through the winter. Already established when the warm spring weather arrives, dense clumps of cheatgrass deprive native species and crops of soil moisture and mineral nutrients. It also produces seeds earlier and in greater abundance than its competitors.

▼ Figure 14 **Cheatgrass, an invasive plant.**

After cheatgrass seeds mature in early summer, the plants become extremely dry and flammable, creating abundant fuel that is easily ignited by lightning or a stray spark. Cheatgrass fires are more intense and occur much more frequently than the fires that native plants have evolved to tolerate. After a few fire cycles, the native plants are gone, robbing more than 150 species of birds and mammals of the food and shelter they derive from sagebrush. Global climate change is also hastening the transition of rangeland into fields of cheatgrass. Studies have shown that cheatgrass responds to increased CO_2 levels by growing faster and accumulating more tissue, which in turn becomes more fuel for the fires that extend its domain.

For a non-native organism to become invasive, the biotic and abiotic factors of the new environment must be compatible with the organism's needs and tolerances. For example, Burmese pythons set loose in South Florida—either accidently released by damaging storms or deliberately freed by disenchanted pet owners—found a hot, humid climate similar to their native area. Prey such as birds, mammals, reptiles, and amphibians are readily available, especially in the Everglades. As a result, South Florida is now home to a burgeoning population of the giant reptiles (**Figure 15**). Burmese pythons released in a less favorable environment might survive for a short time, but would not be able to establish a population. ☑

▼ **Figure 15 A Burmese python.** This 9-foot-long snake was captured in Florida after devouring a pet cat.

Biological Control of Pests

The absence of biotic factors that limit population growth, such as pathogens, predators, or herbivores, may contribute to the success of invasive species. Accordingly, efforts to eliminate or control these troublesome organisms often focus on **biological control**, the intentional release of a natural enemy to attack a pest population. Agricultural researchers have long been interested in identifying potential biological agents to control insects, weeds, and other organisms that reduce crop yield.

Biological control has been effective in numerous instances, especially with invasive insects and plants. In one classic success story, beetles were brought in to combat St. John's wort, a perennial (long-lived) European weed that invaded the western United States. By the 1940s, St. John's wort (also known as Klamath weed) had overgrown millions of acres of rangeland and pasture, leaving few edible plants for grazing livestock. Researchers imported leaf beetles from the plant's native region that feed exclusively on St. John's wort. The shiny, pea-sized insects reduced the weed to less than 5% of its former abundance, restoring the land's value to ranchers.

One potential pitfall of biological control is the danger that an imported control agent may be as invasive as its target. One cautionary tale comes from introducing the mongoose (**Figure 16**) to control rats. Rats that originated in India and northern Asia were accidentally transported around the world and became invasive in many places. For sugarcane growers, rat infestation meant massive crop damage. Cane planters imported the small Indian mongoose, a fierce little carnivore, to deal with the problem. In time, mongooses were introduced to dozens of natural habitats, including all of the largest Caribbean and Hawaiian islands—and became invasive themselves. Mongooses are not picky eaters, and they have voracious appetites. On island after island, populations of reptiles, amphibians, and ground-nesting birds have declined or vanished as mongoose populations have grown and spread. They also prey on domestic poultry and ruin crops, costing millions of dollars a year. Clearly, rigorous research is needed to assess the safety and efficacy of potential biological control agents.

◄ **Figure 16 A small Indian mongoose.**

Biological Invasions THE PROCESS OF SCIENCE

Can Biological Control Defeat Kudzu?

Let's take a brief look at the search for a biological agent to control kudzu, an invasive vine known as "the plant that ate the South" **(Figure 17)**. In the 1930s, the U.S. Department of Agriculture distributed plantings of this Asian import to help control erosion along road cuts and irrigation canals. Today, kudzu covers an estimated 31,000 square kilometers (roughly the combined area of Maryland and Delaware). With its formidable growth rate of up to a foot per day, kudzu climbs over forest trees and blankets the ground in dense greenery. The shoots die back in winter but quickly regenerate from the roots in the spring. Cold winters have limited its acquisition of new territory—the roots don't survive being frozen. However, as global climate change brings warmer winters, kudzu is advancing farther north.

Unlike many invasive species, kudzu does have natural enemies in the United States, but it easily outgrows the damage they inflict. Researchers are investigating the possibility that one of these native pathogens or insects could be manipulated to provide effective control. Several possibilities have already been tested and discarded. For example, experiments showed that larvae of a species of moth have a prodigious appetite for kudzu. Further investigation, however, proved that the larvae actually preferred soybeans—an important crop species closely related to kudzu. At present, a fungal pathogen called *Myrothecium verrucaria* appears to be a promising candidate.

Researchers chose to test *M. verrucaria* because of **observations** that it causes severe disease in other weeds belonging to the same family as kudzu. Preliminary tests in a greenhouse, in controlled environment chambers, and in small outdoor plantings established that *M. verrucaria* kills kudzu when a high enough concentration of *M. verrucaria* spores is sprayed on the plants along with a "wetting agent" (a soap-like substance that reduces the surface tension of water). These findings led researchers to ask the **question**, Will *M. verrucaria* treatment work on an established stand of kudzu in a natural setting? Their **hypothesis** was that the *M. verrucaria* treatment that was most effective in the small outdoor plantings would also be most effective

▲ Figure 17 **Kudzu (*Pueraria lobata*).**

in a natural setting. Their **prediction** was that the treatment that sprayed the highest concentration of spores in combination with a wetting agent would produce the highest death rate. The **results** of this field experiment, which are shown in **Figure 18**, support the hypothesis. However, these experiments are only the initial steps toward biological control of kudzu. A great deal of research is needed to ensure that the method is safe, effective, and practical.

▼ Figure 18 **Biological control of a natural infestation of kudzu with the fungus *Myrothecium verrucaria*.**

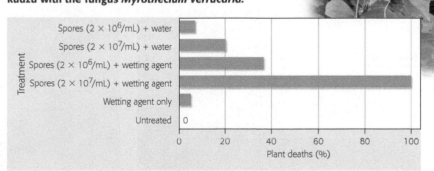

Integrated Pest Management

In contrast to enterprises such as fisheries, which harvest resources from natural ecosystems, agricultural operations create their own highly managed ecosystems. A typical crop population consists of genetically similar individuals (a monoculture) planted in close proximity to each other—a banquet laid out for the many plant-eating animals and pathogenic bacteria, viruses, and fungi in the community. The tilled, fertile ground nurtures weeds as well as crops. Thus, farmers wage an eternal war against pests that compete with their crop for soil minerals, water, and light; that siphon nutrients from the growing plants; or that consume their leaves, roots, fruits, or seeds. At home, you may be engaged in combat against pests on a smaller scale as you attempt to eradicate the weeds, insects, fungi, and bacteria that attack your lawn and garden or the mosquitoes that make your summer evenings miserable.

Like invasive species, most crop pests have an opportunistic life history pattern that enables them to rapidly take advantage of a favorable habitat. The history of agriculture abounds with examples of devastating pest outbreaks. For example, the boll weevil (**Figure 19**) is an insect that feeds on cotton plants both as larvae and as adults. Its unstoppable spread across the southern United States in the early 1900s severely damaged local economies and had a lasting impact on the region. The folklore of the invasion includes the song "The Boll Weevil Blues," which has been recorded by many artists, including the White Stripes. Viruses, fungi, bacteria, nematodes, and other plant-eating insects can cause massive damage as well.

When synthetic herbicides and insecticides such as DDT were developed in the 1940s, they quickly became the method of choice in agriculture. However, chemical solutions to pest problems bring numerous problems of their own. These chemicals are pollutants that can be carried great distances by air or water currents. In addition, natural selection may result in populations that are not affected by a pesticide. Furthermore, most insecticides kill both the pest and its natural predators. Because prey species often have a higher reproductive rate than predators, pest populations rapidly rebound before their predators can reproduce. There may be other unintended damage as well, such as killing pollinators that are essential for both agricultural and natural ecosystems.

Integrated pest management (IPM) uses a combination of biological, chemical, and cultural methods for sustainable control of agricultural pests. Researchers are also investigating IPM approaches to invasive species. IPM relies on knowledge of the population ecology of the pest and its associated predators and parasites, as well as plant growth dynamics. In contrast to traditional methods of pest control, IPM advocates tolerating a low level of pests rather than attempting total eradication. Thus, many pest control measures are aimed at lowering the habitat's carrying capacity for the pest population by using pest-resistant varieties of crops, mixed-species plantings, and crop rotation to deprive the pest of a dependable food source. Biological control is also used when possible. For example, many gardeners release ladybird beetles to control aphid infestations (**Figure 20**). Pesticides are applied when necessary, but adherence to the principles of IPM prevents the overuse of chemicals. ☑

☑ CHECKPOINT

Why is integrated pest management considered a more sustainable method of pest control than the use of chemicals alone?

Answer: Use of pesticides may result in resistant pest populations, which makes the pesticides less effective. Also, pesticide use is unsustainable in the long run because of problems with pollution.

▲ Figure 19 **A boll weevil on a damaged boll (seed pod) of a cotton plant.**

▲ Figure 20 **Ladybird beetles feeding on aphids.** Each of these voracious predators can eat as many as 50 aphids per day.

Human Population Growth

The History of Human Population Growth

Now that we have examined the regulation of population growth in other organisms, what about our own species? Let's begin by looking at the history of the human population and then consider some current and future trends in population growth.

In the few seconds it takes you to read this sentence, approximately 21 babies will be born somewhere in the world and 9 people will die. An imbalance between births and deaths is the cause of population growth (or decline), and as the line graph in **Figure 21** shows, the human population is expected to continue increasing for at least the next several decades. The bar graph in Figure 21 tells a different part of the story. The number of people added to the population each year has been declining since the 1980s. How do we explain these patterns of human population growth?

Let's begin with the rise in world population from approximately 480 million people in 1500 to the current population of more than 7 billion. In the exponential population growth model introduced earlier in this chapter, we assumed that the net rate of increase (birth rate minus death rate) was constant—births and deaths were roughly equal. As a result, population growth depended only on the size of the existing population. Throughout most of human history, this assumption held true. Although parents had many children, the death rate was also high, resulting in a rate of increase

only slightly higher than 0. Consequently, human population growth was initially very slow. (If we extended the x-axis of Figure 21 back in time to year 1, when the population was roughly 300 million, the line would be almost flat for 1,500 years.) The 1 billion mark was not reached until the early 1800s. As economic development in Europe and the United States led to advances in nutrition and sanitation, and later, medical care, people took control of their population's growth rate. At first, the death rate decreased while the birth rate remained the same. The net rate of increase rose, and population growth began to pick up steam by the beginning of the 1900s. By midcentury, improvements in nutrition, sanitation, and health care had spread to the developing world, spurring growth at a breakneck pace as birth rates far outstripped death rates.

As the world population skyrocketed from 2 billion in 1927 to 3 billion just 33 years later, some scientists became alarmed. They feared that Earth's carrying capacity would be reached and that density-dependent factors would maintain that population size through human suffering and death. But the overall growth rate peaked in 1962. In the more developed nations, advanced medical care continued to improve survivorship, but effective contraceptives held down the birth rate. As a result, the overall growth rate of the world's population began a downward trend as the difference between birth rate and death rate decreased. In the most developed nations, the overall rate of increase is near zero **(Table 3)**. In the developing world, on the other hand, death rates have dropped, but high birth rates persist. As a result, these populations are growing rapidly—of the 77.7 million people added to the world in 2012, nearly 74 million were in developing nations. Thus, the world population continues to increase. ☑

Counting one person per second, it would take more than 225 years to count all the people alive today.

▲ **Figure 21 Five centuries of human population growth, projected to 2050.**

Table 3	Population Trends in 2012		
Population	**Birth Rate per 1,000**	**Death Rate per 1,000**	**Growth Rate (%)**
World	1	7.9	1.1
More developed countries	11.2	10.1	0.3
Less developed countries	20.8	7.4	1.3

Age Structures

Age structures, which were introduced at the beginning of this chapter, are helpful for predicting a population's future growth. **Figure 22** shows the estimated and projected age structures of Mexico's population in 1989, 2012, and 2035. In these diagrams, the area to the left of each vertical line represents the number of males in each age-group; females are represented on the right side of the line. The three different colors represent the portion of the population in their prereproductive years (0–14), prime reproductive years (15–44), and postreproductive years (45 and older). Within each of these broader groups, each horizontal bar represents the population in a 5-year age-group.

In 1989, each age-group was larger than the one above it, indicating a high birth rate. The pyramidal shape of this age structure is typical of a population that is growing rapidly. In 2012, the population's growth rate was lower; notice that the three youngest (bottommost) age-groups are roughly the same size. However, the population continues to be affected by its earlier expansion. This situation, which results from the increased proportion of women of childbearing age in the population, is known as **population momentum**. Girls who were 0–14 years old in the 1989 age structure (outlined in pink) were in their reproductive prime in 2012, and girls who were 0–14 years old in 2012 (outlined in blue) will carry the legacy of rapid growth forward to 2035. Putting the brakes on a rapidly expanding population is like stopping a freight train; the actual event takes place long after the decision to do it was made. Even when fertility—the number of live births over a woman's lifetime—is reduced to replacement rate (an average of two children per female), the total population size will continue to increase for several decades. Thus, the percentage of individuals under the age of 15 gives a rough idea of future growth. In less developed countries, about 28% of the population is in this age-group. In contrast, 16.5% of the population of more developed nations is under the age of 15. Population momentum also explains why the total population size worldwide (line graph in Figure 21) continues to increase even though fewer people are added to the population each year, as shown by the bar graph in Figure 21.

Age structure diagrams may also indicate social conditions. For instance, an expanding population has an increasing need for schools, employment, and infrastructure. A large elderly population requires that extensive resources be allotted to health care. Let's look at trends in the age structure of the United States from 1989 to 2035 **(Figure 23)**. The noticeable bulge in the 1989 population (yellow screen) corresponds to the "baby boom" that lasted for about two decades after World War II ended in 1945. The large number of children swelled school enrollments, prompting construction of new schools and creating a demand for teachers. On the other hand, graduates who were born near the end of the boom faced stiff competition for jobs. Because they make up such a large segment of the population, boomers have had an enormous influence on social,

▼ Figure 22 **Population momentum in Mexico.**

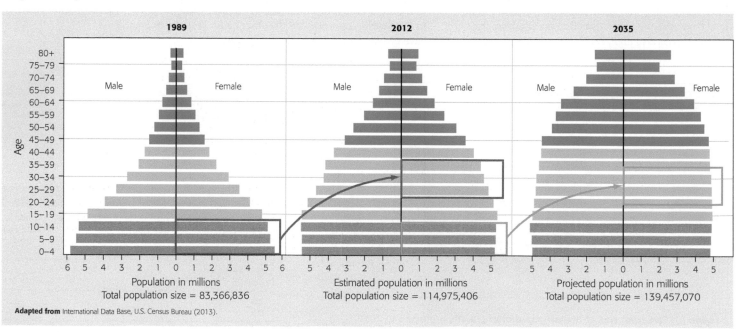

Adapted from International Data Base, U.S. Census Bureau (2013).

▼ **Figure 23 Age structures for the United States in 1989, 2012 (estimated), and 2035 (projected).**

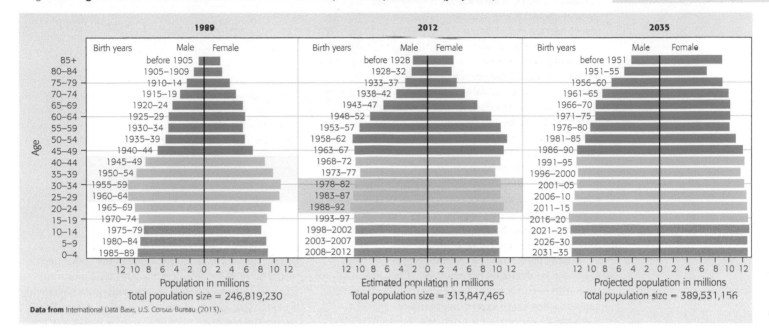

economic, and political trends. They also produced a boomlet of their own, seen in the 0–4 age-group in 1989 and the bump (pink screen) in the 2012 age structure.

Where are the baby boomers now? The leading edge has reached retirement age, which will place pressure on programs such as Medicare and Social Security. In 2012, 60% of the U.S. population was between 20 and 64, the ages most likely to be in the workforce, and 13.5% was over 65. In 2035, the percentages are projected to be 54 and 20, respectively. In part, the increase in the elderly population results from people living longer. The percentage of the population over 80, which was 2.7% in 1985, is projected to rise to nearly 6%—more than 23 million people—in 2035. ☑

Our Ecological Footprint

How large a human population can Earth support? Figure 21 shows that the world's population is increasing rapidly, though at a slower rate than it did in the last century. The rate of increase, as well as population momentum, indicates that the populations of most developing nations will continue to increase for the foreseeable future. The U.S. Census Bureau projects a global population of 8 billion within the next 10 years and 9.6 billion by 2050. But these numbers are only part of the story. Trillions of bacteria can live in a petri dish *if* they have

sufficient resources. Do we have sufficient resources to sustain 8 or 9 billion people?

To accommodate all the people expected to live on our planet in the coming decades and improve the diets of those who are currently malnourished or undernourished, world food production must increase dramatically. But agricultural lands are already under pressure. Overgrazing by the world's growing herds of livestock is turning vast areas of grassland into desert. Water use has risen sixfold over the past 70 years, causing rivers to run dry, water for irrigation to be depleted, and levels of groundwater to drop. Changes in precipitation patterns due to global warming are already causing food shortages in some regions of the world. And because so much open space will be needed to support the expanding human population, many other species are expected to become extinct.

The concept of an ecological footprint is one approach to understanding resource availability and usage. An **ecological footprint** is an estimate of the area of land and water required to provide the resources an individual or a nation consumes—for example, food, fuel, and housing—and to absorb the waste it generates, of which carbon emissions are a major component. Comparing our demand for resources with Earth's capacity to renew these resources, or **biocapacity**, gives us a broad view of the sustainability of human activities.

☑ **CHECKPOINT**

Why is the percentage of individuals under the age of 15 a good indication of future population growth?

Answer: These individuals have not yet entered their reproductive years. If they make up a large percentage of the population (a bottom-heavy age structure), future population growth will be high.

When the total area of ecologically productive land on Earth is divided by the global population, we each have a share of about 1.8 global hectares (1 hectare = 2.47 acres; a global hectare is a hectare with world-average ability to produce resources and absorb wastes). When used sustainably, resources such as crops, pastureland, forests, and fishing grounds can regenerate. But according to the World Wildlife Fund, in 2008 (the most recent year for which data are available), the average ecological footprint for the world's population was 2.7 global hectares—roughly 1.5 times the planet's biocapacity per person. By overshooting Earth's biocapacity, we are depleting our resources. The collapse of the northern cod fisheries (see Figure 13) illustrates what happens when usage exceeds regenerative capacity.

Figure 24 compares the ecological footprints of several countries to the world average footprint (pink line) and Earth's biocapacity (green line). Affluent nations such as the United States and Australia consume a disproportionate amount of resources (Figure 25). By this measure, the ecological impact of affluent nations is potentially as damaging as unrestrained population growth in the developing world. So the problem is not just overpopulation, but overconsumption. The

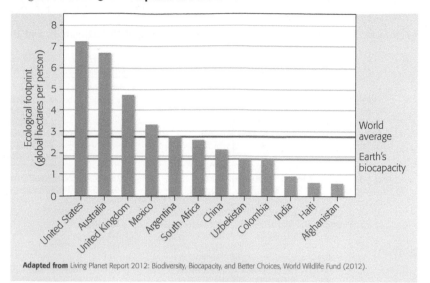

▼ Figure 24 **Ecological footprints of several countries.**

Adapted from Living Planet Report 2012: Biodiversity, Biocapacity, and Better Choices, World Wildlife Fund (2012).

world's richest countries, with 15% of the global population, account for 36% of humanity's total footprint. Some researchers estimate that providing everyone with the same standard of living as the United States would require the resources of more than four planet Earths.

To stay within the planet's regenerative capacity, all of humanity would have to live like an average citizen of Colombia or Uzbekistan.

If you would like to learn about your personal resource consumption, a number of online quizzes can provide a rough estimate of your ecological footprint. Like carbon footprint calculators, these tools are useful for learning how to reduce your environmental impact. ☑

The average American generates about 40 pounds of trash per week, almost three times as much as the average Colombian.

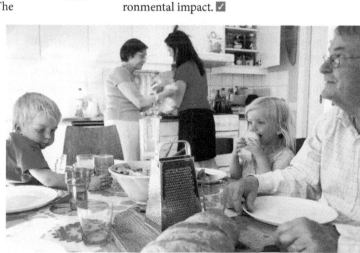

▲ Figure 25 **Mealtime in an Afghan (left) and an American household (right).** Notice the differences in consumer goods and in resources used for food preparation.

Biological Invasions EVOLUTION CONNECTION

Humans as an Invasive Species

The magnificent pronghorn antelope (*Antilocapra americana*) is the descendant of ancestors that roamed the open plains and shrub deserts of North America millions of years ago (Figure 26). With strides that cover 6 m (20 feet) or more at its top speed of 97 km/h (60 mph), it is easily the fastest mammal on the continent. The pronghorn's speed is more than a match for its major predator, the wolf, which typically takes adults that have been weakened by age or illness. What selection pressure promoted such extravagant speed? Ecologists hypothesize that the pronghorn's ancestors were running from the now-extinct American cheetah, a fleet-footed predator that bore some similarities to the more familiar African cheetah.

Cheetahs were not the only danger in the pronghorn's environment. During the Pleistocene epoch, which lasted from 1.8 million to 10,000 years ago, North America was also home to an intimidating list of other predators: lions, jaguars, saber-toothed cats with canines up to 7 inches long, and towering short-faced bears, which stood 11 feet tall and weighed three-quarters of a ton. There were plenty of potential prey for these fearsome predators, including massive ground sloths, bison with horns that spread 10 feet, elephant-like mammoths, a variety of horses and camels, and several species of pronghorns. Of all these species of large mammals, only *Antilocapra americana* remained at the end of the Pleistocene. The others went extinct during a relatively brief period of time that coincided with the spread of humans throughout North America. Although the cause of the extinctions has been hotly disputed, many scientists think that the human invasion, combined with climate change at the end of the last ice age, was responsible. Taken together, changes in the biotic and abiotic environments happened too rapidly for an evolutionary response by these large mammals.

The role of humans in the Pleistocene extinctions was merely a preview of things to come. The human population continues to increase, colonizing almost every corner of the globe. Like other invasive species, we change the environment of the other organisms that share our habitats. As the scope and speed of human-induced environmental changes increase, extinctions are occurring at an accelerating pace.

▼ Figure 26 **A pronghorn antelope racing across the North American plains.**

Chapter Review

■ SUMMARY OF KEY CONCEPTS

An Overview of Population Ecology

A population consists of all the members of a species living in the same place at the same time. Population ecology focuses on the factors that influence a population's size, density, age structure, and growth rate.

Population Density

Population density, the number of individuals of a species per unit area or volume, can be estimated by a variety of sampling techniques.

Population Age Structure

A graph showing the distribution of individuals in different age-groups often provides useful information about the population.

Life Tables and Survivorship Curves

A life table tracks the chance of an individual in a population surviving to various ages. Survivorship curves can be classified into three general types.

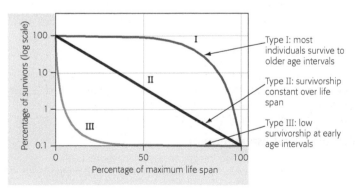

Evolution: Life History Traits as Adaptations

Life history traits are shaped by evolutionary adaptation. Most populations probably fall between the extreme opportunistic life histories (reach sexual maturity rapidly; produce many offspring; little or no parental care) of many insects and the equilibrial life histories (develop slowly and produce few, well-cared-for offspring) of many larger-bodied species.

Population Growth Models

The Exponential Population Growth Model: The Ideal of an Unlimited Environment

Exponential population growth is the accelerating increase that occurs when growth is unlimited. The exponential model predicts that the larger a population becomes, the faster it grows.

The Logistic Population Growth Model: The Reality of a Limited Environment

Logistic population growth occurs when growth is slowed by limiting factors. The logistic model predicts that a population's growth rate will be low when the population size is either small or large and highest when the population is at an intermediate level relative to the carrying capacity.

Regulation of Population Growth

Over the long term, most population growth is limited by a mixture of density-independent factors, which affect the same percentage of individuals regardless of population size, and density-dependent factors, which intensify as a population increases in density. Some populations have regular boom-and-bust cycles.

Applications of Population Ecology

Conservation of Endangered Species

Endangered and threatened species are characterized by very small population sizes. One approach to conservation is identifying and attempting to supply the critical combination of habitat factors needed by the population.

Sustainable Resource Management

Resource managers apply principles of population ecology to help determine sustainable harvesting practices.

Invasive Species

Invasive species are non-native organisms that spread far beyond their original point of introduction and cause environmental and economic damage. Typically, invasive species have an opportunistic life history pattern.

Biological Control of Pests

Biological control, the intentional release of a natural enemy to attack a pest population, is sometimes effective against invasive species. However, prospective control agents can themselves become invasive.

Integrated Pest Management

Crop scientists have developed integrated pest management (IPM) strategies—combinations of biological, chemical, and cultural methods—to deal with agricultural pests.

Human Population Growth

The History of Human Population Growth

The human population grew rapidly during the 1900s and is currently more than 7 billion. A shift from high birth and death rates to low birth and death rates has lowered the rate of growth in more developed countries. In developing nations, death rates have dropped, but birth rates are still high.

Age Structures

The age structure of a population affects its future growth. The wide base of the age structure of Mexico in 1989—the 0–14 age-group—predicts continued population growth in the next generation. Population momentum is the continued growth that occurs after a population's high fertility rate has been reduced to replacement rate; it is a result of girls in the 0–14 age-group reaching their childbearing years. Age structures may also indicate social and economic trends, as in the age structure on the right below.

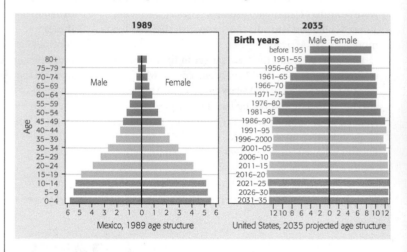

Our Ecological Footprint

An ecological footprint represents the amount of land and water needed to produce the resources used by an individual or nation. There is a huge disparity between resource consumption in more developed and less developed nations.

MasteringBiology®

For practice quizzes, BioFlix animations, MP3 tutorials, video tutors, and more study tools designed for this text, go to MasteringBiology®

SELF-QUIZ

1. What two values would you need to know to figure out the human population density of your community?

2. If members of a species produce a large number of offspring but provide minimal parental care, then a Type _____ survivorship curve is expected. In contrast, if members of a species produce few offspring and provide them with long-standing care, then a Type _____ survivorship curve is expected.

3. Use this graph of the idealized exponential and logistic growth curves to complete the following.

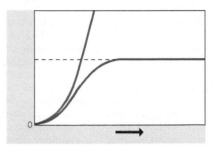

a. Label the axes and curves on the graph.
b. What does the dotted line represent?
c. For each curve, indicate and explain where population growth is the most rapid.
d. Which of these curves better represents global human population growth?

4. Which of the following describes the effects of a density-dependent limiting factor?
a. A forest fire kills all the pine trees in a patch of forest.
b. Early rainfall triggers the explosion of a locust population.
c. Drought decimates a wheat crop.
d. Rabbits multiply, and their food supply begins to dwindle.

5. Which life history pattern is typical of invasive species?

6. Skyrocketing growth of the human population since the beginning of the Industrial Revolution appears to be mainly a result of
a. migration to thinly settled regions of the globe.
b. better nutrition boosting the birth rate.
c. a drop in the death rate due to better nutrition and health care.
d. the concentration of humans in cities.

7. According to the ecological footprint study produced by the World Wildlife Fund in 2008,
a. the carrying capacity of the world is 10 billion.
b. the current demand on global resources by more developed countries is less than the resources available in those countries.
c. the ecological footprint of the United States is more than twice the world average.
d. nations with the largest ecological footprints have the fastest population growth rates.

THE PROCESS OF SCIENCE

8. If researchers establish that *Myrothecium verrucaria* is an effective biological control agent against kudzu, they must then show that the fungus will not harm desirable species such as soybeans (a close relative of kudzu). Describe experiments that could fulfill this purpose.

9. Interpreting Data The graph below shows data for population trends in Mexico from 1890 to 2012, with projected trends for 2012–2050. How has Mexico's rate of population growth changed over this time period? How is it expected to change by midcentury? Describe Mexico's projected age structure in 2050.

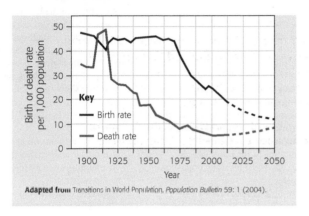

Adapted from Transitions in World Population, *Population Bulletin* 59: 1 (2004).

BIOLOGY AND SOCIETY

10. Experts are enlisting the help of citizen scientists in the battle against invasive species. For example, in 2014, the Florida Fish and Wildlife Commission released a phone app for reporting lionfish sightings, data that will help target fish for removal. A phone app to identify and report the locations of invasive species at more than 100 sites across the United States and Canada is available at www.whatsinvasive.org. Other citizen science projects are listed at www.birds.cornell.edu/citscitoolkit/projects/find/projects-invasive-species. Using these sites or other resources, determine which invasive species are of greatest concern in your area. Learn how to identify them, and find out what control measures are being taken.

11. The tiger, mountain gorilla, spotted owl, giant panda, snow leopard, and grizzly bear are all endangered by human encroachment on their habitats. Why might these animals, which all have equilibrial life history traits, be more easily endangered than animals with opportunistic life history traits? What general type of survivorship curve would you expect these species to exhibit? Explain your answer.

12. Affluent, more developed nations consume a disproportionate amount of Earth's resources and produce a disproportionate amount of wastes, including carbon dioxide and other greenhouse gases that are causing global climate change. The consequences of climate change include rising sea level, drought, and extreme weather events. Do you think affluent countries should responsible for helping poorer, less developed countries bear the financial burden of these consequences?

Glossary

age structure
The relative number of individuals of each age in a population.

biocapacity
Earth's capacity to produce the resources such as food, water, and fuel consumed by humans and to absorb human-generated waste.

biological control
The intentional release of a natural enemy to attack a pest population.

carrying capacity
The maximum population size that a particular environment can sustain.

density-dependent factor
A limiting factor whose effects intensify with increasing population density.

density-independent factor
A limiting factor whose occurrence and effects are not related to population density.

ecological footprint
An estimate of the amount of land required to provide the resources, such as food, water, fuel, and housing, that an individual or a nation consumes and to absorb the waste it generates.

endangered species
As defined in the U.S. Endangered Species Act, a species that is in danger of extinction throughout all or a significant portion of its range.

equilibrial life history (*ē-kwi-lib'-rē-ul*)
The pattern of reaching sexual maturity slowly and producing few offspring but caring for the young; often seen in long-lived, large-bodied species.

exponential population growth
A model that describes the expansion of a population in an ideal, unlimited environment.

intraspecific competition
Competition between individuals of the same species for the same limited resources.

invasive species
A non-native species that has spread far beyond the original point of introduction and causes environmental or economic damage by colonizing and dominating suitable habitats.

life history
The traits that affect an organism's schedule of reproduction and survival.

life table
A listing of survivals and deaths in a population in a particular time period and predictions of how long, on average, an individual of a given age will live.

limiting factor
An environmental factor that restricts the number of individuals that can occupy a particular habitat, thus holding population growth in check.

logistic population growth
A model that describes population growth that decreases as population size approaches carrying capacity.

opportunistic life history
The pattern of reproducing when young and producing many offspring that receive little or no parental care; often seen in short-lived, small-bodied species.

population density
The number of individuals of a species per unit area or volume of the habitat.

population momentum
In a population in which fertility (the number of live births over a woman's lifetime) averages two children (replacement rate), the continuation of population growth as girls reach their reproductive years.

survivorship curve
A plot of the number of individuals that are still alive at each age in the maximum life span; one way to represent the age-specific death rate.

threatened species
As defined in the U.S. Endangered Species Act, a species that is likely to become endangered in the foreseeable future throughout all or a significant portion of its range.

Credits

Self-Quiz Answers

1. the number of people and the land area in which they live
2. III; I
3. **a.** The x-axis is time; the y-axis is the number of individuals; the red curve represents exponential growth; the blue curve represents logistic growth.
   b. carrying capacity
   c. In exponential growth, the size of the population increases more and more rapidly. In logistic growth, the population grows fastest when it is about one-half the carrying capacity.
   d. exponential growth curve, though the worldwide growth rate is slowing
4. d
5. opportunistic
6. c
7. c

Communities and Ecosystems

From Chapter 20 of *Campbell Essential Biology with Physiology*, Fifth Edition. Eric J. Simon, Jean L. Dickey, Kelly A. Hogan, Jane B. Reece. Copyright © 2016 by Pearson Education, Inc. All rights reserved.

Communities and Ecosystems

Why Ecology Matters

Tuna fish, which eat high on the food chain, are likely to be contaminated with mercury and other toxins.

◄ Producing the beef for a hamburger (top) requires eight times as much land as producing the soybeans for a soyburger (bottom).

▲ The atoms in your body might have been part of a dinosaur that lived 75 million years ago.

▲ Human encroachment on tropical rain forests has brought new diseases such as Ebola to human populations.

Biodiversity in Decline BIOLOGY AND SOCIETY

Why Biodiversity Matters

As the human population has expanded, hundreds of species have become extinct and thousands more are threatened with extinction. These changes represent a loss in biological diversity, or biodiversity. Biodiversity loss goes hand in hand with the disappearance of natural ecosystems. Only about a quarter of Earth's land surfaces remain untouched by human alterations. We see the evidence of our impact on natural ecosystems every day. We live and work in altered landscapes. And though we may be less aware of it, our impact on the oceans is also extensive.

What is the value of biodiversity? Most people appreciate the direct benefits provided by certain ecosystems. For example, you probably know that we use resources—such as water, wood, and fish—that come from natural or near-natural ecosystems. These resources have economic value, as the massive 2010 oil spill in the Gulf of Mexico dramatically demonstrated. Billions of dollars were lost by fishing, recreation, and other industries as a result of the disaster. But human well-being also depends on less obvious services that healthy ecosystems provide. The coastal wetlands affected by the Gulf oil spill normally act as a buffer against hurricanes, reduce the impact of flooding, and filter pollutants. The wetlands also furnish nesting sites for birds and marine turtles and breeding areas and nurseries for a wide variety of fish and shellfish. Natural ecosystems provide other services as well—such as recycling

A 2014 oil spill in Galveston Bay, Texas, threatened bird sanctuaries on the nearby Bolivar Peninsula, home of this snowy egret.

nutrients, preventing erosion and mudslides, controlling agricultural pests, and pollinating crops. Some scientists have attempted to assign an economic value to these benefits. They arrived at an average annual value of ecosystem services of $33 trillion, almost twice the global gross national product for the year they published their results. Although rough, these estimates make the important point that we cannot afford to take biodiversity for granted.

In this chapter, we'll examine the interactions among organisms and how those relationships determine the characteristics of communities. On a larger scale, we'll explore the dynamics of ecosystems. Finally, we'll consider how scientists are working to save biodiversity. And throughout the chapter, you'll learn how an understanding of ecology can help us manage Earth's resources wisely.

The Loss of Biodiversity

As mentioned previously, **biodiversity** is short for biological diversity, the variety of living things. It includes genetic diversity, species diversity, and ecosystem diversity. Thus, the loss of biodiversity encompasses more than just the fate of individual species.

Genetic Diversity

The genetic diversity within a population is the raw material that makes microevolution and adaptation to the environment possible. If local populations are lost, then the number of individuals in the species declines, and so do the genetic resources for that species. Severe reduction in genetic variation threatens the survival of a species. When an entire species is lost, so are all of its unique genes.

The enormous genetic diversity of all the organisms on Earth has great potential benefit for people. Many researchers and biotechnology leaders are enthusiastic about the potential that genetic "bioprospecting" holds for future development of new medicines, industrial chemicals, and other products. Bioprospecting may also hold the key to the world's food supply. For example, researchers are currently scrambling to stop the spread of a deadly new strain of wheat stem rust, a fungal pathogen that has devastated harvests in eastern Africa and central Asia. At least 75% of the wheat varieties planted worldwide are susceptible to this pathogen, but researchers hope to find a resistance gene in the wild relatives of wheat (**Figure 1**). ☑

Species Diversity

In view of the damage we are doing to the biosphere, ecologists believe that we are pushing species toward extinction at an alarming rate. The present rate of species loss may be as much as 100 times higher than at any time in the past 100,000 years. Some researchers estimate that at the current rate of destruction, over half of all currently living plant and animal species will be gone by the end of this century. **Figure 2** shows two recent victims. The International Union for the Conservation of Nature (IUCN) compiles scientific assessments of the conservation status of species worldwide. Here are some examples of where things stand:

- Approximately 13% of the 10,004 bird species and almost a quarter of the 4,667 mammalian species assessed are threatened with extinction.

- More than 20% of freshwater fishes in the world either have become extinct during human history or are seriously threatened.

- Roughly 40% of all assessed amphibian species are in danger of extinction.

- Of the approximately 20,000 known plant species in the United States, 200 species have become extinct since dependable records have been kept. More than 10,000 plant species worldwide are in danger of extinction.

▼ Figure 1 Einkorn wheat, one of the wild relatives of modern cultivated varieties.

☑ CHECKPOINT

How does the loss of genetic diversity endanger a population?

Answer: A population with decreased genetic diversity has less ability to evolve in response to environmental change.

▼ Figure 2 Recent additions to the list of human-caused extinctions.

Clouded leopard. In 2013, scientists gave up hope that the Formosan clouded leopard, a subspecies found only on the island of Taiwan, still exists. This photo shows a similar subspecies living in a zoo.

A Chinese river dolphin. This former resident of the Yangtze River, also known as a baiji, fell victim to pollution and habitat loss. The baiji was declared extinct in 2006 after a two-year search failed to find any remaining.

Ecosystem Diversity

Ecosystem diversity is the third component of biological diversity. Recall that an ecosystem includes both the organisms and the abiotic factors in a particular area. Because of the network of interactions among populations of different species within an ecosystem, the loss of one species can have a negative effect on the entire ecosystem. The disappearance of natural ecosystems results in the loss of **ecosystem services**, functions performed by an ecosystem that directly or indirectly benefit people. These vital services include air and water purification, climate regulation, and erosion control. For example, forests absorb and store carbon from the atmosphere, a service that vanishes when forests are destroyed or degraded. Coral reefs not only are rich in species diversity **(Figure 3)** but also provide a wealth of benefits to people, including food, storm protection, and recreation. An estimated 20% of the world's coral reefs have already been destroyed by human activities. A study published in 2011 found that 75% of the remaining reefs are threatened, a percentage expected to top 90% by 2030 if current abuses continue. ☑

▼ Figure 3 **A coral reef, a colorful display of biodiversity.**

Causes of Declining Biodiversity

Ecologists have identified four main factors responsible for the loss of biodiversity: habitat destruction and fragmentation, invasive species, overexploitation, and pollution. The ever-expanding size and dominance of the human population are at the root of all four factors. In addition, scientists expect global climate change to become a leading cause of extinctions in the near future.

Habitat Destruction

The massive destruction and fragmentation of habitats caused by agriculture, urban development, forestry, and mining pose the single greatest threat to biodiversity **(Figure 4)**. According to the IUCN, habitat destruction affects more than 85% of all birds, mammals, and amphibians that are threatened with extinction. The destruction of its forest habitat, along with trade in its gorgeous pelt, doomed the Formosan clouded leopard. The remaining subspecies of clouded leopard, which inhabit the forests of Southeast Asia, are also vulnerable to extinction as a result of deforestation. We'll take a closer look at the consequences of habitat fragmentation later in this chapter.

Invasive Species

Ranking second behind habitat destruction as a cause of biodiversity loss is the introduction of invasive species. Uncontrolled population growth of human-introduced species has caused havoc when the introduced species have competed with, preyed on, or parasitized native species. The lack of interactions with other species that could keep the newcomers in check is often a key factor in a non-native species becoming invasive.

▼ Figure 4 **Habitat destruction.** In a controversial method known as mountaintop removal, mining companies blast the tops off of mountains and then scoop out coal. The earth removed from the mountain is dumped into a neighboring valley.

Overexploitation

Unsustainable marine fisheries demonstrate how people can overexploit wildlife by harvesting at rates that exceed the ability of populations to rebound. American bison, Galápagos tortoises, and tigers are among the many terrestrial species whose numbers have been drastically reduced by excessive commercial harvesting, poaching, and sport hunting. Overharvesting also threatens some plants, including rare trees such as mahogany and rosewood that produce valuable wood.

Pollution

Air and water pollution (**Figure 5**) is a contributing factor in declining populations of hundreds of species worldwide. The global water cycle can transport pollutants from terrestrial to aquatic ecosystems hundreds of miles away. Pollutants that are emitted into the atmosphere may be carried aloft for thousands of miles before falling to earth in the form of acid precipitation. ☑

☑ CHECKPOINT

What are the four main causes of declining biodiversity?

Answer: habitat destruction, invasive species, overexploitation, and pollution

▲ Figure 5 **A pelican stuck in oil from the 2010 Gulf of Mexico disaster.** Wildlife is often the most visible casualty of pollution, but the impact extends throughout the ecosystem.

Community Ecology

On your next walk through a field or woodland, or even across campus or your own backyard, observe the variety of species present. You may see birds in trees, butterflies on flowers, dandelions in the grass of a lawn, or lizards darting for cover as you approach. Each of these organisms interacts with other organisms as it carries out its life activities. An organism's biotic environment includes not just individuals from its own population, but also populations of other species living in the same area. Ecologists call such an assemblage of species living close enough together for potential interaction a **community**. In **Figure 6**, the lion, the zebra, the hyena, the vultures, the plants, and the unseen microbes are all members of an ecological community in Kenya.

Interspecific Interactions

Our study of communities begins with **interspecific interactions**—that is, interactions between species. Interspecific interactions can be classified according to the effect on the populations concerned, which may be helpful (**+**) or harmful (**−**). In some cases, two populations in a community vie for a resource such as food or space. The effect of this interaction is generally negative for both species (**−/−**) because neither species has access to the full range of resources offered by the habitat. On the other hand, some interspecific interactions benefit both parties (**+/+**). For example, the interactions between flowers and their pollinators are mutually beneficial. In a third type of interspecific interaction, one species exploits another species as a source of food. The effect of this interaction is clearly beneficial to one population and harmful to the other (**+/−**). In the next several pages, you will learn more about these interspecific interactions and how they affect communities. You will also see that interspecific interactions can be powerful agents of natural selection.

▼ Figure 6 **Diverse species interacting in a Kenyan savanna community.**

Interspecific Competition (–/–)

In the logistic model of population growth , increasing population density reduces the amount of resources available for each individual. This intraspecific (within-species) competition for limited resources ultimately limits population growth. In **interspecific competition** (between-species competition), the population growth of a species may be limited by the population densities of competing species as well as by the density of its own population (intraspecific competition).

What determines whether populations in a community compete with each other? Each species has an **ecological niche**, defined as its total use of the biotic and abiotic resources in its environment. For example, the ecological niche of a small bird called the Virginia's warbler (**Figure 7a**) includes its nest sites and nest-building materials, the insects it eats, and climatic conditions such as the amount of precipitation and the temperature and humidity that enable it to survive. In other words, the ecological niche encompasses everything the Virginia's warbler needs for its existence. The ecological niche of the orange-crowned warbler (**Figure 7b**) includes some of the same resources used by the Virginia's warbler. Consequently, when these two species inhabit the same area, they are competitors.

Ecologists investigated the effects of interspecific competition between populations of these two birds in a community in central Arizona. When they removed either Virginia's warblers or orange-crowned warblers from the study site, members of the remaining species were significantly more successful in raising their offspring. This study showed that interspecific competition can have a direct, negative effect on reproductive fitness.

If the ecological niches of two species are too similar, they cannot coexist in the same place. Ecologists call

this the **competitive exclusion principle**, a concept introduced by Russian ecologist G. F. Gause, who demonstrated this effect with an elegant series of experiments. Gause used two closely related species of protists, *Paramecium caudatum* and *P. aurelia*. First, he established the carrying capacity for each species separately under the conditions used to grow them in the laboratory (**Figure 8**, top graph). Then he grew the two species in the same habitat. Within two weeks, the *P. caudatum* population had crashed (bottom graph). Gause concluded that the requirements of these two species were so similar that the superior competitor—in this case, *P. aurelia*—deprived *P. caudatum* of essential resources. ✓

▼ Figure 8 **Competitive exclusion in laboratory populations of *Paramecium*.**

Paramecium aurelia

Paramecium caudatum

▼ Figure 7 **Species that use similar resources.**

(a) **Virginia's warbler**

(b) **Orange-crowned warbler**

Mutualism (+/+)

In **mutualism**, both species benefit from an interaction. Some mutualisms occur between symbiotic species—those in which the organisms have a close physical association with each other. For example, in the symbiotic root-fungus associations known as mycorrhizae, the fungus delivers mineral nutrients to the plant and receives organic nutrients in return. Coral reef ecosystems depend on the mutualism between certain species of coral animals and millions of unicellular algae that live in the cells of each coral polyp **(Figure 9)**. Reefs are constructed by successive generations of colonial corals that secrete an external calcium carbonate skeleton. The sugars that the algae produce by photosynthesis provide at least half of the energy used by the coral animals. This energy input enables the coral to form new skeleton rapidly enough to outpace erosion and competition for space from fast-growing seaweeds. In return, the algae gain a secure shelter that allows access to light. They also use the coral's waste products, including CO_2 and ammonia, a valuable source of nitrogen. Mutualism can also occur between species that are not symbiotic, such as flowers and their pollinators.

▲ **Figure 9 Mutualism.** The cells of coral polyps are inhabited by unicellular algae.

Predation (+/−)

Predation refers to an interaction in which one species (the predator) kills and eats another (the prey). Because predation has such a negative impact on the reproductive success of the prey, numerous adaptations for predator avoidance have evolved in prey populations through natural selection. For example, some prey species, such as the pronghorn antelope, run fast enough to escape their predators. Others, such as rabbits, flee into shelters. Still other prey species rely on mechanical defenses, such as the porcupine's sharp quills or the hard shells of clams and oysters.

Adaptive coloration is a type of defense that has evolved in many species of animals. Camouflage, called **cryptic coloration**, makes potential prey difficult to spot against its background **(Figure 10)**. **Warning coloration**, bright patterns of yellow, red, or orange in combination with black, often marks animals with effective chemical defenses. Predators learn to associate these color patterns with undesirable consequences, such as a noxious taste or painful sting, and avoid potential prey with similar markings. The vivid colors of the poison dart frog **(Figure 11)**, an inhabitant of Costa Rican rain forests, warn of noxious chemicals in the frog's skin.

A prey species may also gain significant protection through mimicry, a "copycat" adaptation in which one species looks like another. For example, the pattern of alternating red, black, and yellow rings of the harmless scarlet king snake resembles the bold color pattern of the venomous eastern coral snake **(Figure 12)**. Some insects have combined protective coloration with adaptations of body structures in elaborate disguises. For instance, there are insects that resemble twigs, leaves, and bird droppings. Some even do a passable imitation of a vertebrate. For example, the colors on the dorsal side of certain caterpillars are an effective camouflage,

▼ **Figure 10 Cryptic coloration.** Camouflage conceals the pygmy seahorse from predators.

▼ **Figure 11 Warning coloration of a poison dart frog.**

▲ **Figure 12 Mimicry in snakes.** The color pattern of the nonvenomous scarlet king snake (left) is similar to that of the venomous eastern coral snake (right).

but when disturbed, the caterpillars flip over to reveal the snakelike eyespots of their ventral side **(Figure 13)**. Eyespots that resemble vertebrate eyes are common in several groups of moths and butterflies. A flash of these large "eyes" startles would-be predators. In other species, an eyespot may deflect a predator's attack away from vital body parts.

Herbivory (+/−)

Herbivory is the consumption of plant parts or algae by an animal. Although herbivory is not usually fatal to plants, a plant whose body parts have been partially eaten by an animal must expend energy to replace the loss. Consequently, numerous defenses against herbivores have evolved in plants. Spines and thorns are obvious anti-herbivore devices, as anyone who has plucked a rose from a thorny rosebush or brushed against a spiky cactus knows. Chemical toxins are also very common in plants. Like the chemical defenses of animals, toxins in plants are distasteful, and herbivores learn

to avoid them. Among such chemical weapons are the poison strychnine, produced by a tropical vine called *Strychnos toxifera*; morphine, from the opium poppy; nicotine, produced by the tobacco plant; mescaline, from peyote cactus; and tannins, from a variety of plant species. Other defensive compounds that are not toxic to humans but may be distasteful to herbivores are responsible for the familiar flavors of peppermint, cloves, and cinnamon **(Figure 14)**. Some plants even produce chemicals that cause abnormal development in insects that eat them. Chemical companies have taken advantage of the poisonous properties of certain plants to produce pesticides. For example, nicotine is used as an insecticide. ☑

▼ **Figure 13 An insect mimicking a snake.** When disturbed, this sphinx moth larva flips over (left), revealing eyespots that resemble a snake (right).

▼ **Figure 14 Flavorful plants.**

Peppermint. Parts of the peppermint plant yield a pungent oil.

Cloves. The cloves used in cooking are the flower buds of this plant.

Cinnamon. Cinnamon comes from the inner bark of this tree.

Parasites and Pathogens (+/−)

Both plants and animals may be victimized by parasites or pathogens. These interactions are beneficial to one species (the parasite or pathogen) and harmful to the other, known as the host. A **parasite** lives on or in a **host** from which it obtains nourishment. Invertebrate parasites include flatworms, such as flukes and tapeworms, and a variety of roundworms, which live inside a host organism's body. External parasites, such as ticks, lice, mites, and mosquitoes, attach to their victims temporarily to feed on blood or other body fluids. Plants are also attacked by parasites, including roundworms and aphids, tiny insects that tap into the phloem to suck plant sap. In any parasite population, reproductive success is greatest for individuals that are best at locating and feeding on their hosts. For example, some aquatic leeches first locate a host by detecting movement in the water and then confirm its identity based on the host's body temperature and chemical cues on its skin.

Pathogens are disease-causing bacteria, viruses, fungi, or protists that can be thought of as microscopic parasites. Non-native pathogens, whose impact can be rapid and dramatic, have provided some opportunities to investigate the effects of pathogens on communities. In one example, ecologists studied the consequences of the epidemic of chestnut blight, a disease caused by a protist. The loss of chestnuts, massive canopy trees that once dominated many forest communities in North America, had a significant impact on community composition and structure. Trees such as oaks and hickories that had formerly competed with chestnuts became more numerous; overall, the diversity of tree species increased. Dead chestnut trees also furnished niches for other organisms, such as insects, cavity-nesting birds, and, eventually, decomposers. ✓

☑ **CHECKPOINT**

How is the interaction between a parasite and its host similar to predator-prey and herbivore-plant interactions?

Answer: In all three interactions, one species benefits and the other is harmed (+/−); specifically, one species exploits another as a source of food.

Trophic Structure

Now that we have looked at how populations in a community interact with one another, let's consider the community as a whole. The feeding relationships among the various species in a community are referred to as its **trophic structure**. A community's trophic structure determines the passage of energy and nutrients from plants and other photosynthetic organisms to herbivores and then to predators. The sequence of food transfer between trophic levels is called a **food chain**.

Figure 15 shows two food chains, one terrestrial and one aquatic. At the bottom of both chains is the trophic level that supports all others. This level consists of autotrophs, which ecologists call **producers**. Photosynthetic producers transform light energy to chemical energy stored in the bonds of organic compounds. Plants are the main producers on land. In water, the main producers are photosynthetic protists and cyanobacteria, collectively called phytoplankton. Multicellular algae and aquatic plants are also important producers in shallow waters. In a few communities, such as those surrounding hydrothermal vents, the producers are chemosynthetic prokaryotes.

All organisms in trophic levels above the producers are heterotrophs, or consumers. All consumers depend directly or indirectly on the output of producers. **Herbivores**, which eat plants, algae, or phytoplankton, are **primary consumers**. Primary consumers on land include grasshoppers and many other insects, snails, and certain vertebrates, such as grazing mammals and birds that eat seeds and fruits. In aquatic environments, primary consumers include a variety of zooplankton (mainly protists and microscopic animals such as small shrimps) that eat phytoplankton.

▼ **Figure 15 Examples of food chains.** The arrows trace the transfer of food from one trophic level to the next in terrestrial and aquatic communities.

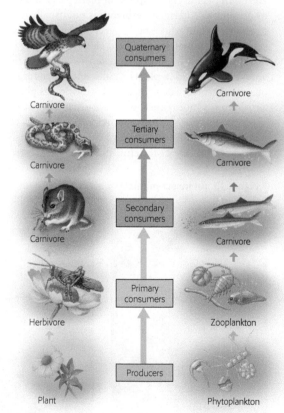

Quaternary consumers

Tertiary consumers

Secondary consumers

Primary consumers

Producers

Carnivore

Carnivore

Carnivore

Herbivore

Plant

A terrestrial food chain

Carnivore

Carnivore

Carnivore

Zooplankton

Phytoplankton

An aquatic food chain

Above the primary consumers, the trophic levels are made up of **carnivores**, which eat the consumers from the level below. On land, **secondary consumers** include many small mammals, such as the mouse shown in Figure 15 eating an herbivorous insect, and a great variety of birds, frogs, and spiders, as well as lions and other large carnivores that eat grazers. In aquatic communities, secondary consumers are mainly small fishes that eat zooplankton. Higher trophic levels include **tertiary consumers** (third-level consumers), such as snakes that eat mice and other secondary consumers. Most communities have secondary and tertiary consumers. As the figure indicates, some also have a higher level—**quaternary consumers** (fourth-level consumers). These include hawks in terrestrial communities and killer whales in the marine environment. There are no fifth-level consumers—you'll find out why shortly.

Figure 15 shows only those consumers that eat living organisms. Some consumers derive their energy from **detritus**, the dead material left by all trophic levels, including animal wastes, plant litter, and dead bodies. Different organisms consume detritus in different stages of decay. **Scavengers**, which are large animals such as crows and vultures, feast on carcasses left behind by predators or speeding cars. The diet of **detritivores** is made up primarily of decaying organic material. Earthworms and millipedes are examples of detritivores. **Decomposers**, mainly prokaryotes and fungi, secrete enzymes that digest molecules in organic material and convert them to inorganic forms. Enormous numbers of microscopic decomposers in the soil and in the mud at the bottom of lakes and oceans break down organic materials to inorganic compounds—the raw materials used by plants and phytoplankton to make new organic materials that may eventually become food for consumers. Many gardeners keep a compost pile, using the services of detritivores and decomposers to break down organic material from kitchen scraps and yard trimmings (Figure 16).

▼ **Figure 16 Compost bin in a garden.** As it decays, the rich organic material of compost provides a slow-release source of inorganic nutrients for plants.

Biological Magnification

Organisms can't metabolize many of the toxins produced by industrial wastes or applied as pesticides; after consumption, the chemicals remain in the body. These toxins become concentrated as they pass through a food chain, a process called **biological magnification**. **Figure 17** shows the biological magnification of chemicals called PCBs (organic compounds used in electrical equipment until 1977) in a Great Lakes food chain. Zooplankton—the base of the pyramid—feed on phytoplankton contaminated by PCBs in the water. Smelt (small fish) feed on contaminated zooplankton. Because each smelt consumes many zooplankton, the concentration of PCBs is higher in smelt than in zooplankton. For the same reason, the concentration of PCBs in trout is higher than in smelt. The top-level predators—herring gulls in this example—have the highest concentrations of PCBs in the food chain and are the organisms most severely affected by any toxic compounds in the environment. In this case, fewer of the contaminated eggs hatched, resulting in a decline in the reproductive success of herring gulls. Many other synthetic chemicals that cannot be degraded by microorganisms, including DDT and mercury, can also become concentrated through biological magnification.

Tuna fish, which eat high on the food chain, are likely to be contaminated with mercury and other toxins.

◄ **Figure 17 Biological magnification of PCBs in a Great Lakes food chain in the early 1960s.** Eating top-level consumers, such as tuna, swordfish, and sharks, from contaminated waters can cause health problems for people, especially during pregnancy.

Concentration of PCBs

Herring gull eggs 124 ppm

Lake trout 4.83 ppm

Smelt 1.04 ppm

Zooplankton 0.123 ppm

Phytoplankton 0.025 ppm

Food Webs

Few, if any, communities are so simple that they are characterized by a single, unbranched food chain. Several types of primary consumers usually feed on the same plant species, and one species of primary consumer may eat several different plants. Such branching of food chains occurs at the other trophic levels as well. Thus, the feeding relationships in a community are woven into elaborate **food webs**.

Consider the grasshopper mouse in **Figure 18**, the secondary consumer shown crunching on a grasshopper in Figure 15. Its diet also includes plants, making it a primary consumer, too. It is an **omnivore**, an animal that eats producers as well as consumers of different levels. The rattlesnake that eats the mouse also feeds on more than one trophic level. The blue arrow leading to the rattlesnake indicates that it eats primary consumers—it is a secondary consumer. The purple arrow shows that it eats secondary consumers, so it is also a tertiary consumer. Sound complicated? Actually, Figure 18 shows a simplified food web. An actual food web would involve many more organisms at each trophic level, and most of the animals would have a more diverse diet than shown in the figure. ☑

☑ **CHECKPOINT**
You're eating a pizza. At which trophic level(s) are you feeding?

Answer: You're a primary consumer when you eat flour (in the crust) and tomato sauce, and you're a secondary consumer when you eat cheese or meat on the pizza.

► **Figure 18 A simplified food web for a Sonoran desert community.** As in the food chains of Figure 15, the arrows in this web indicate "who eats whom," the direction of nutrient transfers. We also continue the color-coding introduced in Figure 15 for the trophic levels and food transfers.

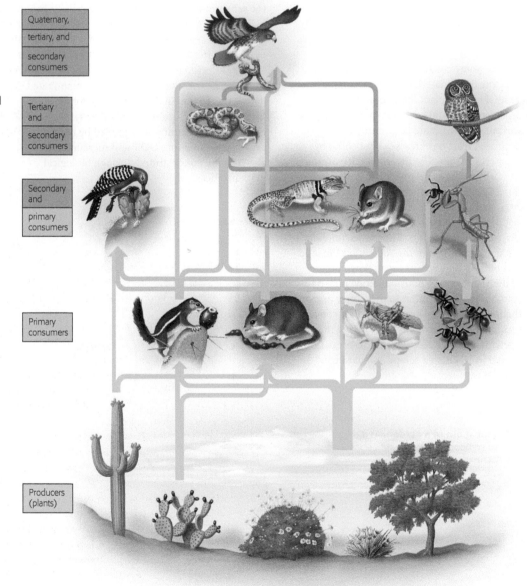

Quaternary, tertiary, and secondary consumers

Tertiary and secondary consumers

Secondary and primary consumers

Primary consumers

Producers (plants)

Species Diversity in Communities

The **species diversity** of a community—the variety of species that make up the community—has two components. The first component is **species richness**, or the number of different species in the community. The other component is the **relative abundance** of the different species, the proportional representation of each species in a community. To understand why both components are important for describing species diversity, imagine walking through the woodlands shown in **Figure 19**. On the path through woodland A, you would pass by four different species of trees, but most of the trees you encounter would be the same species. Now imagine walking on a path through woodland B. You would see the same four species of trees that you saw in woodland A—the species richness of the two woodlands is the same. However, woodland B might seem more diverse to you because no single species predominates. As **Figure 20** shows, the relative abundance of one species in woodland A is much higher than the relative abundances of the other three species. In woodland B, all four species are equally abundant. As a result, species diversity is greater in woodland B. Because plants provide food and shelter for many animals, a diverse plant community promotes animal diversity.

Although the abundance of a dominant species such as a forest tree can have an impact on the diversity of

▼ **Figure 19 Which woodland is more diverse?**

Woodland A

Woodland B

◄ **Figure 20 Relative abundance of tree species in woodlands A and B.**

other species in the community, a nondominant species may also exert control over community composition. A **keystone species** is a species whose impact on its community is much larger than its total mass or abundance indicates. The term *keystone species* was derived from the wedge-shaped stone at the top of an arch that locks the other pieces in place. If the keystone is removed, the arch collapses. A keystone species occupies an ecological niche that holds the rest of its community in place.

To investigate the role of a potential keystone species in a community, ecologists compare diversity when the species is present to that when it is absent. Experiments by Robert Paine in the 1960s were among the first to provide evidence of the keystone species effect. Paine manually removed a predator, a sea star of the genus *Pisaster* (**Figure 21**), from experimental areas within the intertidal zone of the Washington coast. The result was that *Pisaster*'s main prey, a mussel, outcompeted many of the other shoreline organisms (algae, barnacles, and snails, for instance) for the important resource of space on the rocks. The number of different organisms present in experimental areas dropped from more than 15 species to fewer than 5 species.

Ecologists have identified other species that play a key role in ecosystem structure. For instance, the decline of sea otters off the western coast of Alaska allowed populations of sea urchins, their main prey, to increase. The greater abundance of sea urchins, which consume seaweeds such as kelp, has resulted in the loss of many of the kelp "forests" and the diversity of marine life that they support. In many ecosystems, however, ecologists are just beginning to understand the complex relationships among species; the value of an individual species may not be apparent until it is gone. ☑

▼ **Figure 21 A *Pisaster* sea star.**

☑ **CHECKPOINT**

How could a community appear to have relatively little diversity even though it is rich in species?

Answer: if one or a few of the diverse species accounted for almost all the organisms in the community, with the other species being rare

Disturbances in Communities

Most communities are constantly changing in response to disturbances. **Disturbances** are episodes that damage biological communities, at least temporarily, by destroying organisms and altering the availability of resources such as mineral nutrients and water. Examples of natural disturbances are storms, fires, floods, and droughts.

Small-scale natural disturbances often have positive effects on a biological community. For example, when a large tree falls in a windstorm, it creates new habitats **(Figure 22)**. More light may now reach the forest floor, giving small seedlings the opportunity to grow; the depression left by the tree's roots may fill with water and be used as egg-laying sites by frogs, salamanders, and numerous insects.

People are by far the most significant agents of ecological disturbance today. One consequence of human-caused disturbance is the emergence of previously unknown infectious diseases. Three-quarters of emerging diseases have jumped to humans from another vertebrate species. In many cases, people come into contact with these pathogens through activities such as clearing land for agriculture, building roads, or hunting in previously isolated ecosystems. HIV, which may have been transmitted to people from the blood of primates butchered for food, is probably the best-known example.

Others include potentially fatal hemorrhagic fevers, such as Ebola. Habitat destruction may also cause pathogen-carrying animals to venture closer to human dwellings in search of food. ☑

> Human encroachment on tropical rain forests has brought new diseases such as Ebola to human populations.

Ecological Succession

Communities change drastically following a severe disturbance that strips away vegetation and even soil. The disturbed area may be colonized by a variety of species, which are gradually replaced by a succession of other species, in a process called **ecological succession**.

Ecological succession that begins in a virtually lifeless area with no soil is called **primary succession (Figure 23)**. Examples of such areas are cooled lava flows on volcanic islands and the rubble left by a retreating glacier. Often the only life-forms initially present are autotrophic bacteria. Lichens and mosses, which grow from windblown spores, are commonly the first multicellular producers to colonize the area. Soil develops gradually as rocks weather and organic matter accumulates from the decomposing remains of the early colonizers. Lichens and mosses are eventually overgrown by grasses and shrubs that sprout from seeds blown in from nearby areas or carried in by animals. Finally, the area is colonized by plants that become the

▼ **Figure 22 A small-scale disturbance.** When this tree fell during a windstorm, its root system and the surrounding soil uplifted, resulting in a depression that filled with water. The dead tree, the root mound, and the water-filled depression are new habitats.

▼ **Figure 23 Primary succession underway on a lava flow in Volcanoes National Park, Hawaii.**

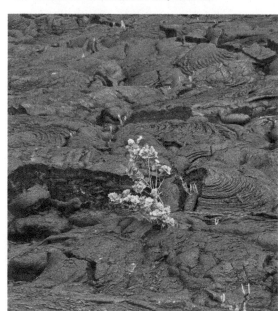

community's prevalent form of vegetation. Primary succession can take hundreds or thousands of years.

Secondary succession occurs where a disturbance has destroyed an existing community but left the soil intact. For example, secondary succession occurs as areas recover from floods or fires (**Figure 24**). Disturbances that lead to secondary succession are also caused by human activities. Even before colonial times, people were clearing the temperate deciduous forests of eastern North America for agriculture and settlements. Some of this land was later abandoned as the soil was depleted of its chemical nutrients or the residents moved west to new territories. Whenever human intervention stops, secondary succession begins. ☑

▼ Figure 24 **Secondary succession after a fire.**

☑ **CHECKPOINT**

What is the main abiotic factor that distinguishes primary from secondary succession?

Answer: absence of soil (primary succession) versus presence of soil (secondary succession) at the onset of succession

Ecosystem Ecology

In addition to the community of species in a given area, an **ecosystem** includes all the abiotic factors, such as energy, soil characteristics, and water. Let's look at a small-scale ecosystem—a terrarium—to see how the community interacts with these abiotic factors (**Figure 25**). A terrarium microcosm exhibits the two major processes that sustain all ecosystems: energy flow and chemical cycling. **Energy flow** is the passage of energy through the components of the ecosystem. **Chemical cycling** is the use and reuse of chemical elements such as carbon and nitrogen within the ecosystem.

Energy enters the terrarium in the form of sunlight (yellow arrows). Plants (producers) convert light energy to chemical energy through the process of photosynthesis. Animals (consumers) take in some of this chemical energy in the form of organic compounds when they eat the plants. Detritivores and decomposers in the soil obtain chemical energy when they feed on the dead remains of plants and animals. Every use of chemical energy by organisms involves a loss of some energy to the surroundings in the form of heat (red arrows). Because so much of the energy captured by photosynthesis is lost as heat, this ecosystem would run out of energy if it were not powered by a continuous inflow of energy from the sun.

In contrast to energy flow, chemical cycling (blue arrows in Figure 25) involves the transfer of materials within the ecosystem. While most ecosystems have a constant input of energy from sunlight or another source, the supply of the chemical elements used to construct molecules is limited. Chemical elements such as carbon and nitrogen are cycled between the abiotic components of the ecosystem, including air, water, and soil, and the biotic components of the ecosystem (the community). Plants acquire these elements in inorganic

form from the air and soil and use them to construct organic molecules. Animals, such as the snail in Figure 25, consume some of these organic molecules. When the plants and animals become detritus, decomposers return most of the elements to the soil and air in inorganic form. Some elements are also returned to the air and soil as the by-products of plant and animal metabolism.

In summary, both energy flow and chemical cycling involve the transfer of substances through the trophic levels of the ecosystem. However, energy flows through, and ultimately out of, ecosystems, whereas chemicals are recycled within and between ecosystems.

▼ Figure 25 **A terrarium ecosystem.** Though it is small and artificial, this sealed terrarium illustrates the two major ecosystem processes: energy flow and chemical cycling.

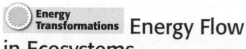 Energy Flow in Ecosystems

All organisms require energy for growth, maintenance, reproduction, and, in many species, locomotion. In this section, we take a closer look at energy flow through ecosystems. Along the way, we'll answer two key questions: What limits the length of food chains? and How do lessons about energy flow apply to people's use of resources?

Primary Production and the Energy Budgets of Ecosystems

Each day, Earth receives about 10^{19} kcal of solar energy, the energy equivalent of about 100 million atomic bombs. Most of this energy is absorbed, scattered, or reflected by the atmosphere or by Earth's surface. Of the visible light that reaches plants, algae, and cyanobacteria, only about 1% is converted to chemical energy by photosynthesis.

Ecologists call the amount, or mass, of living organic material in an ecosystem the **biomass**. The rate at which an ecosystem's producers convert solar energy to the chemical energy stored in organic compounds is called **primary production**. The primary production of the entire biosphere is roughly 165 billion tons of biomass per year.

Different ecosystems vary considerably in their primary production **(Figure 26)** as well as in their contribution to the total production of the biosphere. Tropical rain forests are among the most productive terrestrial ecosystems and contribute a large portion of the planet's overall production of biomass. Coral reefs also have

very high production, but their contribution to global production is small because they cover such a small area. Interestingly, even though the open ocean has very low production, it contributes the most to Earth's total primary production because of its huge size—it covers 65% of Earth's surface area. Whatever the ecosystem, primary production sets the spending limit for the energy budget of the entire ecosystem because consumers must acquire their organic fuels from producers. Now let's see how this energy budget is divided among the different trophic levels in an ecosystem's food web. ☑

Ecological Pyramids

When energy flows as organic matter through the trophic levels of an ecosystem, much of it is lost at each link in the food chain. Consider the transfer of organic matter from plants (producers) to herbivores (primary consumers). In most ecosystems, herbivores manage to eat only a fraction of the plant material produced, and they can't digest all of what they do consume. For example, a caterpillar feeding on leaves passes about half the energy in the leaves as feces **(Figure 27)**. Another 35% of the energy is expended in cellular respiration. Only about 15% of the energy in the caterpillar's food is transformed into caterpillar biomass. Only this biomass (and the energy it contains) is available to the consumer that eats the caterpillar.

Figure 28, called a **pyramid of production**, illustrates the cumulative loss of energy with each transfer in a food chain. Each tier of the pyramid represents all of the organisms in one trophic level, and the width of each tier indicates how much of the chemical energy of the tier below is actually incorporated into the organic matter of that trophic level. Note that producers convert only about 1% of the energy in the sunlight available to them to primary production. In this generalized

☑ CHECKPOINT

Deserts and semidesert scrub cover about the same amount of surface area as tropical rain forests but contribute less than 1% of Earth's primary production, while rain forests contribute 22%. Explain this difference.

Answer: Primary production is measured in g/m²/yr. A square meter of tropical rain forest produces more than 20 times as much biomass as a square meter of desert or semidesert scrub.

▼ **Figure 26 Primary production of different ecosystems.**
Primary production is the amount of biomass created by the producers of an ecosystem over a unit of time, in this case a year. Aquatic ecosystems are color-coded blue in these histograms; terrestrial ecosystems are green.

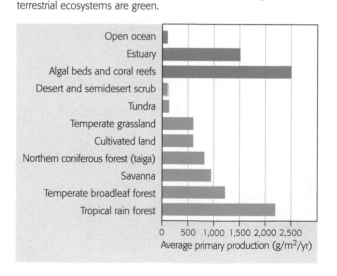

► **Figure 27**
What becomes of a caterpillar's food?
Only about 15% of the calories of plant material this herbivore consumes will be stored as biomass available to the next link in the food chain.

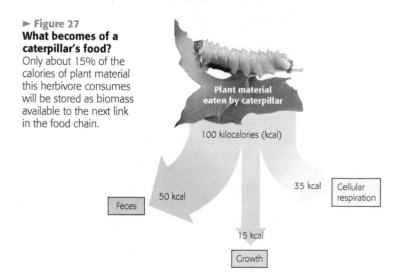

▼ Figure 28 **An idealized pyramid of production.**

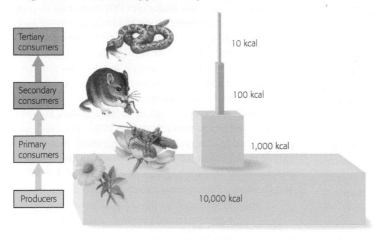

Tertiary
consumers

Secondary
consumers

Primary
consumers

Producers

10 kcal

100 kcal

1,000 kcal

10,000 kcal

1,000,000 kcal of sunlight

pyramid, 10% of the energy available at each trophic level becomes incorporated into the next higher level. Actual efficiencies of energy transfer are usually in the range of 5–20%. In other words, 80–95% of the energy at one trophic level never reaches the next.

An important implication of this stepwise decline of energy in a trophic structure is that the amount of energy available to top-level consumers is small compared with that available to lower-level consumers. Only a tiny fraction of the energy stored by photosynthesis flows through a food chain to a tertiary consumer, such as a snake feeding on a mouse. This explains why top-level consumers such as lions and hawks require so much geographic territory: It takes a lot of vegetation to support trophic levels so many steps removed from photosynthetic production. You can also understand why most food chains are limited to three to five levels; there is simply not enough energy at the very top of an ecological pyramid to support another

trophic level. There are, for example, no nonhuman predators of lions, eagles, and killer whales; the biomass in populations of these top-level consumers is insufficient to supply yet another trophic level with a reliable source of nutrition.

Ecosystem Energetics and Human Resource Use

The dynamics of energy flow apply to the human population as much as to other organisms. The two production pyramids in **Figure 29** are based on the same generalized model used to construct Figure 28, with roughly 10% of the energy in each trophic level available for consumption by the next trophic level. The pyramid on the left shows energy flow from producers (represented by corn) to people as primary consumers—vegetarians. The pyramid on the right illustrates energy flow from the same corn crop, with people as secondary consumers, eating beef. Clearly, the human population has less energy available to it when people eat at higher trophic levels than as primary consumers.

Worldwide, only about 20% of agricultural land is used to produce plants for direct human consumption. The rest of the land produces food for livestock. In either case, large-scale agriculture is environmentally expensive. Land is cleared of its native vegetation; fossil fuels are burned; chemical fertilizers and pesticides are applied; and in many regions, water is used for irrigation. Currently, people in many countries cannot afford to buy meat and are vegetarians by necessity. As nations become more affluent, the demand for meat increases—and so do the environmental costs of food production. ☑

Producing the beef for a hamburger requires eight times as much land as producing the soybeans for a soyburger.

▼ Figure 29 **Food energy available to the human population at different trophic levels.**

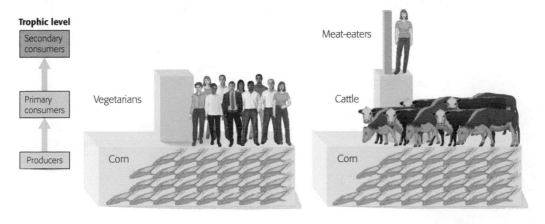

Trophic level

Secondary
consumers

Primary
consumers

Producers

Vegetarians

Corn

Meat-eaters

Cattle

Corn

☑ **CHECKPOINT**

Why is the energy at different trophic levels represented as a pyramid in Figure 28?

Answer: Energy is lost with each transfer from one trophic level to the next. Thus, the collective amount of energy at the producer level (the base of the pyramid) is greater than the collective amount of energy at the level of primary consumers, and so on.

Chemical Cycling in Ecosystems

The sun (or in some cases Earth's interior) supplies ecosystems with a continual input of energy, but aside from an occasional meteorite, there are no extraterrestrial sources of chemical elements. Life, therefore, depends on the recycling of chemicals. While an organism is alive, much of its chemical stock changes continuously, as nutrients are acquired and waste products are released. Atoms present in the complex molecules of an organism at the time of its death are returned to the environment by the action of decomposers, replenishing the pool of inorganic nutrients that plants and other producers use to build new organic matter (Figure 30). In a sense, each living thing only borrows an ecosystem's chemical elements, returning what is left in its body after it dies. Let's take a closer look at how chemicals cycle between organisms and the abiotic components of ecosystems.

The General Scheme of Chemical Cycling

Because chemical cycles in an ecosystem involve both biotic components (organisms and nonliving organic material) and abiotic (geologic and atmospheric) components, they are called **biogeochemical cycles**. Figure 31 is a general scheme for the cycling of a mineral nutrient within an ecosystem. Note that the cycle has an **abiotic reservoir** (white box) where a chemical accumulates or is stockpiled outside of living organisms. The atmosphere, for example, is an abiotic reservoir for carbon. The water of aquatic ecosystems contains dissolved carbon, nitrogen, and phosphorus compounds.

Let's trace our way around our general biogeochemical cycle. ❶ Producers incorporate chemicals from the abiotic reservoir into organic compounds. ❷ Consumers feed on the producers, incorporating some of the chemicals into their own bodies. ❸ Both producers and consumers release some chemicals back to the environment in waste products. ❹ Decomposers play a central role by breaking down the complex organic molecules in detritus such as plant litter, animal

wastes, and dead organisms. The products of this metabolism are inorganic molecules that replenish the abiotic reservoirs. Geologic processes such as erosion and the weathering of rock also contribute to the abiotic reservoirs. Producers use the inorganic molecules from abiotic reservoirs as raw materials for synthesizing new organic molecules (carbohydrates and proteins, for example), and the cycle continues.

Biogeochemical cycles can be local or global. Soil is the main reservoir for nutrients in a local cycle, such as phosphorus. In contrast, for those chemicals that spend part of their time in gaseous form—carbon and nitrogen are examples—the cycling is essentially global. For instance, some of the carbon a plant acquires from the air may have been released into the atmosphere by the respiration of a plant or animal on another continent.

Now let's examine three important biogeochemical cycles more closely: the cycles for carbon, phosphorus, and nitrogen. As you study the cycles, look for the four basic steps we described, as well as the geologic processes that move chemicals around and between ecosystems. In all the diagrams, the main abiotic reservoirs appear in white boxes. ☑

> The atoms in your body might have been part of a dinosaur that lived 75 million years ago.

▼ Figure 30 **Plant growth on fallen tree.** In the temperate rain forest of Olympic National Park, in Washington State, plants—including other trees—quickly take advantage of the mineral nutrients supplied by decomposing "nurse logs."

▼ Figure 31 **General scheme for biogeochemical cycles.**

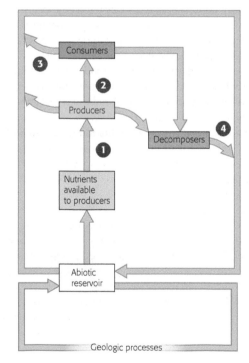

The Carbon Cycle

Carbon, the major ingredient of all organic molecules, has an atmospheric reservoir and cycles globally. Other abiotic reservoirs of carbon include fossil fuels and dissolved carbon compounds in the oceans. The reciprocal metabolic processes of photosynthesis and cellular respiration, are mainly responsible for the cycling of carbon between the biotic and abiotic worlds (Figure 32). ① Photosynthesis removes CO_2 from the atmosphere and incorporates it into organic molecules, which are ② passed along the food chain by consumers. ③ Cellular respiration returns CO_2 to the atmosphere. ④ Decomposers break down the carbon compounds in detritus; that carbon, too, is eventually released as CO_2. On a global scale, the return of CO_2 to the atmosphere by respiration closely balances its removal by photosynthesis. However, increasing levels of CO_2 caused by ⑤ the burning of wood and fossil fuels (coal and petroleum) are contributing to global climate change.

The Phosphorus Cycle

Organisms require phosphorus as an ingredient of nucleic acids, phospholipids, and ATP and (in vertebrates) as a mineral component of bones and teeth. In contrast to the carbon cycle and the other major biogeochemical cycles, the phosphorus cycle does not have an atmospheric component. Rocks are the only source of phosphorus for terrestrial ecosystems; in fact, rocks that have high phosphorus content are mined for fertilizer.

At the center of Figure 33, ① the weathering (breakdown) of rock gradually adds inorganic phosphate (PO_4^{3-}) to the soil. ② Plants absorb dissolved phosphate from the soil and assimilate it by building the phosphorus atoms into organic compounds. ③ Consumers obtain phosphorus in organic form by eating plants. ④ Phosphates are returned to the soil by the action of decomposers on animal waste and the remains of dead plants and animals. ⑤ Some of the phosphates drain from terrestrial ecosystems into the sea, where they may settle and eventually become part of new rocks. Phosphorus removed from the cycle in this way will not be available to living organisms until ⑥ geologic processes uplift the rocks and expose them to weathering.

Phosphates move from land to aquatic ecosystems much more rapidly than they are replaced, and soil characteristics may also decrease the amount of phosphate available to plants. As a result, phosphate is a limiting factor in many terrestrial ecosystems. Farmers and gardeners often use phosphate fertilizer, such as crushed phosphate rock or bone meal (finely ground bones from slaughtered livestock or fish), to boost plant growth.

▼ Figure 32 **The carbon cycle.**

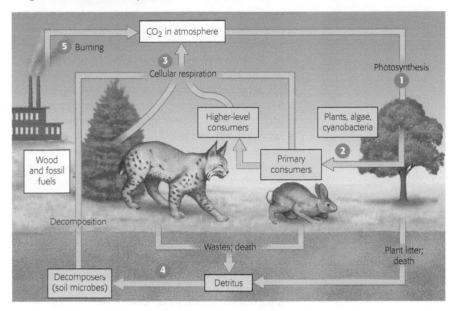

▼ Figure 33 **The phosphorus cycle.**

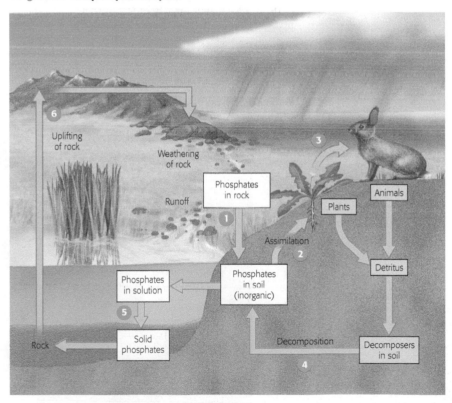

The Nitrogen Cycle

As an ingredient of proteins and nucleic acids, nitrogen is essential to the structure and functioning of all organisms. Nitrogen has two abiotic reservoirs, the atmosphere and the soil. The atmospheric reservoir is huge; almost 80% of the atmosphere is nitrogen gas (N_2). However, plants cannot use nitrogen gas. The process of **nitrogen fixation** converts gaseous N_2 to ammonia (NH_3). NH_3 then picks up another H^+ to become ammonium (NH_4^+), which plants can assimilate. Most of the nitrogen available in natural ecosystems comes from biological fixation performed by certain bacteria. Without these organisms, the reservoir of usable soil nitrogen would be extremely limited.

Figure 34 illustrates the actions of two types of nitrogen-fixing bacteria. ❶ Some bacteria live symbiotically in the roots of certain species of plants, supplying their hosts with a direct source of usable nitrogen. The largest group of plants with this mutualistic relationship is the legumes, a family that includes peanuts and soybeans. Many farmers improve soil fertility by alternating crops of legumes, which add nitrogen to the soil, with plants such as corn that require nitrogen fertilizer. ❷ Free-living bacteria in soil or water fix nitrogen, resulting in NH_4^+.

❸ After nitrogen is fixed, some of the ammonium is taken up and used by plants. ❹ Nitrifying bacteria in the soil also convert some of the ammonium to nitrate (NO_3^-), ❺ which is more readily acquired by plants. Plants use this nitrogen to make molecules such as amino acids, which are then incorporated into proteins.

❻ When an herbivore (represented here by a rabbit) eats a plant, it digests the proteins into amino acids and then uses the amino acids to build the proteins it needs. Higher-order consumers get nitrogen from the organic molecules of their prey. Because animals form nitrogen-containing waste products during protein metabolism, consumers excrete some nitrogen into the soil or water. The urine that rabbits and other mammals excrete contains urea, a nitrogen compound that is widely used as fertilizer.

Organisms that are not consumed eventually die and become detritus, which is decomposed by bacteria and fungi. ❼ The decomposition of organic compounds releases ammonium into the soil, replenishing that abiotic reservoir. Under low-oxygen conditions, however, ❽ soil bacteria known as denitrifying bacteria strip the oxygen atoms from nitrates, releasing N_2 back into the atmosphere and depleting the soil of usable nitrogen.

Human activities are disrupting the nitrogen cycle by adding more nitrogen to the biosphere each year than natural processes do. Combustion of fossil fuels and modern agricultural practices are two major sources of nitrogen. For example, many farmers use enormous amounts of synthetic nitrogen fertilizer to supplement natural nitrogen. However, less than half the fertilizer applied is actually used by the crop plants. Some nitrogen escapes to the atmosphere, where it forms nitrous oxide (N_2O), a gas that contributes to global warming. And as you'll learn next, nitrogen fertilizers also pollute aquatic systems. ☑

☑ **CHECKPOINT**

What are the abiotic reservoirs of nitrogen? In what form does nitrogen occur in each reservoir?

Answer: atmosphere: N_2; soil: NH_4^+ and NO_3^-

▼ Figure 34 **The nitrogen cycle.**

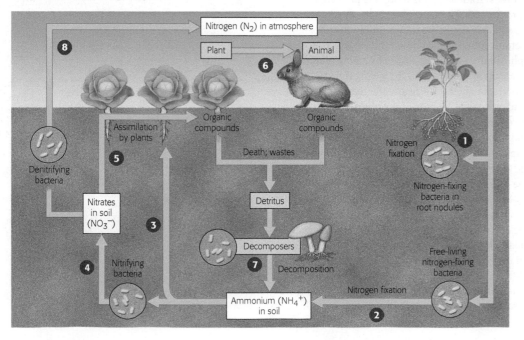

Nutrient Pollution

Low nutrient levels, especially of phosphorus and nitrogen, often limit the growth of algae and cyanobacteria in aquatic ecosystems. Nutrient pollution occurs when human activities add excess amounts of these chemicals to aquatic ecosystems.

In many areas, phosphate pollution comes from agricultural fertilizers and runoff of animal waste from livestock feedlots (where hundreds of animals are penned together). Phosphates are also a common ingredient in dishwasher detergents, making the outflow from sewage-treatment facilities—which also contains phosphorus from human waste—a major source of phosphate pollution. Phosphate pollution of lakes and rivers results in heavy growth of algae and cyanobacteria **(Figure 35)**. Microbes consume a great deal of oxygen as they decompose the extra biomass, a process that depletes the water of oxygen. These changes lead to reduced diversity of aquatic species and a much less appealing body of water.

A major source of nitrogen pollution is the large amount of inorganic nitrogen fertilizers routinely applied to crops, lawns, and golf courses. Plants take up some of the nitrogen compounds, and denitrifiers convert some to atmospheric N_2, but nitrate is not bound tightly by soil particles and is easily washed out of the soil by rain or irrigation. As a result, chemical fertilizers often exceed the soil's natural recycling capacity. Runoff from the manure in high-density livestock facilities, such as cattle feedlots and hog farms, is another significant source of nitrogen pollution. Nitrogen pollution may also come from sewage treatment facilities when extreme conditions (such as unusual storms) or malfunctioning equipment prevent them from meeting water quality standards.

In an example of how far-reaching this problem can be, nitrogen runoff from Midwestern farm fields has been linked to an annual summer "dead zone" in the Gulf of Mexico **(Figure 36)**. Vast algal blooms extend outward from where the Mississippi River deposits its nutrient-laden waters. As the algae die, decomposition of the huge quantities of biomass diminishes the supply of dissolved oxygen over an area that ranges from 13,000 km^2 to 22,000 km^2 (from roughly the size of Connecticut to the size of New Jersey). Oxygen depletion disrupts benthic communities, displacing fish and invertebrates that can move and killing organisms that are attached to the substrate. More than 400 recurring and permanent coastal dead zones totaling approximately 245,000 km^2 (about the area of Michigan) have been documented worldwide. ☑

☑ **CHECKPOINT**

How does the excessive addition of mineral nutrients to a pond eventually result in the loss of most fish in the pond?

Answer: Excessive mineral nutrients initially cause population explosions of algae and the organisms that feed on them. The respiration of so much life, especially of the microbes decomposing all the organic refuse, consumes most of the lake's oxygen, which the fish require.

▼ **Figure 35 Algal growth resulting from nutrient pollution.** The flat green area in this photo is not a lawn, but rather the surface of a polluted pond.

▼ **Figure 36 The Gulf of Mexico dead zone.**

Light blue lines represent rivers draining into the Mississippi River (shown in bright blue). Nitrogen runoff carried by these rivers ends up in the Gulf of Mexico. In the images below, red and orange indicate high concentrations of phytoplankton. Bacteria feeding on dead phytoplankton deplete the water of oxygen, creating a "dead zone."

Summer

Winter

Conservation and Restoration Biology

As we have seen, many of the environmental problems facing us today have been caused by human enterprises. But the science of ecology is not just useful for telling us how things have gone wrong. Ecological research is also the foundation for finding solutions to these problems and for reversing the negative consequences of ecosystem alteration. Thus, we conclude by highlighting these beneficial applications of ecological research.

Conservation biology is a goal-oriented science that seeks to understand and counter the loss of biodiversity. Conservation biologists recognize that biodiversity can be sustained only if the evolutionary mechanisms that have given rise to species and communities of organisms continue to operate. Thus, the goal is not simply to preserve individual species but to sustain ecosystems, where natural selection can continue to function, and to maintain the genetic variability on which natural selection acts. The expanding field of **restoration ecology** uses ecological principles to develop methods of returning degraded areas to their natural state.

Biodiversity "Hot Spots"

Conservation biologists are applying their understanding of population, community, and ecosystem dynamics in establishing parks, wilderness areas, and other legally protected nature reserves. Choosing locations for these protected zones often focuses on **biodiversity hot spots**. These relatively small areas have a large number of

endangered and threatened species and an exceptional concentration of **endemic species**, species that are found nowhere else. Together, the "hottest" of Earth's biodiversity hot spots, shown in **Figure 37**, total less than 1.5% of Earth's land surface but are home to a third of all species of plants and vertebrates. For example, all of Earth's lemurs—more than 50 species—are endemic to Madagascar, a large island off the eastern coast of Africa. In fact, almost all of the mammals, reptiles, amphibians, and plants that inhabit Madagascar are endemic. There are also hot spots in aquatic ecosystems, such as certain river systems and coral reefs. Because biodiversity hot spots can also be hot spots of extinction, they rank high on the list of areas demanding strong global conservation efforts.

Concentrations of species provide an opportunity to protect many species in very limited areas. However, the "hot spot" designation tends to favor the most noticeable organisms, especially vertebrates and plants. Invertebrates and microorganisms are often overlooked. Furthermore, species endangerment is a global problem, and focusing on hot spots should not detract from efforts to conserve habitats and species diversity in other areas. Finally, even the protection of a nature reserve does not shield organisms from the effects of climate change or other threats, such as invasive species or infectious disease. To stem the tide of biodiversity loss, we will have to address environmental problems globally as well as locally. ☑

☑ **CHECKPOINT**

What is a biodiversity hot spot?

Answer: a relatively small area with a disproportionately large number of species, including endangered species

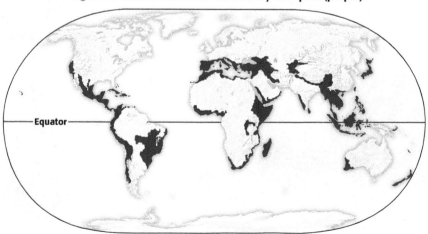

▼ Figure 37 **Earth's terrestrial biodiversity hot spots (purple).**

Equator

Conservation at the Ecosystem Level

In the past, most conservation efforts focused on saving individual species, and this work continues. More and more, however, conservation biology aims at sustaining the biodiversity of entire communities and ecosystems. On an even broader scale, conservation biology considers the biodiversity of whole landscapes. Ecologically, a **landscape** is a regional assemblage of interacting ecosystems, such as an area with forest, adjacent fields, wetlands, streams, and streamside habitats. **Landscape ecology** is the application of ecological principles to the study of land-use patterns. Its goal is to make ecosystem conservation a functional part of the planning for land use.

Edges between ecosystems are prominent features of landscapes, whether natural or altered by people (**Figure 38**). Edges have their own sets of physical conditions—such as soil type and surface features—that differ from the ecosystems on either side of them. Edges also may have their own type and amount of disturbance. For instance, the edge of a forest often has more blown-down trees than a forest interior because the edge is less protected from strong winds. Because of their specific physical features, edges also have their own communities of organisms. Some organisms thrive in edges because they require resources found only there. For instance, whitetail deer browse on woody shrubs found in edges between woods and fields, so their populations often expand when forests are logged or fragmented by development.

Edges can have both positive and negative effects on biodiversity. A recent study in a tropical rain forest in western Africa indicated that natural edge communities are important sites of speciation. On the other hand, landscapes where human activities have produced edges often have fewer species.

Another important landscape feature, especially where habitats have been severely fragmented, is the **movement corridor**, a narrow strip or series of small clumps of suitable habitat connecting otherwise isolated patches. In places where there is extremely heavy human impact, artificial corridors are sometimes constructed (**Figure 39**). Corridors can promote dispersal and help sustain populations, and they are especially important to species that migrate between different habitats seasonally. But a corridor can also be harmful—as, for example, in the spread of disease, especially among small subpopulations in closely situated habitat patches. ✓

▼ Figure 38 Edges between ecosystems within a landscape.

Natural edges. Forests border grassland ecosystems in Lake Clark National Park, Alaska.

Edges created by human activity. Forest edges surround farmland in the Cotswolds region of south central England.

☑ CHECKPOINT

How is a landscape different from an ecosystem?

Answer: A landscape is more inclusive in that it consists of several interacting ecosystems in the same region.

► Figure 39 An artificial corridor. This bridge over a road provides an artificial corridor for animals in Banff National Park, Canada.

Biodiversity in Decline THE PROCESS OF SCIENCE

How Does Tropical Forest Fragmentation Affect Biodiversity?

Long-term studies are essential for learning how we might best conserve biodiversity and other natural resources. One site for such studies is the Biological Dynamics of Forest Fragmentation Project (BDFFP), a 1,000-km² ecological "laboratory" located deep in the Amazonian forest of Brazil. When the project was begun in 1979, laws required landowners who cleared forest for ranching or other agricultural operations to leave scattered tracts of untouched forest. Biologists recruited some of these landowners to create reserves in isolated fragments of 1 ha (roughly 2.5 acres), 10 ha, and 100 ha. Figure 40 shows some of these forest "islands." Before each area was isolated from the main forest, a small army of specialists inventoried the organisms present and measured the trees.

Hundreds of researchers have used the BDFFP sites to investigate the effects of forest fragmentation on all

▼ Figure 40 **Fragments of forest in the Amazon that were created as part of the Biological Dynamics of Forest Fragmentation Project.** The patch of forest on the right is a 1-ha (2.5-acre) fragment.

levels of ecological study. The initial **observations** for these investigations were gleaned from the results of other ecological studies—for example, the effects of fragmentation in temperate forests or differences in the biodiversity of small islands compared with mainland ecosystems. These observations led many researchers to ask the **question**, How does fragmentation of tropical forests affect species diversity within the fragments? Based on previous research on numerous species, a reasonable **hypothesis** might be that species diversity declines as the size of the forest fragment decreases. An ecologist studying large predators such as jaguars and pumas, which require large hunting territories, might therefore make the **prediction** that predators will be found only in the largest areas. The BDFFP is unique because it allows researchers to test their predictions with new observations that compare species diversity in forest fragments with a comparable control: species diversity in the same area when it was intact. An undisturbed area of 25,400 acres is also available for comparison with fragmented areas. In addition, data can be collected over a period of years or even decades.

Since the BDFFP was established, scientists have studied many different groups of plants and animals. In general, the **results** have shown that fragmentation of forest into smaller pieces leads to a decline in species diversity. Species richness decreases as a result of local extinctions of many species of large mammals, insects, and insectivorous birds. The population density of remaining species often declines. Researchers also documented edge effects, such as those described in the previous section. Changes in abiotic factors along the fragment edges, including increased wind disturbance, higher temperature, and decreased soil moisture, played a role in community alterations. For example, ecologists found that tree mortality was higher than normal at fragment edges. They also observed changes in the composition of communities of invertebrates that inhabit the soil and leaf litter.

Restoring Ecosystems

One of the major strategies in restoration ecology is **bioremediation**, the use of living organisms to detoxify polluted ecosystems. For example, bacteria have been used to clean up old mining sites and oil spills. Researchers are also investigating the potential of using plants to remove toxic substances such as heavy metals and organic pollutants (for example, PCBs) from contaminated soil (Figure 41).

Some restoration projects have the broader goal of returning ecosystems to their natural state. Such projects may involve replanting vegetation, fencing out non-native animals, or removing dams that restrict water flow. Hundreds of restoration projects are currently under way in the United States. One of the most ambitious endeavors is the Kissimmee River Restoration Project in south-central Florida.

The Kissimmee River was once a shallow, meandering river that wound its way from Lake Kissimmee southward into Lake Okeechobee. During about half of the year, the river flooded into a wide floodplain, creating wetlands that provided habitat for large numbers of birds, fishes, and invertebrates. And as the floods deposited the river's load of nutrient-rich silt on the floodplain, they boosted soil fertility and maintained the water quality of the river.

Between 1962 and 1971, the U.S. Army Corps of Engineers converted the 166-km wandering river to a straight canal 9 m deep, 100 m wide, and 90 km long. This project, designed to allow development on the floodplain, drained approximately 31,000 acres of wetlands, with significant negative impacts on fish and wetland bird populations. Without the marshes to help filter and reduce agricultural runoff, the river transported phosphates and other excess nutrients from Lake Okeechobee to the Everglades ecosystem to the south.

The restoration project involves removing water-control structures such as dams, reservoirs, and channel modifications and filling in about 35 km of the canal (Figure 42). The first phase of the project was completed in 2004; the rest is scheduled to be completed in 2015. The photo shows a section of the Kissimmee canal that has been plugged, diverting flow into the remnant river channels. Birds and other wildlife have returned in unexpected numbers to the 11,000 acres of wetlands that have been restored. The marshes are filled with native vegetation, and game fishes again swim in the river channels. ☑

☑ CHECKPOINT

The water in the Kissimmee River eventually flows into the Everglades. How will the Kissimmee River Restoration Project affect water quality in the Everglades ecosystem?

Answer: Wetlands filter agricultural runoff, which prevents nutrient pollution from flowing downstream. By restoring this ecosystem service, the project will improve water quality in the Everglades.

▼ Figure 41 **Bioremediation using plants.**
A researcher from the U.S. Department of Agriculture investigates the use of canola plants to reduce toxic levels of selenium in contaminated soil.

▼ Figure 42 **The Kissimmee River Restoration Project.**

Former canal

The Goal of Sustainable Development

As the world population grows and becomes more affluent, the demand for the "provisioning" services of ecosystems, such as food, wood, and water, is increasing. Although these demands are currently being met, they are satisfied at the expense of other critical ecosystem services, such as climate regulation and protection against natural disasters. Clearly, we have set ourselves and the rest of the biosphere on a precarious path into the future. How can we achieve **sustainable development**—development that meets the needs of people today without limiting the ability of future generations to meet their needs?

Many nations, scientific associations, corporations, and private foundations have embraced the concept of sustainable development. The Ecological Society of America, the world's largest organization of ecologists, endorses a research agenda called the Sustainable Biosphere Initiative. The goal of this initiative is to acquire the ecological information necessary for the responsible development, management, and conservation of Earth's resources. The research agenda includes the search for ways to sustain the productivity of natural and artificial ecosystems and studies of the relationship between biological diversity, global climate change, and ecological processes.

Sustainable development depends on more than continued research and application of ecological knowledge. It also requires that we connect the life sciences with the social sciences, economics, and humanities. Conservation of biodiversity is only one side of sustainable development; the other side is improving the human condition. Public education and the political commitment and cooperation of nations are essential to the success of this endeavor.

An awareness of our unique ability to alter the biosphere and jeopardize the existence of other species, as well as our own, may help us choose a path toward a sustainable future. The risk of a world without adequate natural resources for all its people is not a vision of the distant future. It is a prospect for your children's lifetime, or perhaps even your own. But although the current state of the biosphere is grim, the situation is far from hopeless. Now is the time to take action by aggressively pursuing greater knowledge about the diversity of life on our planet and by joining with others in working toward long-term sustainability **(Figure 43)**. ☑

☑ **CHECKPOINT**

What is meant by sustainable development?

Answer: development that meets current needs while ensuring an adequate supply of natural and economic resources for future generations

▼ Figure 43 **Working toward sustainability.**

Students at the University of Virginia sorted trash from dumpsters to promote recycling. Recycling just one aluminum can saves enough energy to power a laptop for five hours.

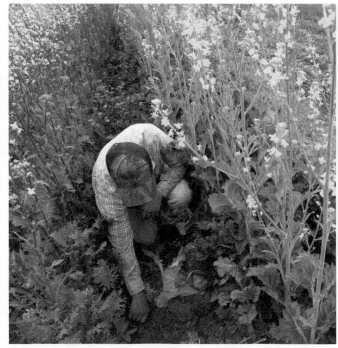

A student at California State University, Fresno, pulls weeds in a plot of mustard and kale plants at the university's organic farm.

Biodiversity in Decline EVOLUTION CONNECTION

Can Biophilia Save Biodiversity?

For millions of years, the diversity of life has flourished via evolutionary adaptation in response to environmental change. For many species, however, the pace of evolution can't match the breakneck speed at which humans are changing the environment. Perhaps those species are doomed to extinction. Or perhaps they can be saved by one human characteristic that works in their favor: biophilia.

Biophilia, which literally means "love of life," is a term that Edward O. Wilson, one of the world's foremost experts on biodiversity and conservation, uses for the human desire to affiliate with other life in its many forms. People develop close relationships with pets, nurture houseplants, invite avian visitors with backyard feeders, and flock to zoos, gardens, and nature parks **(Figure 44)**. Our attraction to pristine landscapes with clean water and lush vegetation is also testimony to our biophilia. Wilson proposes that our biophilia is innate, an evolutionary product of natural selection acting on a brainy species whose survival depended on a close connection to the environment and a practical appreciation of plants and animals. We evolved in natural environments rich in biodiversity, and we still have an affinity for such settings.

It will come as no surprise that many biologists have embraced the concept of biophilia. After all, these are people who have turned their passion for nature into careers. But biophilia strikes a chord with biologists for another reason. If biophilia is evolutionarily embedded in our genome, then there is hope that we can become better custodians of the biosphere. If we all pay more attention to our biophilia, a new environmental ethic could catch on among individuals and societies. And that ethic is a resolve never to knowingly allow a single species to become extinct as a result of our actions or any ecosystem to be destroyed as long as there are reasonable ways to prevent it. Yes, we should be motivated to preserve biodiversity because we depend on it for food, medicine, building materials, fertile soil, flood control, habitable climate, drinkable water, and breathable air. But maybe we can also work harder to prevent the extinction of other forms of life just because it is the ethical thing for us to do.

Biophilia is a fitting capstone for this chapter. Modern biology is the scientific extension of our human tendency to feel connected to and curious about all forms of life. People are most likely to save what they appreciate, and most likely to appreciate what they understand. We hope that our discussion of biodiversity has deepened your biophilia and broadened your education.

▼ **Figure 44 Biophilia.** Whether we seek other organisms in their own habitats or invite them into ours, we clearly find pleasure in the diversity of life.

Chapter Review

SUMMARY OF KEY CONCEPTS

The Loss of Biodiversity

THE COMPONENTS OF BIODIVERSITY		
Genetic Diversity	**Species Diversity**	**Ecosystem Diversity**
Loss of genetic diversity threatens the survival of a species and eliminates potential benefits to people.	The current rate of species extinctions is extremely high compared to the rate of natural extinctions over the past 100,000 years.	Destruction of ecosystems results in the loss of essential ecosystem services.

Causes of Declining Biodiversity

Habitat destruction is the leading cause of extinctions. Invasive species, over-exploitation, and pollution are also significant factors.

Community Ecology

Interspecific Interactions

Populations in a community interact in a variety of ways that can be generally categorized as being beneficial (**+**) or harmful (**−**) to the populations. Because **+/−** interactions (exploitation of one species by another species) may have such a negative impact on the individual that is harmed, defensive evolutionary adaptations are common.

Trophic Structure

The trophic structure of a community defines the feeding relationships among organisms. These relationships are sometimes organized into food chains or food webs. In the process of biological magnification, toxins become more concentrated as they are passed up a food chain to the top predators.

Increasing PCB concentration

Species Diversity in Communities

Diversity within a community includes species richness and relative abundance of different species. A keystone species is a species that has a great impact on the composition of the community despite a relatively low abundance or biomass.

Disturbances in Communities

Disturbances are episodes that damage communities, at least temporarily, by destroying organisms or altering the availability of resources such as mineral nutrients and water. People are the most significant cause of disturbances today.

Ecological Succession

The sequence of changes in a community after a disturbance is called ecological succession. Primary succession occurs where a community arises in a virtually lifeless area with no soil. Secondary succession occurs where a disturbance has destroyed an existing community but left the soil intact.

INTERACTIONS BETWEEN SPECIES IN A COMMUNITY					
Interspecific Interaction	**Effect on Species 1**	**Effect on Species 2**	**Interspecific Interaction**	**Effect on Species 1**	**Effect on Species 2**
Competition	−	−	**Exploitation** Predation	+	−
Mutualism	+	+	Herbivory	+	−
			Parasites and Pathogens	+	−

Ecosystem Ecology

Energy Transformations: Energy Flow in Ecosystems

An ecosystem is a biological community and the abiotic factors with which the community interacts. Energy must flow continuously through an ecosystem, from producers to consumers and decomposers. Chemical elements can be recycled between an ecosystem's living community and the abiotic environment. Trophic relationships determine an ecosystem's routes of energy flow and chemical cycling.

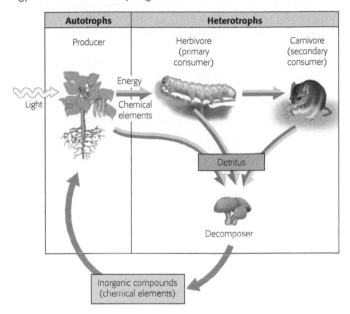

Primary production is the rate at which plants and other producers build biomass. Ecosystems vary considerably in their productivity. Primary production sets the spending limit for the energy budget of the entire ecosystem because consumers must acquire their organic fuels from producers. In a food chain, only about 10% of the biomass at one trophic level is available to the next, resulting in a pyramid of production.

Approximately 90% loss of energy at each trophic level

Energy

When people eat producers instead of consumers, less photosynthetic production is required, which reduces the impact on the environment.

Interconnections within Systems: Chemical Cycling in Ecosystems

Biogeochemical cycles involve biotic and abiotic components. Each circuit has an abiotic reservoir through which the chemical cycles. Some chemical elements require "processing" by certain microorganisms before they are available to plants as inorganic nutrients. A chemical's specific route through an ecosystem varies with the element and the trophic structure of the ecosystem. Phosphorus is not very mobile and is cycled locally. Carbon and nitrogen spend part of their time in gaseous form and are cycled globally. Runoff of nitrogen and phosphorus, especially from agricultural land, causes algal blooms in aquatic ecosystems, lowering water quality and sometimes depleting the water of oxygen.

Conservation and Restoration Biology

Biodiversity "Hot Spots"

Conservation biology is a goal-oriented science that seeks to counter the loss of biodiversity. The front lines for conservation biology are biodiversity "hot spots," relatively small geographic areas that are especially rich in endangered species.

Conservation at the Ecosystem Level

Increasingly, conservation biology aims at sustaining the biodiversity of entire communities, ecosystems, and landscapes. Edges between ecosystems are prominent features of landscapes, with positive and negative effects on biodiversity. Corridors can promote dispersal and help sustain populations.

Restoring Ecosystems

In some cases, ecologists use microbes or plants to remove toxic substances, such as heavy metals, from ecosystems. Ecologists are working to revitalize some ecosystems by planting native vegetation, removing barriers to wildlife, and other means. The Kissimmee River Restoration Project is an attempt to undo the ecological damage done when the river was engineered into straight channels.

The Goal of Sustainable Development

Balancing the needs of people with the health of the biosphere, sustainable development has the goal of long-term prosperity of human societies and the ecosystems that support them.

MasteringBiology®

For practice quizzes, BioFlix animations, MP3 tutorials, video tutors, and more study tools designed for this text, go to MasteringBiology®

SELF-QUIZ

1. Currently, the number one cause of biodiversity loss is _____.
2. According to the concept of competitive exclusion,
   a. two species cannot coexist in the same habitat.
   b. extinction or emigration is the only possible result of competitive interactions.
   c. intraspecific competition results in the success of the best-adapted individuals.
   d. two species cannot share the same niche in a community.

3. The concept of trophic structure emphasizes the
   a. prevalent form of vegetation.
   b. keystone species concept.
   c. feeding relationships within a community.
   d. species richness of the community.

4. Match each organism with its trophic level (you may choose a level more than once).
   a. alga
   b. grasshopper
   c. zooplankton
   d. eagle
   e. fungus

   1. decomposer
   2. producer
   3. tertiary consumer
   4. secondary consumer
   5. primary consumer

5. Why are the top predators in food chains most severely affected by pesticides such as DDT?

6. Over a period of many years, grass grows on a sand dune, then shrubs grow, and then eventually trees grow. This is an example of ecological _____.

7. According to the pyramid of production, why is eating grain-fed beef a relatively inefficient means of obtaining the energy trapped by photosynthesis?

8. Local conditions, such as heavy rainfall or the removal of plants, may limit the amount of nitrogen, phosphorus, or calcium available to a particular terrestrial ecosystem, but the amount of carbon available to the ecosystem is seldom a problem. Why?

9. A _____ is a local grouping of interacting ecosystems with several adjacent habitats.

10. Movement corridors are
   a. strips or clumps of habitat that connect isolated fragments.
   b. landscapes that include several different ecosystems.
   c. edges or boundaries between ecosystems.
   d. buffer zones that protect the long-term viability of protected areas.

THE PROCESS OF SCIENCE

11. An ecologist studying desert plants performed the following experiment. She staked out two identical plots that included a few sagebrush plants and numerous small annual wildflowers. She found the same five wildflower species in similar numbers in both plots. Then she enclosed one of the plots with a fence to keep out kangaroo rats, the most common herbivores in the area. After two years, four species of wildflowers were no longer present in the fenced plot, but one wildflower species had increased dramatically. The unfenced control plot had not changed significantly in species composition. Using the concepts discussed in the chapter, what do you think happened?

12. Imagine that you have been chosen as the biologist for the design team implementing a self-contained space station to be assembled in orbit. It will be stocked with the organisms you choose, creating an ecosystem that will support you and five other people for two years. Describe the main functions you expect the organisms to perform. List the types of organisms you would select, and explain why you chose them.

13. Interpreting Data In a classic study, John Teal measured energy flow in a salt marsh ecosystem. The table below shows some of his results.

Form of energy	Kcal/m²/yr	Efficiency of energy transfer (%)
Sunlight	600,000	n/a
Chemical energy in producers	6,585	
Chemical energy in primary consumers	81	

Data from: J. M. Teal, Energy Flow in the Salt Marsh Ecosystem of Georgia. *Ecology* 43: 614–24 (1962).

   a. Calculate the efficiency of energy transfer by the producers. That is, what percentage of the energy in sunlight was converted into chemical energy and incorporated into plant biomass?
   b. Calculate the efficiency of energy transfer by the primary consumers. What percentage of the energy in plant biomass was incorporated into the bodies of the primary consumers? What became of the rest of the energy (see Figure 27)?
   c. How much energy is available for secondary consumers? Based on the efficiency of energy transfer by primary consumers, estimate how much energy will be available to tertiary consumers.
   d. Draw a pyramid of production for the producers, primary consumers, and secondary consumers for this ecosystem (see Figure 28).

BIOLOGY AND SOCIETY

14. Some organizations are starting to envision a sustainable society—one in which each generation inherits sufficient natural and economic resources and a relatively stable environment. The Worldwatch Institute, an environmental policy organization, estimates that we must reach sustainability by the year 2030 to avoid economic and environmental collapse. In what ways is our current system not sustainable? What might we do to work toward sustainability, and what are the major roadblocks to achieving it? How would your life be different in a sustainable society?

15. The Biological Dynamics of Forest Fragmentation Project, which has contributed so much to our understanding of threats to biodiversity, is itself endangered. Encouraged by Brazilian government agencies, urban sprawl and intensive forest settlement are closing in on the study site. Activities such as clear-cutting, burning, hunting, and logging threaten the integrity of the surrounding forest. Researchers at the BDFFP, which is jointly operated by a Brazilian research agency and the Smithsonian Tropical Research Institute, hope that they can bring attention to the problem through the Brazilian media and pressure the government into protecting the project. How would you argue the importance of protecting the BDFFP against ecologically destructive activities in a letter to a newspaper editor or to a government official?

16. Some scientists have argued that livestock production is the single greatest threat to biodiversity. What concepts that you learned about in this chapter might be used to support this contention?

Glossary

abiotic reservoir (*ā'bī-ot'-ik*)
The part of an ecosystem where a chemical, such as carbon or nitrogen, accumulates or is stockpiled outside of living organisms.

biodiversity
The variety of living things; includes genetic diversity, species diversity, and ecosystem diversity.

biodiversity hot spot
A small geographic area that contains a large number of threatened or endangered species and an exceptional concentration of endemic species (those found nowhere else).

biogeochemical cycle
Any of the various chemical circuits occurring in an ecosystem, involving both biotic and abiotic components of the ecosystem.

biological magnification
The accumulation of persistent chemicals in the living tissues of consumers in food chains.

biomass
The amount, or mass, of living organic material in an ecosystem.

biophilia
The human desire to affiliate with other life in its many forms.

carnivore
An animal that mainly eats other animals. *See also* herbivore; omnivore.

chemical cycling
The use and reuse of chemical elements such as carbon within an ecosystem.

competitive exclusion principle
The concept that populations of two species cannot coexist in a community if their niches are nearly identical. Using resources more efficiently and having a reproductive advantage, one of the populations will eventually outcompete and eliminate the other.

conservation biology
A goal-oriented science that seeks to understand and counter the loss of biodiversity.

cryptic coloration
Adaptive coloration that makes an organism difficult to spot against its background.

decomposer
An organism that secretes enzymes that digest molecules in organic material and convert them to inorganic form.

detritivore (*di-trī'-tuh-vor*)
An organism that consumes dead organic matter (detritus).

detritus (*di-trī'-tus*)
Dead organic matter.

ecological niche
The sum of a species' use of the biotic and abiotic resources in its environment.

ecological succession
The process of biological community change resulting from disturbance; transition in the species composition of a biological community, often following a flood, fire, or volcanic eruption. *See also* primary succession; secondary succession.

ecosystem service
Function performed by an ecosystem that directly or indirectly benefits people.

endemic species
A species whose distribution is limited to a specific geographic area.

energy flow
The passage of energy through the components of an ecosystem.

food chain
The sequence of food transfers between the trophic levels of a community, beginning with the producers.

food web
A network of interconnecting food chains.

herbivore
An animal that eats mainly plants and/or algae. *See also* carnivore; omnivore.

herbivory
The consumption of plant parts or algae by an animal.

host
An organism that is exploited by a parasite or pathogen.

interspecific competition
Competition between populations of two or more species that require similar limited resources.

interspecific interaction
Any interaction between members of different species.

keystone species
A species whose impact on its community is much larger than its biomass or abundance indicates.

landscape
A regional assemblage of interacting ecosystems.

landscape ecology
The application of ecological principles to the study of land-use patterns; the scientific study of the biodiversity of interacting ecosystems.

movement corridor
A series of small clumps or a narrow strip of quality habitat (usable by organisms) that connects otherwise isolated patches of quality habitat.

mutualism
An interspecific interaction in which both partners benefit.

nitrogen fixation
The conversion of atmospheric nitrogen (N_2) to ammonia (NH_3). NH_3 then picks up another H^+ to become NH_4^+ (ammonium), which plants can absorb and use.

omnivore
An animal that eats both plants and animals. *See also* carnivore; herbivore.

predation
An interaction between species in which one species, the predator, kills and eats the other, the prey.

primary consumer
An organism that eats only autotrophs; an herbivore.

primary production
The amount of solar energy converted to the chemical energy stored in organic compounds by autotrophs in an ecosystem during a given time period.

primary succession
A type of ecological succession in which a biological community begins in an area without soil. *See also* secondary succession.

pyramid of production
A diagram depicting the cumulative loss of energy with each transfer in a food chain.

quaternary consumer (*kwot'-er-nār-ē*)
An organism that eats tertiary consumers.

relative abundance
The proportional representation of a species in a biological community; one component of species diversity.

restoration ecology
A field of ecology that develops methods of returning degraded ecosystems to their natural state.

scavenger
An animal that feeds on the carcasses of dead animals.

secondary consumer
An organism that eats primary consumers.

secondary succession
A type of ecological succession that occurs where a disturbance has destroyed an existing biological community but left the soil intact. *See also* primary succession.

species diversity
The variety of species that make up a biological community; the number and relative abundance of species in a biological community.

species richness
The total number of different species in a community; one component of species diversity.

sustainable development
Development that meets the needs of people today without limiting the ability of future generations to meet their needs.

tertiary consumer (*ter'-shē-ār-ē*)
An organism that eats secondary consumers.

trophic structure (*trō'-fik*)
The feeding relationships among the various species in a community.

warning coloration
The bright color pattern, often yellow, red, or orange in combination with black, of animals that have effective chemical defenses.

Credits

Credits are listed in the order of appearance.

PHOTO CREDITS

opening photo bottom left Philippe Psaila/Science Source; **opening photo center left** Ming-Hsiang Chuang/Shutterstock; **opening photo center right** Joe Tucciarone/Science Source; **opening photo center** Jag_cz/Shutterstock; **opening photo center** Frannyanne/Shutterstock; **center right** Amar and Isabelle Guillen - Guillen Photo LLC/Alamy; **top left** Amar and Isabelle Guillen - Guillen Photo LLC/Alamy; **1** James King-Holmes/Science Source; **2 left** Gerard Lacz/Age Fotostock; **2 right** Mark Carwardine/Getty Images; **3** Andre Seale/Age Fotostock; **4** American Folklife Center, Library of Congress; **5** Gerald Herbert/AP Images; **6** Richard D. Estes/Science Source; **7a** Jim Zipp/Science Source **7b** Tim Zurowski/All Canada Photos/Superstock; **8 top** M. I. Walker/Science Source; **8 bottom** M. I. Walker/Science Source; **9** Jurgen Freund/Nature Picture Library; **10** Eric Lemar/Shutterstock; **11** P. Wegner/ARCO/Age Fotostock; **12 left** Robert Hamilton/Alamy; **12 right** Barry Mansell/Nature Picture Library; **13 left** Dante Fenolio/Science Source; **13 right** Peter J. Mayne; **14 top left** Bildagentur-online/TH Foto-Werbung/Science Source; **14 top right** Luca Invernizzi Tetto/Age Fotostock; **14 bottom** ImageState/Alamy; **16** audaxl/Shutterstock; **21** Mark Conlin/Vwpics/Visual&Written SL/Alamy; **22** Todd Sieling/Corvus Consulting; **23** HiloFoto/Getty Images; **24** AdstockRF/Universal Images Group Limited/Alamy; **30** Wing-Chi Poon; **35** Michael Marten/Science Source; **36 top** NASA/Goddard Space Flight Center; **36 bottom left** NASA Goddard Space Flight Center; **36 bottom right** NASA Goddard Space Flight Center; **38 bottom** Matthew Dixon/Shutterstock; **39** Alan Sirulnikoff/Science Source; **40** R. O. Bierregaard, Jr., Biology Department, University of North Carolina, Charlotte; **41** United States Department of Agriculture; **42** South Florida Water Management District; **43 left** Andrew_Shurtleff/The Daily Progress/AP Images; **43 right** The Fresno Bee/ZUMA Press, Inc/Alamy; **44 top right** Juliet Shrimpton/Age Fotostock; **44 bottom left** Matt Jeppson/Shutterstock; **44 bottom right** Image Source/Getty Images; **Biodiversity table left top to bottom** James King-Holmes/Science Source; Gerard Lacz/Age Fotostock; Andre Seale/Age Fotostock; **Interactions table left top to bottom** Jim Zipp/Science Source; Tim Zurowski/All Canada Photos/Superstock; Jurgen Freund/Nature Picture Library; **Interactions table right top to bottom** Outdoor-Archiv/Kukulenz/Alamy; Jean Dickey; Renaud Visage/Getty Images.

ILLUSTRATION AND TEXT CREDITS

Data from J. M. Teal, "Energy Flow in the Salt Marsh Ecosystem of Georgia," *Ecology*, 43:614–624 (1962); **43:** © Pearson Education, Inc.

Self-Quiz Answers

1. habitat destruction
2. d
3. c
4. a2, b5, c5, d3 or d4, e1
5. because the pesticides become concentrated in their prey
6. succession
7. Only 10% of the energy trapped by photosynthesis is turned into biomass by the plant, and only 10% of that energy is turned into the meat of a grazing animal. Therefore, grain-fed beef provides only about 1% of the energy captured by photosynthesis.
8. Many nutrients come from the soil, but carbon comes from the air.
9. landscape
10. a

Index